SIGNALS, SYSTEMS AND COMMUNICATION

B. P. LATHI

Associate Professor of Electrical Engineering
Bradley University

John Wiley & Sons, Inc.
New York · London · Sydney

To
Dr. George S. Bahrs
and
Dr. M. E. Van Valkenburg

Preface

The importance of signal analysis (frequency analysis of signals) in modern theory of linear systems and communication theory cannot be overstressed. The study of signals leads into the analysis of linear systems and frequency transform methods, on one hand; on the other hand, it leads directly into communication theory. Despite the awareness of this unifying principle, traditionally the two aspects have, in general, been treated independently. I believe that the greatest benefit can be derived by studying both of these aspects together. This book presents a unified treatment of the analysis of linear systems (frequency-domain analysis of lumped and distributed systems) and basic communication principles (modulation, demodulation, correlation, noise, information transmission). For such an integrated approach, it is necessary to have a deeper appreciation of signal analysis than is customarily given in introductory treatments. Here an attempt is made not only to develop the significant results in signal analysis mathematically, but also to present intuitive and qualitative interpretations of such results.

This book emphasizes the physical appreciation of the concepts rather than mathematical manipulation. There is generally a tendency to treat engineering subjects as a branch of applied mathematics. This approach ignores the physical meaning behind various derivations. The view based upon abstract postulates is a necessity in the field of mathematics, since it is characterized by a certain set of internally consistent postulates, not necessarily related to physical observations. In the engineering and physical sciences, on the other hand, every discipline is founded upon a set of hypotheses related to a physical reality. Thus, a purely mathematical approach that ignores the underlying physical phenomena deprives one of a physical appreciation and, consequently, of a better understanding of the subject matter. I wholeheartedly agree with the following sentiments of Professor Sergei Schelkunoff.

Mathematics suggests rigor, and students may get an erroneous idea that rigor assures truth in the domain of physics. What is even worse, they may come to believe that mere algebraic manipulation of symbols constitutes rigor and assures the correctness of results. The faith in such manipulation can grow to such an extent that students may accept results which are obviously wrong from the physical point of view, without looking over their solutions in search of an error. Students should be encouraged to develop a habit of sound, even more than rigorous thinking.*

There are certain significant differences in the approach in this book from that generally used in other texts. The point of view here tends to be more physical than axiomatic. For example, in conventional treatments, the frequency-domain analysis of linear systems has been approached from the operational point of view. In such a presentation, the Laplace transform is introduced arbitrarily, and is viewed as a mathematical operation which simplifies the solution of integrodifferential equations. However, the Laplace transform remains a dark mystery to the student and yields very little insight. It is based upon a set of postulates that have little, if anything, to do with classical dynamics. Guillemin calls this a blackbox approach.†

In contrast to this approach the bilateral Laplace transform, in this book, is developed as an extension of the Fourier transform to complex frequencies. The unilateral Laplace transform is then derived as a special case of the bilateral Laplace transform. All the transforms are developed as tools for representing a given signal as a continuous sum (integral) of everlasting or eternal exponential (or sinusoidal) functions (exponentials existing in the entire interval $-\infty$ to ∞). For example, the Fourier transform expresses a signal as a continuous sum of exponentials (or sinusoids of real frequencies (along the $j\omega$ axis), whereas the bilaterial Laplace transform expresses a signal as a continuous sum of eternal exponentials of complex frequencies in general. The unilateral Laplace transform has the same interpretation as that of the bilateral Laplace transform except that the signals in the unilateral case are causal functions (exist only for $t > 0$). The transform of a signal signifies its frequency contents and is, therefore, also known as the spectral density function. Throughout the book the unity between all the three transforms has been emphasized.

A linear system is characterized by its transfer function which, in reality, is the response of the system to an eternal exponential signal. Since for a linear system the principle of superposition holds true, the response to an arbitrary signal is obtained as a continuous sum of the responses of the system to the eternal exponential components of the signal. Thus, a physical interpretation

---

* S. Schelkunoff, *Electromagnetic Fields*, page vii, Blaisdell, New York, 1963.

† E. A. Guilleman, *Theory of Linear Physical Systems*, page IX, Wiley, New York, 1963.

exists for quantities such as transfer function, the transform of the signal, and the response which leads to better appreciation and deeper insight into the subject. Both of the approaches mentioned above are treated and compared, although the latter (physical) is emphasized throughout the book.

The concepts of transfer function and frequency analysis are extended to distributed parameter systems. This approach proves very effective, since it allows one to view the systems with distributed parameters merely as an extension of the lumped parameter system whose transfer function varies with space coordinates.

The time- and frequency-convolution theorems are among the most powerful tools in frequency analysis. They permit an easy derivation of many important results in such diverse topics as analysis of linear systems, modulation, filtering, sampling, correlation, etc. Experience shows, however, that the concept of convolution presented under its integral definition is rather confusing to a beginner. Hence, most authors tend to avoid the use of convolution, particularly in communication theory. I feel, however, that the concept of convolution is too pervasive a phenomenon in the physical sciences and mathematics to be omitted. Moreover, with the growing interest in time-domain analysis (state variable approach) in recent years, the convolution integral has assumed an extremely significant position. It is hoped that this book will form an effective foundation for a more abstract approach of state variable methods. Although the concept of convolution is somewhat difficult for a beginner to understand, it can be mastered with heavy emphasis upon graphical interpretation. What is more significant: the student starts taking delight in the adventure of convolving, once he has mastered it. This book stresses the convolution concept and its application to the areas of linear-system analysis and communication theory. A complete chapter is devoted to the introduction of the convolution integral.

The basic concepts of information theory, such as *the unit of information, the channel capacity,* have been introduced purely from physical concepts of the nature of information.

Many examples are presented to illustrate clearly the theoretical results. In view of the present-day availability of electronic computers, the numerical computational techniques pertaining to the subject are described. In the text, most of the results in the earlier chapters have been derived for linear electrical circuits only. However, a general term "system" is deliberately used to emphasize the fact that the results hold true for any linear system.

This textbook is primarily written for advanced undergraduates who have had an elementary course in circuits or system analysis. An understanding of the book requires only a modest background in calculus and elementary circuits. Hence it can be an effective text for self-study by practicing engineers who are interested in the analysis of linear systems and communication theory.

While preparing the book, I received a great deal of assistance from many people. My greatest debt of gratitude is to my students. Their enthusiasm for studying this material in note form exceeded my own in presenting it to them. They detected some minor errors in the manuscript. I am equally indebted to Professor M. E. Van Valkenburg of the University of Illinois and Professor R. E. Scott of Northeastern University, who read most of the manuscript and made many constructive suggestions. I am also grateful to Professor T. J. Higgins of the University of Wisconsin, who read galley proofs and pointed out a number of errors. Other helpful suggestions were received from my colleagues, particularly from Professor J. L. Jones and Professor D. R. Schertz. I am indebted also to Professor Philip Weinberg, the head of the Electrical Engineering Department at Bradley University, for his encouragement. I am pleased to acknowledge invaluable assistance from Mrs. Evabeth Stone, Sue Keele, and Mrs. Evelyn Kahrs, who typed the manuscript, and from Richard Curran, Dennis Gaushell, Kenneth Moran, and Robert Thompson who assisted in proofreading and preparation of illustrations.

B. P. LATHI

Peoria, Illinois, 1965

Contents

CHAPTER 6   FREQUENCY ANALYSIS OF LINEAR SYSTEMS   203

SIGNALS, SYSTEMS
AND COMMUNICATION

chapter 1

Linear Systems

Linear systems constitute a very small fraction of the entire group of systems observed in nature. Yet they are very important for engineers and scientists. This is because most nonlinear systems can be approximated by linear systems over a limited range. Familiar examples are Ohm's law and Hooke's law. From solid-state theory, it is known that current through a conductor is not linearly proportional to the voltage across it. But for small values of currents the behavior can be closely approximated by a linear one. Similarly for almost all active networks the input and output signals bear linear relationships for small signals but this is not true for large signals.

The handling of nonlinear systems in the present state of the art is rather difficult. There are no straight-forward methods of analysis and no general solutions. Each situation and boundary condition needs individual solution. Analysis of linear systems is highly developed. A linear system can be characterized by linear algebraic equations, difference equations, or differential equations. Most of this text is devoted to the study of systems that are characterized by differential equations.

First, we shall discuss the common characteristics of linear systems and the consequences of linearity.

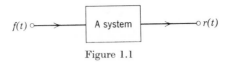

Figure 1.1

1.1 PROPERTIES OF LINEAR SYSTEMS

For every system there is an input signal (or driving function) and an output signal (or response function) (Fig. 1.1). A system processes the input signal in a certain fashion to yield the output signal. The word linear at once suggests that the response of a linear system should change linearly with the driving function (note that this is not the same as saying that the response should be linearly proportional to the driving function, although this is a special case of linearity); that is, if $r(t)$ is the response to $f(t)$ then $kr(t)$ is the response to $kf(t)$. Symbolically, if

$$f(t) \rightarrow r(t)$$

then
$$kf(t) \rightarrow kr(t) \qquad (1.1)$$

The linear system, however, implies more than Eq. 1.1. We define a linear system as a system for which it is true that if $r_1(t)$ is a response to $f_1(t)$ and $r_2(t)$ is a response to $f_2(t)$ then $r_1(t) + r_2(t)$ is a response to $f_1(t) + f_2(t)$, irrespective of the choice of $f_1(t)$ and $f_2(t)$. Symbolically, if

$$f_1(t) \rightarrow r_1(t)$$
$$f_2(t) \rightarrow r_2(t)$$

then
$$f_1(t) + f_2(t) \rightarrow r_1(t) + r_2(t) \qquad (1.2)$$

Equation 1.2 actually expresses the principle of superposition symbolically. Thus linear systems are characterized by the property of superposition. We may consider Eq. 1.2 as the defining equation of a linear system; that is, a system is linear if and only if it satisfies Eq. 1.2, irrespective of the choice of $f_1(t)$ and $f_2(t)$.

Sometimes the condition is stated in the form,

$$\alpha f_1(t) + \beta f_2(t) \rightarrow \alpha r_1(t) + \beta r_2(t) \qquad (1.3)$$

irrespective of the choice of $f_1(t)$, $f_2(t)$ and constants α and β. This will be seen to be exactly equivalent to Eq. 1.2. Note that Eq. 1.2 is stronger than and implies Eq. 1.1.

1.2 CLASSIFICATION OF LINEAR SYSTEMS

Linear systems may further be classified into lumped and distributed systems. They may also be classified as time-invariant and time-variant systems. We shall briefly discuss these classifications.

Lumped and Distributed Systems

A system is a collection of individual elements interconnected in a particular way. A lumped system consists of lumped elements. In a lumped model the energy in the system is considered to be stored or dissipated in distinct isolated elements (resistors, capacitors, inductors, masses, springs, dashpots, etc.). Also, it is assumed that the disturbance initiated at any point is propagated instantaneously at every point in the system. In electrical systems this implies that the dimensions of elements are very small compared to the wavelength of the signals to be transmitted. Analogous implication holds for mechanical systems. In a lumped electrical element, the voltage across the terminals and the current through it are related through a lumped parameter. In contrast to lumped systems we have distributed systems such as transmission lines, waveguides, antennas, semiconductor devices, beams, etc., where it is not possible to describe a system by lumped parameters. Moreover, in such systems it takes a finite amount of time for a disturbance at one point to be propagated to the other point. We thus have to deal not only with the independent variable time t but also the space variable x. The descriptive equations for distributed systems are therefore partial differential equations in contrast to ordinary differential equations describing lumped systems.

All electrical systems can be studied rigorously in terms of electromagnetic fields by using Maxwell's equations. Blind application of Maxwell's equations would, however, make the solutions to many common problems unmanageable. Lumped element circuit theory is really an approximation of electromagnetic wave theory or Maxwell's equations. This approximation is valid as long as the dimensions of the circuit are small compared to the wavelengths of the signals to be transmitted.[1] Thus, at high frequencies the lumped element circuit concept breaks down and the system has to be represented as a distributed system. One should not lose sight of this limitation on the circuit theory. The systems to be studied in this text largely fall under the category of lumped systems. Distributed-parameter systems are discussed in Chapter 9.

Time-Invariant and Time-Variant Systems

As already mentioned, linear systems can also be classified into time-invariant and time-variant systems. The systems whose parameters do not change with time are called constant-parameter or time-invariant systems. Most of the systems observed in practice belong to this category.

[1] For further discussion on this topic, see Simon Ramo and John R. Whinnery, *Fields and Waves in Modern Radio*, 2nd ed., Wiley, New York, 1953.

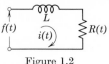

Figure 1.2

Linear time-invariant systems are characterized by linear equations (algebraic, differential, or difference equations) with constant coefficients. Circuits using passive elements are an example of time-invariant systems. On the other hand, we have systems whose parameters change with time and are therefore called variable parameter or time-variant (also time-dependent) systems. Linear time-variant systems are characterized by linear equations with time-dependent coefficients in general. An example of a simple linear time-variant system is shown in Fig. 1.2. The driving function $f(t)$ is a voltage source applied at the input terminals of a series R-L circuit where the resistor $R(t)$ is a function of time. The response is the current $i(t)$. Note that the principle of superposition must apply for a system to qualify as a linear system whether time-variant or time-invariant. The reader may convince himself that the system shown in Fig. 1.2 is a linear system. A linear modulator is another example of linear time-variant system. In this case the gain of the modulator is proportional to the modulating signal.

The system characterized by Eq. 1.4

$$\frac{d^2r}{dt^2} + a\frac{dr}{dt} + br = f(t) \tag{1.4}$$

is a linear time-invariant system, whereas the system characterized by Eq. 1.5

$$\frac{d^2r}{dt^2} + \frac{dr}{dt} + (2t + 1)r = f(t) \tag{1.5}$$

is a linear time-variant system. Note that both these systems satisfy the principle of superposition. This can be easily verified from Eqs. 1.4 and 1.5.

It is evident that for a time-invariant system if a driving function $f(t)$ yields a response function $r(t)$, then the same driving function delayed by time T will yield the same response function as before, but delayed by time T. Symbolically, if

$$f(t) \to r(t)$$

then

$$f(t - T) \to r(t - T)$$

$$\tag{1.6}$$

This property is obvious, in view of the time invariance of the system parameters. Time-variant systems, however, do not in general satisfy Eq. 1.6.

I.3 REVIEW OF TIME-DOMAIN ANALYSIS OF LINEAR SYSTEMS

Lumped-linear time-invariant systems are characterized by linear differential equations with constant coefficients. In the case of electrical circuits these equations can be obtained from Kirchhoff's laws and the voltage-current relationships of individual circuit elements. The resulting equations can be solved by using classical methods. This approach is called time-domain analysis because the independent variable in these equations is time. As the reader, no doubt, is familiar with these techniques, the details of this approach will not be discussed here. Only a brief review will be given.[2]

For electrical circuits (as well as other analogous systems), it is possible to write the equilibrium equations characterizing the system in a number of ways. All these possible sets of equations can be classified either as mesh (loop) or node equations. In each circuit there is a certain number of independent meshes and nodes. If e is the total number of active and passive elements in a circuit, and n the total number of nodes, then M and N the number of independent meshes and nodes, respectively, are given by

$$M = e - n + 1$$
$$N = n - 1 \tag{1.7}$$

Therefore, for a given network, there are M independent mesh equations and N independent node equations. Each of these equations is a linear differential equation with constant coefficients.

As mentioned earlier, there are many possible sets of mesh and node equations. A particular set is chosen according to convenience and requirements. The analysis problem thus reduces to a solution of these M or N simultaneous differential equations depending upon whether a set of mesh or node equations is chosen.

We shall illustrate the procedure by a simple example. The network shown in Fig. 1.3 will be analyzed by a mesh method. In this network e, the total number of active and passive elements is 6, and n, the total number of nodes is 5. Hence M, the number of independent loops, is

$$M = 6 - 5 + 1 = 2$$

[2] For a detailed treatment, see any introductory text on circuit theory. See, for instance, E. Brenner and M. Javid, *Analysis of Electric Circuits*, McGraw-Hill, New York, 1959, and M. E. Van Valkenberg, *Network Analysis*, Prentice-Hall, Englewood Cliffs, N.J., 2nd ed. 1964.

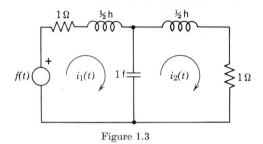

Figure 1.3

The two loops are chosen as shown in Fig. 1.3. We can now write the loop equations in terms of loop currents $i_1(t)$, $i_2(t)$, and the driving voltage $f(t)$, using Kirchhoff's voltage law and the voltage-current relationship of individual circuit elements.

$$i_1(t) + 0.5\frac{di_1}{dt} + \int [i_1(t) - i_2(t)]\, dt = f(t)$$

$$\int [i_2(t) - i_1(t)]\, dt + 0.5\frac{di_2}{dt} + i_2(t) = 0 \tag{1.8}$$

We need to solve this set of two simultaneous integrodifferential equations in two unknowns $i_1(t)$ and $i_2(t)$. We may eliminate $i_2(t)$ from the first equation and $i_1(t)$ from the second equation to obtain two equations each having only one unknown. This can be conveniently done by using operational notation. We replace the differential operator d/dt by an algebraic operator p, and the operation of integration with respect to t is replaced by $1/p$.
Thus

$$p = \frac{d}{dt}, \qquad p^n = \frac{d^n}{dt^n}$$

$$pf(t) = \frac{df}{dt}, \qquad p^n f(t) = \frac{d^n f}{dt^n}$$

$$\frac{1}{p}f(t) = \int f(t)\, dt, \quad \frac{1}{p^n}f(t) = \int\int \cdots \int\int f(t)\, dt^n$$

According to this notation, Eqs. 1.8 are transformed to

$$\left(1 + 0.5p + \frac{1}{p}\right)i_1(t) - \frac{1}{p}i_2(t) = f(t)$$

$$-\frac{1}{p}i_1(t) + \left(1 + 0.5p + \frac{1}{p}\right)i_2(t) = 0 \tag{1.9}$$

The set of simultaneous integrodifferential equations is thus converted into a set of simultaneous algebraic equations using operational notation.

We can now eliminate variables $i_1(t)$ and $i_2(t)$ from appropriate equations. Application of Cramer's rule to Eqs. 1.9 yields

$$(p^3 + 4p^2 + 8p + 8)i_1(t) = (2p^2 + 4p + 4)f(t)$$

and $\hspace{8cm}$ (1.10)

$$(p^3 + 4p^2 + 8p + 8)i_2(t) = 4f(t)$$

Note that Eqs. 1.10 are actually not algebraic equations but differential equations. When the variable p is replaced by the differential operator d/dt, Eqs. 1.10 are transformed to

$$\frac{d^3 i_1}{dt^3} + 4\frac{d^2 i_1}{dt^2} + 8\frac{di_1}{dt} + 8i_1(t) = 2\frac{d^2 f}{dt^2} + 4\frac{df}{dt} + 4f(t)$$

$$\frac{d^3 i_2}{dt^2} + 4\frac{d^2 i_2}{dt^2} + 8\frac{di_2}{dt} + 8i_2(t) = 4f(t)$$

(1.11)

These equations can now be solved by classical methods.

The above example indicates the nature of differential equations characterizing lumped linear time-invariant systems. In general, in the analysis of lumped linear time-invariant systems we encounter differential equations of the form

$$a_m\frac{d^m i}{dt^m} + a_{m-1}\frac{d^{m-1} i}{dt^{m-1}} + \cdots + a_1\frac{di}{dt} + a_0 i(t)$$

$$= b_n\frac{d^n f}{dt^n} + b_{n-1}\frac{d^{n-1} f}{dt^{n-1}} + \cdots + b_1\frac{df}{dt} + b_0 f(t) \quad (1.12)$$

In terms of operational notation this equation can be expressed as

$$(a_m p^m + a_{m-1}p^{m-1} + \cdots + a_1 p + a_0)i(t)$$

$$= (b_n p^n + b_{n-1}p^{n-1} + \cdots + b_1 p + b_0)f(t) \quad (1.13)$$

Equation 1.13 is a linear differential equation with constant coefficients and can be solved by classical methods. The solution consists of two components: (1) the source-free component, and (2) the component due to source. The source-free component $i_f(t)$ is obtained when the source $f(t)$ is made zero in Eq. 1.13. Thus, $i_f(t)$ is the solution of equation

$$(a_m p^m + a_{m-1}p^{m-1} + \cdots + a_1 p + a_0)i_f(t) = 0 \quad (1.14)$$

The component due to source $i_s(t)$ is the solution of equation

$$(a_m p^m + a_{m-1}p^{m-1} + \cdots + a_1 p + a_0)i_s(t)$$

$$= (b_n p^n + b_{n-1}p^{n-1} + \cdots + b_1 p + b_0)f(t) \quad (1.15)$$

The complete solution $i(t)$ of Eq. 1.13 is the sum of these two components

$$i(t) = i_f(t) + i_s(t) \quad (1.16)$$

It is easy to see that $i(t)$, as given in Eq. 1.16, satisfies Eq. 1.13. The reader may convince himself by substituting Eq. 1.16 in Eq. 1.13 and using Eqs. 1.14 and 1.15.

We shall briefly indicate a method of obtaining the solution to Eq. 1.14 (the source-free component) and Eq. 1.15 (the component due to source).

It can be shown that the general solution of Eq. 1.14 is given by[3]

$$i_f(t) = k_1 e^{p_1 t} + k_2 e^{p_2 t} + \cdots + k_m e^{p_m t} \tag{1.17}$$

where $k_1, k_2, \ldots, k_m$ are arbitrary constants and $p_1, p_2, \ldots, p_m$ are the roots of the polynomial

$$a_m p^m + a_{m-1} p^{m-1} + \cdots + a_1 p + a_0 = 0 \tag{1.18}$$

There are several methods available for obtaining the component due to source.[4] Here we shall discuss briefly the method of undetermined coefficients. This method is relatively simple and is applicable to a large variety of driving functions. This technique can be applied when the driving function $f(t)$ is such that it yields only a finite number of independent derivatives. In such cases, the component due to source can be assumed to be a linear combination of $f(t)$ and all its higher derivatives:

$$i_s(t) = c_1 f(t) + c_2 \frac{df}{dt} + c_3 \frac{d^2 f}{dt^2} + \cdots + c_{r+1} \frac{d^r f}{dt^r} \tag{1.19}$$

where only the first r derivatives of $f(t)$ are independent. The coefficients $c_1, c_2, \ldots, c_r$ are obtained by substituting Eq. 1.19 in Eq. 1.15 and equating the coefficients of the similar terms, on both sides.

We shall illustrate the use of these techniques in the solution of the network in Fig. 1.3. For this network we shall assume a specific driving function $f(t)$ to be $t^2 u(t)$. The differential equation for the loop current $i_1(t)$ is given by (Eq. 1.10):

$$(p^3 + 4p^2 + 8p + 8)i_1(t) = (2p^2 + 4p + 4)t^2 u(t) \tag{1.20}$$

To obtain the source-free component $i_f(t)$ we must find the roots of the polynomial

$$p^3 + 4p^2 + 8p + 8 = 0 \tag{1.21}$$

This polynomial can be factored as

$$(p + 2)(p^2 + 2p + 4) = 0 \tag{1.22}$$

---

[3] See, for instance, A. Bronwell, *Advanced Mathematics in Physics and Engineering*, page 45, McGraw-Hill, New York, 1953.

[4] A. Bronwell, cited in ref. 3, pp. 49–58. In mathematical context, the source-free component is called the complementary function and the component due to source is referred to as the particular integral.

Hence the roots of the polynomial (1.21) are

$$-2 \quad \text{and} \quad (-1 \pm j\sqrt{3})$$

The source-free component $i_f(t)$ is given by

$$i_f(t) = k_1 e^{-2t} + k_2 e^{(-1+j\sqrt{3})t} + k_3 e^{(-1-j\sqrt{3})t} \tag{1.23}$$

where k_1, k_2, and k_3 are arbitrary constants to be determined from the initial conditions of the network.

To determine the component due to source, we observe that for $f(t) = t^2 u(t)$ only the first two derivatives of $f(t)$ are independent and nonzero. Hence the component due to source may be assumed to be of the form:

$$i_s(t) = c_1 f(t) + c_2 \frac{df}{dt} + c_3 \frac{d^2 f}{dt^2} \tag{1.24}$$

$$= [c_1 t^2 + 2c_2 t + 2c_3] u(t) \tag{1.25}$$

Substitution of Eq. 1.25 in Eq. 1.20 yields

$$(p^3 + 4p^2 + 8p + 8)(c_1 t^2 + 2c_2 t + 2c_3) u(t)$$
$$= (2p^2 + 4p + 4) t^2 u(t) \quad (1.26)$$

Recall that the symbol p represents the operation of differentiation. Carrying out the actual operation of differentiation in Eq. 1.26 we get

$$8(c_1 + 2c_2 + 2c_3) + 16(c_1 + c_2)t + 8c_1 t^2 = 4 + 8t + 4t^2$$

Equating the like powers of t on both sides, we get

$$8c_1 + 16c_2 + 16c_3 = 4$$
$$16c_1 + 16c_2 = 8$$
$$8c_1 = 4$$

From this set of simultaneous equations we obtain

$$c_1 = \tfrac{1}{2}, \qquad c_2 = c_3 = 0$$

Hence

$$i_s(t) = \tfrac{1}{2} t^2 u(t)$$

The complete solution of $i_1(t)$ is thus given by

$$i_1(t) = i_f(t) + i_s(t)$$
$$= k_1 e^{-2t} + k_2 e^{(-1+j\sqrt{3})t} + k_3 e^{(-1-j\sqrt{3})t} + \tfrac{1}{2} t^2 u(t) \quad (1.27)$$

The arbitrary constants k_1, k_2, and k_3 are determined from the initial conditions of the circuit. Let the initial conditions be given as

$$i_1(0) = 0, \qquad \frac{di_1}{dt}(0) = 4, \qquad \frac{d^2 i_1}{dt^2}(0) = 1 \tag{1.28}$$

Also

$$i_1(0), \quad \frac{di_1}{dt}(0), \quad \text{and} \quad \frac{d^2i_1}{dt^2}(0)$$

can be obtained from Eq. 1.27 by successive differentiation. Equating these values to the initial conditions expressed in Eq. 1.28, we get

$$k_1 = 2; \qquad k_2 = (-1 - j\sqrt{3}), \qquad k_3 = (-1 + j\sqrt{3})$$

Substituting these values in Eq. 1.27, we get

$$i_1(t) = 2e^{-2t} + (-1 - j\sqrt{3})e^{(-1+j\sqrt{3})t} + (-1 + j\sqrt{3})e^{(-1-j\sqrt{3})t} + \tfrac{1}{2}t^2u(t)$$

$$= 2e^{-2t} - 2e^{-t}(\cos\sqrt{3}t - \sqrt{3}\sin\sqrt{3}t) + \tfrac{1}{2}t^2u(t)$$

Similar techniques may be used to obtain $i_2(t)$ from Eq. 1.10.

Exponential Driving Function

If the driving function $f(t)$ is an exponential function of time, a great deal of simplification is effected in the solution of the component due to source. Since, for an exponential function, all the derivatives are also exponential functions of the same form, none of the derivatives are independent. Hence the component due to source must be of the same form as the driving function itself.

$$i_s(t) = cf(t) \tag{1.29}$$

Thus, if

$$f(t) = e^{st}$$

$$i_s(t) = ce^{st}$$

The constant c can be obtained by substituting Eq. 1.29 in Eq. 1.15. This yields

$$(a_m p^m + a_{m-1}p^{m-1} + \cdots + a_1 p + a_0)ce^{st}$$
$$= (b_n p^n + b_{n-1}p^{n-1} + \cdots + b_1 p + b_0)e^{st} \tag{1.30}$$

Note that

$$pe^{st} = \frac{d}{dt}e^{st} = se^{st}$$

and

$$p^r e^{st} = s^r e^{st}$$

Substituting these results in Eq. 1.30, we get

$$(a_m s^m + a_{m-1}s^{m-1} + \cdots + a_1 s + a_0)c$$
$$= (b_n s^n + b_{n-1}s^{n-1} + \cdots + b_1 s + b_0)$$

Hence

$$c = \frac{b_n s^n + b_{n-1} s^{n-1} + \cdots + b_1 s + b_0}{a_m s^m + a_{m-1} s^{m-1} + \cdots + a_1 s + a_0} \tag{1.31}$$

$$= H(s) \tag{1.32}$$

Hence the component due to source for an exponential driving function e^{st} is given by $H(s)e^{st}$ where $H(s)$ is given by Eq. 1.31. This is a very significant result, and is the basis of the frequency-domain analysis to be discussed in the next few chapters. It states that for an exponential driving function, the response component due to source is also an exponential function of the same form as the driving function.

As an example, we shall again consider the network in Fig. 1.3. The driving function $f(t)$ will now be assumed to be e^{st}. The loop currents $i_1(t)$ and $i_2(t)$ can be found from the differential Eqs. 1.10. We shall now evaluate the current $i_1(t)$. The source-free component of this current is obtained by making $f(t)$ equal to zero. We have already found this component in Eq. 1.23. The component due to source is $i_s(t)$ given by (Eq. 1.29):

$$i_s(t) = ce^{st}$$

where c is found from Eq. 1.31. From Eqs. 1.31 and 1.10 it follows that

$$c = \frac{2s^2 + 4s + 4}{s^3 + 4s^2 + 8s + 8}$$

Hence the component due to source is

$$i_s(t) = \frac{2s^2 + 4s + 4}{s^3 + 4s^2 + 8s + 8} e^{st}$$

The complete response $i_1(t)$ is given by

$$i_1(t) = i_f(t) + i_s(t)$$

$$= k_1 e^{-2t} + k_2 e^{(-1+j\sqrt{3})t} + k_3 e^{(-1-j\sqrt{3})t} + \frac{2s^2 + 4s + 4}{s^3 + 4s^2 + 8s + 8} e^{st}$$

where k_1, k_2, and k_3 are arbitrary constants to be determined from the initial conditions.

1.4 THE TRANSIENT AND THE STEADY-STATE COMPONENTS OF THE RESPONSE

The two components of the response referred to in the previous section are also designated in various ways in the literature. For a stable system, the source-free component always decays with time.[5] In fact, a stable system is defined as one whose source-free component decays with time. For this reason, the source-free component is also designated as the transient component and the component due to source is called the steady-state component.[6] Throughout this book, the terms source-free component and transient component will be used synonymously. Similarly, the terms component due to source and steady-state component will mean the same thing.

The source-free component is obtained by making the driving function go to zero. It is obvious that this component is independent of the driving function, and depends only on the nature of the system. Thus, the source-free component is characteristic of the system itself. This is the response which a system can sustain itself without a driving function $[f(t) = 0]$. This is, therefore, a response that is characteristic of the system, and is also known as the *natural response* of the system. The component due to source (the steady-state component), on the other hand, depends upon the nature of the system and the driving function. This component of response is not the natural response of the system but is forced upon it by the external driving function. For this reason, this component is also referred to as the *forced response*.

To reiterate: the source-free response, the transient response, and the natural response are synonymous terms and represent the component of the response when the driving function is made zero; the response due to source, the steady-state response, and the forced response mean the same thing and represent the component of response due to the driving function.

---

[5] An exception to this is an idealized lossless system where the source-free component may have a constant amplitude.

[6] I must caution the reader here regarding the definition of the transient and the steady-state components. Presently there are no standard definitions for these terms and different authors define them in different ways.

chapter 2

The Exponential Signal in Linear Systems

In the previous chapter the system under consideration was analyzed by solving the integrodifferential equations characterizing the system. This approach is very general and can be used to analyze any system, whether linear or nonlinear. The differential equations encountered in the analysis of linear systems are linear differential equations (such as those observed in Chapter 1) and are relatively easy to handle. For nonlinear systems, however, the equilibrium equations characterizing the system are non-linear differential equations and are rather difficult to solve. This approach is characterized by the fact that the independent variable is time t, and hence this method is known as the time-domain analysis. In this book we are concerned strictly with linear systems. The characteristics of a linear system may change with time (time-variant linear systems) or may be constant (time-invariant linear systems). We shall be mainly interested in time-invariant systems, since most of the linear systems fall under this category.

The most important feature that distinguishes a linear system is the applicability of the principle of superposition. This principle applies to linear systems only. Thus far we have not exploited this property in analyzing linear systems. We naturally expect that the use of this property should simplify the analysis and this indeed is the case. Since the principle of superposition is the basis of the techniques to be discussed, we shall restate the property.

For a linear system, if $r_1(t)$ is the response to a driving function $f_1(t)$ and if $r_2(t)$ is the response of the same system to another driving function $f_2(t)$ then, according to the principle of superposition, $r_1(t) + r_2(t)$ will be the response of the system to a driving function $f_1(t) + f_2(t)$, irrespective of the choice of $f_1(t)$ and $f_2(t)$. This apparently innocent-looking principle has far-reaching implications and opens many avenues for analyzing linear systems. This principle implies that if we want to find the response of a system to a complex driving function, we may separate this function into a number of simple components, that is, represent the given function as a sum of simpler functions. The response of the system to each simple component may be evaluated with less difficulty. The desired response is then the sum of all the responses to the individual components. The next important question is: What component functions shall we use to represent a given function? It is evident *that the component functions must belong to a class of functions so that it should be possible to represent any arbitrary driving function encountered in practice as a sum (discrete or continuous) of component functions.* There are a number of classes of functions that satisfy this requirement. For example, it is possible to represent any arbitrary function as a continuous sum of exponential functions, impulse functions, step functions, ramp functions, and other functions of higher powers of t. The uses of impulse, step, ramp, and other higher-order functions lead to analysis techniques that will be treated later in Chapter 10, concerning convolution integral. First we shall consider the case of exponential functions. Generally, any driving function $f(t)$, encountered in practice, can be expressed as a sum (discrete or continuous) of exponential functions. The response of a linear system to a general exponential driving function can be easily determined. By virtue of linearity, the principle of superposition applies, and the response of the system to any driving function $f(t)$ can be evaluated as a sum (discrete or continuous) of the responses of the system to individual exponential components of $f(t)$. This approach will be called the *frequency analysis approach or the frequency domain analysis.*

2.1 THE EXPONENTIAL FUNCTION

The exponential function is perhaps the most important function to engineers, physicists, and mathematicians alike. This is because the exponential function has almost a magiclike property that its derivative and the integral yield the function itself. For example,

$$\frac{d}{dt} e^t = \int e^t \, dt = e^t \tag{2.1}$$

This function has been liberally used by engineers and physicists starting from such simple applications as phasors in steady-state circuits to more sophisticated application of the Schrödinger equation in quantum mechanics. Many of the phenomena observed in nature can be described by exponential functions. It is therefore natural that we choose exponential functions for the purpose of analyzing linear systems by the principle of superposition. We must, however, justify the choice on more firm grounds. It turns out that the main reason for using exponential functions in analyzing linear systems can be attributed to certain important properties of that function. They are as follows.

(1) Every function or waveform encountered in practice can always be expressed as a sum (discrete or continuous) of various exponential functions.

(2) The response of a linear time invariant system to an exponential function e^{st} is also an exponential function[1] $H(s)e^{st}$.

By exponential function, we mean a function

$$Ae^{st} \qquad (-\infty < t < \infty) \qquad\qquad (2.2)$$

where s is complex in general and the function is eternal, that is, it exists in the entire interval $(-\infty < t < \infty)$. The complex quantity s, the index of the exponential, is known as the complex frequency. The reason for this designation will become clear later. Note that since s is complex in general, the following functions can also be categorized as exponential functions:

(a) A constant, $k = ke^{ot}$
(b) A monotonic exponential, e^{at}
(c) A sinusoidal function, $\sin \omega t = (1/2j)(e^{j\omega t} - e^{-j\omega t})$
(d) An exponentially varying sinusoid,

$$e^{-at} \sin \omega t = \frac{1}{2j} [e^{(-a+j\omega)t} - e^{(-a-j\omega)t}]$$

Exponential functions, therefore, cover a variety of important waveforms encountered in practice. In general, the exponent s is complex:

$$s = \sigma + j\omega \qquad\qquad (2.3)$$

Therefore

$$e^{st} = e^{(\sigma+j\omega)t}$$
$$= e^{\sigma t}e^{j\omega t}$$

---

[1] There is a certain limitation on this statement. It is true only if the transient component of the system decays faster than the magnitude of the function e^{st}.

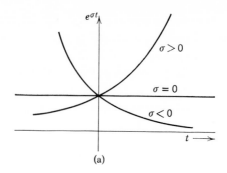

(a)

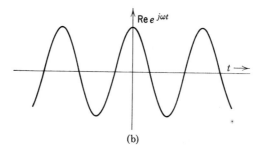

(b)

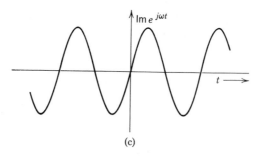

(c)

Figure 2.1

The waveforms of e^{st} depend upon the nature of s. If s is real (that is, if $\omega = 0$), then e^{st} is given by $e^{\sigma t}$ and can be represented by monotonically increasing or decreasing function of time (Fig. 2.1a), depending upon whether $\sigma > 0$ or $\sigma < 0$. On the other hand, if s is imaginary (that is, $\sigma = 0$), then e^{st} is given by $e^{j\omega t}$. The function $e^{j\omega t}$ is complex and has real and imaginary parts:

$$e^{j\omega t} = \cos \omega t + j \sin \omega t$$

Thus

$$\text{Re} \, (e^{j\omega t}) = \cos \omega t$$

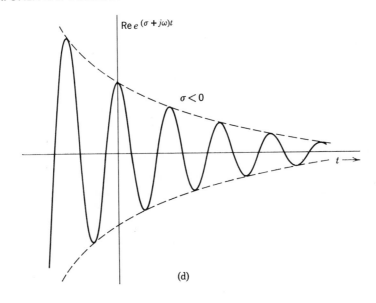

(d)

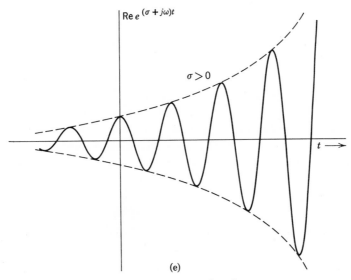

(e)

Figure 2.1 (*continued*)

and

$$\text{Im} \ (e^{j\omega t}) = \sin \ \omega t$$

The function $e^{j\omega t}$ can, therefore, be represented graphically by a real part and an imaginary part. Each of these functions is a sinusoidal function of frequency ω and has a constant amplitude (Figs. 2.1*b* and 2.1*c*).

We can extend this discussion to the case where s is complex, that is, both σ and ω are nonzero, as follows:

$$e^{st} = e^{\sigma t} e^{j \omega t}$$

$$= e^{\sigma t}(\cos \omega t + j \sin \omega t)$$

$$= e^{\sigma t} \cos \omega t + j e^{\sigma t} \sin \omega t$$

Therefore, the function e^{st} has real and imaginary parts when s is complex. Here, both functions $e^{\sigma t} \cos \omega t$ and $e^{\sigma t} \sin \omega t$ represent functions oscillating at angular frequency ω, with the amplitude increasing or decreasing exponentially depending upon whether σ is positive or negative (Figs. 2.1d and 2.1e).

If s is imaginary, then e^{st} is represented by $e^{j \omega t}$ where ω connotes the frequency of the signal. This same concept is extended to the case when s is complex. We call the variable s in the function e^{st} the complex frequency. This designation, however, is slightly misleading because we always associate the term frequency with a periodic function. Now when the variable s is real (that is, $\omega = 0$), then e^{st} is represented by $e^{\sigma t}$ which increases or decreases monotonically (Fig. 2.1a). Yet, according to this designation, the signal $e^{\sigma t}$ has a frequency σ. It will be more appropriate to say that the frequency of the signal e^{st} is given by the imaginary part of the variable s. To emphasize this distinction, it is often said that ω is the real frequency of the signal e^{st}. Throughout this text the complex variable s will be referred to as the complex frequency. The complex frequency can be conveniently represented on a plane as shown in Fig. 2.2. The horizontal axis is the real axis (σ axis) and the vertical axis is the imaginary axis (ω axis). Notice that the frequencies of exponential signals with monotonically increasing or decreasing amplitudes (Fig. 2.1a) are represented on the real axis (σ axis.) The frequencies of sinusoidally oscillating signals of constant amplitude (Figs. 2.1b and 2.1c) are represented on the imaginary axis (ω axis). For the functions shown in Figs. 2.1d and 2.1e, the frequency s is complex and does not lie on either axis. For Fig. 2.1d, σ is negative and s lies to the left of the imaginary axis. On the other hand, for Fig. 2.1e, σ is positive and s lies to the right of the imaginary axis. Note that for $\sigma > 0$, the amplitudes of the functions increase exponentially and for $\sigma < 0$, the amplitude decays exponentially. Thus, the s plane is distinguished into two parts: the left half plane (LHP), which represents exponentially decaying signals, and the right half plane (RHP), which represents exponentially growing signals.

Thus, each point on the complex frequency plane corresponds to a certain mode of the exponential function. At this point one may wonder

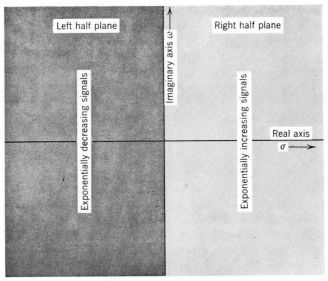

Figure 2.2   The s plane.

about the frequencies lying along the $-j\omega$ axis. The frequencies of the signals represented along the $-j\omega$ axis appear to be negative according to our designation of the frequency. What is a negative frequency? By its very definition, the frequency is an inherently positive quantity. The number of times that a function passes through a fixed point, say zero, in 1 second is always positive. How shall we then interpret a negative frequency? The confusion arises because we are defining the frequency not as number of cycles per second of a particular waveform but as an index of the exponential function. Hence the negative frequencies are associated with negative exponents. It should be noted that signals of negative and positive frequencies can be combined to obtain real functions. Thus

$$e^{j\omega t} + e^{-j\omega t} = 2 \cos \omega t \qquad (2.4)$$

Similarly, signals of two complex conjugate frequencies $(\sigma + j\omega)$ and $(\sigma - j\omega)$ can form real signals:

$$e^{(\sigma+j\omega)t} + e^{(\sigma-j\omega)t} = 2e^{\sigma t} \cos \omega t \qquad (2.5)$$

This result is quite significant. It will be seen in the next chapter that any real function of time encountered in practice can always be expressed as a continuous sum of exponential functions which occur in pairs with complex conjugate frequencies.[2]

---

[2] It can be shown by using the theory of complex variables that although a real function of time can be represented by the continuous sum of complex exponential functions occurring in pairs of complex conjugate frequencies, it is not a necessary condition.

Exponential functions possess another very important property, known as orthogonality. The full implications of this property will be discussed in Chapter 3. A consequence of it, however, is that any function of time $f(t)$ can be represented by the sum (discrete or continuous) of various eternal exponential functions. It will be shown that any periodic function can be expressed as a sum of discrete exponential functions.

$$f(t) = C_1 e^{s_1 t} + C_2 e^{s_2 t} + \cdots + C_n e^{s_n t} + \cdots + \qquad (-\infty < t < \infty)$$
$$= \sum_r C_r e^{s_r t} \qquad\qquad\qquad\qquad\qquad\qquad (2.6)$$

Here C represents the amplitude of the rth exponential of frequency s_r. Any nonperiodic function can be expressed as a continuous sum of external exponential functions as:

eternal

$$f(t) = \int_{S_A}^{S_B} C(s) e^{st}\, ds \qquad (-\infty < t < \infty) \qquad (2.7)$$

Here $C(s)$ expresses the amplitude distribution of various exponentials. Note that Eq. 2.7 is an extension of Eq. 2.6. In Eq. 2.6, $f(t)$ is expressed as the sum of discrete exponential components of frequencies $s_1, s_2, \ldots, s_r$, etc., whereas in Eq. 2.7, $f(t)$ is expressed as a continuous sum of the exponentials of all the frequencies lying along the path from s_A to s_B. The amplitude distribution of various exponentials along this path is given by $C(s)$. This topic will be discussed in detail in Chapter 3.

In all this discussion it is important to realize that the exponentials that we are talking about are eternal, that is, they exist in the entire interval $(-\infty < t < \infty)$. Any function $f(t)$ can be expressed as a sum (discrete or continuous) of these eternal exponentials. Let us consider a function $f(t)$ which exists only for $t > 0$ and is identically zero for $t < 0$. One might wonder whether it will be possible to express such a function in terms of a sum of eternal functions, which exist over the entire interval $(-\infty < t < \infty)$. The answer is yes. Such functions can always be expressed as a sum of eternal exponential functions. These exponential functions add in such a way as to cancel one another for $t < 0$ and yield the desired function for $t > 0$.

2.2 RESPONSE OF LINEAR SYSTEMS TO EXPONENTIAL FUNCTIONS

It was indicated in Chapter 1 that the response of a linear system has two components: the source-free component and the component due to source. These components are commonly called the transient component and the steady-state component, respectively. The nature of the transient component is characteristic of the system alone, whereas the nature of the steady-state component depends upon the system and the driving function as well.

It was also shown in Chapter 1 that the steady-state response of a linear system to a driving function e^{st} is given by $H(s)e^{st}$, which is an exponential function of the same frequency. As an example, consider a series R-L circuit driven by a voltage source e^{st} as shown in Fig. 2.3. Assume that $i(t)$ is our response function. The loop equation for this network is given by

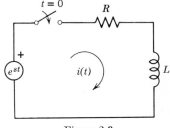

Figure 2.3

$$Ri(t) + L\frac{di}{dt} = e^{st} \qquad (2.8)$$

Equation 2.8 can be solved by techniques discussed in Chapter 1. The general solution for $i(t)$ is given by

$$i(t) = Ae^{-Rt/L} + \frac{e^{st}}{(R + Ls)} \qquad (2.9)$$

where A is an arbitrary constant which can be determined from the initial conditions.

Let

$$\frac{1}{(R + Ls)} = H(s)$$

Then

$$i(t) = Ae^{-Rt/L} + H(s)e^{st}$$

Notice that the response $i(t)$ has two components: $Ae^{-Rt/L}$, the transient component whose nature is characteristic of the network alone, and the steady-state component $H(s)e^{st}$, which has the same frequency as that of the driving function. The frequency of the transient component is $-R/L$ and hence this component decays with time. For every stable system, the transient component decays with time.[3] The steady-state component $H(s)e^{st}$ may or may not decay with time, depending upon the value of s. If it is assumed that the transient component decays faster than the steady-state component, then after a long time the transient

[3] In fact, a stable system, by definition, has the decaying transient component. See Chapter 7 for more discussion.

component will become negligible compared to the steady-state component. In other words, the steady-state component will dominate the transient component.[4]

In the previous example, if

$$\text{Re } s = \sigma > -\frac{R}{L} \tag{2.10}$$

then it is evident that after a long time, the magnitude of $e^{-Rt/L}$ will become negligible compared to the magnitude of e^{st}. Under these conditions the steady-state component will dominate the transient component, and hence after a sufficiently long time the response of the system to the exponential function e^{st} will consist entirely of the steady-state component $H(s)e^{st}$.

If the magnitude of the exponential function e^{st} decays slower than the transient component of the system, then the signal e^{st} is said to satisfy the dominance condition. For the example of the R-L circuit considered above, Eq. 2.10 gives the dominance condition.

Now, suppose the driving function e^{st} were applied at $t = -\infty$ instead of $t = 0$ and, further, suppose that the transient component decays faster than the function $e^{\sigma t}$; that is, if the dominance condition is satisfied, then at any finite time t, the transient component would have vanished and the response will consist entirely of the steady-state component $H(s)e^{st}$, which is also an exponential function of frequency s. We therefore reach a very important conclusion: *the response of a linear system to an eternal exponential function* $e^{st}(-\infty < t < \infty)$ *consists entirely of an exponential function of the same frequency.* Of course, it is understood that the statement is true only for those values of s which will satisfy the dominance condition. There is thus a minimum value of σ, say σ_m, for which the conclusion is valid. The complex frequency s of the driving function e^{st} must satisfy

$$\text{Re } s > \sigma_m \tag{2.11}$$

We can demonstrate this easily for the case of R—L circuit in Fig. 2.3. Let this circuit be switched on at $t = T$ and assume that the initial energy storage is zero, that is $i(T) = 0$. From Eq. 2.9, we get

$$i(T) = A\, e^{-RT/L} + \frac{e^{sT}}{R + Ls} = 0$$

---

[4] This discussion is not restricted to stable systems, but applies as well to unstable systems where the transient component grows with time. In such cases we choose the exponential function e^{st} which also grows with time at a faster rate than the transient component. The steady-state component thus will dominate the transient component. In such cases, s must lie in the right half of the complex frequency plane.

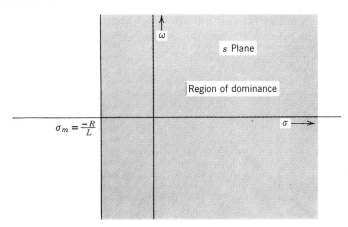

Figure 2.4

Hence

$$A = \frac{-e^{(s+R/L)T}}{R + Ls}$$

If the circuit is switched on at $T = -\infty$, then obviously $A = 0$ provided $\mathrm{Re}\, s > -R/L$

and

$$i(t) = H(s)e^{st} \qquad (2.12)$$

Note that if $\mathrm{Re}\, s < -R/L$ (that is if the dominance condition is not satisfied), $A = \infty$ and the response $i(t)$ to an eternal exponential is infinity. The reader can easily show that these results are valid for any initial condition.

We have seen in Chapter 1, that for an exponential driving function e^{st}, the response component due to source is of the form $H(s)e^{st}$. We have shown this valid for lumped-linear systems (such systems can be described by ordinary linear differential equations with constant coefficients). This result, however is general and holds for any linear time-invariant system, whether a lumped or a distributed parameter system. We shall now give a general proof of this inference for any linear time-invariant system. In fact, it will be shown that this property of exponential functions follows as a consequence of linearity and the time invariance of the system. Let a driving function $e^{st}(-\infty < t < \infty)$ be applied to a linear time-invariant system. The response function will, in general, be a function of s and t and will be denoted by $r_e(s, t)$. Thus

$$e^{st} \rightarrow r_e(s, t)$$

Let us define

$$H(s, t) = \frac{r_e(s, t)}{e^{st}}$$

then

$$r_e(s, t) = H(s, t)e^{st} \qquad (2.13)$$

Suppose now we apply a driving function which is a delayed exponential, that is, $e^{s(t-T)}$. Because the system is time invariant, the response will also be delayed by time T. Thus the new response will be

$$r_e(s, t - T) = H(s, t - T)e^{s(t-T)} \qquad (2.14)$$

But the delayed driving function $e^{s(t-T)}$ can be expressed as the product of the original driving function e^{st} with the complex constant e^{-sT}. That is,

$$e^{s(t-T)} = e^{st}e^{-sT}$$

Hence, by the property of linearity, the response to the delayed function must be the product of the original response $r_e(s, t)$ with the complex constant e^{-sT}. That is,

$$r_e(s, t - T) = r_e(s, t)e^{-sT}$$
$$= H(s, t)e^{s(t-T)} \qquad (2.15)$$

From Eqs. 2.14 and 2.15, it follows that

$$H(s, t - T) = H(s, t)$$

for all values of T.

This is only possible if $H(s, t)$ is independent of time. Under this condition, H is a function of s alone and $H(s, t)$ may be simply expressed as $H(s)$.

Therefore, from Eq. 2.13, we have

$$r_e(s, t) = H(s)e^{st} \qquad (2.16)$$

$H(s)$ is called the *transfer function* of the system. We have thus proved the result for a general linear time-invariant system.

The discussion, thus far, regarding the transfer function $H(s)$ may create some confusion. It must be clearly understood that if a driving function e^{st} is applied to a system at any finite time, say $t = 0$, then the response of the system will consist of a transient component as well as the steady-state component $H(s)e^{st}$. If, however, the exponential signal e^{st} is applied at $t = -\infty$ (that is, the eternal exponential signal), then at any finite time the response will be given entirely by $H(s)e^{st}$ (provided, of course, that the dominance condition is satisfied). This distinction should be properly understood. We shall repeat it once again. The response of a linear time-invariant system to an eternal exponential signal e^{st} is $H(s)e^{st}$, where $H(s)$ is called the transfer function of the system. If, however, the exponential signal e^{st} is applied at some finite time, then the response will consist of a transient component and a steady-state component $H(s)e^{st}$. *The steady-state component of response, therefore, becomes the entire response when the signal is applied at* t $= -\infty$, *and provided that the dominance condition is satisfied.*

One may wonder about the value of the eternal exponential function at $t = -\infty$. The function e^{st} has a unit value at $t = 0$ regardless of the value of s. If s lies in RHP, the function vanishes at $t = -\infty$, whereas for values of s lying in LHP, the function goes to infinity at $t = -\infty$. Thus, in either case, it appears that the eternal exponential function is undefined at $-\infty$. Under such conditions it is meaningless to talk about exciting a system by eternal exponential function at $t = -\infty$. We can solve this dilemma by a limiting process. Instead of considering the signal as starting at $t = -\infty$, we can assume that it starts at $t = -T$ where T is arbitrarily large but finite. If T is made large enough, all the results discussed previously hold true.

2.3 FOUNDATIONS OF THE FREQUENCY-ANALYSIS APPROACH

We are now in a position to discuss an entirely different approach to the analyzing of linear systems. This method exploits the principle of superposition to advantage in linear-system analysis.

If $H(s)$ is the transfer function of a given linear system then the response of the system to an eternal exponential function e^{st} is given by $H(s)e^{st}$. Assume that we wish to find the response of this system to a certain driving function $f(t)$. By virtue of the property of orthogonality of the exponential function, $f(t)$ can be expressed as a sum (either discrete or continuous) of eternal exponential functions. Consider first the discrete case. If $f(t)$ is a periodic function over the entire interval $(-\infty < t < \infty)$, then it can be expressed as a discrete sum:

$$f(t) = C_1 e^{s_1 t} + C_2 e^{s_2 t} + \cdots + C_n e^{s_n t} + \cdots$$
$$= \sum_r C_r e^{s_r t} \qquad (-\infty < t < \infty) \tag{2.17}$$

According to the principle of superposition, the response of the system to $f(t)$ will be given by a sum of the responses of the system to individual exponential components. The response $r(t)$ is therefore given by

$$r(t) = C_1 H(s_1)e^{s_1 t} + C_2 H(s_2)e^{s_2 t} + \cdots + C_r H(s_r)e^{s_r t} + \cdots$$
$$= \sum_r C_r H(s_r)e^{s_r t} \qquad (-\infty < t < \infty) \tag{2.18}$$

If, however, $f(t)$ is a nonperiodic function, then it can be expressed as a continuous sum of eternal exponential functions, that is,

$$f(t) = \int_{s_A}^{s_B} C(s)e^{st}\, ds$$

The response $r(t)$ will also be given by a continuous sum of the responses of the system to individual exponential components:

$$r(t) = \int_{s_A}^{s_B} H(s)C(s)e^{st}\,ds \qquad (-\infty < t < \infty) \qquad (2.19)$$

Note that it is tacitly assumed in this discussion that the variable s in the above equations lies in the region of validity, that is, in the region in the s plane where the magnitude of e^{st} decays slower than the transient component of the system.[5] This region is also known as the region of convergence for the reasons explained in Chapter 5.

Observe that the response $r(t)$ of the system to a driving function $f(t)$ must contain the transient as well as the steady-state components. However, it is evident from Eq. 2.19 that by using the frequency-analysis approach it is possible to express $r(t)$ entirely in terms of $H(s)$, the steady-state response of the system to the driving function e^{st}.

The response $r(t)$ in Eq. 2.19 is expressed as a continuous sum of eternal exponential functions. Now consider a case where the driving function $f(t)$ exists only for $t > 0$ and is zero for $t < 0$. For a physical system, if the driving function starts at $t = 0$, then its response $r(t)$ must also be zero for $t < 0$. However, Eq. 2.19 expresses $r(t)$ as a continuous sum of exponentials which exist in the entire interval $(-\infty < t < \infty)$. This may appear rather strange. However, if $f(t) = 0$ for $t < 0$, then it turns out that the continuous sum of exponential functions in Eq. 2.19 yields zero value for $t < 0$ and the desired value of $r(t)$ for $t > 0$.

In order to discuss further the topic of frequency-analysis techniques, we must first develop the tools for expressing any arbitrary waveform as a sum (discrete or continuous) of eternal exponential functions. This is accomplished by the techniques of frequency transforms, which will be fully discussed in the next three chapters. Hence, we shall postpone the study of frequency-analysis techniques until the end of Chapter 5. The quantity of great importance in the frequency-analysis approach is obviously the transfer function $H(s)$. The techniques for evaluating the transfer function of a system will now be developed.

2.4 THE TRANSFER FUNCTION OF A SYSTEM

In the frequency-analysis approach, the response of a system can be evaluated from the knowledge of the driving function and the transfer function of the system. It therefore follows in this approach that the

---

[5] It can be shown from the theory of complex variables that this condition is sufficient but not necessary. See the discussion in Section 5.6.

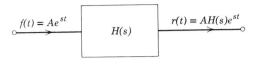

Figure 2.5

system is characterized by its transfer function $H(s)$ and, hence, this function is a very important quantity. We shall devote this section to the techniques of evaluating the transfer function of a given system.

Let us review the definition of the transfer function $H(s)$ of a system. The response of a linear time-invariant system to a driving function $e^{st}(-\infty < t < \infty)$ is given by $H(s)e^{st}$. Thus, by definition, the transfer function of a system is the ratio of the response function to the driving function when the driving function is of the form $Ae^{st}(-\infty < t < \infty)$. It should be remembered that the concept of transfer function is meaningful to linear systems alone. If the driving function

$$f(t) = Ae^{st} \qquad (-\infty < t < \infty)$$

then the response function

$$r(t) = AH(s)e^{st}$$

and the transfer function

$$H(s) = \frac{AH(s)e^{st}}{Ae^{st}} = \frac{r(t)}{f(t)} \tag{2.20}$$

Thus, if the input function to a system is Ae^{st}, then its output function will be $AH(s)e^{st}$ (Fig. 2.5). The ratio of the output amplitude to the input amplitude is also sometimes called the gain of the system. The transfer function $H(s)$ is therefore the gain of a system when the input function is of the form Ae^{st}.

The basic definition of $H(s)$, as expressed in Eq. 2.20, can be used to evaluate the transfer function of a system. Before proceeding any further, it is necessary to comment about the system characterization by a transfer function. By definition, the transfer function of a system is the ratio of the response function to the driving function when the driving function is of the form Ae^{st}. For a given system, however, there are a number of positions where a driving function may be applied and where a response may be observed. Thus, for a given system, the transfer function is not a unique quantity unless the location of excitation (driving point or the input terminals) and of the response (response point or the output terminals) are specified. In any system, an excitation at a specific location causes different responses in different positions of the system.

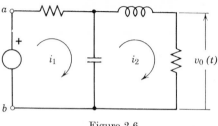

Figure 2.6

The transfer function, which is the ratio of the response to the excitation (for exponential functions), would therefore be different for responses at different positions in the system. It is therefore necessary to qualify the transfer function of a system by specifying the locations of excitation and response. In a network, for example, an exponential excitation at some terminal will cause different currents in different loops. If any one of the loop currents is considered as the response, then the transfer function will be different for different loop currents. In Fig. 2.6, for example, one may consider either i_1, i_2, or the voltage v_0 as the response when a driving function is a voltage applied across terminals ab. It is evident that there will be a different transfer function for each of these quantities considered as a response.

In this chapter we shall deal exclusively with the lumped time-invariant parameter systems that are described by ordinary linear differential equations with constant coefficients such as those encountered in Chapter 1. Distributed parameter systems will be considered in Chapter 9.

We shall now turn to the techniques of evaluating a transfer function of a system.

Transfer Function from the System's Equations

A transfer function can be readily evaluated from the knowledge of the equations describing the system. It was shown in Chapter 1 that, for a lumped-linear system, the relationship between the driving function $f(t)$ and the response function $r(t)$ can, in general, be expressed as

$$a_m \frac{d^m r}{dt^m} + a_{m-1} \frac{d^{m-1} r}{dt^{m-1}} + \cdots + a_1 \frac{dr}{dt} + a_0 r(t)$$

$$= b_n \frac{d^n f}{dt^n} + b_{n-1} \frac{d^{n-1} f}{dt^{n-1}} + \cdots + a_1 \frac{df}{dt} + a_0 f(t) \quad (2.21)$$

If

$$f(t) = e^{st} \quad (-\infty < t < \infty)$$

then
$$r(t) = H(s)e^{st}$$

and
$$\frac{d^k}{dt^k} f(t) = s^k e^{st}$$

$$\frac{d^k}{dt^k} r(t) = s^k H(s)e^{st}$$
(2.22)

Substitution of Eq. 2.22 in Eq. 2.21 yields

$$(a_m s^m + a_{m-1}s^{m-1} + \cdots + a_1 s + a_0)H(s)e^{st}$$
$$= (b_n s^n + b_{n-1}s^{n-1} + \cdots + b_1 s + b_0)$$

Therefore
$$H(s) = \frac{b_n s^n + b_{n-1}s^{n-1} + \cdots + b_1 s + b_0}{a_m s^m + a_{m-1}s^{m-1} + \cdots + a_1 s + a_0}$$
(2.23)

Note that if we substitute s^k for (d^k/dt^k) in the original differential Eq. 2.21, we get

$$(a_m s^m + a_{m-1}s^{m-1} + \cdots + a_1 s + a_0)r(t)$$
$$= (b_n s^n + b_{n-1}s^{n-1} + \cdots + b_1 s + b_0)f(t)$$

and
$$\frac{r(t)}{f(t)} = \frac{b_n s^n + b_{n-1}s^{n-1} + \cdots + b_1 s + b_0}{a_m s^m + a_{m-1}s^{m-1} + \cdots + a_1 s + a_0}$$
(2.24)

It is evident from Eqs. 2.23 and 2.24 that if we replace (d^k/dt^k) by s^k in the original system equation, then the ratio $r(t)/f(t)$ yields the desired transfer function $H(s)$. If the equation also contains integrals, then the kth integral should be replaced by s^{-k}, that is,

$$\int \cdots \int \int dt^k \text{ should be replaced by } s^{-k}.$$

Example 2.1

A driving voltage $v(t)$ is applied across the series R-L-C network (Fig. 2.7). If the current i is taken as the response, find the transfer function.

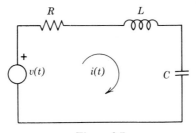

Figure 2.7

The integrodifferential equation of the system is given by

$$Ri(t) + L\frac{di}{dt} + \frac{1}{C}\int i\,dt = v(t) \tag{2.25}$$

Replacing (d/dt) by s and $\int dt$ by $1/s$ we get

$$\left(R + Ls + \frac{1}{Cs}\right)i = v(t) \tag{2.26}$$

The transfer function by definition is the ratio i/v. Thus

$$H(s) = \frac{i}{v} = \frac{1}{R + Ls + 1/Cs} \tag{2.27}$$

Note that we could have obtained the transfer function $H(s)$ for this problem from the basic definition. Let

$$v(t) = e^{st} \tag{2.28}$$

then

$$i(t) = H(s)e^{st} \tag{2.29}$$

Substituting Eqs. 2.28 and 2.29 in Eq. 2.25, we get

$$RH(s)e^{st} + LsH(s)e^{st} + \frac{1}{Cs}H(s)e^{st} = e^{st} \tag{2.30}$$

From Eq. 2.30, we get

$$H(s) = \frac{1}{R + Ls + 1/Cs} \tag{2.31}$$

From Eq. 2.23, it is evident that the transfer function $H(s)$ of a lumped-parameter linear system, in general, can be represented as a ratio of two finite polynomials of integral powers of s and with real coefficients. Such functions are known as rational algebraic fractions. The two polynomials in Eq. 2.23 may be factored as

$$H(s) = \frac{b_n}{a_m}\frac{(s - z_1)(s - z_2)\cdots(s - z_n)}{(s - p_1)(s - p_2)\cdots(s - p_m)} \tag{2.32}$$

Values of s for which $H(s) = 0$ are called the zeros of $H(s)$ and, similarly, the values of s for which $H(s)$ goes to infinity are called the poles of the transfer function. Thus, $z_1, z_2, \ldots, z_n$ are the zeros and $p_1, p_2, \ldots, p_m$ are the poles of the transfer function $H(s)$ in Eq. 2.32. The poles and zeros may be real or complex. If they are complex, they must occur in complex conjugate pairs in order to have all the coefficients $b_1, b_2, \ldots, b_n$ and $a_1, a_2, \ldots, a_m$ in Eq. 2.23 real coefficients.

The transfer functions of distributed-parameter systems in general contain nonintegral powers of s and transcendental functions of s such as $1/\sqrt{s^2 + a^2}$, $e^{k\sqrt{s}}$, etc.

Transfer Function from Immittance Functions

Evaluation of a transfer function is considerably facilitated by the application of *immittance functions*. The use of these functions yields the transfer function directly without the necessity of writing the differential equation for the system. Immittance functions, in reality, are the transfer functions of the individual elements of the system. Thus, in an electrical circuit, every element such as a resistor, a capacitor, and an inductor has a transfer function. If a voltage is applied across each of these elements, the response will be a current through these elements. An exponential voltage across each of these elements will naturally yield an exponential response (that is, current) as a consequence of the properties of linearity and time invariance of these elements. When we consider the exponential current through each of these elements as the driving function and the resultant voltage as the response function, then the transfer function for each element is the ratio of the voltage to the current and this ratio is called the *generalized impedance* of that element. (From now on it will be identified simply as an impedance.)

Thus, if i (the current through the element) is given by

$$i(t) = e^{st}$$

then the voltage v, across the terminals of the element as a result of this current, is given by an exponential function:

$$v(t) = Z(s)e^{st}$$

that is,

$$\frac{v(t)}{i(t)} = Z(s) \tag{2.33}$$

where $Z(s)$ is called the impedance of the element. Note that Eq. 2.33 is true only when i is an exponential function of the form Ae^{st}.

If, on the other hand, we consider the exponential voltage across the terminals of an element as the driving function and the resultant current as the response function, then the transfer function for the element is the ratio of the current to the voltage and this ratio is called the *generalized admittance*, $Y(s)$, of an element.

Thus, if

$$v(t) = e^{st}$$

then

$$i(t) = Y(s)e^{st}$$

and

$$\frac{i(t)}{v(t)} = Y(s) \tag{2.34}$$

Note that $Y(s) = 1/Z(s)$.

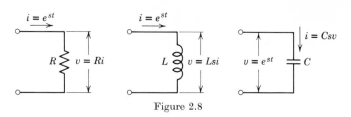

Figure 2.8

A general term *immittance function* is used to refer to either impedance or admittance functions. It should be borne in mind that immittance functions are used only in reference to exponential driving and response functions. Impedance is therefore the ratio of the voltage across the terminals to the current flowing through these terminals, only when these signals are exponential of the form Ae^{st}.

Let us find the immittance functions for passive electrical elements: a resistor, an inductor, and a capacitor.

(a) For a resistor R, the voltage and current are related by

$$v = iR$$

If

$$i(t) = e^{st}$$

then

$$v(t) = Re^{st}$$

Thus

$$Z(s) = \frac{v(t)}{i(t)} = R$$

and

$$Y(s) = \frac{i(t)}{v(t)} = \frac{1}{R} = G$$

(b) For an inductor:

$$v(t) = L\frac{di}{dt}$$

if

$$i(t) = e^{st}$$

then

$$v(t) = Lse^{st}$$

Thus

$$Z(s) = \frac{v(t)}{i(t)} = Ls$$

and

$$Y(s) = \frac{i(t)}{v(t)} = \frac{1}{Ls}$$

(c) For a capacitor:

$$i(t) = C\frac{dv}{dt}$$

if

$$v(t) = e^{st},$$

then

$$i(t) = Cse^{st}$$

Thus

$$Y(s) = \frac{i(t)}{v(t)} = Cs,$$

and

$$Z(s) = \frac{v(t)}{i(t)} = \frac{1}{Cs}$$

Various Combinations of Impedances

The concept of immittance functions for a single element can be extended to various combinations of elements. Consider the case of two impedances $Z_1(s)$ and $Z_2(s)$ in series as shown in Fig. 2.9a. If a voltage

$$v(t) = e^{st}$$

is applied across the series combination, and i is the current through the combined element, then

$$i(t) = \frac{v(t)}{Z(s)}$$

where Z is the impedance of the two elements in series. The immittances are functions of variable s. From now on, for convenience, we shall omit the explicit functional notation. Thus, notations Z and Y will always be understood as $Z(s)$ and $Y(s)$. If v_1 and v_2 are the voltages across impedances Z_1 and Z_2 respectively, then by definition

$$v_1(t) = i(t)Z_1 \tag{2.35a}$$

$$v_2(t) = i(t)Z_2 \tag{2.35b}$$

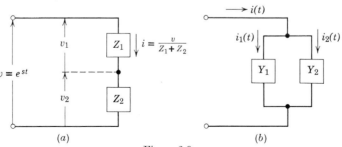

(a)   (b)

Figure 2.9

and

$$v(t) = i(t)Z \tag{2.35c}$$

but

$$v(t) = v_1(t) + v_2(t)$$
$$= i(t)(Z_1 + Z_2) \tag{2.35d}$$

Hence

$$Z = Z_1 + Z_2$$

Thus, the net impedance of two elements in series is the sum of the impedances of individual elements. The result may be extended to any number of elements in series.

Note that from Eqs. 2.35a and 2.35d, it follows that

$$v_1(t) = \frac{Z_1}{Z_1 + Z_2} v(t) \tag{2.36a}$$

Similarly

$$v_2(t) = \frac{Z_2}{Z_1 + Z_2} v(t) \tag{2.36b}$$

Equations 2.36a and 2.36b give the voltage across the individual elements in terms of the net voltages across the series combination. Thus the total voltage divides across the two elements as given by Eqs. 2.36a and 2.36b. If there are n elements with impedances $Z_1, Z_2, \ldots, Z_n$ in series, then the impedance of all the elements in series is given by

$$Z_T = Z_1 + Z_2 + \cdots + Z_n \tag{2.37}$$

If Ve^{st} is the voltage across all n elements, then the voltage across the terminals of the rth element with impedance Z_r is given by

$$v_r(t) = \frac{Z_r}{Z_1 + Z_2 + \cdots + Z_n} Ve^{st}$$
$$= \frac{Z_r}{Z_T} Ve^{st} \tag{2.38}$$

Similarly, for two admittances Y_1 and Y_2 in shunt, it can be shown that the net admittance Y is given by

$$Y = Y_1 + Y_2 \tag{2.39}$$

Note that if Z_1 and Z_2 are the impedances of the two elements in shunt, then

$$Z_1 = \frac{1}{Y_1} \quad \text{and} \quad Z_2 = \frac{1}{Y_2} \tag{2.40}$$

and the total impedance $Z = 1/Y$. Then, from Eqs. 2.39 and 2.40, it follows that

$$Z = \frac{Z_1 Z_2}{Z_1 + Z_2}$$

It can also be shown that the total current $i(t)$ divides between the two shunt elements (Fig. 2.9b) as given by

$$i_1(t) = \frac{Y_1 i(t)}{Y_1 + Y_2} = \frac{Z_2 i(t)}{Z_1 + Z_2}$$

and   (2.41)

$$i_2(t) = \frac{Y_2 i(t)}{Y_1 + Y_2} = \frac{Z_1 i(t)}{Z_1 + Z_2}$$

If there are n elements with admittances $Y_1, Y_2, \ldots, Y_n$, connected in shunt, then the net admittance of this combination is given by

$$Y_T = Y_1 + Y_2 + \cdots + Y_n$$

If Ie^{st} is the current entering this combination, then the current through the rth element with admittance Y_r is given by

$$i_r(t) = \frac{Y_r}{Y_1 + Y_2 + \cdots + Y_n} Ie^{st}$$

$$= \frac{Y_r}{Y_T} Ie^{st} \qquad\qquad (2.42)$$

We shall now demonstrate the utility of immittance functions in the evaluation of the transfer function of a system.

Example 2.2

The driving voltage $v(t)$ is applied across the terminals ab and the response function is the voltage $v_0(t)$ across terminals db of a network shown in Fig. 2.10. Let us find the transfer function of this network using immittance functions.

Assume an exponential voltage v across terminals ab. According to Kirchhoff's voltage law, the sum of voltages across the terminals ac and cb must be equal to v, and the voltage divides across terminals ac and cb according to the voltage division rule of Eqs. 2.36a and 2.36b. The net impedance across

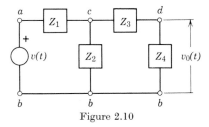

Figure 2.10

terminals ac is Z_1 and that across cb is the shunt combination of impedance Z_2 and $(Z_3 + Z_4)$. Therefore, the net admittance across cb is given by

$$Y_{cb} = \frac{1}{Z_2} + \frac{1}{Z_3 + Z_4}$$

$$= \frac{Z_2 + Z_3 + Z_4}{Z_2(Z_3 + Z_4)}$$

and

$$Z_{cb} = \frac{1}{Y_{cb}} = \frac{Z_2(Z_3 + Z_4)}{Z_2 + Z_3 + Z_4}$$

Voltage v_{cb}, across terminals cb, is given by

$$v_{cb} = \frac{Z_{cb}}{Z_1 + Z_{cb}} v = \frac{\dfrac{Z_2(Z_3 + Z_4)}{Z_2 + Z_3 + Z_4}}{Z_1 + \dfrac{Z_2(Z_3 + Z_4)}{Z_2 + Z_3 + Z_4}} v$$

$$= \frac{Z_2(Z_3 + Z_4)}{Z_1(Z_2 + Z_3 + Z_4) + Z_2(Z_3 + Z_4)} v$$

The voltage v_{cb} again divides itself across terminals cd and db according to the voltage division rule,

$$v_0(t) = \frac{Z_4}{Z_3 + Z_4} v_{cb}$$

$$= \frac{Z_2 Z_4}{Z_1(Z_2 + Z_3 + Z_4) + Z_2(Z_3 + Z_4)} v$$

The transfer function $H(s)$ is given by

$$H(s) = \frac{v_0}{v} = \frac{Z_2 Z_4}{Z_1(Z_2 + Z_3 + Z_4) + Z_2(Z_3 + Z_4)} \tag{2.43}$$

Let us evaluate the transfer function of a network shown in Fig. 2.11. Note that this network is similar to that in Fig. 2.10, where

$$Z_1 = R_1, \quad Z_2 = \frac{1}{Cs}, \quad Z_3 = Ls, \quad Z_4 = R_2$$

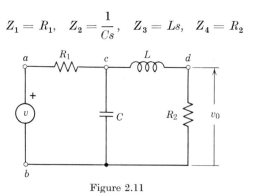

Figure 2.11

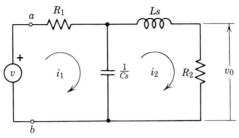

Figure 2.12

Substituting these values in Eq. 2.43, we get

$$H(s) = \frac{R_2/Cs}{R_1\left(\dfrac{1}{Cs} + Ls + R_2\right) + \dfrac{1}{Cs}\left(Ls + R_2\right)}$$

$$= \frac{R_2}{R_1(LCs^2 + R_2Cs + 1) + (R_2 + Ls)} \tag{2.44}$$

Alternately, the transfer function $H(s)$ for the network in Fig. 2.11 may be evaluated by using loop or node equations. We take advantage of the fact that if the signals are exponential functions, then the voltage across any element is given by the product of the impedance of the element with the current passing through the element.

Thus for each element

$$v = iZ.$$

We shall denote all the elements by their impedances as shown in Fig. 2.12. It will be assumed that an exponential voltage $v = Ve^{st}$ is applied across terminals ab and the exponential currents i_1 and i_2 are the two loop currents. The loop equations for the network are

$$v = i_1\left(R_1 + \frac{1}{Cs}\right) - i_2\left(\frac{1}{Cs}\right)$$

$$0 = -i_1\left(\frac{1}{Cs}\right) + i_2\left(R_2 + Ls + \frac{1}{Cs}\right) \tag{2.45}$$

The solution of simultaneous Eqs. 2.45 by Cramer's rule yields

$$i_2 = \frac{v}{R_1(LCs^2 + R_2Cs + 1) + (R_2 + Ls)}$$

and

$$H(s) = \frac{v_0}{v} = \frac{R_2 i_2}{v} = \frac{R_2}{R_1(LCs^2 + R_2Cs + 1) + (R_2 + Ls)} \tag{2.46}$$

This is the same result as that obtained in Eq. 2.44. The transfer function may be found in a similar way using node equations.

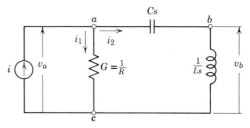

Figure 2.13

Example 2.3

Find the transfer function of a network shown in Fig. 2.13. The driving current i is applied across nodes ac, and the response is the voltage across nodes bc.

All the elements are represented by their admittances in Fig. 2.13.

This problem can be solved by two methods: by inspection, and by using node equations.

We shall assume that the input current i is Ie^{st}. This current divides into two branches according to the current division rule in Eq. 2.42. It is evident that

$$i_2 = \frac{1/(Ls + 1/Cs)}{G + 1/(Ls + 1/Cs)}\, i$$

$$= \frac{Cs}{G(LCs^2 + 1) + Cs}\, i$$

and

$$H(s) = \frac{v_b}{i} = \frac{Lsi_2}{i} = \frac{LCs^2}{G(LCs^2 + 1) + Cs} \tag{2.47}$$

Alternately, we write the two node equations for nodes a and b and the datum node c.

$$i = (G + Cs)v_a - Csv_b$$

$$0 = -Csv_a + \left(Cs + \frac{1}{Ls}\right)v_b \tag{2.48}$$

The solution of Eqs. 2.48 by Cramer's rule yields

$$v_b = \frac{LCs^2 i}{G(LCs^2 + 1) + Cs}$$

and

$$H(s) = \frac{v_b}{i} = \frac{LCs^2}{G(LCs^2 + 1) + Cs} \tag{2.49}$$

This is the same result as that obtained in Eq. 2.47.

2.5 STEADY-STATE RESPONSE OF LINEAR SYSTEMS TO SINUSOIDAL EXCITATIONS

The steady-state response of a linear system to sinusoidal functions $\cos \omega t$ and $\sin \omega t$ is of great importance. The solution to this problem is made considerably easier by examining the steady-state response of the system to the exponential function $e^{j\omega t}$.

The steady-state response of a system to the exponential driving function e^{st} was found to be $H(s)e^{st}$. It therefore follows that the steady-state response of the system to a function $e^{j\omega t}$ will be $H(j\omega)e^{j\omega t}$.

Now suppose that the steady-state response of the system to the driving function $\cos \omega t$ is $R_c(t)$ and that the steady-state response to the function $\sin \omega t$ is $R_s(t)$. We shall represent this symbolically:

$$\begin{aligned} \cos \omega t &\to R_c(t) \\ \sin \omega t &\to R_s(t) \end{aligned} \tag{2.50}$$

It follows from the property of linearity and the principle of superposition that the steady-state response of the system to a driving function $(\cos \omega t + j \sin \omega t)$ will be given by $R_c(t) + jR_s(t)$. Symbolically,

$$(\cos \omega t + j \sin \omega t) \to R_c(t) + jR_s(t) \tag{2.51}$$

But since

$$(\cos \omega t + j \sin \omega t) = e^{j\omega t}$$

it follows that the steady-state response of the system to a driving function $e^{j\omega t}$ is $R_c(t) + jR_s(t)$. However, it is given that the steady-state response of the system to the signal $e^{j\omega t}$ is $H(j\omega)e^{j\omega t}$. Therefore, it follows that

$$R_c(t) + jR_s(t) = H(j\omega)e^{j\omega t} \tag{2.52}$$

Since $R_c(t)$ and $R_s(t)$ are both real functions of the variable t, it is evident that

$$R_c(t) = \operatorname{Re}\left[H(j\omega)e^{j\omega t}\right]$$

and

$$R_s(t) = \operatorname{Im}\left[H(j\omega)e^{j\omega t}\right]$$

We therefore conclude that the steady-state response of the system to driving functions $\cos \omega t$ and $\sin \omega t$ is given by $\operatorname{Re}\left[H(j\omega)e^{j\omega t}\right]$ and $\operatorname{Im}\left[H(j\omega)e^{j\omega t}\right]$, respectively. Symbolically,

$$\operatorname{Re} e^{j\omega t} = \cos \omega t \to \operatorname{Re}\left[H(j\omega)e^{j\omega t}\right] \tag{2.53}$$

$$\operatorname{Im} e^{j\omega t} = \sin \omega t \to \operatorname{Im}\left[H(j\omega)e^{j\omega t}\right] \tag{2.54}$$

$H(j\omega)$ is complex in general and can be expressed in polar form as

$$H(j\omega) = |H(j\omega)|\, e^{j\theta(\omega)}$$

and   (2.55)

$$H(j\omega)e^{j\omega t} = |H(j\omega)|\, e^{j(\omega t + \theta)}$$

Therefore

$$\text{Re}\,[H(j\omega)e^{j\omega t}] = |H(j\omega)| \cos (\omega t + \theta)$$

and   (2.56)

$$\text{Im}\,[H(j\omega)e^{j\omega t}] = |H(j\omega)| \sin (\omega t + \theta)$$

As a result, the steady-state response of the system to a driving function $\cos \omega t$ is given by $|H(j\omega)| \cos (\omega t + \theta)$, and the steady-state response to a driving function $\sin \omega t$ is given by $|H(j\omega)| \sin (\omega t + \theta)$. Symbolically,

$$\cos \omega t \rightarrow |H(j\omega)| \cos (\omega t + \theta)$$
$$\sin \omega t \rightarrow |H(j\omega)| \sin (\omega t + \theta)$$ (2.57)

In general,

$$\cos (\omega t + \varphi) \rightarrow |H(j\omega)| \cos (\omega t + \varphi + \theta)$$

The term $|H(j\omega)|$ therefore represents the magnitude of the response to a unit sinusoidal function, and it is evident from Eq. 2.57 that the response function is shifted in phase by angle θ from the driving function. As can be seen from Eq. 2.55, the angle θ is the phase angle of $H(j\omega)$. That is,

$$\underline{/H(j\omega)} = \theta$$

Note that a sinusoidal function is not restricted to the function $\sin \omega t$ alone. Any circular function such as $\cos \omega t$, $\sin (\omega t + \varphi)$, $\cos (\omega t + \alpha)$, etc. is called a sinusoidal function. The knowledge of $H(j\omega)$ is therefore sufficient to evaluate the steady-state response of a linear system to a sinusoidal driving function. Very often it is stated that the response of a linear system to a unit sinusoidal signal is $H(j\omega)$. This statement is meaningless unless it is understood in the proper context. The response of a system to any real function must be real and, hence, $H(j\omega)$ cannot be a response of a real function. What we actually mean by the response being $H(j\omega)$ is that the magnitude of the response is $|H(j\omega)|$ and is shifted in phase from the driving function by $\underline{/H(j\omega)}$. If we represent the response function and the driving functions by phasors, then the ratio of two phasors is given by $H(j\omega)$.

Example 2.4

A sinusoidal voltage V of 10 volts at angular frequency of $\omega = 1$ radian/second is applied across a series combination of 1-ohm resistor and 1-henry inductor as shown in Fig. 2.14. Find the steady-state current I.

The transfer function which relates voltage and current is the admittance $Y(s)$.

$$I = Y(s)V$$

The admittance of the network seen across terminals ab is $1/(1 + s)$. For sinusoidal signal $s = j\omega$ and admittance $Y(j\omega)$ is given by

$$Y(j1) = \frac{1}{1 + j1} = \frac{1 - j1}{2}$$

and

$$I = \frac{1 - j1}{2} V$$

$$= \frac{(1 - j1)}{2} 10$$

$$= 5(1 - j1)$$

$$= 5\sqrt{2} \left/ -\frac{\pi}{4} \right. \qquad (2.58)$$

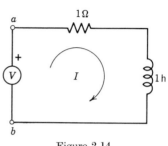

Figure 2.14

Again the answer in Eq. 2.58 is meaningless unless correctly understood. If the input voltage is 10 cos t, then the steady-state response current will be given by $5\sqrt{2} \cos (t - \pi/4)$, and if the input voltage is 10 sin t, then the current will be $5\sqrt{2} \sin (t - \pi/4)$, and so on.

Since $H(j\omega)$ completely specifies the steady-state response of the system to any sinusoidal driving function, it is customary to evaluate the response of the system to signal $e^{j\omega t}$ and state that this represents the response of the system to sinusoidal signal. The meaning behind such a statement must be clearly understood.

PROBLEMS

1. If the driving function is a voltage across terminals aa', and the response function is the voltage across terminals bb' (Fig. P-2.1), determine the following things.

(a) Find the transfer function (1) from the integrodifferential equations of the system, and (2) by using impedance functions.

(b) Find the steady-state response to the sinusoidal signal input.

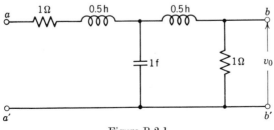

Figure P-2.1

2. Find the steady-state output voltage $v_0(t)$ for a network shown in Fig. P-2.2 when the driving voltage $v(t)$ is given by

$$v(t) = \text{(a) } E_0 \cos \omega t$$
$$\text{(b) } E_0 \sin \omega t$$
$$\text{(c) } E_2 \cos \omega t + E_2 \sin \omega t$$

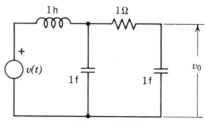

Figure P-2.2

3. For a linear system, the transfer function $H(s)$ is given by

$$H(s) = \frac{N(s)}{(s - P_1)(s - P_2) \cdots (s - P_m)}$$

It is given that

$$\text{Re } P_1 > \text{Re } P_2 > \text{Re } P_3 > \cdots > \text{Re } P_m$$

The response of this system to an eternal exponential function e^{st} is $H(s)e^{st}$.

(a) Show that this statement is valid for values of s given by

$$\text{Re } s > \text{Re } P_1$$

(b) What is the region of validity for network in Problem 1?

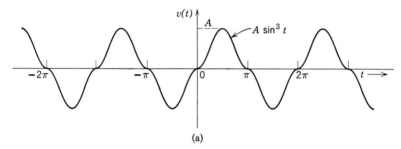

(a)

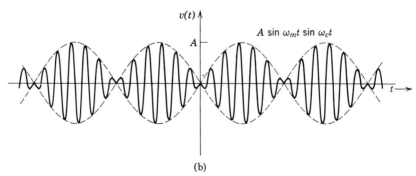

(b)

Figure P-2.4

4. Express the voltage $v(t)$, shown in Fig. P-2.4a, as a discrete sum of eternal exponential functions. Hence, find the current through a series R-L-C circuit when a voltage $v(t)$ is applied across its terminals. Repeat the problem for $v(t)$ shown in Fig. P-2.4b.

5. Show that the response of a system to the eternal exponential signal e^{st} is infinity if the complex frequency variable s does not satisfy the dominance condition.

chapter 3

Signal Representation by Discrete Exponentials: The Fourier Series

The success of the frequency-analysis approach depends upon our ability to represent a given function of time as a sum of various exponential functions. We shall devote the next three chapters to the development of such techniques.

3.1 ANALOGY BETWEEN VECTORS AND SIGNALS

A problem is better understood or better remembered if it can be associated with some familiar phenomenon. Therefore we always search for analogies while studying a new problem. In the study of abstract problems, analogies are very helpful, particularly if the problem can be shown to be analogous to some concrete phenomenon. It is then easy to gain some insight into the new problem from the knowledge of the analogous phenomenon. Fortunately, there is a perfect analogy between vectors and signals which leads to a better understanding of signal analysis. We shall now briefly review the properties of vectors.

Vectors

A vector is specified by magnitude and direction. We shall denote all vectors by boldface type and their magnitudes by lightface type, for example, **A** is a certain vector with magnitude A. Consider two vectors

$\mathbf{V}_1$ and $\mathbf{V}_2$ as shown in Fig. 3.1. Let the component of $\mathbf{V}_1$ along $\mathbf{V}_2$ be given by $C_{12}\mathbf{V}_2$. How do we interpret physically the component of one vector along the other vector? Geometrically the component of a vector $\mathbf{V}_1$ along the vector $\mathbf{V}_2$ is obtained by drawing a perpendicular from the end of $\mathbf{V}_1$ on the vector $\mathbf{V}_2$, as shown in Fig. 3.1. The vector $\mathbf{V}_1$ can now be expressed in terms of vector $\mathbf{V}_2$.

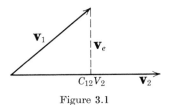

Figure 3.1

$$\mathbf{V}_1 = C_{12}\mathbf{V}_2 + \mathbf{V}_e \qquad (3.1a)$$

However, this is not the only way of expressing vector $\mathbf{V}_1$ in terms of vector $\mathbf{V}_2$. Figure 3.2 illustrates two of the infinite alternate possibilities. Thus, in Fig. 3.2a,

$$\mathbf{V}_1 = C_1\mathbf{V}_2 + \mathbf{V}_{e_1} \qquad (3.1b)$$

and in Fig. 3.2b,

$$\mathbf{V}_1 = C_2\mathbf{V}_2 + \mathbf{V}_{e_2} \qquad (3.1c)$$

In each representation, $\mathbf{V}_1$ is represented in terms of $\mathbf{V}_2$ plus another vector, which will be called the error vector. If we are asked to approximate the vector $\mathbf{V}_1$ by a vector in the direction of $\mathbf{V}_2$, then $\mathbf{V}_e$ represents the error in this approximation. For example, in Fig. 3.1 if we approximate $\mathbf{V}_1$ by $C_{12}\mathbf{V}_2$, then the error in the approximation is $\mathbf{V}_e$. If $\mathbf{V}_1$ is approximated by $C_1\mathbf{V}_2$ as in Fig. 3.2a, then the error is given by $\mathbf{V}_{e_1}$, and so on. What is so unique about the representation in Fig. 3.1? It is immediately evident from the geometry of these figures that the error vector is smallest in Fig. 3.1. We can now formulate a quantitative definition of a component of a vector along another vector. The component of a vector $\mathbf{V}_1$ along the vector $\mathbf{V}_2$ is given by $C_{12}\mathbf{V}_2$, where C_{12} is chosen such that the error vector is minimum.

Let us now interpret physically the component of one vector along another. It is clear that the larger the component of a vector along the other vector, the more closely do the two vectors resemble each other in their directions, and the smaller is the error vector. If the component of a vector $\mathbf{V}_1$ along $\mathbf{V}_2$ is $C_{12}\mathbf{V}_2$, then the magnitude of C_{12} is an indication

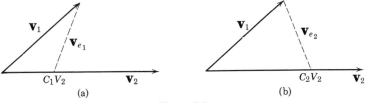

Figure 3.2

of the similarity of the two vectors. If C_{12} is zero, then the vector has no component along the other vector and, hence, the two vectors are mutually perpendicular. Such vectors are known as *orthogonal vectors*. Orthogonal vectors are thus independent vectors. If the vectors are orthogonal, then the parameter C_{12} is zero.

For convenience, we define the dot product of two vectors $\mathbf{A}$ and $\mathbf{B}$ as

$$\mathbf{A} \cdot \mathbf{B} = AB \cos \theta$$

where θ is the angle between vectors $\mathbf{A}$ and $\mathbf{B}$. It follows from the definition that

$$\mathbf{A} \cdot \mathbf{B} = \mathbf{B} \cdot \mathbf{A}$$

According to this notation,

$$\text{the component of } \mathbf{A} \text{ along } \mathbf{B} = A \cos \theta = \frac{\mathbf{A} \cdot \mathbf{B}}{B}$$

and

$$\text{the component of } \mathbf{B} \text{ along } \mathbf{A} = B \cos \theta = \frac{\mathbf{A} \cdot \mathbf{B}}{A}$$

Similarly

$$\text{the component of } \mathbf{V}_1 \text{ along } \mathbf{V}_2 = \frac{\mathbf{V}_1 \cdot \mathbf{V}_2}{V_2}$$

$$= C_{12} V_2$$

Therefore

$$C_{12} = \frac{\mathbf{V}_1 \cdot \mathbf{V}_2}{V_2{}^2} = \frac{\mathbf{V}_1 \cdot \mathbf{V}_2}{\mathbf{V}_2 \cdot \mathbf{V}_2} \tag{3.2}$$

Note that if $\mathbf{V}_1$ and $\mathbf{V}_2$ are orthogonal then

$$\mathbf{V}_1 \cdot \mathbf{V}_2 = 0 \tag{3.3}$$

and

$$C_{12} = 0.$$

Signals

The concept of vector comparison and orthogonality can be extended to signals.[1] Let us consider two signals, $f_1(t)$ and $f_2(t)$. Suppose we want to approximate $f_1(t)$ in terms of $f_2(t)$ over a certain interval $(t_1 < t < t_2)$ as follows.

$$f_1(t) \simeq C_{12} f_2(t) \qquad \text{for} \quad (t_1 < t < t_2) \tag{3.4}$$

---

[1] We shall often use the terms signals and functions interchangeably. A signal is a function of time. However, there is one difference between signals and functions. A function $f(t)$ can be a multivalued function of variable t. But the physical signal is always a single-valued function of t. Hence, whenever we use a term function, it will be understood that it is a single-valued function of the independent variable.

How shall we choose C_{12} in order to achieve the best approximation? Obviously, we must find C_{12} such that the error between the actual function and the approximated function is minimum over the interval $(t_1 < t < t_2)$. Let us define an *error function* $f_e(t)$ as

$$f_e(t) = f_1(t) - C_{12}f_2(t) \tag{3.5}$$

One possible criterion for minimizing the error $f_e(t)$ over the interval t_1 to t_2 is to minimize the average value of $f_e(t)$ over this interval; that is, to minimize

$$\frac{1}{(t_2 - t_1)} \int_{t_1}^{t_2} [f_1(t) - C_{12}f_2(t)] \, dt$$

However, this criterion is inadequate because there can be large positive and negative errors present that may cancel one another in the process of averaging and give the false indication that the error is zero. For example, if we approximate a function $\sin t$ with a null function $f(t) = 0$ over an interval 0 to 2π, the average error will be zero, indicating wrongly that $\sin t$ can be approximated to zero over the interval 0 to 2π without any error. This situation can be corrected if we choose to minimize the average (or the mean) of the square of the error instead of the error itself. Let us designate the average of $f_e^2(t)$ by ε.

$$\varepsilon = \frac{1}{(t_2 - t_1)} \int_{t_1}^{t_2} f_e^2(t) \, dt = \frac{1}{(t_2 - t_1)} \int_{t_1}^{t_2} [f_1(t) - C_{12}f_2(t)]^2 \, dt \tag{3.6}$$

To find the value of C_{12} which will minimize ε, we must have

$$\frac{d\varepsilon}{dC_{12}} = 0 \tag{3.7}$$

that is,

$$\frac{d}{dC_{12}} \left\{ \frac{1}{(t_2 - t_1)} \int_{t_1}^{t_2} [f_1(t) - C_{12}f_2(t)]^2 \, dt \right\} = 0 \tag{3.8}$$

Changing the order of integration and differentiation, we get

$$\frac{1}{(t_2 - t_1)} \left[\int_{t_1}^{t_2} \frac{d}{dC_{12}} f_1^2(t) \, dt - 2 \int_{t_1}^{t_2} f_1(t)f_2(t) \, dt + 2C_{12} \int_{t_1}^{t_2} f_2^2(t) \, dt \right] = 0 \tag{3.9}$$

The first integral is obviously zero, and hence Eq. 3.9 yields

$$C_{12} = \frac{\displaystyle\int_{t_1}^{t_2} f_1(t)f_2(t) \, dt}{\displaystyle\int_{t_1}^{t_2} f_2^2(t) \, dt} \tag{3.10}$$

Observe the similarity between Eqs. 3.10 and 3.2, which expresses C_{12} for vectors.

By analogy with vectors, we say that $f_1(t)$ has a component of waveform $f_2(t)$, and this component has a magnitude C_{12}. If C_{12} vanishes, then the signal $f_1(t)$ contains no component of signal $f_2(t)$ and we say that the two functions are orthogonal over the interval (t_1, t_2). It therefore follows that the two functions $f_1(t)$ and $f_2(t)$ are *orthogonal* over an interval (t_1, t_2) if

$$\int_{t_1}^{t_2} f_1(t) f_2(t) \, dt = 0 \qquad (3.11)$$

Observe the similarity between Eq. 3.11 derived for orthogonal functions and Eq. 3.3 derived for orthogonal vectors.

We can easily show that the functions $\sin n\omega_0 t$ and $\sin m\omega_0 t$ are orthogonal over any interval $(t_0, t_0 + 2\pi/\omega_0)$ for integral values of n and m. Consider the integral I:

$$m \neq n$$

$$
\begin{aligned}
I &= \int_{t_0}^{t_0+2\pi/\omega_0} \sin n\omega_0 t \, \sin m\omega_0 t \, dt \\
&= \int_{t_0}^{t_0+2\pi/\omega_0} \tfrac{1}{2}[\cos (n-m)\omega_0 t - \cos (n+m)\omega_0 t] \, dt \\
&= \frac{1}{2\omega_0}\left[\frac{1}{(n-m)} \sin (n-m)\omega_0 t - \frac{1}{(n+m)} \sin (n+m)\omega_0 t\right]_{t_0}^{t_0+2\pi/\omega_0}
\end{aligned}
$$

Since n and m are integers, $(n-m)$ and $(n+m)$ are also integers. In such a case the integral I is zero. Hence the two functions are orthogonal. Similarly, it can be shown that $\sin n\omega_0 t$ and $\cos m\omega_0 t$ are orthogonal functions and $\cos n\omega_0 t$, $\cos m\omega_0 t$ are also mutually orthogonal.

Example 3.1

A rectangular function $f(t)$ is defined by (Fig. 3.3):

$$f(t) = \begin{cases} 1, & (0 < t < \pi) \\ -1, & (\pi < t < 2\pi) \end{cases}$$

Approximate this function by a waveform $\sin t$ over the interval $(0, 2\pi)$ such that the mean square error is minimum.

Solution. The function $f(t)$ will be approximated over the interval $(0, 2\pi)$, as

$$f(t) \simeq C_{12} \sin t$$

We shall find the optimum value of C_{12} which will minimize the mean square error in this approximation. According to Eq. 3.10 to minimize the mean

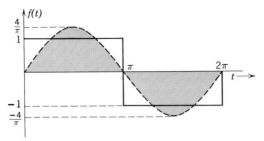

Figure 3.3

square error:

$$C_{12} = \frac{\displaystyle\int_0^{2\pi} f(t)\sin t\, dt}{\displaystyle\int_0^{2\pi} \sin^2 t\, dt}$$

$$= \frac{1}{\pi}\left[\int_0^{\pi} \sin t\, dt + \int_{\pi}^{2\pi} -\sin t\, dt\right]$$

$$= \frac{4}{\pi}$$

Thus

$$f(t) \simeq \frac{4}{\pi}\sin t$$

represents the best approximation of $f(t)$ by a function $\sin t$ which will minimize the mean square error.

By analogy with vectors, we may say that the rectangular function $f(t)$ shown in Fig. 3.3 has a component of function $\sin t$ and the magnitude of this component is $4/\pi$.

What is the significance of orthogonality of two functions? In the case of vectors, orthogonality implies that one vector has no component along the other. Similarly, a function does not contain any component of the form of the function which is orthogonal to it. If we try to approximate a function by its orthogonal function, the error will be larger than the original function itself, and it is better to approximate a function with a null function $f(t) = 0$ rather than with a function orthogonal to it. Hence the optimum value of $C_{12} = 0$ in such a case.

Graphical Evaluation of a Component of One Function in the Other

It is possible to evaluate the component of a function in the other function by graphical means, using Eq. 3.10. Suppose two functions $f_1(t)$ and $f_2(t)$ are known graphically, and it is desired to evaluate the component of waveform $f_2(t)$ contained in signal $f_1(t)$ over a period $(0, T)$.

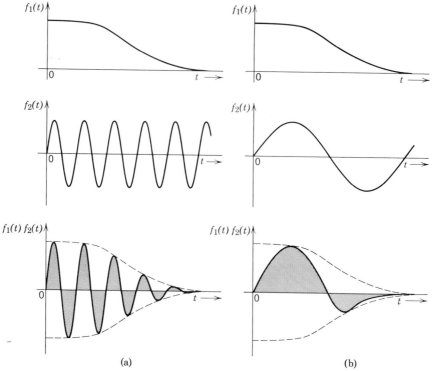

Figure 3.4   Graphical evaluation of the component of waveform $f_2(t)$ in a signal $f_1(t)$.

We know that this component is given by $C_{12}f_2(t)$; that is, $f_1(t)$ contains the component of function $f_2(t)$ of magnitude C_{12}, given by

$$C_{12} = \frac{\displaystyle\int_0^T f_1(t)f_2(t)\,dt}{\displaystyle\int_0^T f_2{}^2(t)\,dt}$$

The integral in the numerator in this equation can be found by multiplying the two functions and evaluating the area under the product curve as shown in Fig. 3.4. The denominator integral can be evaluated by finding the area under the function $[f_2(t)]^2$ in a similar way.

It is evident that if $f_1(t)$ varies much more slowly than $f_2(t)$, the area under the curve $f_1(t)f_2(t)$ will be very small since the positive and negative areas will be approximately equal and will tend to cancel each other as shown in Fig. 3.4a. Hence, $f_1(t)$ contains a small component of $f_2(t)$. If, however, $f_1(t)$ varies at about the same rate as $f_2(t)$, then the area under the product curve $f_1(t)f_2(t)$ will be much larger, as shown in Fig. 3.4b, and hence $f_1(t)$ will contain a large component of function $f_2(t)$. This result is also intuitively obvious, since if two functions vary at about the same rate, there must be a great deal of similarity between the two functions, and hence $f_1(t)$ will contain a large component of the function $f_2(t)$.

Orthogonal Vector Space

The analogy between vectors and signals may be extended further. Let us now consider a three-dimensional vector space described by rectangular coordinates, as shown in Fig. 3.5. We shall designate a vector of unit length along the x axis by $\mathbf{a}_x$. Similarly, unit vectors along the y and z axes will be designated by $\mathbf{a}_y$ and $\mathbf{a}_z$, respectively. Since the magnitude of vectors $\mathbf{a}_x$, $\mathbf{a}_y$, and $\mathbf{a}_z$ is unity, it follows that for any general vector $\mathbf{A}$:

$$\text{The component of } \mathbf{A} \text{ along the } x \text{ axis} = \mathbf{A} \cdot \mathbf{a}_x$$
$$\text{The component of } \mathbf{A} \text{ along the } y \text{ axis} = \mathbf{A} \cdot \mathbf{a}_y$$
$$\text{The component of } \mathbf{A} \text{ along the } z \text{ axis} = \mathbf{A} \cdot \mathbf{a}_z$$

A vector $\mathbf{A}$ drawn from the origin to a general point (x_0, y_0, z_0) in space has components x_0, y_0, and z_0 along the x, y, and z axes, respectively. We can express this vector $\mathbf{A}$ in terms of its components along the three mutually perpendicular axes:

$$\mathbf{A} = x_0\mathbf{a}_x + y_0\mathbf{a}_y + z_0\mathbf{a}_z$$

Any vector in this space can be expressed in terms of the three vectors $\mathbf{a}_x$, $\mathbf{a}_y$, and $\mathbf{a}_z$.

Since the three vectors $\mathbf{a}_x$, $\mathbf{a}_y$, and $\mathbf{a}_z$ are mutually perpendicular, it follows that

$$\mathbf{a}_x \cdot \mathbf{a}_y = \mathbf{a}_y \cdot \mathbf{a}_z = \mathbf{a}_z \cdot \mathbf{a}_x = 0$$

and $\qquad\qquad\qquad\qquad\qquad\qquad\qquad\qquad\qquad\qquad$ (3.12)

$$\mathbf{a}_x \cdot \mathbf{a}_x = \mathbf{a}_y \cdot \mathbf{a}_y = \mathbf{a}_z \cdot \mathbf{a}_z = 1$$

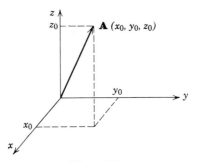

Figure 3.5

The properties of the three vectors, as expressed by Eq. 3.12, can be succinctly expressed by

$$\mathbf{a}_m \cdot \mathbf{a}_n = \begin{cases} 0 & m \neq n \\ 1 & m = n \end{cases} \qquad (3.13)$$

where m and n can assume any value x, y, and z.

Now we make an important observation. If the coordinate system has only two axes, x and y, then the system is inadequate to express a general vector $\mathbf{A}$ in terms of the components along these axes. This system can only express two components of vector $\mathbf{A}$. Therefore, it is necessary that to express any general vector $\mathbf{A}$ in terms of its coordinate components, the system of coordinates must be complete. In this case there must be three coordinate axes.

A single straight line represents a one-dimensional space; a single plane represents a two-dimensional space; and our universe, in general, has three dimensions of space. We may extend our concepts as developed here to a general n-dimensional space. Such a physical space, of course, does not exist in nature. Nevertheless, there are many analogous problems that may be viewed as n-dimensional problems. For example, a linear equation in n-independent variables may be viewed as a vector expressed in terms of its components along n mutually perpendicular coordinates.

If unit vectors along these n mutually perpendicular coordinates are designated as $\mathbf{x}_1$, $\mathbf{x}_2$, . . . , $\mathbf{x}_n$ and a general vector $\mathbf{A}$ in this n dimensional space has components C_1, C_2, . . . , C_n respectively along these n coordinates, then

$$\mathbf{A} = C_1\mathbf{x}_1 + C_2\mathbf{x}_2 + C_3\mathbf{x}_3 + \cdots + C_n\mathbf{x}_n \qquad (3.14)$$

All the vectors $\mathbf{x}_1$, $\mathbf{x}_2$, . . . , $\mathbf{x}_n$ are mutually orthogonal, and the set must be complete in order for any general vector $\mathbf{A}$ to be represented by Eq. 3.14. The condition of orthogonality implies that the dot product of any two vectors $\mathbf{x}_n$ and $\mathbf{x}_m$ must be zero, and the dot product of any vector with itself must be unity. This is the direct extension of Eq. 3.13 and can be expressed as

$$\mathbf{x}_m \cdot \mathbf{x}_n = \begin{cases} 0 & m \neq n \\ 1 & m = n \end{cases} \qquad (3.15)$$

The constants C_1, C_2, C_3, . . . , C_n in Eq. 3.14 represent the magnitudes of the components of $\mathbf{A}$ along the vectors $\mathbf{x}_1$, $\mathbf{x}_2$, $\mathbf{x}_3$, . . . , $\mathbf{x}_n$ respectively. It follows that

$$C_r = \mathbf{A} \cdot \mathbf{x}_r \qquad (3.16)$$

This result can also be obtained by taking the dot product of both sides in Eq. 3.14 with vector $\mathbf{x}_r$. We have

$$\mathbf{A} \cdot \mathbf{x}_r = C_1 \mathbf{x}_1 \cdot \mathbf{x}_r + C_2 \mathbf{x}_2 \cdot \mathbf{x}_r + \cdots + C_r \mathbf{x}_r \cdot \mathbf{x}_r + \cdots + C_n \mathbf{x}_n \cdot \mathbf{x}_r \quad (3.17)$$

From Eq. 3.15 it follows that all the terms of the form $C_j \mathbf{x}_j \cdot \mathbf{x}_r (j \neq r)$ on the right-hand side of Eq. 3.17 are zero. Therefore

$$\mathbf{A} \cdot \mathbf{x}_r = C_r \mathbf{x}_r \cdot \mathbf{x}_r = C_r \quad (3.18)$$

We call the set of vectors $(\mathbf{x}_1, \mathbf{x}_2, \ldots, \mathbf{x}_n)$ an *orthogonal vector space*. In general, the product $\mathbf{x}_m \cdot \mathbf{x}_n$ can be some constant k_m instead of unity. *(m = n)* When k_m is unity, the set is called normalized orthogonal set, or *orthonormal vector space*. Therefore, in general, for orthogonal vector space $\{\mathbf{x}_r\} \cdots (r = 1, 2, \ldots n)$ we have

$$\mathbf{x}_m \cdot \mathbf{x}_n = \begin{cases} 0 & m \neq n \\ k_m & m = n \end{cases} \quad (3.19)$$

For an orthogonal vector space, Eq. 3.18 is modified to

$$\mathbf{A} \cdot \mathbf{x}_r = C_r \mathbf{x}_r \cdot \mathbf{x}_r = C_r k_r$$

and

$$C_r = \frac{\mathbf{A} \cdot \mathbf{x}_r}{k_r}$$

We shall now summarize the results of our discussion. For an orthogonal vector space $\{\mathbf{x}_r\} \cdots (r = 1, 2, \ldots)$

$$\mathbf{x}_m \cdot \mathbf{x}_n = \begin{cases} 0 & m \neq n \\ k_m & m = n \end{cases} \quad (3.20)$$

If this vector space is complete, then any vector $\mathbf{F}$ can be expressed as

$$\mathbf{F} = C_1 \mathbf{x}_1 + C_2 \mathbf{x}_2 + \cdots + C_r \mathbf{x}_r + \cdots \quad (3.21)$$

where

$$C_r = \frac{\mathbf{F} \cdot \mathbf{x}_r}{k_r} = \frac{\mathbf{F} \cdot \mathbf{x}_r}{\mathbf{x}_r \cdot \mathbf{x}_r} \quad (3.22)$$

Orthogonal Signal Space

We shall now apply certain concepts of vector space to gain some intuition about signal analysis. We have seen that any vector can be expressed as a sum of its components along n mutually orthogonal vectors, provided these vectors formed a complete set of coordinate system. We therefore suspect that it may be possible to express any function $f(t)$ as a sum of its components along a set of mutually orthogonal functions if these functions form a complete set. We shall now show that this indeed is the case.

Approximation of a Function by a Set of Mutually Orthogonal Functions

Let us consider a set of n functions $g_1(t)$, $g_2(t)$, $\ldots$, $g_n(t)$ which are orthogonal to one another over an interval t_1 to t_2; that is,

$$\int_{t_1}^{t_2} g_j(t)g_k(t) = 0 \qquad j \neq k \tag{3.23a}$$

and let

$$\int_{t}^{t_2} g_j{}^2(t) \, dt = K_j \tag{3.23b}$$

Let an arbitrary function $f(t)$ be approximated over an interval (t_1, t_2) by a linear combination of these n mutually orthogonal functions.

$$f(t) \simeq C_1 g_1(t) + C_2 g_2(t) + \cdots + C_k g_k(t) + \cdots + C_n g_n(t) \tag{3.24}$$

$$= \sum_{r=1}^{n} C_r g_r(t) \tag{3.25}$$

For the best approximation we must find the proper values of constants C_1, C_2, $\ldots$, C_n such that ε, the mean square of $f_e(t)$, is minimized.

By definition,

$$f_e(t) = f(t) - \sum_{r=1}^{n} C_r g_r(t)$$

and

$$\varepsilon = \frac{1}{t_2 - t_1} \int_{t_1}^{t_2} \left[f(t) - \sum_{r=1}^{n} C_r g_r(t) \right]^2 dt \tag{3.26}$$

It is evident from Eq. 3.26 that ε is a function of C_1, C_2, $\ldots$, C_n and to minimize ε, we must have

$$\frac{\partial \varepsilon}{\partial C_1} = \frac{\partial \varepsilon}{\partial C_2} = \cdots = \frac{\partial \varepsilon}{\partial C_j} = \cdots = \frac{\partial \varepsilon}{\partial C_n} = 0 \tag{3.27}$$

Let us consider the equation:

$$\frac{\partial \varepsilon}{\partial C_j} = 0 \tag{3.28}$$

Since $(t_2 - t_1)$ is constant, Eq. 3.28 may be expressed as

$$\frac{\partial}{\partial C_j} \left\{ \int_{t_1}^{t_2} \left[f(t) - \sum_{r=1}^{n} C_r g_r(t) \right]^2 dt \right\} = 0 \tag{3.29}$$

When we expand the integrand, we note that all the terms arising due to the cross product of the orthogonal functions are zero by virtue of orthogonality; that is, all the terms of the form $\int g_j(t)g_k(t) \, dt$ are zero as expressed in Eq. 3.23. Similarly, the derivative with respect to C_j of all the terms that do not contain C_j are zero; that is,

$$\frac{\partial}{\partial C_j} \int_{t_1}^{t_2} f^2(t)\, dt = \frac{\partial}{\partial C_j} \int_{t_1}^{t_2} C_r{}^2 g_r{}^2(t)\, dt = \frac{\partial}{\partial C_j} \int_{t_1}^{t_2} C_r f(t) g_r(t)\, dt = 0 \quad (3.30)$$

This leaves only two nonzero terms in Eq. 3.29 as follows:

$$\frac{\partial}{\partial C_j} \int_{t_1}^{t_2} [-2C_j f(t) g_j(t) + C_j{}^2 g_j{}^2(t)]\, dt = 0 \quad (3.31)$$

Changing the order of differentiation and integration in Eq. 3.31, we get

$$2 \int_{t_1}^{t_2} f(t) g_j(t)\, dt = 2C_j \int_{t_1}^{t_2} g_j{}^2(t)\, dt \quad (3.32)$$

Therefore

$$C_j = \frac{\displaystyle\int_{t_1}^{t_2} f(t) g_j(t)\, dt}{\displaystyle\int_{t_1}^{t_2} g_j{}^2(t)\, dt} \quad (3.33a)$$

$$= \frac{1}{K_j} \int_{t_1}^{t_2} f(t) g_j(t)\, dt \quad (3.33b)$$

We may summarize this result as follows. Given a set of n functions $g_1(t)$, $g_2(t)$, $\ldots$, $g_n(t)$ mutually orthogonal over the interval (t_1, t_2), it is possible to approximate an arbitrary function $f(t)$ over this interval by a linear combination of these n functions.

$$f(t) \simeq C_1 g_1(t) + C_2 g_2(t) + \cdots + C_n g_n(t)$$

$$= \sum_{r=1}^{n} C_r g_r(t) \quad (3.34)$$

For the best approximation, that is, the one that will minimize the mean of the square error over the interval, we must choose the coefficients $C_1, C_2, \ldots, C_n$, etc. as given by Eq. 3.33.

Evaluation of Mean Square Error

Let us now find the value of ε when optimum values of coefficients $C_1, C_2, \ldots, C_n$ are chosen according to Eq. 3.33. By definition,

$$\varepsilon = \frac{1}{(t_2 - t_1)} \int_{t_1}^{t_2} \left[f(t) - \sum_{r=1}^{n} C_r g_r(t) \right]^2 dt \quad (3.35)$$

$$= \frac{1}{(t_2 - t_1)} \left[\int_{t_1}^{t_2} f^2(t)\, dt + \sum_{r=1}^{n} C_r{}^2 \int_{t_1}^{t_2} g_r{}^2(t)\, dt \right.$$

$$\left. - 2\sum_{r=1}^{n} C_r \int_{t_1}^{t_2} f(t) g_r(t)\, dt \right] \quad (3.36)$$

But from Eqs. 3.33a and 3.33b it follows that

$$\int_{t_1}^{t_2} f(t) g_r(t) \, dt = C_r \int_{t_1}^{t_2} g_r^2(t) \, dt = C_r K_r \qquad (3.37)$$

Substituting Eq. 3.37 in Eq. 3.36, we get

$$\varepsilon = \frac{1}{(t_2 - t_1)} \left[\int_{t_1}^{t_2} f^2(t) \, dt + \sum_{r=1}^{n} C_r^2 K_r - 2 \sum_{r=1}^{n} C_r^2 K_r \right]$$

$$= \frac{1}{(t_2 - t_1)} \left[\int_{t_1}^{t_2} f^2(t) \, dt - \sum_{r=1}^{n} C_r^2 K_r \right] \qquad (3.38)$$

$$= \frac{1}{(t_2 - t_1)} \left[\int_{t_1}^{t_2} f^2(t) \, dt - (C_1^2 K_1 + C_2^2 K_2 + \cdots + C_n^2 K_n) \right] \qquad (3.39)$$

One can therefore evaluate the mean-square error by using Eq. 3.39.

Representation of a Function by a Closed or a Complete Set of Mutually Orthogonal Functions

It is evident from Eq. 3.39 that if we increase n, that is, if we approximate $f(t)$ by a larger number of orthogonal functions, the error will become smaller. But by its very definition, ε is a positive quantity; hence in the limit as the number of terms is made infinity, the sum $\sum_{r=1}^{\infty} C_r^2 K_r$ may converge to the integral

$$\int_{t_1}^{t_2} f^2(t) \, dt$$

and then ε vanishes. Thus

$$\int_{t_1}^{t_2} f^2(t) \, dt = \sum_{r=1}^{\infty} C_r^2 K_r \qquad (3.40)$$

Under these conditions $f(t)$ is represented by the infinite series:

$$f(t) = C_1 g_1(t) + C_2 g_2(t) + \cdots + C_r g_r(t) + \cdots \qquad (3.41)$$

The infinite series on the right-hand side of Eq. 3.40 thus converges to $f(t)$ such that the mean square of the error is zero. The series is said to *converge in the mean*. Note that the representation of $f(t)$ is now exact.

A set of functions $g_1(t)$, $g_2(t)$, ..., $g_r(t)$ mutually orthogonal over the interval (t_1, t_2) is said to be a complete or a closed set if there exists no function $x(t)$ for which it is true that

$$\int_{t_1}^{t_2} x(t) g_k(t) \, dt = 0 \qquad \text{for} \quad k = 1, 2, \ldots$$

If a function $x(t)$ could be found such that the above integral is zero, then obviously $x(t)$ is orthogonal to each member of the set $\{g_r(t)\}$ and, consequently, is itself a member of the set. Evidently the set cannot be complete without $x(t)$ being its member.

Let us now summarize the results of this discussion. For a set $\{g_r(t)\}$, $(r = 1, 2, \ldots)$ mutually orthogonal over the interval (t_1, t_2),

$$\int_{t_1}^{t_2} g_m(t)g_n(t)\, dt = \begin{cases} 0 & \text{if } m \neq n \\ K_m & \text{if } m = n \end{cases} \tag{3.42}$$

If this function set is complete, then any function $f(t)$, can be expressed as

$$f(t) = C_1 g_1(t) + C_2 g_2(t) + \cdots + C_r g_r(t) + \cdots \tag{3.43}$$

where

$$C_r = \frac{\displaystyle\int_{t_1}^{t_2} f(t)g_r(t)\, dt}{K_r} = \frac{\displaystyle\int_{t_1}^{t_2} f(t)g_r(t)\, dt}{\displaystyle\int_{t_1}^{t_2} g_r^2(t)\, dt} \tag{3.44}$$

Comparison of Eqs. 3.42 to 3.44 with Eqs. 3.20 to 3.22 brings out forcefully the analogy between vectors and signals. Any vector can be expressed as a sum of its components along n mutually orthogonal vectors, provided these vectors form a complete set. Similarly, any function $f(t)$ can be expressed as a sum of its components along mutually orthogonal functions, provided these functions form a closed or a complete set.

In the analogy of vectors and signals the dot product of two vectors is analogous to the integral of the product of two signals, that is,

$$\mathbf{A} \cdot \mathbf{B} \sim \int_{t_1}^{t_2} f_A(t) f_B(t)\, dt$$

It follows that the square of the length A of a vector $\mathbf{A}$ is analogous to the integral of the square of a function, that is,

$$\mathbf{A} \cdot \mathbf{A} = A^2 \sim \int_{t_1}^{t_2} f_A^2(t)\, dt$$

If a vector is expressed in terms of its mutually orthogonal components. the square of the length is given by the sum of the squares of the lengths of the component vectors. An analogous result holds true for signals, This is precisely expressed by Eq. 3.40 (Parseval's theorem). Since the component functions are not orthonormal, the right-hand side is $\Sigma\, C_r^2 K_r^2$ instead of $\Sigma\, C_r^2$. For an orthonormal set, $K_r = 1$. Equation 3.40 is thus analogous to the case where a vector is expressed in terms of its components along mutually orthogonal vectors whose length squares are $K_1, K_2, \ldots, K_r \ldots$, etc.

Equation 3.43 shows that $f(t)$ contains a component of signal $g_r(t)$, and this component has a magnitude C_r. Representation of $f(t)$ by a set of infinite mutually orthogonal functions is called *generalized Fourier series representation*[2] of $f(t)$.

Orthogonality in Complex Functions

In the above discussion, we have considered only real functions of real variable. If $f_1(t)$ and $f_2(t)$ are complex functions of real variable t, then it can be shown that $f_1(t)$ can be approximated by $C_{12}f_2(t)$ over an interval (t_1, t_2).

$$f_1(t) \simeq C_{12}f_2(t)$$

The optimum value of C_{12} to minimize the mean-square error magnitude is given by[3]

$$C_{12} = \frac{\int_{t_1}^{t_2} f_1(t) f_2{}^*(t)\, dt}{\int_{t_1}^{t_2} f_2(t) f_2{}^*(t)\, dt} \tag{3.45}$$

where $f_2{}^*(t)$ is a complex conjugate of $f_2(t)$.

It is evident from Eq. 3.45 that two complex functions $f_1(t)$ and $f_2(t)$ are orthogonal over the interval (t_1, t_2) if[4]

$$\int_{t_1}^{t_2} f_1(t) f_2{}^*(t)\, dt = \int_{t_1}^{t_2} f_1{}^*(t) f_2(t)\, dt = 0 \tag{3.46}$$

For a set of complex functions $\{g_r(t)\}$, $(r = 1, 2, \ldots)$ mutually orthogonal over the interval (t_1, t_2):

$$\int_{t_1}^{t_2} g_m(t) g_n{}^*(t)\, dt = \begin{cases} 0 & \text{if } m \neq n \\ K_m & \text{if } m = n \end{cases} \tag{3.47}$$

If this set of functions is complete, then any function $f(t)$ can be expressed as

$$f(t) = C_1 g_1(t) + C_2 g_2(t) + \cdots + C_r g_r(t) + \cdots \tag{3.48}$$

where

$$C_r = \frac{1}{K_r} \int_{t_1}^{t_2} f(t) g_r{}^*(t)\, dt \tag{3.49}$$

---

[2] R. V. Churchill, *Fourier Series and Boundary Value Problems*, pp. 57–58, McGraw-Hill, New York, 1963.

[3] See, for instance, S. Mason and H. Zimmerman, *Electronic Circuits, Signals and Systems* pp. 199–200, Wiley, New York, 1960.

[4] When two complex functions $f_1(t)$ and $f_2(t)$ satisfy Eq. 3.46, they are sometimes referred to as orthogonal functions in the Hermitian sense.

If the set of functions is real, then $g_r{}^*(t) = g_r(t)$ and all the results for complex functions reduce to those obtained for real functions in Eqs. 3.42 to 3.44.

Example 3.2

As an example we shall again consider the rectangular function of Example 3.1 as shown in Fig. 3.3. This function was approximated by a single function $\sin t$. We shall now see how the approximation improves when a large number of mutually orthogonal functions are used. It was shown previously that functions $\sin n\omega_0 t$ and $\sin m\omega_0 t$ are mutually orthogonal over the interval $(t_0, t_0 + 2\pi/\omega_0)$ for all integral values of n and m. Hence, it follows that a set of functions $\sin t$, $\sin 2t$, $\sin 3t$, etc. are mutually orthogonal over the interval $(0, 2\pi)$. The rectangular function in Fig. 3.3 will now be approximated by a finite series of sinusoidal functions.

$$f(t) \simeq C_1 \sin t + C_2 \sin 2t + \cdots + C_n \sin nt$$

The constants C_r can be evaluated by using Eq. 3.33.

$$C_r = \frac{\displaystyle\int_0^{2\pi} f(t) \sin rt \, dt}{\displaystyle\int_0^{2\pi} \sin^2 rt \, dt}$$

$$= \frac{1}{\pi}\left[\int_0^{\pi} \sin rt \, dt - \int_{\pi}^{2\pi} \sin rt \, dt\right]$$

$$= \frac{4}{\pi r} \qquad \text{if } r \text{ is odd}$$

$$= 0 \qquad \text{if } r \text{ is even}$$

Thus, $f(t)$ is approximated by

$$f(t) = \frac{4}{\pi}\left[\sin t + \tfrac{1}{3}\sin 3t + \tfrac{1}{5}\sin 5t + \tfrac{1}{7}\sin 7t + \cdots\right] \qquad (3.50)$$

Figure 3.6 shows the actual function and the approximated function when the function is approximated with one, two, three, and four terms respectively in Eq. 3.50. For the given number of terms of the form $\sin rt$, these are the optimum approximations which minimize the mean-square error. As we increase the number of terms, the approximation improves and the mean-square error diminishes. For infinite terms the mean-square error is zero.[5]

Let us evaluate the error ε in these approximations. From Eq. 3.39,

$$\varepsilon = \frac{1}{(t_2 - t_1)}\left[\int_{t_1}^{t_2} f^2(t) \, dt - C_1{}^2 K_1 - C_2{}^2 K_2 - \cdots\right]$$

[5] The Fourier series fails to converge at the points of discontinuity, and hence even though the number of terms is increased, the approximated function shows large amounts of ripples at the points of discontinuity. This is known as the *Gibbs phenomenon*.

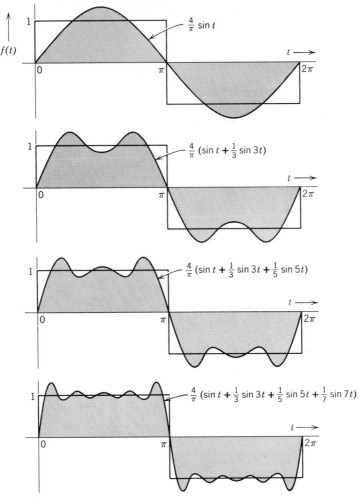

Figure 3.6 Approximation of a rectangular function by orthogonal functions.

In this case

$$(t_2 - t_1) = 2\pi$$

$$f(t) = \begin{cases} 1, & (0 < t < \pi) \\ -1, & (\pi < t < 2\pi) \end{cases}$$

Therefore

$$\int_0^{2\pi} f^2(t)\, dt = 2\pi$$

Also

$$C_r = \begin{cases} \dfrac{4}{\pi r} & \text{if } r \text{ is odd} \\ \\ 0 & \text{if } r \text{ is even} \end{cases}$$

and

$$K_r = \int_0^{2\pi} \sin^2 rt \, dt = \pi$$

Therefore, for one-term approximation:

$$\varepsilon_1 = \frac{1}{2\pi}\left[2\pi - \left(\frac{4}{\pi}\right)^2 \pi\right] = 0.19$$

For two-term approximation:

$$\varepsilon_2 = \frac{1}{2\pi}\left[2\pi - \left(\frac{4}{\pi}\right)^2 \pi - \left(\frac{4}{3\pi}\right)^2 \pi\right] = 0.1$$

For three-term approximation:

$$\varepsilon_3 = \frac{1}{2\pi}\left[2\pi - \left(\frac{4}{\pi}\right)^2 \pi - \left(\frac{4}{3\pi}\right)^2 \pi - \left(\frac{4}{5\pi}\right)^2 \pi\right] = 0.0675$$

and

$$\varepsilon_4 = \frac{1}{2\pi}\left[2\pi - \left(\frac{4}{\pi}\right)^2 \pi - \left(\frac{4}{3\pi}\right)^2 \pi - \left(\frac{4}{5\pi}\right)^2 \pi - \left(\frac{4}{7\pi}\right)^2 \pi\right] = 0.051$$

and so on.

It can be easily seen that in this case the mean-square error diminishes rapidly as the number of terms is increased.

3.2 SOME EXAMPLES OF ORTHOGONAL FUNCTIONS

Representation of a function over a certain interval by a linear combination of mutually orthogonal functions is called Fourier series representation of a function. There exist, however, a large number of sets of orthogonal functions, and hence a given function may be expressed in terms of different sets of orthogonal functions. In vector space this is analogous to the representation of a given vector in different sets of coordinate systems. Each set of orthogonal functions corresponds to a coordinate system. Some of the examples of sets of orthogonal functions are trigonometric functions, exponential functions, Legendre polynomials, Jacobi polynomials, etc. Bessel functions also form a special kind of orthogonal functions.[6]

[6] Bessel functions are orthogonal with respect to a weighting function. See, for instance, W. Kaplan, *Advanced Calculus*, Addison-Wesley, Cambridge, Mass., 1953.

Legendre Fourier Series

A set of Legendre polynomials $P_n(x)$, $(n = 0, 1, 2, \ldots)$ forms a complete set of mutually orthogonal functions over an interval $(-1 < t < 1)$.

These polynomials can be defined by Rodrigues formula.

$$P_n(t) = \frac{1}{2^n n!} \frac{d^n}{dt^n} (t^2 - 1)^n, \qquad n = (0, 1, 2, \cdots)$$

It follows from this equation that

$$P_0(t) = 1; \qquad\qquad P_1(t) = t$$
$$P_2(t) = (\tfrac{3}{2}t^2 - \tfrac{1}{2}); \qquad P_3(t) = (\tfrac{5}{2}t^3 - \tfrac{3}{2}t)$$

and so on.

We may verify the orthogonality of these polynomials by showing that

$$\int_{-1}^{1} P_m(t) P_n(t)\, dt = \begin{cases} 0 & m \neq n \\[2mm] \dfrac{2}{2m + 1} & m = n \end{cases} \tag{3.51}$$

We can express a function $f(t)$ in terms of Legendre polynomial over an interval $(-1 < t < 1)$ as:

$$f(t) = C_0 P_0(t) + C_1 P_1(t) + \cdots + \cdots \tag{3.52}$$

where

$$C_r = \frac{\displaystyle\int_{-1}^{1} f(t) P_r(t)\, dt}{\displaystyle\int_{-1}^{1} P_r{}^2(t)\, dt}$$

$$= \frac{2r + 1}{2} \int_{-1}^{1} f(t) P_r(t)\, dt \tag{3.53}$$

Note that although the series representation is valid over the region -1 to 1, it can be extended to any region by the appropriate change in variable.

Example 3.3

Let us consider the rectangular function shown in Fig. 3.7. This function can be represented by Legendre Fourier series:

$$f(t) = C_0 P_0(t) + C_1 P_1(t) + \cdots + C_r P_r(t) + \cdots$$

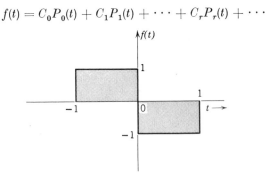

Figure 3.7

The coefficients $C_0, C_1, C_2, \ldots, C_r$ etc. may be found from Eq. 3.53. We have

$$f(t) = \begin{cases} 1 & \cdots (-1 < t < 0) \\ -1 & \cdots (0 < t < 1) \end{cases}$$

and

$$C_0 = \tfrac{1}{2} \int_{-1}^{1} f(t)\, dt = 0$$

$$C_1 = \tfrac{3}{2} \int_{-1}^{1} t f(t)\, dt$$

$$= \tfrac{3}{2} \left(\int_{-1}^{0} t\, dt - \int_{1}^{0} t\, dt \right)$$

$$= -\tfrac{3}{2}$$

$$C_2 = \tfrac{5}{2} \int_{-1}^{1} f(t)\, (\tfrac{3}{2}t^2 - \tfrac{1}{2})\, dt$$

$$= \tfrac{5}{2} \left[\int_{-1}^{0} \tfrac{3}{2} t^2 - \tfrac{1}{2}\, dt + \int_{0}^{1} - (\tfrac{3}{2} t^2 - \tfrac{1}{2})\, dt \right]$$

$$= 0$$

It can be shown, in general, that for even values of r,

$$C_r = 0$$

that is,

$$C_0 = C_2 = C_4 = C_6 = \cdots = 0 \qquad (3.54)$$

$$C_3 = \tfrac{7}{2} \int_{-1}^{1} f(t)(\tfrac{5}{2}t^3 - \tfrac{3}{2}t)\, dt$$

$$= \tfrac{7}{2} \left[\int_{-1}^{0} \tfrac{5}{2}t^3 - \tfrac{3}{2}t\, dt + \int_{0}^{1} - (\tfrac{5}{2}t^3 - \tfrac{3}{2}t) \right] dt$$

$$= \tfrac{7}{8}$$

In a similar way the coefficients $C_5, C_7 \cdots$ etc. may be evaluated. We now have

$$f(t) = -\tfrac{3}{2}t + \tfrac{7}{8}(\tfrac{5}{2}t^3 - \tfrac{3}{2}t) + \cdots \qquad (3.55)$$

Trigonometric Fourier Series

We have already shown that functions $\sin \omega_0 t$, $\sin 2\omega_0 t$, etc. form an orthogonal set over any interval $(t_0, t_0 + 2\pi/\omega_0)$. This set, however, is not complete. This is evident from the fact a function $\cos n\omega_0 t$ is orthogonal to $\sin m\omega_0 t$ over the same interval. Hence, to complete the set, we must include cosine as well as sine functions. It can be shown that the composite set of functions consisting of a set $\cos n\omega_0 t$ and $\sin n\omega_0 t$ for $(n = 0, 1, 2, \ldots)$ forms a complete orthogonal set. Note that for $n = 0$, $\sin n\omega_0 t$ is zero, but $\cos n\omega_0 t = 1$. Thus we have a complete orthogonal set represented by functions 1, $\cos \omega_0 t$, $\cos 2\omega_0 t$, $\ldots$, $\cos n\omega_0 t$, $\ldots$; $\sin \omega_0 t$, $\sin 2\omega_0 t$, $\ldots$, $\sin n\omega_0 t$, $\ldots$, etc. It therefore follows that any function $f(t)$ can be represented in terms of these functions over any interval $(t_0, t_0 + 2\pi/\omega_0)$. Thus

$$f(t) = a_0 + a_1 \cos \omega_0 t + a_2 \cos 2\omega_0 t + \cdots + a_n \cos n\omega_0 t + \cdots$$
$$+ b_1 \sin \omega_0 t + b_2 \sin 2\omega_0 t + \cdots + b_n \sin n\omega_0 t + \cdots$$
$$+ (t_0 < t < t_0 + 2\pi/\omega_0) \quad (3.56)$$

For convenience we shall denote $2\pi/\omega_0$ by T. Equation 3.56 can be expressed as

$$f(t) = a_0 + \sum_{n=1}^{\infty} (a_n \cos n\omega_0 t + b_n \sin n\omega_0 t), \quad (t_0 < t < t_0 + T)$$
$$(3.57)$$

Equation 3.57 is the trigonometric Fourier series representation of $f(t)$ over an interval $(t_0, t_0 + T)$. The various constants a_n and b_n are given by

$$a_n = \frac{\int_{t_0}^{(t_0+T)} f(t) \cos n\omega_0 t \, dt}{\int_{t_0}^{(t_0+T)} \cos^2 n\omega_0 t \, dt} \quad (3.58)$$

and

$$b_n = \frac{\int_{t_0}^{(t_0+T)} f(t) \sin n\omega_0 t \, dt}{\int_{t_0}^{(t_0+T)} \sin^2 n\omega_0 t \, dt} \quad (3.59)$$

If we let $n = 0$ in Eq. 3.58, we get

$$a_0 = \frac{1}{T} \int_{t_0}^{t_0+T} f(t) \, dt \quad (3.60a)$$

We also have

$$\int_{t_0}^{t_0+T} \cos^2 n\omega_0 t \, dt = \int_{t_0}^{t_0+T} \sin^2 n\omega_0 t \, dt = \frac{T}{2}$$

Therefore

$$a_n = \frac{2}{T} \int_{t_0}^{t_0+T} f(t) \cos n\omega_0 t \, dt \quad (3.60b)$$

$$b_n = \frac{2}{T} \int_{t_0}^{t_0+T} f(t) \sin n\omega_0 t \, dt \quad (3.60c)$$

The constant term a_0 in the series is given by Eq. 3.60a. It is evident that a_0 is the average value of $f(t)$ over the interval $(t_0, t_0 + T)$. Thus, a_0 is the d-c component of $f(t)$ over this interval.

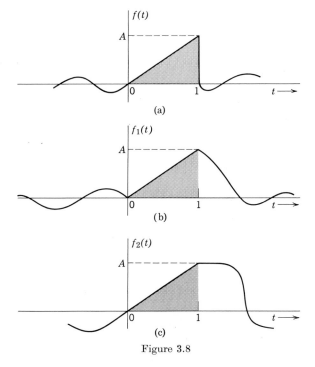

Figure 3.8

Example 3.4

We shall now expand a function $f(t)$ shown in Fig. 3.8a by trigonometric Fourier series over the interval $(0, 1)$. It is evident that $f(t) = At$ $(0 < t < 1)$, the interval $T = 1$, and $\omega_0 = 2\pi/T = 2\pi$. We must choose $t_0 = 0$. Thus

$$f(t) = a_0 + a_1 \cos 2\pi t + a_2 \cos 4\pi t + \cdots + a_n \cos 2\pi n t + \cdots$$
$$+ b_1 \sin 2\pi t + b_2 \sin 4\pi t + \cdots + b_n \sin 2\pi n t + \cdots \qquad (3.61)$$

Various coefficients in the series in Eq. 3.61 can be found by using Eqs. 3.60a to 3.60c.

$$a_0 = \frac{1}{T} \int_0^T f(t)\, dt = 1 \int_0^1 At\, dt = \frac{A}{2} \qquad (3.62a)$$

Similarly

$$a_n = \frac{2}{1} \int_0^1 At \cos 2\pi n t\, dt$$

$$= \frac{A}{2\pi^2 n^2} [\cos 2\pi n t + 2\pi n t \sin 2\pi n t]_0^1 = 0 \qquad (3.62b)$$

$$b_n = \frac{2}{1} \int_0^1 At \sin 2\pi n t\, dt$$

$$= \frac{A}{2\pi^2 n^2} [\sin 2\pi n t - 2\pi n t \cos 2\pi n t]_0^1 = \frac{-A}{\pi n} \qquad (3.62c)$$

Since $a_n = 0$ for all values of n, all the cosine terms in series in Eq. 3.61 are zero. The coefficients of the sine terms are given by Eq. 3.62c. The series in Eq. 3.61 may now be expressed as

$$f(t) = \frac{A}{2} - \frac{A}{\pi} \sin 2\pi t - \frac{A}{2\pi} \sin 4\pi t - \frac{A}{3\pi} \sin 6\pi t - \cdots$$

$$- \frac{A}{n\pi} \sin 2\pi n t - \cdots - \qquad (0 < t < 1)$$

$$= \frac{A}{2} - \frac{A}{\pi} \sum_{n=1}^{\infty} \frac{\sin 2\pi n t}{n}, \qquad (0 < t < 1) \qquad (3.63)$$

We have thus expressed $f(t)$ in terms of its components over the interval $(0, 1)$. From Eq. 3.63 it is evident that $f(t)$ has a d-c component $A/2$. In addition, $f(t)$ has components of sinusoidal functions $\sin 2\pi t$, $\sin 4\pi t$ etc. with magnitudes of $-A/\pi$, $-A/2\pi$ etc., respectively.

We note here that the series in Eq. 3.61 will also represent any other functions identical to $f(t)$ over the interval $(0, 1)$. Thus the functions $f_1(t)$ and $f_2(t)$ in Figs. 3.8b and 3.8c are identical to $f(t)$ over the interval $(0, 1)$, and hence both these functions can also be represented over the interval $(0, 1)$ by the series in Eq. 3.63.

Exponential Fourier Series

It can be easily shown that a set of exponential functions $\{e^{jn\omega_0 t}\}$, $(n = 0, \pm 1, \pm 2, \ldots)$ is orthogonal over an interval $(t_0, t_0 + 2\pi/\omega_0)$ for any value of t_0. Note that this is a set of complex functions. We can demonstrate the orthogonality of this set by considering the integral:

$$I = \int_{t_0}^{t_0 + 2\pi/\omega_0} (e^{jn\omega_0 t})(e^{jm\omega_0 t})^* \, dt = \int_{t_0}^{t_0 + 2\pi/\omega_0} e^{jn\omega_0 t} e^{-jm\omega_0 t} \, dt \qquad (3.64)$$

If $n = m$, the integral I is given by

$$I = \int_{t_0}^{t_0 + 2\pi/\omega_0} dt = \frac{2\pi}{\omega_0}$$

If $n \neq m$, the integral in Eq. 3.64 is given by

$$I = \frac{1}{j(n-m)\omega_0} e^{j(n-m)\omega_0 t} \bigg|_{t_0}^{t_0 + 2\pi/\omega_0}$$

$$= \frac{1}{j(n-m)\omega_0} e^{j(n-m)\omega_0 t_0} [e^{j2\pi(n-m)} - 1]$$

Since both n and m are integers, $e^{j2\pi(n-m)}$ is equal to unity and hence the integral is zero.

$$I = 0$$

Thus

$$\int_{t_0}^{t_0+2\pi/\omega_0} e^{jn\omega_0 t}(e^{jm\omega_0 t})^* \, dt = \begin{cases} \dfrac{2\pi}{\omega_0} & m = n \\[2mm] 0 & m \neq n \end{cases} \qquad (3.65)$$

As before, let

$$\frac{2\pi}{\omega_0} = T$$

It is evident from Eq. 3.65 that the set of functions

$$\{e^{jn\omega_0 t}\}, \qquad (n = 0, \pm 1, \pm 2, \ldots)$$

is orthogonal over the interval $(t_0, t_0 + T)$ where $T = 2\pi/\omega_0$. Further, it can be shown that this is a complete set. It is therefore possible to represent an arbitrary function $f(t)$ by a linear combination of exponential functions over an interval $(t_0, t_0 + T)$:

$$f(t) = F_0 + F_1 e^{j\omega_0 t} + F_2 e^{j2\omega_0 t} + \cdots + F_n e^{jn\omega_0 t} + \cdots$$
$$+ F_{-1} e^{-j\omega_0 t} + F_{-2} e^{-j2\omega_0 t} + \cdots + F_{-n} e^{-jn\omega_0 t} + \cdots$$

for

$$= \sum_{n=-\infty}^{\infty} F_n e^{jn\omega_0 t} \qquad (t_0 < t < t_0 + T) \qquad (3.66)$$

where $\omega_0 = 2\pi/T$ and the summation in Eq. 3.66 is for integral values of n from $-\infty$ to ∞, including zero. Representation of $f(t)$ by exponential series, as shown in Eq. 3.66, is known as exponential Fourier series representation of $f(t)$ over the interval $(t_0, t_0 + T)$. The various coefficients in this series can be evaluated by using Eq. 3.49.

$$F_n = \frac{\displaystyle\int_{t_0}^{t_0+T} f(t)(e^{jn\omega_0 t})^* \, dt}{\displaystyle\int_{t_0}^{t_0+T} e^{jn\omega_0 t}(e^{jn\omega_0 t})^* \, dt}$$

$$= \frac{\displaystyle\int_{t_0}^{t_0+T} f(t)e^{-jn\omega_0 t} \, dt}{\displaystyle\int_{t_0}^{t_0+T} e^{jn\omega_0 t}e^{-jn\omega_0 t} \, dt}$$

$$= \frac{1}{T} \int_{t_0}^{t_0+T} f(t)e^{-jn\omega_0 t} \, dt \qquad (3.67)$$

We could also have obtained this same result directly by multiplying both sides of Eq. 3.66 by $e^{-jn\omega_0 t}$ and integrating with respect to t over the interval $(t_0, t_0 + T)$. By virtue of orthogonality, all the terms except one, on the right-hand side, vanish and yield the expression for F_n as in Eq. 3.67.

Summarizing the results: any given function $f(t)$ may be expressed as a discrete sum of exponential functions $\{e^{jn\omega_0 t}\}$, $(n = 0, \pm 1, \pm 2, \ldots)$ over an interval $t_0 < t < t_0 + T$, $(\omega_0 = 2\pi/T)$.

$$f(t) = \sum_{n=-\infty}^{\infty} F_n e^{jn\omega_0 t} \qquad (t_0 < t < t_0 + T) \qquad (3.68)$$

where

$$F_n = \frac{1}{T} \int_{t_0}^{t_0+T} f(t)e^{-jn\omega_0 t}\, dt \qquad (3.69)$$

Example 3.5

We shall again consider the triangular function $f(t)$ shown in Fig. 3.8. This function will now be represented by exponential Fourier series. We have

$$f(t) = At \qquad (0 < t < 1)$$

The interval $T = 1$ second and $t_0 = 0$. Also, $\omega_0 = 2\pi/T = 2\pi$. The exponential Fourier series representation of $f(t)$ is given by

$$f(t) = \sum_{n=-\infty}^{\infty} F_n e^{j2n\pi t}, \qquad (0 < t < 1)$$

The coefficients F_n may be found from Eq. 3.69. Here, $t_0 = 0$ and $T = 1$. Therefore

$$F_n = \int_0^1 Ate^{-j2n\pi t}\, dt \qquad (3.70)$$

$$= \frac{A}{4\pi^2 n^2}\left[\frac{e^{-j2n\pi t}}{1}(j2n\pi t + 1)\right]_0^1$$

$$= \frac{A}{4\pi^2 n^2}[e^{-j2\pi n}(j2\pi n + 1) - 1]$$

Since $e^{-j2\pi n} = 1$, we have

$$F_n = \frac{jA}{2\pi n} \qquad (3.71)$$

Thus

$$F_1 = \frac{jA}{2\pi}, \qquad F_2 = \frac{jA}{4\pi}, \ldots, \text{etc.}$$

and

$$F_{-1} = \frac{-jA}{2\pi}, \qquad F_{-2} = \frac{-jA}{4\pi}$$

Note that it is not possible to obtain F_0 by directly substituting $n = 0$ in Eq. 3.71. We shall use Eq. 3.70 to evaluate F_0 by letting $n = 0$. Thus

$$F_0 = \int_0^1 At \, dt = \frac{A}{2}$$

Therefore

$$f(t) = \frac{A}{2} + \frac{jA}{2\pi} e^{j2\pi t} + \frac{jA}{4\pi} e^{j4\pi t} + \frac{jA}{6\pi} e^{j6\pi t} + \cdots + \frac{jA}{2\pi n} e^{j2\pi n} + \cdots$$

$$- \frac{jA}{2\pi} e^{-j2\pi t} - \frac{jA}{4\pi} e^{j4\pi t} - \frac{jA}{6\pi} e^{-j6\pi t} - \cdots - \frac{jA}{2\pi n} e^{-j2\pi nt} - \cdots \qquad (3.72)$$

$$= \frac{A}{2} + \frac{jA}{2\pi} \sum_{n=-\infty}^{\infty} \frac{1}{n} e^{j2\pi nt} \qquad (0 < t < 1) \qquad (3.73)$$

This is the exponential Fourier series representation of $f(t)$ shown in Fig. 3.8 over an interval $(0, 1)$.

3.3 RELATIONSHIP BETWEEN THE TRIGONOMETRIC AND THE EXPONENTIAL FOURIER SERIES

As a specific example, we expanded over an interval $(0, 1)$ the triangular function in Fig. 3.8 by the trigonometric Fourier series (Eq. 3.63) and the exponential Fourier series (Eq. 3.73). One cannot fail to observe the similarity between these two series. Indeed, the two series are identical. This can be easily seen. The exponential series in Eq. 3.73 can be expressed alternately as follows:

$$f(t) = \frac{A}{2} + \frac{jA}{2\pi} \sum_{n=1}^{\infty} \left(\frac{1}{n} e^{j2\pi nt} - \frac{1}{n} e^{-j2\pi nt} \right), \qquad (0 < t < 1)$$

$$= \frac{A}{2} + \frac{jA}{2\pi} \sum_{n=1}^{\infty} \frac{1}{n} (2j \sin 2\pi nt) \qquad (0 < t < 1)$$

$$= \frac{A}{2} - \frac{A}{\pi} \sum_{n=1}^{\infty} \frac{1}{n} \sin 2\pi nt \qquad (0 < t < 1)$$

This is exactly the trigonometric series in Eq. 3.63. What is true for this specific case is true in general. The trigonometric and exponential Fourier series are merely two different ways of expressing the same series, and the one can be obtained from the other merely by expressing sinusoidal functions in exponential form or exponential functions in sinusoidal form and rearranging the terms. This can be easily shown. Consider a general exponential Fourier series:

$$f(t) = \sum_{n=-\infty}^{\infty} F_n e^{jn\omega_0 t} \qquad (t_0 < t < t_0 + T)$$

$$= F_0 + F_1 e^{j\omega_0 t} + F_2 e^{j2\omega_0 t} + F_3 e^{j3\omega_0 t} + \cdots + F_n e^{jn\omega_0 t} + \cdots$$

$$+ F_{-1} e^{-j\omega_0 t} + F_{-2} e^{-j2\omega_0 t} + F_{-3} e^{-j3\omega_0 t} + \cdots + F_{-n} e^{-jn\omega_0 t} + \cdots$$

$$(3.74)$$

Note that

$$F_n = \frac{1}{T} \int_{t_0}^{t_0+T} f(t) e^{-jn\omega_0 t} \, dt \qquad (3.75)$$

It follows that

$$F_{-n} = \frac{1}{T} \int_{t_0}^{t_0+T} f(t) e^{jn\omega_0 t} \, dt \qquad (3.76)$$

It is evident from Eqs. 3.75 and 3.76 that

$$F_n = F_{-n}{}^* \qquad (3.77)$$

Let

$$F_n = \alpha_n + j\beta_n$$

Then

$$(3.78)$$

$$F_{-n} = \alpha_n - j\beta_n$$

Substituting Eq. 3.78 in Eq. 3.74 and rearranging the terms, we get

$$f(t) = F_0 + [(\alpha_1 + j\beta_1)e^{j\omega_0 t} + (\alpha_1 - j\beta_1)e^{-j\omega_0 t}] + [(\alpha_2 + j\beta_2)e^{j2\omega_0 t}$$

$$+ (\alpha_2 - j\beta_2)e^{-j2\omega_0 t}] + \cdots + [(\alpha_n + j\beta_n)e^{jn\omega_0 t}$$

$$+ (\alpha_n - j\beta_n)e^{-jn\omega_0 t}] \cdots$$

$$= F_0 + \sum_{n=1}^{\infty} [\alpha_n(e^{jn\omega_0 t} + e^{-jn\omega_0 t}) + j\beta_n(e^{jn\omega_0 t} - e^{jn\omega_0 t})]$$

$$= a_0 + \sum_{n=1}^{\infty} (a_n \cos n\omega_0 t + b_n \sin n\omega_0 t)$$

where

$$a_0 = F_0$$

$$a_n = 2\alpha_n = (F_n + F_{-n}) \qquad (3.79)$$

and

$$b_n = -2\beta_n = j(F_n - F_{-n})$$

Conversely

$$F_n = \tfrac{1}{2}(a_n - jb_n)$$

and

$$(3.80)$$

$$F_{-n} = \tfrac{1}{2}(a_n + jb_n)$$

Thus, using Eqs. 3.79 and 3.80, it is possible to convert an exponential Fourier series into a trigonometric one and vice versa. Using Eqs. 3.75, 3.76, and 3.79 it can be easily shown that

$$a_0 = \frac{1}{T} \int_{t_0}^{t_0+T} f(t) \, dt$$

$$a_n = \frac{2}{T} \int_{t_0}^{t_0+T} f(t) \cos n\omega_0 t \, dt \qquad (3.81)$$

$$b_n = \frac{2}{T} \int_{t_0}^{t_0+T} f(t) \sin n\omega_0 t \, dt$$

This is the same result as that in Eqs. 3.60a to 3.60c.

3.4 REPRESENTATION OF A PERIODIC FUNCTION BY THE FOURIER SERIES OVER THE ENTIRE INTERVAL ($-\infty < t < \infty$)

Thus far we have been able to represent a given function $f(t)$ by the Fourier series over a finite interval $(t_0, t_0 + T)$. Outside this interval the function $f(t)$ and the corresponding Fourier series need not be equal. The equality between $f(t)$ and its series holds only over the interval $(t_0, t_0 + T)$. If, however, the function $f(t)$ happens to be periodic, it can be shown that the equality holds over the entire interval[7] ($-\infty < t < \infty$). This can be easily shown by considering some function $f(t)$ and its exponential Fourier series representation over an interval $(t_0, t_0 + T)$.

$$f(t) = \sum_{n=-\infty}^{\infty} F_n e^{jn\omega_0 t} \qquad (t_0 < t < t_0 + T) \qquad (3.82)$$

where

$$\omega_0 = \frac{2\pi}{T}$$

The equality in Eq. 3.82 holds only over the interval $(t_0 < t < t_0 + T)$. The two sides of the equation need not be equal outside this interval. Let us denote the function represented on the right-hand side of Eq. 3.82 by $\varphi(t)$. Thus

$$f(t) = \varphi(t) \qquad (t_0 < t < t_0 + T)$$

where

$$\varphi(t) = \sum_{n=-\infty}^{\infty} F_n e^{jn\omega_0 t} \qquad \text{(for all values of } t\text{)} \qquad (3.83)$$

[7] This statement is true only for the exponential and the trigonometric Fourier series representation. From now on, we shall be concerned only with the exponential (and trigonometric) Fourier series. Therefore, the term Fourier series will always mean the exponential (or trigonometric) one.

It is simple to show that the function $\varphi(t)$ is a periodic function with period T. Consider the function $\varphi(t + T)$. From Eq. 3.83, we have

$$\varphi(t + T) = \sum_{n=-\infty}^{\infty} F_n e^{jn\omega_0(t+T)}$$

$$= \sum_{n=-\infty}^{\infty} F_n e^{jn\omega_0(t+2\pi/\omega_0)}$$

$$= \sum_{n=-\infty}^{\infty} F_n e^{jn\omega_0 t} e^{j2\pi n}$$

Since n assumes only integral values 0, ± 1, ± 2, etc., it is obvious that $e^{j2\pi n}$ is equal to unity and hence

$$\varphi(t + T) = \sum_{n=-\infty}^{\infty} F_n e^{jn\omega_0 t} = \varphi(t) \tag{3.84}$$

It is apparent from Eq. 3.84 that the function $\varphi(t)$ repeats itself after every T seconds. Such a function is called a *periodic function*. Indeed, Eq. 3.84 may be considered as the definition of a periodic function. A periodic function in variable t satisfies the condition:

$$\varphi(t) = \varphi(t + T) \tag{3.85}$$

The smallest value of T which satisfies the condition of periodicity in Eq. 3.85 is called the period. An example of a periodic function is shown in Fig. 3.9. For this function the condition of periodicity (Eq. 3.85) is satisfied for the smallest value of $T = 1$ second, and hence the period of this function is 1 second.

We have thus shown that the exponential (and trigonometric) Fourier series repeat themselves every T seconds. The exponential Fourier series representation of a triangular function $f(t)$ in Fig. 3.8 is given by Eq. 3.73. In this equation the left-hand and right-hand side are equal only over the

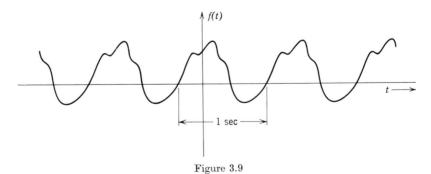

Figure 3.9

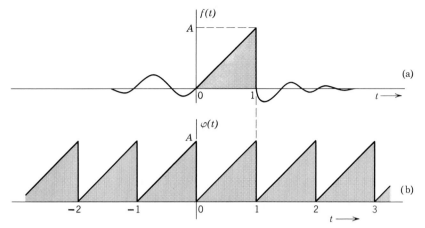

Figure 3.10 Representation of $f(t)$ and its Fourier series over the entire interval $-\infty < t < \infty$).

interval $(0, 1)$. The right-hand side series will be a triangular function repeating itself every 1 second (Fig. 3.10).

If $f(t)$ happens to be a periodic function of period T, then it is evident that it can be represented by an exponential (or trigonometric) Fourier series over the entire interval $(-\infty < t < \infty)$. This is really the statement of the *Fourier theorem*.

A periodic function $f(t)$ with period T can be represented by a Fourier series (exponential or trigonometric) over the entire interval $(-\infty < t < \infty)$. That is, if $f(t) = f(t + T)$, then $f(t)$ can be represented by a series:

$$f(t) = \sum_{n=-\infty}^{\infty} F_n e^{jn\omega_0 t} \qquad (-\infty < t < \infty) \qquad (3.86)$$

where

$$\omega_0 = \frac{2\pi}{T}$$

and

$$F_n = \frac{1}{T} \int_{t_0}^{t_0+T} f(t) e^{-jn\omega_0 t}\, dt \qquad (3.87)$$

Limits of Integration

In Eq. 3.87 the limits of integration are t_0 to $t_0 + T$. The function is integrated over an interval of T seconds. It is immaterial what value of t_0 is chosen in the integral (Eq. 3.87). The value of this integral is independent of the choice of t_0 for a periodic function. This can be easily shown as follows. Let

$$R(t) = f(t) e^{-jn\omega_0 t}$$

Then

$$F_n = \frac{1}{T} \int_{t_0}^{t_0+T} R(t)\, dt \tag{3.88}$$

Since $f(t)$ is a periodic function,

$$f(t + T) = f(t)$$

and it follows that

$$
\begin{aligned}
R(t + T) = f(t + T)\bar{e}^{jn\omega_0(t+T)} &= f(t)\bar{e}^{jn\omega_0 t}e^{j2\pi n} \\
&= f(t)\bar{e}^{jn\omega_0 t} \\
&= R(t)
\end{aligned}
$$

Hence, $R(t)$ is also a periodic function with period T. It is evident from Eq. 3.88 that F_n is the average value of a periodic function $R(t)$ over the interval $(t_0, t_0 + T)$. A glance at any periodic function of period T will show that the average value of such a function is the same over an interval of T seconds, no matter where this interval is chosen. We therefore conclude that the value of F_n is independent of the choice of t_0. If t_0 is chosen to be zero, then

$$F_n = \frac{1}{T} \int_0^T f(t)e^{-jn\omega_0 t}\, dt \tag{3.89}$$

It is quite common, however, to choose $t_0 = -T/2$. Thus

$$F_n = \frac{1}{T} \int_{-T/2}^{T/2} f(t)e^{-jn\omega_0 t}\, dt \tag{3.90}$$

3.5 CONVERGENCE OF THE FOURIER SERIES

We now ask an important question: Is it possible to represent any periodic function by a Fourier series? It is obvious that for the existence of a Fourier series, all the coefficients F_n must exist. Since the magnitude of $e^{-jn\omega_0 t}$ is unity, it is evident from Eq. 3.90 that

$$F_n < \frac{1}{T} \int_{-T/2}^{T/2} |f(t)|\, dt \tag{3.91}$$

Thus, if the integral on the right-hand side of Eq. 3.91 is finite, then F_n must also be finite. Hence the coefficients F_n will exist if $f(t)$ is absolutely integrable over the interval T seconds; that is, if

$$\int_{-T/2}^{T/2} |f(t)|\, dt \tag{3.92}$$

is finite.

This is known as the *weak Dirichlet condition*. If a function satisfies the weak Dirichlet condition, the existence of a Fourier series is guaranteed, but the series may not converge at every point. For example, if the function is infinite at some point, then obviously the series representing the function will be infinite and nonconvergent at that point. Similarly, if the function has an infinite number of maxima and minima in one period, then the function contains an appreciable amount of infinite frequency component and the series will not converge rapidly or uniformly. Thus, for a uniform convergent Fourier series, the function $f(t)$ must remain finite and must have only a finite number of maxima and minima. It may have a finite number of finite discontinuities. These are known as *strong Dirichlet conditions*. The study of convergence is a rather elegant topic in Fourier theory, but it is not immediately relevant to our purpose of analyzing systems. We note here that any periodic waveform that can be generated in the laboratory satisfies strong Dirichlet conditions, and hence possesses a convergent Fourier series. Thus a physical possibility of a periodic waveform is a valid and sufficient condition for the existence of a convergent series.

To reiterate: every periodic function $f(t)$ with period T, which satisfies Eq. 3.92, can be expanded by a Fourier series.

$$f(t) = \sum_{n=-\infty}^{\infty} F_n e^{jn\omega_0 t} \qquad (-\infty < t < \infty) \qquad (3.93)$$

where $\omega_0 = 2\pi/T$. The various coefficients F_0, F_1, ..., F_n, ..., etc., in the series are given by

$$F_n = \frac{1}{T} \int_{-T/2}^{T/2} f(t) e^{-jn\omega_0 t} \, dt \qquad (3.94)$$

The limits of integration in Eq. 3.94 may be chosen as t_0 to $(t_0 + T)$ where t_0 may have any value. This series may also be expressed in trigonometric form:

$$f(t) = a_0 + \sum_{n=1}^{\infty} (a_n \cos n\omega_0 t + b_n \sin n\omega_0 t) \qquad (-\infty < t < \infty) \quad (3.95)$$

The various coefficients a_n and b_n are given by

$$a_0 = \frac{1}{T} \int_{-T/2}^{T/2} f(t) \, dt$$

$$a_n = \frac{2}{T} \int_{-T/2}^{T/2} f(t) \cos n\omega_0 t \, dt \qquad (3.96)$$

$$b_n = \frac{2}{T} \int_{-T/2}^{T/2} f(t) \sin n\omega_0 t \, dt$$

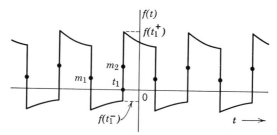

Figure 3.11   A periodic function with jump discontinuities.

There is another interesting property of the Fourier series with regard to the convergence at a point of discontinuity. Assume that a periodic function $f(t)$ has a finite jump discontinuity, as shown in Fig. 3.11. At the points of discontinuity the function has two values depending upon the direction of approach. If a discontinuity occurs at $t = t_1$, then the values of $f(t_1^-)$ and $f(t_1^+)$ differ by the amount of discontinuity. When we expand such a function by a Fourier series, these questions arise: To what value does the series converge at $t = t_1$? Does it converge to $f(t_1^+)$ or to $f(t_1^-)$ or to some other value? It turns out that the series converges to the mean of $f(t_1^+)$ and $f(t_1^-)$; that is, to a value $\frac{1}{2}[f(t_1^+) + f(t_1^-)]$ (why?). These points are shown by dots in Fig. 3.11.

3.6 ALTERNATE FORM OF THE TRIGONOMETRIC SERIES

The trigonometric form may also be represented in a more compact way using only the cosine form. This follows from the trigonometric identity

$$a_n \cos n\omega_0 t + b_n \sin n\omega_0 t = A_n \cos (n\omega_0 t + \varphi_n)$$

where

$$A_n = \sqrt{a_n{}^2 + b_n{}^2} \quad \text{and} \quad \varphi_n = -\tan^{-1}\left(\frac{b_n}{a_n}\right) \tag{3.97}$$

This representation can be easily appreciated by considering the phasor representation of $a_n \cos n\omega_0 t$ and $b_n \sin n\omega_0 t$. The resultant phasor has a magnitude $\sqrt{a_n{}^2 + b_n{}^2}$ and a phase $-\tan^{-1}(b_n/a_n)$.

$$f(t) = a_0 + \sum_{n=1}^{\infty} (a_n \cos n\omega_0 t + b_n \sin n\omega_0 t)$$

$$= a_0 + \sum_{n=1}^{\infty} A_n \cos (n\omega_0 t + \varphi_n) \tag{3.98}$$

where A_n and φ_n can be found from Eq. 3.97.

TABLE 3.1
Fourier Series Representation of a Periodic Function of Period $T(\omega_0 = 2\pi/T)$

Form	Series Representation	Equations for Coefficients	Conversion Formulas
Exponential	$f(t) = \displaystyle\sum_{n=-\infty}^{\infty} F_n e^{jn\omega_0 t}$	$F_n = \dfrac{1}{T}\displaystyle\int_{-T/2}^{T/2} f(t)e^{-jn\omega_0 t}dt$	$F_0 = a_0$ $F_n = \frac{1}{2}(a_n - jb_n)$
Trigonometric	$= a_0 + \displaystyle\sum_{n=1}^{\infty}(a_n \cos n\omega_0 t + b_n \sin n\omega_0 t)$ $= a_0 + \displaystyle\sum_{n=1}^{\infty} A_n \cos(n\omega_0 t + \varphi_n)$	$a_0 = \dfrac{1}{T}\displaystyle\int_{-T/2}^{T/2} f(t)\, dt$ $a_n = \dfrac{2}{T}\displaystyle\int_{-T/2}^{T/2} f(t)\cos n\omega_0 t\, dt$ $b_n = \dfrac{2}{T}\displaystyle\int_{-T/2}^{T/2} f(t)\sin n\omega_0 t\, dt$	$a_n = (F_n + F_{-n})$ $b_n = j(F_n - F_{-n})$ $A_n = \sqrt{a_n^2 + b_n^2}$ $\quad = 2|F_n|$ $\varphi_n = -\tan^{-1}(b_n/a_n)$

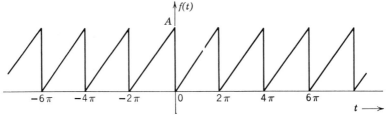

Figure 3.12

A Fourier series representation of a periodic function is really equivalent to separating a periodic function into its component functions. It is evident from Eq. 3.98 that a trigonometric Fourier series separates a periodic function of period T into sinusoidal components of frequency ω_0, $2\omega_0$, $3\omega_0$, ..., $n\omega_0$, etc., where $\omega_0 = 2\pi/T$. The frequency ω_0 is the fundamental angular frequency and the other angular frequencies $2\omega_0$, $3\omega_0$, ..., $n\omega_0$, etc., are the harmonics of ω_0. Hence, the Fourier analysis is also sometimes called the *harmonic analysis*.

Example 3.6

As an example, consider the periodic function $f(t)$ shown in Fig. 3.12. This function has a period $T = 2\pi$ and may be expressed analytically in the region $(0, 2\pi)$:

$$f(t) = \frac{At}{2\pi} \tag{3.99}$$

The period T is 2π and hence the fundamental frequency ω_0 is given by

$$\omega_0 = \frac{2\pi}{T} = 1.$$

It therefore follows that the Fourier series will consist of angular frequency components $\omega = 1, 2, 3$, etc., and hence the series can be represented as

$$f(t) = a_0 + a_1 \cos t + a_2 \cos 2t + \cdots + a_n \cos nt + \cdots$$
$$+ b_1 \sin t + b_2 \sin 2t + \cdots + b_n \sin nt + \cdots \tag{3.100}$$

$$= a_0 + \sum_{n=1}^{\infty} a_n \cos nt + b_n \sin nt \tag{3.101}$$

The various coefficients in this series can be evaluated by using Eq. 3.96. In general, it was shown that the limits of integration in Eq. 3.96 may be chosen as t_0 to $(t_0 + T)$ where t_0 may have any value. In this problem it is more convenient to choose the limits of integration as 0 to 2π ($t_0 = 0$). The reader may convince himself that it is immaterial whether the limits are chosen as $-\pi$ to π or 0 to 2π. Substituting the expression for $f(t)$ in Eq. 3.96 and taking the limits of integration as 0 to 2π, we get

$$a_0 = \frac{A}{2} \tag{3.102a}$$

$$a_n \doteq 0 \tag{3.102b}$$

$$b_n = -A/\pi n \tag{3.102c}$$

It is evident that all the cosine terms are zero. The required series using the coefficients in Eq. 102 is now given by

$$f(t) = \frac{A}{2} - \frac{A}{\pi}\sin t - \frac{A}{2\pi}\sin 2t - \cdots - \frac{A}{n\pi}\sin nt - \cdots \tag{3.103}$$

$$= \frac{A}{2} - \frac{A}{\pi}\sum_{n=1}^{\infty}\frac{1}{n}\sin nt \tag{3.104}$$

The function $f(t)$ has components of frequency $\omega = 1, 2, 3, \ldots$, etc. Notice that the amplitude of the components is inversely proportional to the frequency, and hence the magnitude of lower-frequency components is larger than that at the higher frequencies. This fact can also be demonstrated graphically. The function $f(t)$ contains a component of a signal $\sin nt$. According to Eq. 3.10, the component of $f_1(t)$ of the waveform $f_2(t)$ in the interval (t_1, t_2) is given by

$$C_{12} = \frac{\displaystyle\int_{t_1}^{t_2} f_1(t)f_2(t)\,dt}{\displaystyle\int_{t_1}^{t_2} [f_2(t)]^2\,dt}$$

The component b_n of the waveform $\sin t$ in $f(t)$ in the interval $(0, 2\pi)$ will therefore be given by

$$b_n = \frac{\displaystyle\int_0^{2\pi} f(t)\sin nt}{\displaystyle\int_0^{2\pi} \sin^2 t\,dt}$$

$$= \frac{1}{\pi}\int_0^{2\pi} f(t)\sin nt\,dt$$

This is, of course, the required Fourier coefficient. The graphical evaluation of a component of the waveform $f_2(t)$ contained in signal $f_1(t)$ was discussed in Section 3.1. It is evident that b_n is proportional to the area under the product curve $f(t)\sin nt$ in the region $(0, 2\pi)$. The product curve for values of $n = 1$ and $n = 4$ are shown in Fig. 3.13. Both of these curves have regions of positive and negative area. However for $n = 1$ the negative area is much larger than the positive area and there is a sizable net negative area. On the other hand,

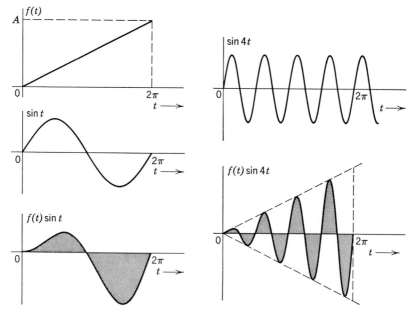

Figure 3.13   Graphical evaluation of the Fourier coefficients.

for $n = 4$, the negative and positive area are of about the same order of magnitude and they tend to cancel out, and hence the net area is much smaller. At still higher frequencies, the cancellation becomes more and more perfect, and the net area becomes smaller and smaller. Therefore, the coefficient b_n becomes smaller at higher frequencies. The magnitudes of components of higher frequency in the signal $f(t)$ are therefore smaller in magnitude (inversely proportional to the frequency).

The above discussion suggests the method for evaluation of Fourier coefficients when a function $f(t)$ is known only graphically. The product curves of $f(t) \cos n\omega_0 t$ and $f(t) \sin n\omega_0 t$ are plotted and $2/T$ times the average values of these areas over one period gives the coefficients a_n and b_n, respectively.

The function $f(t)$ has been expanded by the trigonometric Fourier series in Eq. 3.104. We could just as well have used the exponential form. The exponential series is given by

$$f(t) = \sum_{n=-\infty}^{\infty} F_n e^{jnt} \qquad n = 0, \pm 1, \pm 2, \dots, \text{etc.}$$

The coefficients F_n may be evaluated either from Eq. 3.94 or from the coefficients of the trigonometric series using Eq. 3.80. Either way, it can be shown that

$$F_n = \frac{jA}{2\pi n} \qquad \text{and} \qquad F_0 = a_0 = \frac{A}{2}$$

Thus

$$f(t) = \frac{A}{2} + \frac{jA}{2\pi} e^{jt} + \frac{jA}{4\pi} e^{j2t} + \cdots + \frac{jA}{2n\pi} e^{jnt} + \cdots$$

$$- \frac{jA}{2\pi} e^{-jt} - \frac{jA}{4\pi} e^{-j2t} - \cdots - \frac{jA}{2n\pi} e^{-jnt} - \cdots$$

$$= \frac{A}{2} + \frac{jA}{2\pi} \sum_{n=-\infty}^{\infty} \frac{1}{n} e^{jnt} \qquad (n \text{ integral}) \qquad (3.105)$$

Example 3.7

As a second example we shall expand, by the Fourier series, a periodic function $f(t)$ shown in Fig. 3.14. This is a rectified sine wave and can be represented analytically in region $(0, 1)$ as $f(t) = A \sin \pi t$. We shall expand this function by an exponential Fourier series. The period $T = 1$ second and hence the fundamental frequency ω_0 is given by

$$\omega_0 = \frac{2\pi}{T} = 2\pi$$

The required exponential series is therefore

$$f(t) = F_0 + F_1 e^{j2\pi t} + F_2 e^{j4\pi t} + \cdots + F_n e^{j2n\pi t} + \cdots$$

$$+ F_{-1} e^{-j2\pi t} + F_{-2} e^{-j4\pi t} + \cdots + F_{-n} e^{-j2n\pi t} + \cdots$$

$$= \sum_{n=-\infty}^{\infty} F_n e^{j2n\pi t}$$

The coefficient F_n is given by

$$F_n = \frac{1}{T} \int_0^T f(t) e^{-j2n\pi t} \, dt$$

$$= 1 \int_0^1 A \sin \pi t e^{-j2n\pi t} \, dt$$

$$= \frac{A e^{-j2\pi nt}}{\pi^2 (1 - 4n^2)} (-j2n\pi \sin \pi t - \pi \cos \pi t) \Big|_0^1$$

$$= \frac{-2A}{\pi (4n^2 - 1)}$$

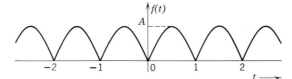

Figure 3.14　Rectified sine wave.

Note that

$$F_0 = \frac{2A}{\pi}$$

The series may now be written as

$$f(t) = \frac{2A}{\pi} - \frac{2A}{\pi}\left(\tfrac{1}{3}e^{j2\pi t} + \tfrac{1}{15}e^{j4\pi t} + \tfrac{1}{35}e^{j6\pi t} + \cdots + \cdots\right)$$

$$-\frac{2A}{\pi}\left(\tfrac{1}{3}e^{-j2\pi t} + \tfrac{1}{15}e^{-j4\pi t} + \tfrac{1}{35}e^{-j6\pi t} + \cdots + \cdots\right) \qquad (3.106)$$

$$= -\frac{2A}{\pi}\sum_{n=-\infty}^{\infty}\frac{1}{(4n^2-1)}e^{j2\pi nt} \qquad (3.107)$$

We could just as well have expanded this function by a trigonometric series. The corresponding coefficients in a trigonometric series may be evaluated directly, using Eqs. 3.96, or may be obtained from the coefficients F_n of exponential series, using Eq. 3.79. By either method, we obtain a trigonometric series which consists only of cosine terms.

$$f(t) = \frac{2A}{\pi} - \frac{4A}{\pi}\left(\tfrac{1}{3}\cos 2\pi t + \tfrac{1}{15}\cos 4\pi t + \tfrac{1}{35}\cos 6\pi t + \cdots\right)$$

Example 3.8

We shall consider one more example of periodic functions $f(t)$ in Fig. 3.15.

$$f(t) = \begin{cases} \dfrac{2A}{\pi}t & (-\pi/2 < t < \pi/2) \\[2mm] \dfrac{2A}{\pi}(\pi - t) & (\pi/2 < t < 3\pi/2) \end{cases}$$

The period $T = 2\pi$. Hence, $\omega_0 = 2\pi/T = 1$. The Fourier series will consist of components of frequencies $\omega = 1, 2, 3, \ldots$, etc.

$$f(t) = a_0 + \sum_{n=1}^{\infty}(a_n \cos nt + b_n \sin nt)$$

It is easy to see, from Fig. 3.15, that it will be convenient to choose limits of integration as $-\pi/2$ to $3\pi/2$ in evaluating the coefficients of the series.

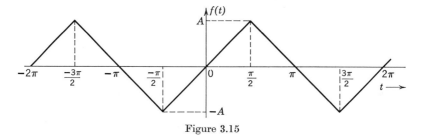

Figure 3.15

The d-c component a_0 is the average value of $f(t)$ over the interval $(-\pi/2, 3\pi/2)$ and is obviously zero.

$$a_n = \frac{1}{\pi} \int_{-\pi/2}^{3\pi/2} f(t) \cos nt \, dt$$

$$= \frac{1}{\pi} \left[\int_{-\pi/2}^{\pi/2} \frac{2A}{\pi} t \cos nt \, dt + \int_{\pi/2}^{3\pi/2} \frac{2A}{\pi} (\pi - t) \cos nt \, dt \right]$$

$$= 0$$

$$b_n = \frac{1}{\pi} \left[\int_{-\pi/2}^{\pi/2} \frac{2A}{\pi} t \sin nt \, dt + \int_{\pi/2}^{3\pi/2} \frac{2A}{\pi} (\pi - t) \sin nt \, dt \right]$$

$$= \frac{8A}{n^2\pi^2} \sin (n\pi/2)$$

Note that for even values of n, $b_n = 0$ and $b_1 = 8A/\pi^2$, $b_3 = -8A/25\pi^2$, etc. Hence

$$f(t) = \frac{8A}{\pi^2} \sin t - \frac{8A}{9\pi^2} \sin 3t + \frac{8A}{25\pi^2} \sin 5t - \frac{8A}{49\pi^2} \sin 7t + \cdots$$

$$= \frac{8A}{\pi^2} (\sin t - \tfrac{1}{9} \sin 3t + \tfrac{1}{25} \sin 5t - \tfrac{1}{49} \sin 7t + \cdots)$$

3.7 SYMMETRY CONDITIONS

In the discussion of the above examples, we found that all the sine terms were zero in the series of Example 3.7, whereas all the cosine terms were zero in that of Example 3.8. This is not a coincidence. A glance at the periodic functions in Examples 3.7 and 3.8 (Figs. 3.14 and 3.15) shows that the former is symmetrical, and the latter is antisymmetrical about the vertical axis passing through the origin. We shall now discuss the effects of symmetry in a Fourier series. It will be shown that if a periodic function is symmetrical about the vertical axis, the corresponding Fourier series contains only cosine terms, whereas if it is antisymmetrical about the vertical axis, the series contains sine terms only. In this connection it is useful to define even- and odd-type functions as follows.

A function $f_e(t)$ is said to be an *even function* of t if

$$f_e(t) = f_e(-t) \tag{3.108}$$

and $f_0(t)$ is said to be an *odd function* of t if

$$f_0(t) = -f_0(-t) \tag{3.109}$$

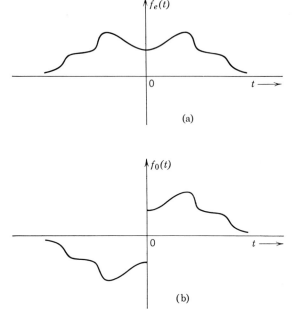

Figure 3.16   Representation of even and odd functions.

An example of even and odd functions is shown in Fig. 3.16. By definition, an even function is symmetrical and an odd function is antisymmetrical about the vertical axis passing through the origin. Note that the odd and even functions need not be periodic. We shall now derive some interesting properties of even and odd functions.

It follows from the definition of even and odd functions that the product of an even and an odd function is an odd function, and that the product of an odd and an odd function is an even function. Similarly, the product of an even and an even function is also an even function. It also follows from these definitions (Eqs. 3.108 and 3.109) that for an even function $f_e(t)$,

$$\int_{-\tau}^{\tau} f_e(t)\, dt = \int_{-\tau}^{0} f_e(t)\, dt + \int_{0}^{\tau} f_e(t)\, dt$$

Letting $t = -x$ in the first integral,

$$\int_{-\tau}^{\tau} f_e(t)\, dt = \int_{0}^{\tau} f_e(-x)\, dx + \int_{0}^{\tau} f_e(t)\, dt$$

But since $f_e(-x) = f_e(x)$, we have

$$\int_{-\tau}^{\tau} f_e(t)\, dt = 2\int_{0}^{\tau} f_e(t)\, dt \tag{3.110}$$

Similarly, for an odd function $f_0(t)$,

$$\int_{-\tau}^{\tau} f_0(t) \, dt = \int_{-\tau}^{0} f_0(t) \, dt + \int_{0}^{\tau} f_0(t) \, dt$$

$$= -\int_{0}^{\tau} f_0(x) \, dx + \int_{0}^{\tau} f_0(t) \, dt$$

$$= 0 \tag{3.111}$$

The results in Eqs. 3.110 and 3.111 are also obvious intuitively. A glance at Fig. 3.16 shows that the area under the even function from $-\tau$ to τ is twice that under 0 to τ, because of the symmetry. Similarly for an anti-symmetric function the total area under $-\tau$ to τ is zero.

We are now in a position to evaluate the effects of various types of symmetry in a periodic function. Let a periodic function $f_e(t)$ be an even function of t (that is, symmetrical about the origin as shown in Fig. 3.14), then the corresponding Fourier series is given by

$$f_e(t) = a_0 + \sum_{n=1}^{\infty} (a_n \cos n\omega_0 t + b_n \sin n\omega_0 t)$$

where

$$a_n = \frac{2}{T} \int_{-T/2}^{T/2} f_e(t) \cos n\omega_0 t \, dt$$

Observe that $\cos n\omega_0 t$ is an even function of t and $f_e(t)$ is also an even function of t. Hence, the product $f_e(t) \cos n\omega_0 t$ is an even function and, according to Eq. 3.110,

$$a_n = \frac{4}{T} \int_{0}^{T/2} f_e(t) \cos n\omega_0 t \, dt \tag{3.112}$$

The coefficient b_n is given by

$$b_n = \frac{2}{T} \int_{-T/2}^{T/2} f_e(t) \sin n\omega_0 t \, dt$$

Since $\sin n\omega_0 t = -\sin(-n\omega_0 t)$, it is an odd function, and hence the product $f_e(t) \sin n\omega_0 t$ is an odd function. Hence, according to Eq. 3.111,

$$b_n = 0$$

It therefore follows that all the sine terms will be zero. A Fourier series for an even periodic function will consist entirely of cosine terms. This type of function was considered in Example 3.7. Let us now consider the odd periodic function $f_0(t)$.

The coefficient a_n is given by

$$a_n = \frac{2}{T} \int_{-T/2}^{T/2} f_0(t) \cos n\omega_0 t \, dt$$

Since $f_0(t)$ is an odd function and $\cos n\omega_0 t$ is an even function, the product $f_0(t) \cos n\omega_0 t$ is an odd function and, according to Eq. 3.111,

$$a_n = 0$$

Similarly, the product $f_0(t) \sin n\omega_0 t$ is an even function, and

$$b_n = \frac{4}{T} \int_0^{T/2} f_0(t) \sin n\omega_0 t \, dt \tag{3.113}$$

Thus, a Fourier series for an odd periodic function will consist entirely of sine terms. This type of function has been discussed in Example 3.8.

Note that if the periodic functions are either even or odd, it is not necessary to integrate over the entire interval $(-T/2, T/2)$ in order to evaluate the coefficients. This is obvious from Eqs. 3.112 and 3.113. One may integrate over the half period only and multiply the results by a factor of 2.

Hidden Symmetry

Often one comes across a periodic function without any apparant form of symmetry, yet it possesses a Fourier series containing only sine or cosine terms. Example 3.6 (Fig. 3.12) illustrates this point. Here the periodic function does not satisfy either of the symmetry conditions, yet the Fourier series (Eq. 3.104) consists of a d-c term and sine terms alone. The reason for this behavior is that the symmetry of this function is obscured by a d-c term. If we subtract a constant $A/2$ from this function, the new function, say $f_n(t)$, is antisymmetrical.

$$f_n(t) = f(t) - \frac{A}{2}$$

The subtraction of a constant from $f(t)$ merely shifts the horizontal axis upward by the amount $A/2$. It is evident that $f_n(t)$ is an odd periodic function and hence the Fourier series of $f_n(t)$ consists entirely of sine terms. Therefore the Fourier series for $f(t)$ consists of a d-c term $(A/2)$ and sine terms alone.

Rotation Symmetry

If the waveshapes of the alternate half cycles are identical but opposite in sign (Fig. 3.17), a *rotation symmetry* exists. This type of symmetry can be expressed analytically as follows:

$$f(t) = -f(t \pm T/2)$$

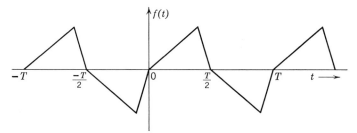

Figure 3.17   Example of rotation symmetry.

It can be readily shown that the Fourier series of a periodic signal with rotation symmetry contains only odd harmonics, that is, ω_0, $3\omega_0$, ..., etc.

Proof:

$$a_n = \frac{2}{T} \int_0^T f(t) \cos n\omega_0 t \, dt$$

$$= \frac{2}{T}\left[\int_0^{T/2} f(t) \cos n\omega_0 t + \int_{T/2}^T f(t) \cos n\omega_0 t \, dt\right]$$

Changing the variable from t to $(t + T/2)$ in the second integral, we get

$$a_n = \frac{2}{T}\left[\int_0^{T/2} f(t) \cos n\omega_0 t + \int_0^{T/2} f(t + T/2) \cos n\omega_0(t + T/2) \, dt\right]$$

Using the property $f(t) = -f(t + T/2)$, we get

$$a_n = \frac{2}{T} \int_0^{T/2} [f(t) \cos n\omega_0 t - f(t) \cos n\omega_0 t \cos n\pi] \, dt$$

$$= \begin{cases} 0 & \text{(for } n \text{ even)} \\ \dfrac{4}{T} \displaystyle\int_0^{T/2} f(t) \cos n\omega_0 t \, dt & \text{(for } n \text{ odd)} \end{cases}$$

Similarly it can be shown that

$$b_n = \begin{cases} 0 & \text{(for } n \text{ even)} \\ \dfrac{4}{T} \displaystyle\int_0^{T/2} f(t) \sin n\omega_0 t \, dt & \text{(for } n \text{ odd)} \end{cases}$$

The waveform in Fig. 3.15 possesses a rotation symmetry. Often the rotation symmetry is obscured by a d-c term. Such is the case of the waveform in Fig. 3.18d. If the d-c component ($A/2$) is removed from this waveform by shifting the horizontal axis upward by $A/2$, the rotation symmetry becomes evident. The Fourier series for this wave has a d-c term ($A/2$) and only the odd harmonics ω_0, $3\omega_0$, $5\omega_0$, ..., etc.

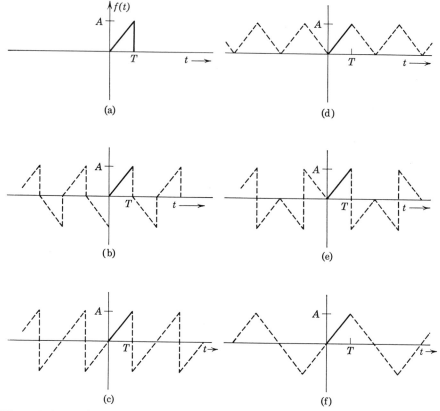

Figure 3.18 (a) $f(t)$. (b) Sine and cosine terms, odd harmonics only ($\omega_0 = \pi/T$). (c) Sine terms only, odd and even harmonics ($\omega_0 = \pi/T$). (d) Cosine terms and odd harmonics only ($\omega_0 = \pi/T$). (e) Cosine terms and odd harmonics only ($\omega_0 = \pi/2T$). (f) Sine terms and odd harmonics only ($\omega_0 = \pi/2T$).

3.8 ALTERNATE FOURIER EXPANSION OF A FUNCTION OVER A FINITE INTERVAL

A function $f(t)$, not necessarily periodic, can be represented by a Fourier series over a certain finite interval. The Fourier series converges to the function $f(t)$ over this interval. Outside this interval the series represents a periodic function repeating itself every T seconds. In certain applications, such as in boundary value problems, it becomes necessary to represent a function $f(t)$ over a finite interval by sine or cosine terms alone. This can be done by constructing a proper periodic function which will be identical to $f(t)$ over the required interval, say $(0, T)$, and satisfying such symmetry conditions as to yield the desired form of series. This is shown in Fig. 3.18. Indeed, it is possible to expand $f(t)$ by a Fourier series with any desired fundamental frequency. A periodic function may be so constructed as to be identical with $f(t)$ over the desired interval $(0, T)$ and having any desired fundamental frequency. In addition, the symmetry conditions may be so chosen as to yield only sine terms, only cosine terms, or both. In most of these applications, it is desired to choose a series that will converge rapidly. The series for a smoother function converges quickly compared to that for functions with discontinuities. The series for the waveforms in Figs. 3.18d and 3.18f, for example, will converge faster than those for the waveforms in Figs. 3.18b, 3.18c, and 3.18e.

3.9 THE COMPLEX FOURIER SPECTRUM

A Fourier series expansion of a periodic function is really equivalent to resolving the function in terms of its components of various frequencies. A periodic function with period T has frequency components of angular frequencies ω_0, $2\omega_0$, $3\omega_0$, $\ldots$, $n\omega_0$, etc., where $\omega_0 = 2\pi/T$. Thus the periodic function $f(t)$ possesses its spectrum of frequencies. If we specify $f(t)$, we can find its spectrum. Conversely, if the spectrum is known, one can find the corresponding periodic function $f(t)$. We therefore have two ways of specifying a periodic function $f(t)$: the time domain representation where $f(t)$ is expressed as a function of time, and the frequency domain representation where the spectrum (that is, the amplitudes of various frequency components) is specified. Note that the spectrum exists only at $\omega = \omega_0$, $2\omega_0$, $3\omega_0$, $\ldots$, etc. Thus the spectrum is not a continuous curve but exists only at some discrete values of ω. It is therefore a *discrete spectrum*, sometimes referred to as a *line spectrum*. We may represent the spectrum graphically by drawing a vertical line at $\omega = \omega_0$, $2\omega_0$, $\ldots$, etc., with their heights proportional to the amplitude of the corresponding frequency component. The discrete frequency spectrum thus appears on a graph as a series of equally spaced vertical lines with heights proportional to the amplitude of the corresponding frequency component.

We can use either the trigonometric or exponential series to represent the spectrum. The exponential form, however, is more useful for our purpose since the very reason for including this chapter is our need to be able to represent a given function as a discrete or continuous sum of exponential functions. In the exponential Fourier series the periodic function is expressed as a sum of exponential functions of frequency 0, $\pm\omega_0$, $\pm 2\omega_0$, $\ldots$, etc. The significance of negative frequencies has already

been pointed out in Chapter 2. Both the signals $e^{j\omega t}$ and $e^{-j\omega t}$ oscillate
at frequency ω. They may, however, be looked upon as two phasors
rotating in opposite directions and, when added, yield a real function of
time. Thus

$$e^{j\omega t} + e^{-j\omega t} = 2 \cos \omega t$$

For a periodic function of period T, the exponential series is given by

$$f(t) = F_0 + F_1 e^{j\omega_0 t} + F_2 e^{j2\omega_0 t} + \cdots + F_n e^{jn\omega_0 t} + \cdots$$
$$+ F_{-1} e^{-j\omega_0 t} + F_{-2} e^{-j2\omega_0 t} + \cdots + F_{-n} e^{-jn\omega_0 t} + \cdots$$

We thus have the frequencies 0, ω_0, $-\omega_0$, $2\omega_0$, $-2\omega_0$, $\ldots$, $n\omega_0$, $-n\omega_0$,
$\ldots$, etc., and the amplitudes of these components are respectively
F_0, F_1, F_{-1}, F_2, F_{-2}, $\ldots$, F_n, F_{-n}, $\ldots$, etc.

In general, the amplitudes F_n are complex, and hence can be described
by magnitude and phase. Therefore, in general, we need two line spectra:
the *magnitude spectrum* and the *phase spectrum* for the frequency domain
representation of a periodic function. In most of the cases, however,
the amplitudes of frequency components are either real or imaginary,
and thus it is possible to describe the function by only one spectrum.

Consider the periodic function in Example 3.7 (Fig. 3.14). This is a
rectified sine wave, and the exponential Fourier series was found to be

$$f(t) = \frac{2A}{\pi} - \frac{2A}{3\pi} e^{j2\pi t} - \frac{2A}{15\pi} e^{j4\pi t} - \frac{2A}{35\pi} e^{j6\pi t} - \cdots$$
$$- \frac{2A}{3\pi} e^{-j2\pi t} - \frac{2A}{15\pi} e^{-j4\pi t} - \frac{2A}{35\pi} e^{j6\pi t} - \cdots$$

The spectrum exists at $\omega = 0$, $\pm 2\pi$, $\pm 4\pi$, $\pm 6\pi$, $\ldots$, etc., and the
corresponding magnitudes are $2A/\pi$, $-2A/3\pi$, $-2A/15\pi$, $-2A/35\pi$, $\ldots$,
etc. Note that all the amplitudes are real and consequently it is necessary
to plot only one spectrum. The required frequency spectrum is shown in
Fig. 3.19. It is evident from this figure that the spectrum is symmetrical
about the vertical axis passing through the origin. This is not a coincidence. We shall presently show that the magnitude spectrum of every
periodic function is symmetrical about the vertical axis passing through
the origin. This can be easily demonstrated. The coefficient F_n is given by

$$F_n = \frac{1}{T} \int_{-T/2}^{T/2} f(t) e^{-jn\omega_0 t} \, dt \tag{3.114}$$

and

$$F_{-n} = \frac{1}{T} \int_{-T/2}^{T/2} f(t) e^{jn\omega_0 t} \, dt \tag{3.115}$$

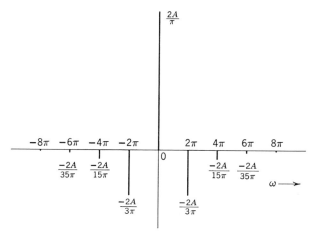

Figure 3.19   Line spectrum of a rectified sine wave.

It is evident from these equations that the coefficients F_n and F_{-n} are complex conjugates of each other, that is,

$$F_n = F_{-n}{}^*; \qquad \text{Hence} \quad |F_n| = |F_{-n}|$$

It therefore follows that the magnitude spectrum is symmetrical about the vertical axis passing through the origin, and hence is an even function of ω.

If F_n is real, then F_{-n} is also real and F_n is equal to F_{-n}. If F_n is complex, let

$$F_n = |F_n| e^{j\theta_n} \qquad\qquad\qquad (3.116a)$$

then

$$F_{-n} = |F_n| e^{-j\theta_n} \qquad\qquad\qquad (3.116b)$$

The phase of F_n is θ_n; however, the phase of F_{-n} is $-\theta_n$. Hence it is obvious that the phase spectrum is antisymmetrical (an odd function) and the magnitude spectrum is symmetrical (an even function) about the vertical axis passing through the origin.

Effect of Time Displacement on the Frequency Spectrum

We shall now investigate the effect on the frequency spectrum of a periodic function caused by a time displacement of the function. Let $f(t)$ be a periodic function with period T, and let the exponential series corresponding to this function be given by

$$f(t) = \sum_{n=-\infty}^{\infty} F_n e^{jn\omega_0 t} \qquad\qquad\qquad (3.117)$$

Let us investigate the frequency spectrum of the function $f(t - \tau)$. From Eq. 3.117 we have

$$f(t - \tau) = \sum_{n=-\infty}^{\infty} F_n e^{jn\omega_0(t-\tau)}$$

$$= \sum_{-\infty}^{\infty} F_n e^{-jn\omega_0\tau} e^{jn\omega_0 t} \tag{3.118}$$

$$= \sum_{-\infty}^{\infty} F_n' e^{jn\omega_0 t} \tag{3.119}$$

where

$$F_n' = F_n e^{-jn\omega_0\tau}$$

If

$$F_n = |F_n| e^{j\theta_n} \tag{3.120}$$

then

$$F_n' = |F_n| e^{j(\theta_n - n\omega_0\tau)} \tag{3.121}$$

From Eq. 3.119 it is evident that $f(t - \tau)$ has the components of frequencies $\omega = 0$, $\pm\omega_0$, $\pm2\omega_0$, ... These are, of course, the same frequencies as those of $f(t)$. It also follows from Eqs. 3.120 and 3.121 that the magnitude of the various frequency components is unchanged, due to time displacement. The phases, however, are different. The time displacement causes a lag of phase by an amount $n\omega_0\tau$ radians in the frequency component $n\omega_0$. We therefore conclude that the time displacement in a periodic function has no effect on the magnitude spectrum, but changes the phase spectrum by an amount of $-n\omega_0\tau$ radians for the component of the frequency $n\omega_0$.

This result is also intuitively obvious. If we shift a periodic function in time, the physical waveform is unchanged except that it is delayed by τ seconds. Hence it must contain the same frequency components but it is delayed by τ seconds. For a sinusoidal signal of frequency $n\omega_0$, a delay of τ seconds is equivalent to a phase shift of $-n\omega_0\tau$ radians. This is obvious, since the signal $\sin n\omega_0 t$ delayed by τ seconds is given by

$$\sin n\omega_0(t - \tau) = \sin (n\omega_0 t - n\omega_0\tau)$$

Thus there is a net phase shift of $-n\omega_0\tau$ seconds.

The Power Spectrum of a Periodic Function

If we assume the periodic function $f(t)$ as a voltage or a current waveform, then the integral

$$\frac{1}{T} \int_{-T/2}^{T/2} f^2(t) \, dt$$

represents the power delivered by $f(t)$ to a 1-ohm resistor. This integral is called the *power* of a periodic signal $f(t)$. The frequency spectrum of $f(t)$ represents the amplitudes of various frequency components of $f(t)$. There is a power associated with each component. Just as we can represent the amplitude spectrum of various frequency components, we can also represent the *power spectrum* corresponding to the power associated with various frequency components in $f(t)$.

Let the exponential Fourier series of $f(t)$ be given by

$$f(t) = \sum_{n=-\infty}^{\infty} F_n e^{jn\omega_0 t} \tag{3.122}$$

Hence it follows that

$$\frac{1}{T} \int_{-T/2}^{T/2} f^2(t)\, dt = \frac{1}{T} \int_{-T/2}^{T/2} f(t) \sum_{n=-\infty}^{\infty} F_n e^{jn\omega_0 t}\, dt$$

The operations of integration and summation on the right-hand side can be interchanged. Hence we obtain

$$\frac{1}{T} \int_{-T/2}^{T/2} f^2(t)\, dt = \frac{1}{T} \sum_{n=-\infty}^{\infty} F_n \int_{-T/2}^{T/2} f(t) e^{jn\omega_0 t}\, dt \tag{3.123}$$

It is evident that the integral on the right-hand side is $T F_{-n}$. Hence

$$\frac{1}{T} \int_{-T/2}^{T/2} f^2(t)\, dt = \sum_{n=-\infty}^{\infty} F_n F_{-n} \tag{3.124}$$

But since $F_n = F_{-n}{}^*$, we have $F_n F_{-n} = |F_n|^2$, and

$$\frac{1}{T} \int_{-T/2}^{T/2} f^2(t)\, dt = \sum_{n=-\infty}^{\infty} |F_n|^2 \tag{3.125}$$

$$= F_0{}^2 + |F_1|^2 + |F_2|^2 + \cdots + |F_n|^2 + \cdots$$
$$+ |F_{-1}|^2 + |F_{-2}|^2 + \cdots + |F_{-n}|^2 + \cdots \tag{3.126}$$

Equation 3.125 really states Parseval's theorem (Eq. 3.40) as applied to the exponential Fourier series.

Equation 3.126 suggests that there is a power associated with each frequency component. The magnitude of power contained in the component of frequency $n\omega_0$ is $|F_n|^2$ and that of $-n\omega_0$ is $|F_{-n}|^2$. But since

$$F_{-n} = F_n{}^*$$

then

$$|F_{-n}|^2 = |F_n|^2 \tag{3.127}$$

Hence the power associated with a component of frequency $n\omega_0$ is the same as that of frequency $-n\omega_0$. Since we know that both signal $e^{jn\omega_0 t}$ and $e^{-jn\omega_0 t}$ represent signals of the same frequency, namely $n\omega_0$, the total power associated with the frequency $n\omega_0$ in the signal is therefore $2\,|F_n|^2$. This can also be readily seen as follows. The two components $F_n e^{jn\omega_0 t}$ and $F_{-n} e^{-jn\omega_0 t}$ together yield a real function of time $f_n(t)$.

$$f_n(t) = F_n e^{jn\omega_0 t} + F_{-n} e^{-jn\omega_0 t}$$

and

$$F_n = |F_n|\, e^{j\theta_n}$$
$$F_{-n} = |F_n|\, e^{-j\theta_n}$$

Therefore

$$f_n(t) = |F_n|\, e^{j(n\omega_0 t + \theta_n)} + |F_n|\, e^{-j(n\omega_0 t + \theta_n)}$$
$$= 2\,|F_n| \cos(n\omega_0 t + \theta_n)$$

The power contained in any sinusoidal signal of amplitude A is $A^2/2$. Consequently the power contained in $2\,|F_n| \cos(n\omega_0 t + \theta_n)$ is $2\,|F_n|^2$. We associate one half of this power to the component $F_n e^{jn\omega_0 t}$. Thus, in general, $|F_n|^2$ represents the power associated with the component $F_n e^{jn\omega_0 t}$. Similarly, the power associated with $F_{-n} e^{-jn\omega_0 t}$ is $|F_{-n}|^2$. Therefore Eq. 3.126 may be interpreted as follows: the power in the periodic signal is equal to the sum of the powers of its components.

We can plot a spectrum of power associated with each frequency component. Obviously, the spectrum is discrete, existing at frequencies $\omega = 0,\ \pm\omega_0,\ \pm 2\omega_0,\ \dots$, etc., and is symmetrical about the vertical axis passing through the origin.

If we denote by P the power of a periodic signal $f(t)$, for convenience, then

$$P = \frac{1}{T} \int_{-T/2}^{T/2} f^2(t)\, dt$$

$$= \sum_{n=-\infty}^{\infty} F_n^{\,2}$$

The power spectrum for the rectified sine wave in Fig. 3.14 can be obtained from Eq. 3.125 and Eq. 3.107.

$$P = \frac{4A^2}{\pi^2} + \frac{4A^2}{9\pi^2} + \frac{4A^2}{225\pi^2} + \cdots + \cdots + \frac{4A^2}{9\pi^2} + \frac{4A^2}{225\pi^2} + \cdots \qquad (3.128)$$

This power spectrum is plotted in Fig. 3.20. It is evident that the power in high frequencies decays rapidly. Indeed, in this example, about 99% of the total power is contained in the d-c component and the first harmonic. All the remaining components account for the residual 1% of the power.

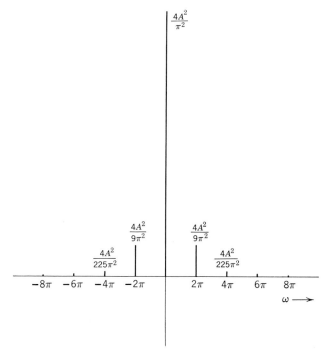

Figure 3.20   Power spectrum of a rectified sine wave.

It is quite obvious that if such a rectified sine wave is passed through a filter which cuts off all the frequencies above ω_0, there will be no noticeable distortion in the output waveform.

Example 3.9

Expand the periodic gate function shown in Fig. 3.21 by the exponential Fourier series and plot the frequency and power spectrum.

Solution. The gate function has a width δ and repeats every T seconds. The function may be described analytically over one period as follows.

$$f(t) = \begin{cases} A & (-\delta/2 < t < \delta/2) \\ 0 & (\delta/2 < t < T - \delta/2) \end{cases}$$

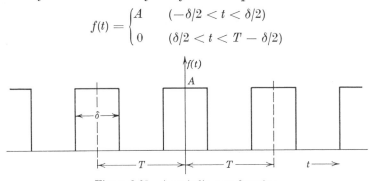

Figure 3.21   A periodic gate function.

For the purpose of integration we shall choose the limits of integration as $-\delta/2$ to $(T - \delta/2)$ for convenience.

$$F_n = \frac{1}{T} \int_{-\delta/2}^{T-\delta/2} f(t) e^{-jn\omega_0 t} \, dt$$

$$= \frac{1}{T} \int_{-\delta/2}^{\delta/2} A e^{-jn\omega_0 t} \, dt$$

$$= \frac{-A}{jn\omega_0 T} e^{-jn\omega_0 t} \Big|_{-\delta/2}^{\delta/2}$$

$$= \frac{2A}{n\omega_0 T} \frac{(e^{jn\omega_0 \delta/2} - e^{-jn\omega_0 \delta/2})}{2j}$$

$$= \frac{2A}{n\omega_0 T} \sin (n\omega_0 \delta/2)$$

$$= \frac{A\delta}{T} \left[\frac{\sin (n\omega_0 \delta/2)}{n\omega_0 \delta/2} \right] \tag{3.129}$$

The function in the bracket has a form $(\sin x)/x$. This function plays an important role in communication theory and is known as the *sampling function*, abbreviated by $Sa(x)$ for convenience.

$$Sa(x) = \frac{\sin x}{x} \tag{3.130}$$

The sampling function is shown in Fig. 3.22. Note that the function oscillates with a period 2π, with a decaying amplitude in either direction of x and has zeros at $x = \pm\pi, \pm 2\pi, \pm 3\pi, \ldots$, etc. From Eq. 3.129 we have

$$F_n = \frac{A\delta}{T} Sa(n\omega_0 \delta/2)$$

But

$$\omega_0 = \frac{2\pi}{T} \quad \text{and} \quad \frac{n\omega_0 \delta}{2} = \frac{n\pi\delta}{T}$$

Hence

$$F_n = \frac{A\delta}{T} Sa\left(\frac{n\pi\delta}{T}\right) \tag{3.131a}$$

and

$$f(t) = \frac{A\delta}{T} \sum_{n=-\infty}^{\infty} {}' Sa\left(\frac{n\pi\delta}{T}\right) e^{jn\omega_0 t} \tag{3.131b}$$

It is evident from Eq. 3.131 that F_n is real, and hence we need only one spectrum for frequency domain representation. Also, since $Sa(x)$ is an even function, it is obvious from Eq. 3.131 that $F_n = F_{-n}$.

The fundamental frequency $\omega_0 = 2\pi/T$. The frequency spectrum is a discrete function and exists only at $\omega = 0, \pm 2\pi/T, \pm 4\pi/T, \pm 6\pi/T, \ldots$, etc.,

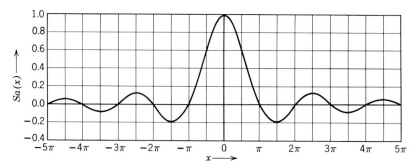

Figure 3.22 The sampling function $Sa(x)$.

and has amplitudes $A\delta/T$, $(A\delta/T)Sa(\pi\delta/T)$, $(A\delta/T)Sa(2\pi\delta/T)$, ..., etc., respectively. We shall consider the spectrum for some specific values of δ and T. The pulse width δ will be taken as $\frac{1}{20}$ second, and the period T will be chosen as $\frac{1}{4}$ second, $\frac{1}{2}$ second, and 1 second, successively.

For $\delta = \frac{1}{20}$ and $T = \frac{1}{4}$ second, Eq. 3.131 is given by

$$F_n = \frac{A}{5} Sa\left(\frac{n\pi}{5}\right)$$

The fundamental frequency $\omega_0 = 2\pi/T = 8\pi$. Thus the spectrum exists at $\omega = 0, \pm 8\pi, \pm 16\pi, \ldots$, etc., and is shown in Fig. 3.23a.

For $\delta = \frac{1}{20}$, $T = \frac{1}{2}$ second,

$$F_n = \frac{A}{10} Sa\left(\frac{n\pi}{10}\right)$$

The spectrum is shown in Fig. 3.23b and exists at frequencies $0, \pm 4\pi, \pm 8\pi, \ldots$, etc.

For $\delta = \frac{1}{20}$, $T = 1$ second,

$$F_n = \frac{A}{20} Sa\left(\frac{n\pi}{20}\right)$$

The spectrum exists at $\omega = 0, \pm 2\pi, \pm 4\pi, \ldots$, etc., and is shown in Fig. 3.23c.

It is evident that as the period T becomes larger and larger, the fundamental frequency $2\pi/T$ becomes smaller and smaller, and hence there are more and more frequency components in a given range of frequency. The spectrum therefore becomes denser as the period T becomes larger. However, the amplitudes of the frequency components become smaller and smaller as T is increased. In the limit as T is made infinity, we have a single rectangular pulse of width δ, and the fundamental frequency becomes zero. The spectrum now becomes continuous and exists at every frequency. Note, however, that the shape of the frequency spectrum does not change with the period T. Thus the envelope of the spectrum depends only upon the pulse shape that repeats at a period T but not upon the period (T) of repetition. In the limit as T is made infinite, the function $f(t)$ consists entirely of one nonrepetitive pulse,

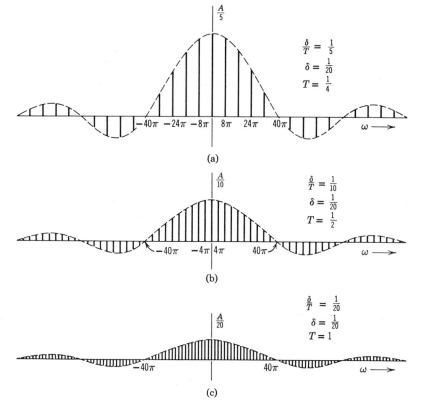

Figure 3.23

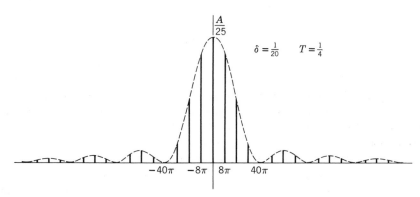

Figure 3.24

and the spectrum thus represents a nonperiodic function over the entire interval $(-\infty < t < \infty)$. We have thus extended the representation of a periodic function by summation of exponential functions to that for a nonperiodic function. This topic will be discussed in detail in the next chapter.

The power spectrum is given by

$$P = \sum_{n=-\infty}^{\infty} |F_n|^2$$

Substituting Eq. 3.131 in the above equation, we get

$$P = \left(\frac{A\delta}{T}\right)^2 \sum_{n=-\infty}^{\infty} \left(Sa\,\frac{n\pi\delta}{T}\right)^2$$

The power associated with the component of frequency $\pm n\omega_0$ is obviously $(A\delta/T)^2 Sa^2(n\pi\delta/T)$. The power spectrum for the case of $\delta = \frac{1}{20}$ and $T = \frac{1}{4}$ is shown in Fig. 3.24.

PROBLEMS

1. Show that over the interval $(0, 2\pi)$ the rectangular function in Fig. 3.3 is orthogonal to signals $\cos t$, $\cos 2t$, . . . , $\cos nt$ for all integral values of n; that is, this function has a zero component of the waveform $\cos nt$ (n integral).

2. Show that if the two signals $f_1(t)$ and $f_2(t)$ are orthogonal over an interval t_1, t_2, then the energy of the signal $[f_1(t) + f_2(t)]$ is equal to the sum of the energies of $f_1(t)$ and $f_2(t)$. The energy of a signal $f(t)$ over the interval (t_1, t_2) is defined as

$$\text{energy} = \int_{t_1}^{t_2} f^2(t)\, dt$$

Extend this result to n number of mutually orthogonal signals.

3. The rectangular function $f(t)$ in Fig. 3.3 is approximated by the signal $(4/\pi) \sin t$. Show that the error function

$$f_e(t) = f(t) - \frac{4}{\pi} \sin t$$

is orthogonal to the function $\sin t$ over the interval $(0, 2\pi)$. Can you give the qualitative reason for this? Hence, show that the energy of $f(t)$ is the sum of energies of $f_e(t)$ and $(4/\pi) \sin t$.

4. Approximate the rectangular function in Fig. 3.3 by Legendre polynomials by the first two nonzero terms. Find the mean square error in the approximation when the approximation has only (a) the first term, (b) the first and the second term, and (c) all the three terms. How does this approximation compare with that obtained by sinusoidal terms (in Eq. 3.50)?

5. Prove that if $f_1(t)$ and $f_2(t)$ are complex functions of a real variable t, then the component of $f_2(t)$ contained in $f_1(t)$ over the interval (t_1, t_2) is given by

$$C_{12} = \frac{\displaystyle\int_{t_1}^{t_2} f_1(t) f_2{}^*(t)\, dt}{\displaystyle\int_{t_1}^{t_2} f_2(t) f_2{}^*(t)\, dt}$$

The component is defined in the usual sense to minimize the magnitude of the mean square error. Now, show that the signals $[f_1(t) - C_{12}f_2(t)]$ and $f_2(t)$ are mutually orthogonal. Can you explain this qualitatively?

6. Find the component of a waveform $\sin \omega_2 t$ contained in another waveform $\sin \omega_1 t$ over the interval $(-T, T)$ for all real values of ω_1 and ω_2 $(\omega_1 \neq \omega_2)$. How does this component change with T? Show that as T is made infinite, the component vanishes. Show that the above result holds for any pair of the functions $\sin \omega_1 t$, $\sin \omega_2 t$, $\cos \omega_1 t$, $\cos \omega_2 t$, $e^{j\omega_1 t}$, $e^{j\omega_2 t}$.

7. The two periodic functions $f_1(t)$ and $f_2(t)$ with zero d-c components have arbitrary waveforms with periods T and $\sqrt{2}T$, respectively. Show that the component in $f_1(t)$ of waveform $f_2(t)$ is zero over the interval $(-\infty < t < \infty)$. Show that the above result is true for any two periodic functions if the ratio of their periods is an irrational number, and provided that either $f_1(t)$ or $f_2(t)$ has a zero average value (zero d-c component).

8. Determine whether the following functions are periodic or nonperiodic. In the case of periodic functions, find the period.

   (a) $a \sin t + b \sin 2t$
   (b) $a \sin 5t + b \cos 8t$
   (c) $a \sin 2t + b \cos \pi t$
   (d) $a \cos 2t + b \sin 7t + c \sin 13t$
   (e) $a \cos t + b \sin \sqrt{2}t$
   (f) $a \sin (3t/2) + b \cos (16t/15) + c \sin (t/29)$
   (g) $(a \sin t)^3$
   (h) $(a \sin 2t + b \sin 5t)^2$

9. Represent the function e^t over the interval $(0 < t < 1)$ by the trigonometric Fourier series and the exponential Fourier series.

10. Represent the triangular function in Fig. P-3.10 by a trigonometric Fourier series over the interval $(-\pi, \pi)$. It is desired to approximate this function by finite terms of the Fourier series. Determine the number of terms that should be

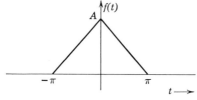

Figure P-3.10

taken in order to reduce the mean square error between the actual and the approximated function to less than 1% of the total energy of $f(t)$.

11. For each of the periodic waveforms shown in Fig. P-3.11, find the Fourier series and sketch the frequency spectrum.

12. A periodic waveform is formed by eliminating the alternate cycle of a sinusoidal waveform as shown in Fig. P-3.12.

   (a) Find the Fourier series (trigonometric or exponential) by direct evaluation of the coefficients.

   (b) If the waveform $f(t)$ is shifted to the left by π seconds, the new waveform $f(t + \pi)$ is an odd function of time whose Fourier series contains only sine terms. Find the Fourier series of $f(t + \pi)$. From this series, now write down the Fourier series for $f(t)$.

   (c) Repeat (b) by shifting $f(t)$ to the right by π seconds.

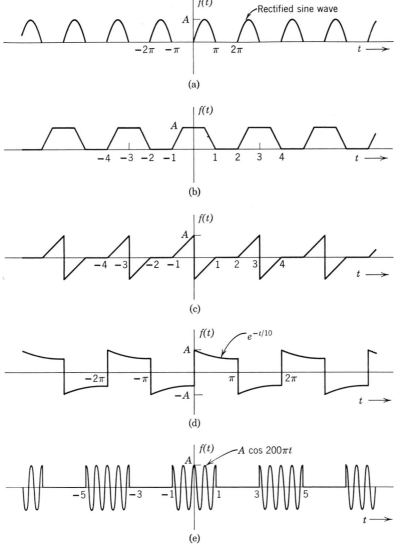

(a)

(b)

(c)

(d)

(e)

Figure P-3.11

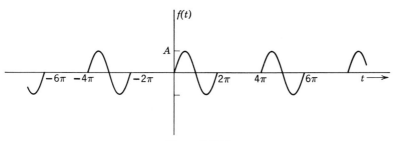

Figure P-3.12

13. A periodic waveform $f(t)$ is formed by inverting every other cycle of a sine wave as shown in Fig. P-3.13.

(a) Find the Fourier series by direct evaluation of the coefficients.

(b) If this waveform $f(t)$ is shifted $\pi/2$ seconds to the right, the new waveform $f(t - \pi/2)$ is an even function of time whose Fourier series contains only cosine terms. Determine the Fourier series for $f(t - \pi/2)$ and from this series find the Fourier series for $f(t)$.

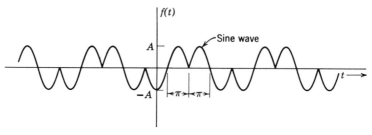

Figure P-3.13

(c) The waveform $f(t + \pi/2)$ is an odd function of time. Determine the Fourier series for $f(t + \pi/2)$ and from this series find the Fourier series for $f(t)$.

(d) This waveform can also be expressed in terms of the waveform encountered in Problem 12 (Fig. P-3.12). Using the results in Problem 12, determine the Fourier series for $f(t)$.

14. Expand the function $f(t)$ shown in Fig. P-3.14 by the trigonometric Fourier series, using the following terms.

(a) The sine and cosine terms of frequencies $\omega = 4, 8, 12, 16, \ldots$, etc., and a constant.

(b) Only the sine terms of frequencies $\omega = 2, 6, 10, 14, \ldots$, etc.

(c) A constant and only the cosine terms of frequencies $\omega = \frac{8}{3}, \frac{16}{3}, 8, \frac{32}{3}, \ldots$, etc.

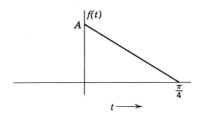

Figure P-3.14

(d) A constant and only the cosine terms of frequencies $\omega = 2, 4, 6, 8, \ldots$, etc.

(e) The sine and cosine terms of frequencies $\omega = 1, 2, 3, 4, \ldots$, etc., and a constant.

(f) Only the sine terms of frequencies $\omega = 1, 3, 5, 7, \ldots$, etc.

If it is desired to approximate $f(t)$ with a finite number of terms in these series, which of the above representations will you prefer? Give a qualitative and quantitative justification.

15. Show that an arbitrary function $f(t)$ can always be expressed as a sum of an even function $f_e(t)$ and an odd function $f_0(t)$.

$$f(t) = f_e(t) + f_0(t)$$

Hence, find the even and odd components of the functions $u(t)$, $e^{-at}u(t)$, and e^{jt}. (*Hint.* $f(t) = \frac{1}{2}[f(t) + f(-t)] + \frac{1}{2}[f(t) - f(-t)]$.)

16. Show that for an even periodic function, the coefficients of the exponential Fourier series are real; also show that for an odd periodic function, the coefficients are imaginary.

17. A Fourier series of a continuous periodic function $f(t)$ is given by

$$f(t) = \sum_{n=-\infty}^{\infty} F_n e^{jn\omega_0 t}$$

Show that the function df/dt is also a periodic function of the same period and may be expressed by a series

$$\frac{df}{dt} = \sum_{n=-\infty}^{\infty} (jn\omega_0 F_n)e^{jn\omega_0 t}$$

If the function $f(t)$ has a zero average value (that is, $F_0 = 0$), then show that its integral is also a periodic function and may be expressed by a series

$$\int f(t)\, dt = \sum_{n=-\infty}^{\infty} \frac{F_n}{jn\omega_0} e^{jn\omega_0 t}$$

18. Find the exponential Fourier series for the periodic functions shown in Fig. P-3.18. How do the coefficients F_n vary with n? Can you explain the results qualitatively, using the results in Problem 17?

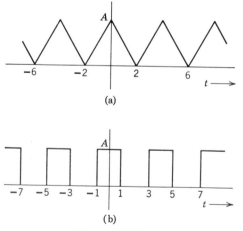

(a)

(b)

Figure P-3.18

19. A periodic function $f(t)$ is given to have components of only the first n harmonics, and all the coefficients of the higher harmonics are zero. Such signals are known as band-limited signals. Show that such a band-limited periodic signal is uniquely specified by its values at any $(2n + 1)$ instants in one period.

20. A periodic voltage $v(t)$ is applied to the input terminal of a series R-L-C circuit shown in Fig. P-3.20. Determine the current $i(t)$ and sketch the line spectra (magnitude and phase) and power spectra if $v(t)$ is given by the following.

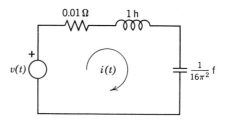

Figure P-3.20

(a) A triangular periodic signal as in Fig. 3.12 but with period 1 sec.
(b) A rectified sine wave in Fig. 3.14.
(c) A triangular periodic signal as in Fig. 3.15 but with period 1 sec.

Sketch the magnitude spectrum for each $v(t)$ and compare them with those of $i(t)$. Comment.

chapter 4

Signal Representation
by Continuous Exponentials:
The Fourier Transform

We set out to analyze signals with one purpose: to be able to represent any signal in terms of exponential functions. The techniques of frequency analysis of linear systems require that every driving function $f(t)$ should be represented as a sum (discrete or continuous) of exponential functions. Thus far we have succeeded only partially in this goal. We can now represent any periodic function $f(t)$, over the entire interval ($-\infty < t < \infty$) as a discrete sum of exponential functions. We can also represent any nonperiodic function in terms of exponential functions over any finite interval ($t_0 < t < t_0 + T$). For the purpose of frequency analysis, however, we need to represent every type of driving function in terms of exponential functions not over a finite interval but over the entire interval ($-\infty, \infty$). This chapter is devoted to the development of the appropriate techniques for such representation. We shall presently see that a nonperiodic signal, in general, can be expressed as a continuous sum (integral) of exponential signals in contrast to the periodic signals which can be represented by a discrete sum of exponential functions.

4.1 REPRESENTATION OF AN ARBITRARY FUNCTION OVER THE ENTIRE INTERVAL ($-\infty ; \infty$): THE FOURIER TRANSFORM

This problem may be approached in two ways. We can express a function $f(t)$ in terms of exponential functions over a finite interval

$(-T/2 < t < T/2)$ and then let T go to infinity. Alternately, we may construct a periodic function of period T so that $f(t)$ represents the first cycle of this periodic waveform. In the limit we let the period T become infinity, and this periodic function then has only one cycle in the interval $(-\infty < t < \infty)$ and is represented by $f(t)$. There is virtually no difference between the two approaches. But the latter approach is more convenient, for it allows us to visualize the limiting process without altering the shape of the frequency spectrum. We have already discussed at some length this limiting process for a periodic gate function in Example 3.9 (Fig. 3.21). It was observed that as the period T is made larger, the fundamental frequency becomes smaller and the frequency spectrum becomes denser; that is, in a given frequency range there are more frequency components. But the amplitudes become smaller. The shape of the frequency spectrum, however, remains unaltered. This can be easily seen from Fig. 3.23 where three values of T ($T = \frac{1}{4}, \frac{1}{2},$ and 1 sec) are considered.

Let us consider a function $f(t)$, as shown in Fig. 4.1. We desire to represent this function as a sum of exponential functions over the entire interval $(-\infty < t < \infty)$. For this purpose we shall construct a new periodic function $f_T(t)$ with period T where the function $f(t)$ repeats itself every T seconds as shown in Fig. 4.2. The period T is made large enough so that there is no overlap between the pulses of the shape of $f(t)$. This new function $f_T(t)$ is a periodic function, and consequently can be represented with an exponential Fourier series. In the limit if

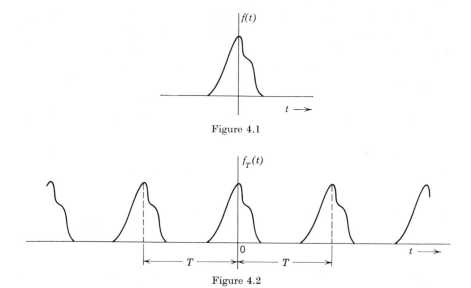

Figure 4.1

Figure 4.2

we let T become infinite, then the pulses in the periodic function repeat after an infinite interval. Hence in the limit $T \to \infty$, $f_T(t)$ and $f(t)$ are identical. That is,

$$\lim_{T \to \infty} f_T(t) = f(t)$$

Thus the Fourier series representing $f_T(t)$ over the entire interval will also represent $f(t)$ over the entire interval if we let $T = \infty$ in this series.

The exponential Fourier series for $f_T(t)$ can be represented as

$$f_T(t) = \sum_{n=-\infty}^{\infty} F_n e^{jn\omega_0 t}$$

where

$$\omega_0 = \frac{2\pi}{T}$$

and

$$F_n = \frac{1}{T} \int_{-T/2}^{T/2} f_T(t) e^{-jn\omega_0 t}\, dt \tag{4.1}$$

The term F_n represents the amplitude of the component of frequency $n\omega_0$. We shall now let T become very large. As T becomes larger, ω_0 (the fundamental frequency) becomes smaller and the spectrum becomes denser. As seen from Eq. 4.1, the amplitudes of individual components become smaller too. The shape of the frequency spectrum, however, is unaltered. We have already observed this behavior for the case of periodic gate functions as shown in Fig. 3.23. In the limit when $T = \infty$, the magnitude of each component becomes infinitesimally small, but now there also are an infinite number of frequency components. The spectrum exists for every value of ω, and is no longer a discrete but a continuous function of ω. To illustrate this point, let us make a slight change in notation here. Let

$$n\omega_0 = \omega_n \tag{4.2}$$

Then F_n is a function of ω_n, and we shall denote F_n by $F_n(\omega_n)$. Further, let

$$T F_n(\omega_n) = F(\omega_n) \tag{4.3}$$

Then

$$f_T(t) = \frac{1}{T} \sum_{n=-\infty}^{\infty} F(\omega_n) e^{j\omega_n t} \tag{4.4}$$

and, from Eqs. 4.1 and 4.3, we have

$$F(\omega_n) = T F_n = \int_{-T/2}^{T/2} f_T(t) e^{-j\omega_n t}\, dt \tag{4.5}$$

Substituting the value $T = 2\pi/\omega_0$ in Eq. 4.4, we get

$$f_T(t) = \frac{1}{2\pi} \sum_{n=-\infty}^{\infty} F(\omega_n)e^{j\omega_n t}\omega_0 \tag{4.6}$$

Equation 4.6 shows that $f_T(t)$ can be expressed as a sum of exponential signals of frequencies ω_1, ω_2, ω_3, . . . , ω_n, . . . , etc. The amplitude of the component of frequency ω_n is $F(\omega_n)\omega_0/2\pi$ (this is equal to F_n). We note, therefore, that the amplitude content in $f_T(t)$ of frequency ω_n is not $F(\omega_n)$, but is proportional to $F(\omega_n)$.

Let us try a graphical interpretation of Eq. 4.6, which represents a discrete sum or a sum of discrete frequency components. Actually, the quantity $F(\omega_n)e^{j\omega_n t}$ is complex in general, and a strict graphical representation will need two plots (real and imaginary plots or magnitude and phase plots). However, we shall assume that the quantity $F(\omega_n)e^{j\omega_n t}$ is real. This will sufficiently indicate our line of reasoning. Figure 4.3 shows such a plot of this quantity as a function of ω. This function exists only at discrete values of ω; that is, at $\omega = \omega_1, \omega_2, \ldots, \omega_n$, etc., where $\omega_n = n\omega_0$.

Each frequency component is separated by distance ω_0. Therefore, the area of the shaded rectangle in Fig. 4.3 is evidently $F(\omega_n)e^{jn\omega_n t}\omega_0$. Equation 4.6 represents the sum of areas under all such rectangles corresponding to $n = -\infty$ to ∞. The sum of rectangular areas represents approximately the area under the dotted curve. The approximation becomes better as ω_0 becomes smaller. In the limit when $T \to \infty$, ω_0 becomes infinitesimally small and may be represented by $d\omega$. The discrete sum in Eq. 4.6 becomes the integral or the area under this curve.

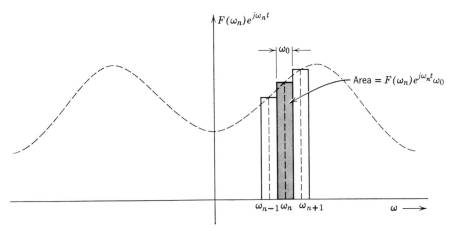

Figure 4.3

The curve now is a continuous function of ω and is given by $F(\omega)e^{j\omega t}$. Also as $T \to \infty$, the function $f_T(t) \to f(t)$ and Eqs. 4.6 and 4.5 become

$$f(t) = \frac{1}{2\pi} \int_{-\infty}^{\infty} F(\omega)e^{j\omega t}\,d\omega \qquad (4.7)$$

where

$$F(\omega) = \int_{-\infty}^{\infty} f(t)e^{-j\omega t}\,dt \qquad (4.8)$$

We have thus succeeded in representing a nonperiodic function $f(t)$ in terms of exponential functions over an entire interval $(-\infty < t < \infty)$. Equation 4.7 represents $f(t)$ as a continuous sum of exponential functions with frequencies lying in the interval $(-\infty < \omega < \infty)$. The amplitude of the component of any frequency ω is proportional to $F(\omega)$. Therefore, $F(\omega)$ represents the frequency spectrum of $f(t)$ and is called the *spectral-density function*. Note, however, that the frequency spectrum now is continuous and exists at all values of ω. The spectral-density function $F(\omega)$ can be evaluated from Eq. 4.8.

Equations 4.7 and 4.8 are usually referred to as the Fourier transform pair. Equation 4.8 is known as the direct Fourier transform of $f(t)$, and Eq. 4.7 is known as the inverse Fourier transform of $F(\omega)$. Symbolically, these transforms are also written as

$$F(\omega) = \mathscr{F}[f(t)] \qquad \text{and} \qquad f(t) = \mathscr{F}^{-1}[F(\omega)] \qquad (4.9)$$

Thus, $F(\omega)$ is the direct Fourier transform of $f(t)$, and $f(t)$ is the inverse Fourier transform of $F(\omega)$, and

$$\mathscr{F}[f(t)] = \int_{-\infty}^{\infty} f(t)e^{-j\omega t}\,dt \qquad (4.10)$$

$$\mathscr{F}^{-1}[F(\omega)] = \frac{1}{2\pi} \int_{-\infty}^{\infty} F(\omega)e^{j\omega t}\,d\omega \qquad (4.11)$$

4.2 SOME REMARKS ABOUT THE CONTINUOUS SPECTRUM FUNCTION

We have expressed a nonperiodic function $f(t)$ as a continuous sum of exponential functions with frequencies in the interval $-\infty$ to ∞. The amplitude of a component of any frequency ω is infinitesimal, but is proportional to $F(\omega)$, where $F(\omega)$ is the spectral density.

The concept of a continuous spectrum is sometimes confusing because we generally picture the spectrum as existing at discrete frequencies and with finite amplitudes in the manner of a periodic function. The continuous spectrum concept can be appreciated by considering the analogous

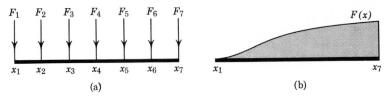

Figure 4.4   (a) A beam loaded at discrete points. (b) A continuously loaded beam.

concrete phenomenon. One familiar example of a continuous distribution is the loading of a beam. Consider a beam loaded with weights F_1, F_2, F_3, ..., F_7 units at uniformly spaced points x_1, x_2, ..., x_7, as shown in Fig. 4.4a. The beam is loaded at 7 discrete points, and the total weight on the beam is given by the sum of these loads at 7 discrete points.

$$W_T = \sum_{r=1}^{7} F_r$$

Next, consider the case of a continuously loaded beam as shown in Fig. 4.4b. The loading density is a function of x, and let it be given by $F(x)$ kg per meter. The total weight on the beam is now given by a continuous sum of the weights, that is, the integral of $F(x)$ over the entire length.

$$W_T = \int_{x_1}^{x_7} F(x)\, dx \qquad \text{kg}$$

In the former case of discrete loading, the weight existed only at discrete points. At other points there was no loading. On the other hand, in the continuously distributed case, the loading exists at every point but, at any one point, the loading is zero. However, the loading in a small distance dx is given by $F(x)\, dx$. Therefore, $F(x)$ represents the relative magnitude of loading at a point x. An exactly analogous situation exists in the case of signals and their frequency spectrum. A periodic signal can be represented by a sum of discrete exponentials with finite amplitudes.

$$f(t) = \sum_{n=-\infty}^{\infty} F_n e^{j\omega_n t} \qquad (\omega_n = n\omega_0)$$

For a nonperiodic function, the distribution of exponentials becomes continuous; that is, the spectrum function exists at every value of ω. At any one frequency ω, the amplitude of that frequency component is zero. The total contribution in an infinitesimal interval $d\omega$ is given by $(1/2\pi)F(\omega)\, d\omega$ and the function $f(t)$ can be expressed in terms of the continuous sum of such infinitesimal components.

$$f(t) = \frac{1}{2\pi} \int_{-\infty}^{\infty} F(\omega) e^{j\omega t}\, d\omega \qquad (4.12)$$

The factor 2π in Eq. 4.12 can be removed if the integration is performed with respect to variable f instead of ω. We have

$$\omega = 2\pi f$$

and

$$d\omega = 2\pi \, df$$

Equation 4.12 may now be expressed as

$$f(t) = \int_{-\infty}^{\infty} F(2\pi f) e^{j2\pi ft} \, df$$

4.3 TIME-DOMAIN AND FREQUENCY-DOMAIN REPRESENTA-TION OF A SIGNAL

The Fourier transform is a tool that resolves a given signal into its exponential components. The function $F(\omega)$ is the direct Fourier transform of $f(t)$ and represents relative amplitudes of various frequency components. Therefore, $F(\omega)$ is the frequency-domain representation of $f(t)$. Time-domain representation specifies a function at each instant of time, whereas frequency-domain representation specifies the relative amplitudes of the frequency components of the function. Either representation uniquely specifies the function. However, the function $F(\omega)$ is complex in general, and needs two plots for its graphical representation.

$$F(\omega) = |F(\omega)| e^{j\theta(\omega)}$$

Thus, $F(\omega)$ may be represented by a magnitude plot $|F(\omega)|$ and a phase plot $\theta(\omega)$. In many cases, however, $F(\omega)$ is either real or imaginary and only one plot is necessary. $F(\omega)$, however, is in general a complex function of ω, and we shall now show that for a real function $f(t)$,

$$F(\omega) = F^*(-\omega)$$

We have

$$F(\omega) = \int_{-\infty}^{\infty} f(t) e^{-j\omega t} \, dt \tag{4.13a}$$

Similarly

$$F(-\omega) = \int_{-\infty}^{\infty} f(t) e^{j\omega t} \, dt \tag{4.13b}$$

From Eqs. 4.13a and 4.13b it follows that if $f(t)$ is a real function of t, then

$$F(\omega) = F^*(-\omega) \tag{4.14}$$

Thus, if

$$F(\omega) = |F(\omega)| e^{j\theta(\omega)}$$

then

$$F(-\omega) = |F(\omega)|e^{-j\theta(\omega)} \tag{4.15}$$

It is evident from the above equations that the magnitude spectrum $F(\omega)$ is an even function of ω, and the phase spectrum $\theta(\omega)$ is an odd function of ω.

4.4 EXISTENCE OF THE FOURIER TRANSFORM

From Eq. 4.10, defining the Fourier transform, it is evident that if $\int_{-\infty}^{\infty} f(t)e^{-j\omega t} dt$ is finite, then the Fourier transform exists. But since the magnitude of $e^{-j\omega t}$ is unity, a sufficient condition for the existence of a Fourier transform of a function $f(t)$ is that

$$\int_{-\infty}^{\infty} |f(t)| dt$$

must be finite. If, however, singularity functions (for example, impulse functions) are allowed, then the above condition of absolute integrability is not always necessary. We shall see later that there are functions that are not absolutely integrable, but that do have transforms. Absolute integrability of $f(t)$ is thus a sufficient but not a necessary condition for the existence of the Fourier transform of $f(t)$.

Functions such as $\sin \omega t$, $\cos \omega t$, $u(t)$, etc., do not satisfy the above condition and, strictly speaking, do not possess the Fourier transform. These functions, however, do have Fourier transforms in the limit.

A function $\sin \omega t$ may be assumed to exist only in the interval $-T/2 < t < T/2$. Under these conditions the function has a Fourier transform as long as T is finite. In the limit we make T very large but finite. It will be shown later that the Fourier transforms for such functions do exist in the limit.

4.5 THE FOURIER TRANSFORM OF SOME USEFUL FUNCTIONS

We shall now evaluate the Fourier transform of a few functions. Most functions of practical importance start at some finite time, say at $t = 0$. For this reason we shall define an important function called Heaviside's unit step function $u(t)$, which is defined as

$$u(t) = \begin{cases} 0 & \text{for } t < 0 \\ 1 & t > 0 \end{cases}$$

The function is shown in Fig. 4.5.

We shall first find the Fourier transform of the exponential function e^{-at}, which starts at $t = 0$ and is zero for $t < 0$. Such a function can be conveniently written as $e^{-at}u(t)$.

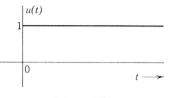

Figure 4.5

$$\mathscr{F}[e^{-at}u(t)] = \int_{-\infty}^{\infty} e^{-at}u(t)e^{-j\omega t} \, dt$$

Since $e^{-at}u(t)$ is zero for $-\infty < t < 0$, we can change the lower limit of the integral from $-\infty$ to 0. Therefore

$$\mathscr{F}[e^{-at}u(t)] = \int_{0}^{\infty} e^{-at}e^{-j\omega t} \, dt$$

$$= \int_{0}^{\infty} e^{-(a+j\omega)t} \, dt$$

$$= \frac{-1}{a + j\omega} e^{-(a+j\omega)t} \Big|_{0}^{\infty} \tag{4.16}$$

$$= \frac{1}{a + j\omega} \tag{4.17}$$

Observe that if a is negative in Eq. 4.16, the expression goes to infinity and the Fourier transform does not exist. This is also seen from the fact that $e^{-at}u(t)$ does not satisfy the condition of absolute integrability if a is negative—in which case the function represents a growing exponential. Thus

$$\mathscr{F}[e^{-at}u(t)] = \frac{1}{a + j\omega} \qquad \text{for} \quad a > 0 \tag{4.18}$$

It follows that the inverse Fourier transform of $1/(a + j\omega)$ is $e^{-at}u(t)$; that is,

$$\mathscr{F}^{-1}\left(\frac{1}{a + j\omega}\right) = e^{-at}u(t) \tag{4.19}$$

Therefore

$$e^{-at}u(t) = \frac{1}{2\pi} \int_{-\infty}^{\infty} \frac{1}{a + j\omega} e^{j\omega t} \, d\omega$$

Both Eqs. 4.18 and 4.19 may be written as a Fourier transform pair:

$$\frac{1}{a + j\omega} = \int_{-\infty}^{\infty} e^{-at}u(t)e^{-j\omega t} \, dt$$

and

$$e^{-at}u(t) = \frac{1}{2\pi} \int_{-\infty}^{\infty} \frac{1}{a + j\omega} e^{j\omega t} \, d\omega$$

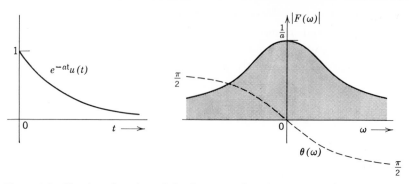

Figure 4.6   The time-domain and the frequency-domain representation of $e^{-at}u(t)$.

The spectral density function of $e^{-at}u(t)$ is therefore given by $1/(a + j\omega)$. Note that this is a complex function and can be expressed as

$$\frac{1}{a + j\omega} = \frac{1}{\sqrt{a^2 + \omega^2}}\, e^{-j\tan^{-1}(\omega/a)}$$

The magnitude function $1/\sqrt{a^2 + \omega^2}$ and the phase function $\theta(\omega) = -\tan^{-1}(\omega/a)$ are shown in Fig. 4.6.

It is evident that the magnitude function is an even function, whereas the phase function is an odd function of ω.

We have thus expressed the signal $e^{-at}u(t)$ in terms of a continuous sum of eternal exponential functions. These exponential components add in such a way as to yield zero value for $t < 0$ and add up to e^{-at} for $t > 0$. Let us consider another function:

$$f(t) = te^{-at}u(t)$$

$$F(\omega) = \mathscr{F}[f(t)] = \int_{-\infty}^{\infty} te^{-at}u(t)e^{-j\omega t}\, dt$$

$$= \int_{0}^{\infty} te^{-at}e^{-j\omega t}\, dt$$

$$= \int_{0}^{\infty} te^{-(a+j\omega)t}\, dt$$

Integration by parts yields

$$F(\omega) = \mathscr{F}[te^{-at}u(t)] = \frac{1}{(a + j\omega)^2} \qquad (a > 0)$$

Therefore

$$\mathscr{F}^{-1}\left[\frac{1}{(a + j\omega)^2}\right] = te^{-at}u(t)$$

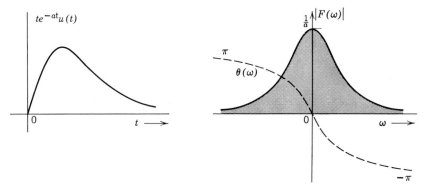

Figure 4.7   The time-domain and the frequency-domain representation of the function $te^{-at}u(t)$.

The spectral-density function $F(\omega)$ may be expressed in terms of magnitude and phase-density functions.

$$F(\omega) = \frac{1}{(a+j\omega)^2} = \frac{1}{a^2+\omega^2}e^{-j2\tan^{-1}(\omega/a)}$$

Figure 4.7 shows the time-domain and frequency-domain representation of $te^{-at}u(t)$.

Transform of a Gate Function

A gate function $G_\tau(t)$ is a rectangular pulse, as shown in Fig. 4.8a, and is defined by

$$G_\tau(t) = \begin{cases} 1 & |t| < \tau/2 \\ 0 & |t| > \tau/2 \end{cases}$$

The Fourier transform of this function is given by

$$F(\omega) = \int_{-\tau/2}^{\tau/2} Ae^{-j\omega t}\,dt$$

$$= \frac{A}{j\omega}\left(e^{j\omega\tau/2} - e^{-j\omega\tau/2}\right)$$

$$= A\tau\,\frac{\sin(\omega\tau/2)}{\omega\tau/2}$$

$$= A\tau\,Sa\,\frac{(\omega\tau)}{2}$$

Note that $F(\omega)$ is a real function and hence can be represented graphically by a single curve (Fig. 4.8b).

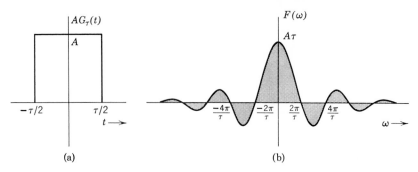

Figure 4.8   (a) A gate function. (b) Transform of a gate function.

4.6 SINGULARITY FUNCTIONS

Consider a unit step voltage applied to a capacitor as shown in Fig. 4.9a. The current i through the capacitor is given by

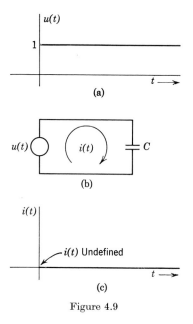

Figure 4.9

$$i = C \frac{dv}{dt}$$

It is easy to see that dv/dt is zero for all values of t except at $t = 0$ where it is undefined. The derivative at $t = 0$ does not exist because the function $u(t)$ is discontinuous at this point. We are in a serious mathematical difficulty, which arises from the idealization of the source as well as the circuit element. If either the source or the capacitor were nonideal, the solution would exist. If, for example, the source voltage were as shown in Fig. 4.10a instead of that shown in Fig. 4.9a, the current through the capacitor would be a pulse of current as shown in Fig. 4.10b. The solution to an ideal unit step voltage does not exist, but it is possible to obtain a solution in the limit by assuming an unideal source as shown in Fig. 4.10a and then letting a go to zero in the limit.

Let us designate the unidealized voltage function by $u_a(t)$. In the limit when a goes to zero, this voltage function becomes a unit step function. The derivative of the function $u_a(t)$ is a rectangular pulse of height $1/a$ and width a. As a varies, the pulse shape varies, but the area

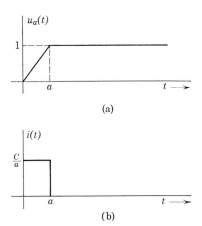

(a)

(b)

Figure 4.10 (a) Unidealized voltage representation. (b) The current pulse through the capacitor due to the unidealized voltage source $u_a(t)$ across it.

of the pulse remains constant. Figure 4.11a shows the sequence of such pulses as a varies. In the limit when a goes to zero, the height of the pulse goes to infinity and the width of the pulse is zero. The area of the pulse, however, remains unity. We define the unit impulse function as the derivative of a unit step function. Since the derivative of an idealized unit step function does not exist, we define the unit impulse function as the limit of the sequence of the derivatives of an unidealized function $u_a(t)$ as a goes to zero. The unit impulse function is denoted by $\delta(t)$.

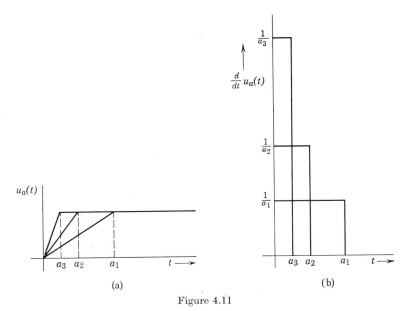

(a)   (b)

Figure 4.11

We therefore have

$$\delta(t) = \lim_{a \to 0} \frac{d}{dt}[u_a(t)]$$

But the function $d/dt[u_a(t)]$ is a rectangular pulse of height $1/a$ and width a. This can be described as

$$\delta(t) = \lim_{a \to 0} \frac{1}{a}[u(t) - u(t - a)]$$

In the limit as a goes to zero, the function $\delta(t)$ assumes the form of a pulse of infinite height and zero width. The area of the pulse, however, remains unity. The function $\delta(t)$ exists only at $t = 0$ and has a zero value of all $t \neq 0$. This fact can be expressed as

$$\delta(t) = 0 \qquad t \neq 0 \Bigg\}$$

and

$$\int_{-\infty}^{\infty} \delta(t)\, dt = 1 \Bigg\} \tag{4.20}$$

Equation 4.20 may be taken as a definition of the unit impulse function. This description of an impulse function is more general and represents the impulse function as a limiting process without any regard to the actual shape of the pulse; that is, it is not necessary to define the impulse

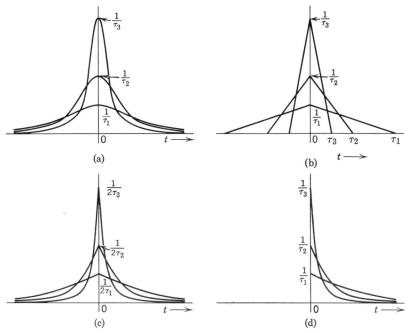

Figure 4.12   (a) Gaussian pulse sequence. (b) Triangular pulse sequence. (c) Two-sided exponential pulse sequence. (d) Single-sided exponential pulse sequence.

function as a limiting form of a rectangular pulse. One may, for example, define $\delta(t)$ as a limiting form of a gaussian pulse, a triangular pulse, an exponential pulse, or many other pulse forms. The significant point is that, in the limit, the function must satisfy Equation 4.20. The rectangular pulse sequence, shown in Fig. 4.11b, is one example. The sequences of some of the pulse forms which satisfy Eq. 4.20 are shown in Fig. 4.12. Figure 4.13 shows the impulse function as a limit of the sequence of a sampling function.

(1) *Gaussian pulse.*

$$\delta(t) = \lim_{\tau \to 0} \frac{1}{\tau} e^{(-\pi t^2/\tau^2)}$$

(2) *Triangular pulse.*

$$\delta(t) = \lim_{\tau \to 0} \frac{1}{\tau} \left[1 - \frac{|t|}{\tau} \right] \cdots |t| < \tau$$
$$= 0 \qquad \cdots |t| > \tau$$

(3) *Exponential pulse.*

$$\delta(t) = \lim_{\tau \to 0} \frac{1}{2\tau} e^{(-|t|/\tau)}$$

or

$$\delta(t) = \lim_{\tau \to 0} \frac{1}{\tau} e^{(-t/\tau)} u(t)$$

(4) *Sampling function.* It can be shown that

$$\int_{-\infty}^{\infty} \frac{k}{\pi} Sa(kt) \, dt = 1 \tag{4.21}$$

As k is made larger and larger, the amplitude of the function $(k/\pi)Sa(kt)$ becomes larger. The function oscillates faster and decays very rapidly away from the origin (Fig. 4.13). In the limit as $k \to \infty$, the function exists only at the origin and the net area under the curve is unity as seen from Eq. 4.21. Hence the sampling function $(k/\pi)Sa(kt)$ becomes an impulse function in the limit as $k \to \infty$.

$$\lim_{k \to \infty} \left[\frac{k}{\pi} Sa(kt) \right] = \delta(t) \tag{4.22}$$

The entire area of an impulse function is concentrated at $t = 0$, and we may write

$$\int_{0^-}^{0^+} \delta(t) \, dt = 1 \tag{4.23}$$

where 0^+ and 0^- denote arbitrarily small values of t approached from the right and the left side, respectively, of the origin. Also note that

$$\int_{0^-}^{0^+} f(t) \, \delta(t) \, dt = f(0) \tag{4.24}$$

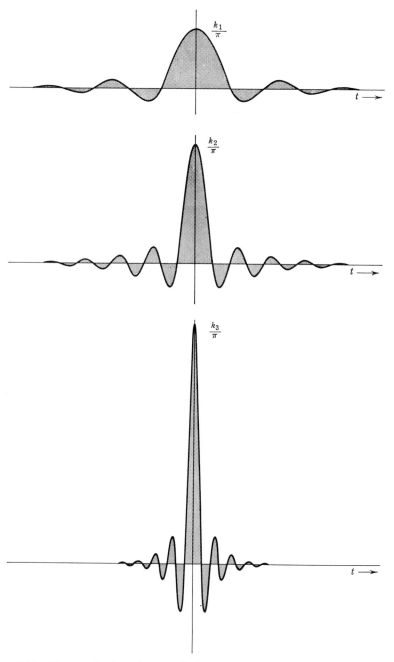

Figure 4.13   The impulse function as a limit of the sequence of a sampling function.

It should be remembered that the impulse function is not a true function in the usual mathematical sense where a function is defined for every value of t. Nevertheless, its formal use leads to results that are capable of physical interpretation. The impulse function is a new concept of a function specified by Eq. 4.20. The impulse function and its derivatives are known as *generalized functions*, and are justified by a relatively new discipline known as the "theory of distribution."[1] The use of the impulse function is very common in physical sciences and engineering to represent such entities as point masses, point charges, point sources, concentrated forces, line sources, surface charges, etc. Actually, in practice, such distributions do not exist, but this idealization simplifies the derivation of result. Besides, the measuring equipment in practice, due to its finite resolution, cannot distinguish between the response of the idealized impulse function and a pulse of small but finite width.

The step function $u(t)$, the impulse function $\delta(t)$, and its higher derivatives are all known as singularity functions.[2]

Derivative of Discontinuous Functions

If a function has a jump discontinuity at a point $t = t_0$, as shown in Fig. 4.14a, then rigorously speaking the function $f(t)$ does not possess a derivative at $t = t_0$. Therefore, a unit step function which has a jump discontinuity at $t = 0$ does not possess a derivative at the origin in a strict mathematical sense. We overcame this difficulty by considering the unit step function as a limit of the sequence of functions which were continuous (Fig. 4.11a). The limit of the derivative of this sequence was found to be an impulse function of unit strength. From this discussion it follows that a function possesses a derivative at a point of jump discontinuity and this derivative is an impulse function of strength equal to the amount of discontinuity. For a unit step function, the amount of discontinuity is unity and the derivative of $u(t)$ is an impulse of unit strength at $t = 0$. Thus

$$\frac{du}{dt} = \delta(t)$$

It follows that

$$\int_{-\infty}^{t} \delta(t)\, dt = u(t)$$

[1] M. J. Lighthill, *An Introduction to Fourier Analysis and Generalized Functions*, Cambridge University Press, New York, 1959; A. Papoulis, *The Fourier Integral and its Applications*, McGraw-Hill, New York, 1962.

[2] For further discussion on higher derivatives of the impulse function, see S. J. Mason and H. J. Zimmermann, *Electronic Circuits, Signals and Systems*, pp. 310–318, Wiley, New York, 1960.

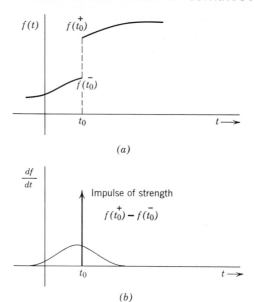

(a)

(b)

Figure 4.14

In Fig. 4.14a the function $f(t)$ has a jump discontinuity at $t = t_0$ of amount $[f(t_0{}^+) - f(t_0{}^-)]$ and therefore the derivative of $f(t)$ at $t = t_0$ is given by

$$\frac{df}{dt}(t_0) = [f(t_0{}^+) - f(t_0{}^-)]\,\delta(t - t_0)$$

Sampling Property of the Impulse Function

The function $\delta(t - t_0)$ is a unit impulse function which exists only at $t = t_0$ and is zero everywhere else. It follows therefore that for a given function $f(t)$:

$$f(t)\,\delta(t - t_0) = f(t_0)\,\delta(t - t_0) \tag{4.25}$$

Hence, multiplication of any function $f(t)$ by an impulse $\delta(t - t_0)$ also yields an impulse of strength $f(t_0)$ at $t = t_0$. From Eq. 4.20, defining an impulse function, it follows that

$$\int_{-\infty}^{\infty} f(t)\,\delta(t - t_0)\,dt = \int_{-\infty}^{\infty} f(t_0)\,\delta(t - t_0)\,dt = f(t_0) \tag{4.26}$$

that is,

$$\int_{-\infty}^{\infty} f(t)\,\delta(t - t_0)\,dt = f(t_0) \tag{4.27}$$

Equation 4.27 expresses the sampling or sifting property of an impulse function. Since $\delta(t - t_0)$ is concentrated at $t = t_0$ and is zero everywhere else, it follows from Eq. 4.27 that

$$\int_{t_0^-}^{t_0^+} f(t)\, \delta(t - t_0)\, dt = f(t_0) \qquad (4.28)$$

and

$$\int_{0^-}^{0^+} f(t)\, \delta(t)\, dt = f(0) \qquad (4.29)$$

The Fourier Transform of an Impulse Function

The Fourier transform of a unit impulse function $\delta(t)$ is given by

$$\mathscr{F}[\delta(t)] = \int_{-\infty}^{\infty} \delta(t)e^{-j\omega t}\, dt \qquad (4.30)$$

From the sampling property of an impulse function expressed in Eq. 4.27, it is evident that the integral on the right-hand side of Eq. 4.30 is unity. Hence

$$\mathscr{F}[\delta(t)] = 1 \qquad (4.31)$$

Therefore, the Fourier transform of a unit impulse function is unity.

It is therefore evident that an impulse function has a uniform spectral density over the entire frequency interval. In other words, an impulse function contains all frequency components with the same relative amplitudes.

The Fourier Transform of a Constant

Let us now find the Fourier transform of a function:

$$f(t) = A$$

This function does not satisfy the condition of absolute integrability. Nevertheless, it has a Fourier transform in the limit. We shall consider the Fourier transform of a gate function of height A and width τ seconds as shown in Fig. 4.8a. In the limit as $\tau \to \infty$, the gate function tends to be a constant function A. The Fourier transform of a constant A is therefore

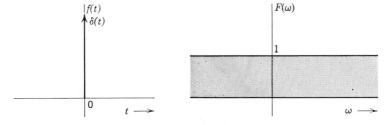

Figure 4.15   An impulse function and its transform.

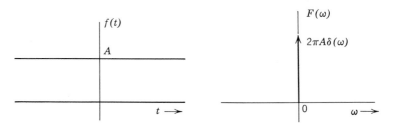

Figure 4.16   A constant and its transform.

the Fourier transform of a gate function $G_\tau(t)$ as $\tau \to \infty$. The Fourier transform of $AG_\tau(t)$ was found to be $A\tau Sa(\omega\tau/2)$. Hence

$$\mathscr{F}[A] = \lim_{\tau \to \infty} A\tau Sa(\omega\tau/2)$$

$$= 2\pi A \lim_{\tau \to \infty} \frac{\tau}{2\pi} Sa(\omega\tau/2)$$

From Eq. 4.22, it follows that the limit of the sampling function above defines an impulse function $\delta(\omega)$. Hence

$$\mathscr{F}[A] = 2\pi A\ \delta(\omega) \qquad (4.32a)$$

and

$$\mathscr{F}[1] = 2\pi\ \delta(\omega) \qquad (4.32b)$$

Thus, when $f(t)$ equals a constant, it contains only a frequency component of $\omega = 0$. This is the logical result, since a constant function is a d-c signal ($\omega = 0$), and does not have any other frequency components.

Transform of Cos $\omega_0 t$ and Sin $\omega_0 t$

The functions $\cos \omega_0 t$ and $\sin \omega_0 t$ also do not satisfy the condition of absolute integrability, yet their Fourier transform exists, and can be found in the limit exactly in the manner used for a constant function above. Consider a function $\cos \omega_0 t$. We shall first consider this function to exist only over the interval $-\tau/2$ to $\tau/2$ and zero outside this interval. In the limit, τ will be made infinity. Therefore

$$\mathscr{F}[\cos \omega_0 t] = \lim_{\tau \to \infty} \int_{-\tau/2}^{\tau/2} \cos \omega_0 t e^{-j\omega t}\, dt$$

$$= \lim_{\tau \to \infty} \int_{-\tau/2}^{\tau/2} \frac{e^{j\omega_0 t} + e^{-j\omega_0 t}}{2} e^{-j\omega t}\, dt$$

$$= \lim_{\tau \to \infty} \frac{\tau}{2}\left[\frac{\sin\left[(\omega - \omega_0)\tau/2\right]}{(\omega - \omega_0)\tau/2} + \frac{\sin\left[(\omega + \omega_0)\tau/2\right]}{(\omega + \omega_0)\tau/2}\right]$$

$$= \lim_{\tau \to \infty} \left\{\frac{\tau}{2} Sa\left[\frac{\tau(\omega - \omega_0)}{2}\right] + \frac{\tau}{2} Sa\left[\frac{\tau(\omega + \omega_0)}{2}\right]\right\} \qquad (4.33)$$

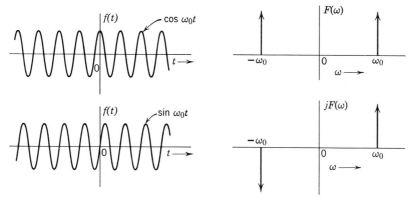

Figure 4.17

In the limit the sampling function becomes an impulse function according to Eq. 4.22, and we have

$$\mathscr{F}(\cos \omega_0 t) = \pi[\delta(\omega - \omega_0) + \delta(\omega + \omega_0)] \qquad (4.34)$$

Similarly, it can be shown that

$$\mathscr{F}(\sin \omega_0 t) = j\pi[\delta(\omega + \omega_0) - \delta(\omega - \omega_0)] \qquad (4.35)$$

Therefore, the Fourier spectrum for these functions consists of two impulses at ω_0 and $-\omega_0$, respectively. It is interesting to see how the spectrum behaves in the limiting process as τ is made infinite. For a finite τ, the spectral density function is given by Eq. 4.33. This spectral-density function is plotted in Fig. 4.18 for the case $\tau = 16\pi/\omega_0$. In other words, it represents the spectral-density function of a signal $\cos \omega_0 t$ which is

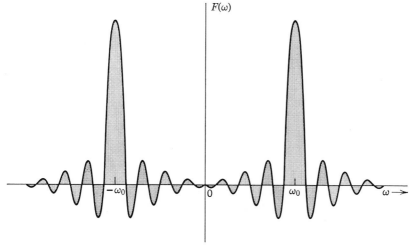

Figure 4.18   The spectral density function of 8 cycles of $\cos \omega_0 t$.

truncated beyond 8 cycles.

$$f(t) = \begin{cases} \cos \omega_0 t & |t| < \dfrac{16\pi}{\omega_0} \\[3mm] 0 & |t| > \dfrac{16\pi}{\omega_0} \end{cases}$$

Note that there is a large concentration of energy at frequencies near $\pm \omega_0$. As we increase the interval τ, the spectral density concentrates more and more around frequencies $\pm \omega_0$. In the limit as $\tau \to \infty$, the spectral density is zero everywhere except at frequencies $\pm \omega_0$ where it is infinite in such a way that the area under the curve at each of these frequencies is π. In the limit the distribution therefore becomes two impulses of strength, π units each, located at frequencies $\pm \omega_0$ as shown in Fig. 4.17. It is evident that the spectral density functions for $\cos \omega_0 t$ and $\sin \omega_0 t$ exist only at $\omega = \omega_0$. This is quite logical since these signals do not contain components of any other frequency. On the other hand, functions $(\cos \omega_0 t)u(t)$ and $(\sin \omega_0 t)u(t)$ do contain components of frequencies other than ω_0. It can be shown that (see Problem 2 at the end of this chapter):

$$\mathscr{F}[(\cos \omega_0 t)u(t)] = \frac{\pi}{2}[\delta(\omega - \omega_0) + \delta(\omega + \omega_0)] + \frac{j\omega}{\omega_0{}^2 - \omega^2} \qquad (4.36)$$

and

$$\mathscr{F}[(\sin \omega_0 t)u(t)] = \frac{\pi}{2j}[\delta(\omega - \omega_0) - \delta(\omega + \omega_0)] + \frac{\omega_0}{\omega_0{}^2 - \omega^2} \qquad (4.37)$$

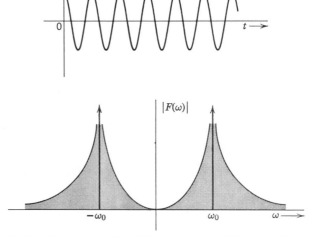

Figure 4.19   The function $\cos \omega_0 t u(t)$ and the magnitude of its spectral density function.

These functions evidently contain a large component of frequency ω_0, but also contain other frequency components.

Apparently, the signals $(\cos \omega_0 t)u(t)$ and $(\sin \omega_0 t)u(t)$ are pure sinusoidal signals, and it may seem rather strange that these functions should contain components of frequencies other than ω_0. We must remember, however, that we are expressing a function in terms of eternal exponential (or eternal sinusoidal) functions existing from $-\infty$ to ∞. The functions $(\cos \omega_0 t)u(t)$ and $(\sin \omega_0 t)u(t)$ are not eternal sinusoidal signals. These functions are zero for values of $t < 0$ and exist only for positive values of t. Hence, in addition to ω_0, they also contain other frequency components. All these eternal frequency components in the spectrum of these functions (Fig. 4.19) add in such a way as to yield zero value for $t < 0$ and $\cos \omega_0 t$ (or $\sin \omega_0 t$) for $t > 0$. If the sinusoidal signals are eternal ($\cos \omega_0 t$ and $\sin \omega_0 t$ in the entire interval $-\infty$ to ∞), then we have already shown in Eqs. 4.34 and 4.35 that they indeed contain components of frequency ω_0 only.

Transform of a Unit Step Function

The unit step function does not satisfy the condition of absolute integrability, and hence its Fourier transform exists in the limit only. In fact, a function $\cos \omega_0 t\, u(t)$ tends to $u(t)$ as ω_0 is made zero.

$$\lim_{\omega_0 \to 0} [(\cos \omega_0 t)u(t)] = u(t)$$

Hence

$$\begin{aligned}
\mathscr{F}[u(t)] &= \lim_{\omega_0 \to 0} \mathscr{F}[(\cos \omega_0 t)u(t)] \\
&= \lim_{\omega_0 \to 0} \left\{ \frac{\pi}{2}\,[\delta(\omega - \omega_0) + \delta(\omega + \omega_0)] + \frac{j\omega}{\omega_0{}^2 - \omega^2} \right\} \\
&= \pi\delta(\omega) + \frac{1}{j\omega}
\end{aligned} \qquad (4.38)$$

The spectral-density function contains an impulse at $\omega = 0$. Thus, the function $u(t)$ contains a large d-c component as expected. In addition, it

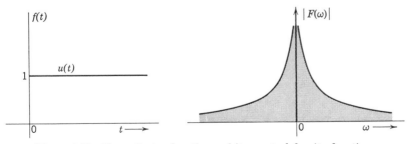

Figure 4.20 The unit step function and its spectral density function.

also has other frequency components (Fig. 4.20). Here again the function $u(t)$ appears to be a constant function, and hence the presence of other frequency components may appear rather strange. However, the function $u(t)$ is not a constant since it is zero for $t < 0$, and there is an abrupt discontinuity at $t = 0$ giving rise to other frequency components. For a true d-c signal, $f(t)$ is a constant for $-\infty < t < \infty$. We have already shown in Eq. 4.32 that such a signal indeed has no other components except d-c ($\omega = 0$).

Transform of an Eternal Exponential $e^{j\omega_0 t}$

We shall now find the Fourier transform of an eternal exponential signal $e^{j\omega_0 t}(-\infty < t < \infty)$. We have

$$e^{j\omega_0 t} = \cos \omega_0 t + j \sin \omega_0 t$$

Hence

$$\mathscr{F}[e^{j\omega_0 t}] = \mathscr{F}[\cos \omega_0 t + j \sin \omega_0 t]$$

Substituting Eqs. 4.34 and 4.35 in the above equation, we get

$$\mathscr{F}[e^{j\omega t}] = \pi[\delta(\omega - \omega_0) + \delta(\omega + \omega_0) - \delta(\omega + \omega_0) + \delta(\omega - \omega_0)]$$
$$= 2\pi\delta(\omega - \omega_0) \tag{4.39}$$

The Fourier transform of $e^{j\omega_0 t}$ is therefore a single impulse of strength 2π at $\omega = \omega_0$. Note that the signal $e^{j\omega_0 t}$ is not a real function of time, and hence it has a spectrum which exists at $\omega = \omega_0$ alone. We have shown previously that for any real function of time, the spectral density function $F(\omega)$ satisfies (see Eq. 4.14):

$$F(\omega) = F^*(-\omega)$$

and

$$|F(\omega)| = |F(-\omega)|$$

Hence, for any real function of time, the magnitude spectrum is an even function of ω, and if there is an impulse at $\omega = \omega_0$, there must exist an impulse at $\omega = -\omega_0$. This is the case for signals $\sin \omega_0 t$ and $\cos \omega_0 t$.

4.7 THE FOURIER TRANSFORM OF A PERIODIC FUNCTION

We have developed a Fourier transform as a limiting case of the Fourier series by letting the period of a periodic function become infinite. We shall now proceed in the opposite direction and show that the Fourier series is just a limiting case of the Fourier transform. This point of view is very useful, since it permits a unified treatment of both the periodic and the nonperiodic functions.

Strictly speaking, the Fourier transform of a periodic function does not exist, since it fails to satisfy the condition of absolute integrability. For any periodic function $f(t)$:

$$\int_{-\infty}^{\infty} |f(t)|\, dt = \infty$$

But the transform does exist in the limit. We have already found the Fourier transform of $\cos \omega_0 t$, $\sin \omega_0 t$ in the limit. We use here exactly the same procedure by assuming that the periodic function exists only in a finite interval $(-\tau/2, \tau/2)$, and in the limit let τ become infinite.

Alternatively, we may express a periodic function by its Fourier series. The Fourier transform of a periodic function is then the sum of Fourier transforms of its individual components. We can express a periodic function $f(t)$ with period T as

$$f(t) = \sum_{n=-\infty}^{\infty} F_n e^{jn\omega_0 t} \qquad \left(\omega_0 = \frac{2\pi}{T}\right)$$

Taking the Fourier transforms of both sides, we have

$$\mathscr{F}[f(t)] = \mathscr{F} \sum_{n=-\infty}^{\infty} F_n e^{jn\omega_0 t}$$

$$= \sum_{n=-\infty}^{\infty} F_n \mathscr{F}(e^{jn\omega_0 t})$$

Substituting the transform of $e^{j\omega_0 t}$ from Eq. 4.39, we get

$$\mathscr{F}[f(t)] = 2\pi \sum_{n=-\infty}^{\infty} F_n \delta(\omega - n\omega_0) \qquad (4.40)$$

This is a significant result. Relation 4.40 states that *the spectral density function or the Fourier transform of a periodic signal consists of impulses located at the harmonic frequencies of the signal and that the strength of each impulse is the same as 2π times the value of the corresponding coefficient in the exponential Fourier series.* The sequence of equidistant impulses is just a limiting form of continuous density function. The result should, of course, be no surprise, since we know that a periodic function contains components only of discrete harmonic frequencies.

Example 4.1

Find the Fourier transform of a periodic gate function (rectangular pulse of width τ seconds and repeating every T seconds). The Fourier series for this function is given by (Eq. 3.131b):

$$f(t) = \sum_{n=-\infty}^{\infty} F_n e^{jn\omega_0 t}$$

where

$$F_n = \frac{A\tau}{T} Sa\left(\frac{n\pi\tau}{T}\right)$$

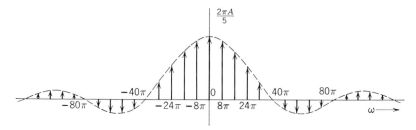

Figure 4.21   The spectral density function of a periodic gate pulse.

From Eq. 4.40, it follows that the Fourier transform of this function is given by

$$\mathscr{F}[f(t)] = \frac{2\pi A\tau}{T} \sum_{n=-\infty}^{\infty} Sa\left(\frac{n\pi\tau}{T}\right) \delta(\omega - n\omega_0) \qquad (4.41)$$

The transform of $f(t)$ therefore consists of impulses located at $\omega = 0, \pm\omega_0,$ $\pm 2\omega_0, \ldots, \pm n\omega_0, \ldots,$ etc. The magnitude of impulse located at $\omega = n\omega_0$ is given by $2\pi(A\tau/T)Sa(n\pi\tau/T)$.

The spectrum for the case of $\tau = \frac{1}{20}$ seconds and $T = \frac{1}{4}$ seconds is shown in Fig. 4.21. Here $\omega_0 = 8\pi$.

Example 4.2

We shall find a Fourier transform of a sequence of equidistant impulses of unit strength and separated by T seconds as shown in Fig. 4.22. This function is very important in sampling theory, and hence it is convenient to denote this function by a special symbol $\delta_T(t)$. Thus

$$\delta_T(t) = \delta(t) + \delta(t - T) + \delta(t - 2T) + \cdots + \delta(t - nT) + \cdots$$
$$+ \delta(t + T) + \delta(t + 2T) + \cdots + \delta(t + nT) + \cdots$$
$$= \sum_{n=-\infty}^{\infty} \delta(t - nT) \qquad (4.42)$$

This is obviously a periodic function with period T. We shall first find the Fourier series for this function.

$$\delta_T(t) = \sum_{n=-\infty}^{\infty} F_n e^{jn\omega_0 t}$$

where

$$F_n = \frac{1}{T} \int_{-T/2}^{T/2} \delta_T(t)e^{-jn\omega_0 t}\, dt$$

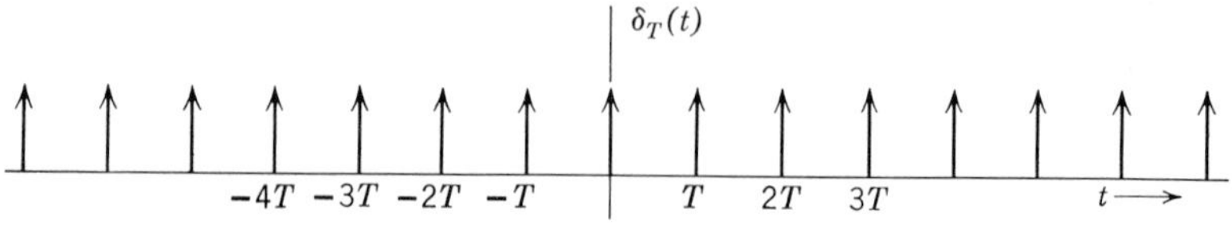

$\delta_T(t)$

$$\quad -4T \quad -3T \quad -2T \quad -T \qquad T \quad 2T \quad 3T \qquad \qquad t\longrightarrow$$

Figure 4.22   The sequence of a uniform equidistant impulse function.

Function $\delta_T(t)$ in the interval $(-T/2,\ T/2)$ is simply $\delta(t)$. Hence

$$F_n = \frac{1}{T} \int_{-T/2}^{T/2} \delta(t) e^{-jn\omega_0 t}\, dt$$

From the sampling property of an impulse function as expressed in Eq. 4.29, the above equation reduces to

$$F_n = \frac{1}{T} \tag{4.43}$$

Consequently, F_n is a constant $(1/T)$. It therefore follows that the impulse train function of period T contains components of frequencies $\omega = 0,\ \pm\omega_0,$ $\pm 2\omega_0, \ldots, \pm n\omega_0, \ldots,$ etc. $(\omega_0 = 2\pi/T)$ in the same amount.

$$\delta_T(t) = \frac{1}{T} \sum_{n=-\infty}^{\infty} e^{jn\omega_0 t} \tag{4.44}$$

To find the Fourier transform of $\delta_T(t)$, we use Eq. 4.40. Since in this case $F_n = 1/T$, it is evident that

$$\mathscr{F}[\delta_T(t)] = 2\pi \sum_{n=-\infty}^{\infty} \frac{1}{T} \delta(\omega - n\omega_0)$$

$$= \frac{2\pi}{T} \sum_{n=-\infty}^{\infty} \delta(\omega - n\omega_0)$$

$$= \omega_0 \sum_{n=-\infty}^{\infty} \delta(\omega - n\omega_0)$$

$$= \omega_0 \delta_{\omega_0}(\omega) \tag{4.45}$$

Relation 4.45 is very significant. It states that the Fourier transform of a unit impulse train of period T is also a train of impulses of strength ω_0 and separated by ω_0 radians $(\omega_0 = 2\pi/T)$. Therefore, the impulse train function is its own transform. The sequence of impulses with periods $T = \frac{1}{2}$, and $T = 1$ second, and their respective transforms are shown in Fig. 4.23. It is evident that as the periods of the impulses increase, the frequency spectrum becomes denser.

The various functions of time and their spectral-density functions are shown in Table 4.1A. Note that for a large number of signals in this table, $F(\omega)$ is

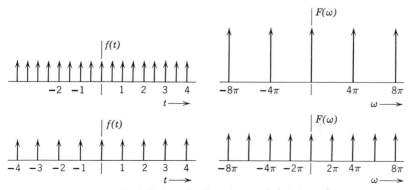

Figure 4.23   Periodic impulse functions and their transforms.

TABLE 4.1A
Various Functions of Time and Their Spectral-Density Functions

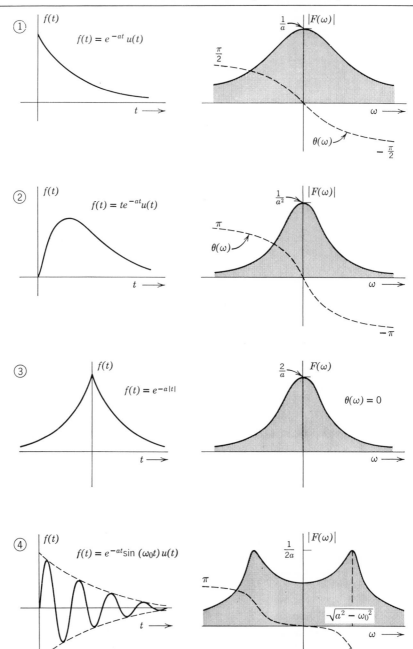

TABLE 4.1A (continued)

⑤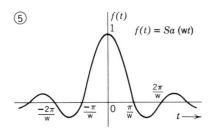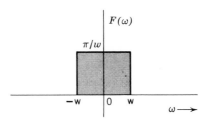

⑥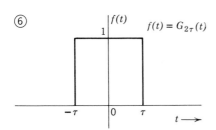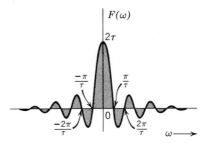

⑦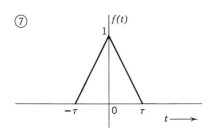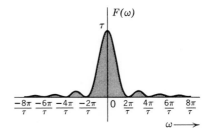

⑧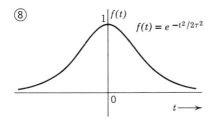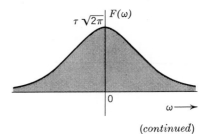

(continued)

TABLE 4.1A (continued)

⑨

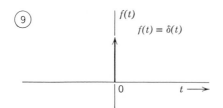

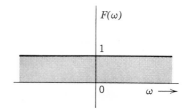

⑩

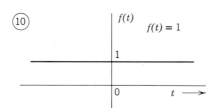

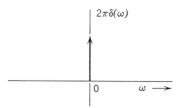

⑪

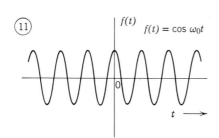

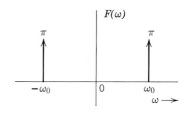

⑫

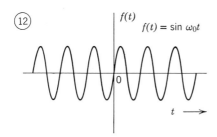

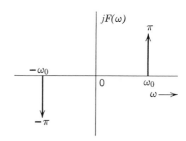

TABLE 4.1A (concluded)

⑬ $f(t)$ $f(t) = \cos \omega_0 t u(t)$

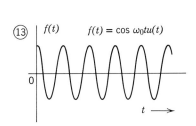

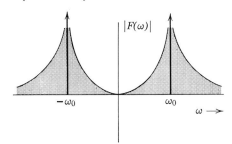

⑭ $f(t)$ $f(t) = \sin \omega_0 t u(t)$

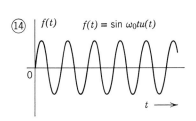

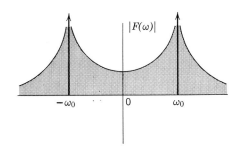

⑮ $f(t)$ $f(t) = u(t)$

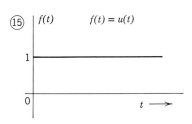

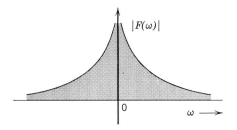

⑯ $f(t)$ $f(t) = \delta_T(t)$

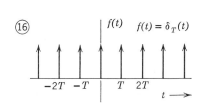

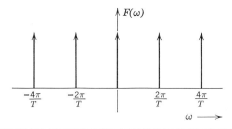

real and hence only one plot is necessary. Transforms of some functions are listed in Table 4.1B.

TABLE 4.1B
Table of Fourier Transforms

$f(t)$	$F(\omega)$
1. $e^{-at}u(t)$	$1/(a + j\omega)$
2. $te^{-at}u(t)$	$1/(a + j\omega)^2$
3. $|t|$	$-2/\omega^2$
4. $\delta(t)$	1
5. 1	$2\pi\,\delta(\omega)$
6. $u(t)$	$\pi\,\delta(\omega) + 1/j\omega$
7. $\cos \omega_0 t\, u(t)$	$\dfrac{\pi}{2}[\delta(\omega - \omega_0) + \delta(\omega + \omega_0)] + \dfrac{j\omega}{\omega_0^2 - \omega^2}$
8. $\sin \omega_0 t\, u(t)$	$\dfrac{\pi}{2j}[\delta(\omega - \omega_0) - \delta(\omega + \omega_0)] + \dfrac{\omega_0}{\omega_0^2 - \omega^2}$
9. $\cos \omega_0 t$	$\pi[\delta(\omega - \omega_0) + \delta(\omega + \omega_0)]$
10. $\sin \omega_0 t$	$j\pi[\delta(\omega + \omega_0) - \delta(\omega - \omega_0)]$
11. $e^{-at} \sin \omega_0 t\, u(t)$	$\dfrac{\omega_0}{(a + j\omega)^2 + \omega_0^2}$
12. $\dfrac{\text{w}}{2\pi} Sa\, \dfrac{(\text{w}t)}{2}$	$G_\text{w}(\omega)$
13. $G_\tau(t)$	$\tau Sa\left(\dfrac{\omega\tau}{2}\right)$
14. $\left.\begin{array}{ll} 1 - \dfrac{|t|}{\tau} & \cdots\ |t| < \tau \\ 0 & \cdots\ |t| > \tau \end{array}\right\}$	$\tau\left[Sa\left(\dfrac{\omega\tau}{2}\right)\right]^2$
15. $e^{-a|t|}$	$\dfrac{2a}{a^2 + \omega^2}$
16. $e^{-(t/2\tau)^2}$	$\tau\sqrt{2\pi}\,e^{-t^2/2\tau^2}$
17. $\delta_T(t)$	$\omega_0\,\delta_{\omega_0}(\omega) \quad \left(\omega_0 = \dfrac{2\pi}{T}\right)$

4.8 SOME PROPERTIES OF THE FOURIER TRANSFORM

The Fourier transform is a tool for expressing a function in terms of its exponential components of various frequencies. It has already been pointed out that the Fourier transform of a function is just another way of specifying the function. We therefore have two descriptions of the same function: the time-domain and frequency-domain descriptions. It is very illuminating to study the effect in one domain caused by certain operations over the function in the other domain. We may ask, for example: If a function is differentiated in the time domain, how is the spectrum of the derivative function related to the spectrum of the function itself? What happens to the spectrum of a function if the function is shifted in the time domain? We shall now seek to evaluate the effects on one domain caused by certain important operations on the function in the other domain.

It is important to point out at this stage that there is a certain amount of symmetry in the equations defining the two domains. This can be easily seen from the equations defining the Fourier transform.

and

$$\left. \begin{array}{l} F(\omega) = \displaystyle\int_{-\infty}^{\infty} f(t)e^{-j\omega t}\, dt \\[2mm] f(t) = \dfrac{1}{2\pi} \displaystyle\int_{-\infty}^{\infty} F(\omega)e^{j\omega t}\, d\omega \end{array} \right\} \tag{4.46}$$

We therefore should expect this symmetry to be reflected in the properties. For example, we expect that the effect on the frequency domain due to differentiation in the time domain should be similar to the effect on the time domain due to differentiation in the frequency domain. We shall see that this indeed is the case.

For convenience, the correspondence between the two domains will be denoted by a double arrow. Thus the notation

$$f(t) \longleftrightarrow F(\omega)$$

denotes that $F(\omega)$ is the direct Fourier transform of $f(t)$ and that $f(t)$ is the inverse Fourier transform of $F(\omega)$ related by Eq. 4.46.

I. Symmetry Property

If
$$f(t) \longleftrightarrow F(\omega)$$
then
$$F(t) \longleftrightarrow 2\pi f(-\omega) \tag{4.47}$$

Proof. From Eq. 4.46 it follows that

$$2\pi f(-t) = \int_{-\infty}^{\infty} F(\omega)e^{-j\omega t}\, d\omega$$

Since ω is a dummy variable in the above integral it may be replaced by another variable x. Therefore

$$2\pi f(-t) = \int_{-\infty}^{\infty} F(x)e^{-jxt}\,dx$$

Hence

$$2\pi f(-\omega) = \int_{-\infty}^{\infty} F(x)e^{-jx\omega}\,dx$$

Replacing the dummy variable x by another variable t, we get

$$2\pi f(-\omega) = \int_{-\infty}^{\infty} F(t)e^{-j\omega t}\,dt$$

$$= \mathscr{F}[F(t)]$$

Hence

$$F(t) \leftrightarrow 2\pi f(-\omega) \tag{4.48}$$

The symmetry property holds perfectly if $f(t)$ is an even function. In that case $f(-\omega) = f(\omega)$ and Eq. 4.48 reduces to

$$F(t) \leftrightarrow 2\pi f(\omega)$$

This property is demonstrated in Fig. 4.24.

It can be easily seen that the Fourier transform of a gate function is a sampling function, whereas the Fourier transform of a sampling function is a gate function. The symmetry property holds for all, even $f(t)$. If $f(t)$ is not an even function, then the symmetry is not so perfect; nevertheless, there is some measure of symmetry, as seen from Eq. 4.48.

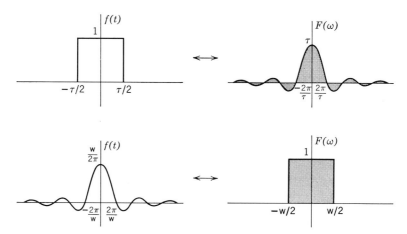

Figure 4.24   Symmetry property of the Fourier transform.

2. Linearity Property

If
$$f_1(t) \leftrightarrow F_1(\omega)$$
$$f_2(t) \leftrightarrow F_2(\omega)$$

then, for any arbitrary constants a_1 and a_2,
$$a_1 f_1(t) + a_2 f_2(t) \leftrightarrow a_1 F_1(\omega) + a_2 F_2(\omega) \tag{4.49}$$

The proof is trivial. The above is also valid for finite sums:
$$a_1 f_1(t) + a_2 f_2(t) + \cdots + a_n f_n(t) \leftrightarrow a_1 F_1(\omega) + a_2 F_2(\omega) + \cdots + a_n F_n(\omega)$$

3. Scaling Property

If
$$f(t) \leftrightarrow F(\omega)$$

then for a real constant a
$$f(at) \leftrightarrow \frac{1}{|a|} F\left(\frac{\omega}{a}\right) \tag{4.50}$$

Proof. For a positive real constant a
$$\mathscr{F}[f(at)] = \int_{-\infty}^{\infty} f(at) e^{-j\omega t} \, dt$$

Let $x = at$. Then, for positive constant a,
$$\mathscr{F}[f(at)] = \frac{1}{a} \int_{-\infty}^{\infty} f(x) e^{(-j\omega/a)x} \, dx \tag{4.51}$$
$$= \frac{1}{a} F\left(\frac{\omega}{a}\right)$$

Hence
$$f(at) \leftrightarrow \frac{1}{a} F\left(\frac{\omega}{a}\right)$$

Similarly, it can be shown that if $a < 0$
$$f(at) \leftrightarrow -\frac{1}{a} F\left(\frac{\omega}{a}\right)$$

Consequently it follows that
$$f(at) \leftrightarrow \frac{1}{|a|} F\left(\frac{\omega}{a}\right)$$

Significance of the Scaling Property. The function $f(at)$ represents function $f(t)$ compressed in the time scale by a factor of a. Similarly, a function $F(\omega/a)$ represents a function $F(\omega)$ expanded in the frequency scale by the same factor a. The scaling-property therefore states that

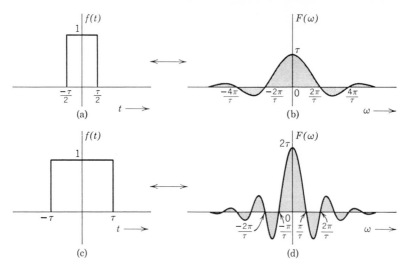

Figure 4.25 Compression in the time domain is equivalent to expansion in the frequency domain.

compression in the time domain is equivalent to expansion in the frequency domain and vice versa. This result is also obvious intuitively, since compression in the time scale by a factor a means that the function is varying rapidly by the same factor, and hence the frequencies of its components will be increased by the factor a. We therefore expect its frequency spectrum to be expanded by the factor a in the frequency scale. Similarly, if a function is expanded in the time scale, it varies slowly, and hence the frequencies of its components are lowered. Thus, the frequency spectrum is compressed. As an example, consider the signal $\cos \omega_0 t$. This signal has frequency components at $\pm \omega_0$. The signal $\cos 2\omega_0 t$ represents compression of $\cos \omega_0 t$ by a factor of two, and its frequency components lie at $\pm 2\omega_0$. It is therefore evident that the frequency spectrum has been expanded by a factor of two. The effect of scaling is demonstrated in Fig. 4.25.

4. Time-Shifting Property

If

$$f(t) \leftrightarrow F(\omega)$$

then

$$f(t - t_0) \leftrightarrow F(\omega)e^{-j\omega t_0} \qquad (4.52)$$

Proof.

$$\mathscr{F}[f(t - t_0)] = \int_{-\infty}^{\infty} f(t - t_0)e^{-j\omega t}\, dt$$

Let

$$t - t_0 = x$$

then

$$\mathscr{F}[f(t - t_0)] = \int_{-\infty}^{\infty} f(x)e^{-j\omega(x+t_0)}\, dx$$

$$= F(\omega)e^{-j\omega t_0}$$

This theorem states that if a function is shifted in the time domain by t_0 seconds, then its magnitude spectrum $F(\omega)$ remains unchanged, but the phase spectrum is changed by an amount $-\omega t_0$. This result is also obvious intuitively, since the shifting of a function in the time domain really does not change the frequency components of the signal but each component is shifted by an amount t_0. A shift of time t_0 for a component of frequency ω is equivalent to a phase shift of $-\omega t_0$.

We may state that a shift of t_0 in the time domain is equivalent to multiplication by $e^{-j\omega t_0}$ in the frequency domain.

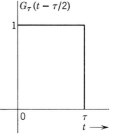

Figure 4.26

Example 4.3

Find the Fourier transform of a rectangular pulse shown in Fig. 4.26. The function in Fig. 4.26 is really a gate function $G_\tau(t)$ shifted by $\tau/2$ seconds. Hence it may be represented as $G_\tau(t - \tau/2)$. From Table 4.1B:

$$G_\tau(t) \longleftrightarrow \tau Sa(\omega\tau/2)$$

Therefore

$$G_\tau(t - \tau/2) \longleftrightarrow \tau Sa(\omega\tau/2)e^{-j\omega\tau/2}$$

5. Frequency-Shifting Property:

If

$$f(t) \longleftrightarrow F(\omega)$$

then

$$f(t)e^{j\omega_0 t} \longleftrightarrow F(\omega - \omega_0) \tag{4.53}$$

Proof.

$$\mathscr{F}[f(t)e^{j\omega_0 t}] = \int_{-\infty}^{\infty} f(t)e^{j\omega_0 t}\, e^{-j\omega t}\, dt$$

$$= \int_{-\infty}^{\infty} f(t)e^{-j(\omega-\omega_0)t}\, dt$$

$$= F(\omega - \omega_0)$$

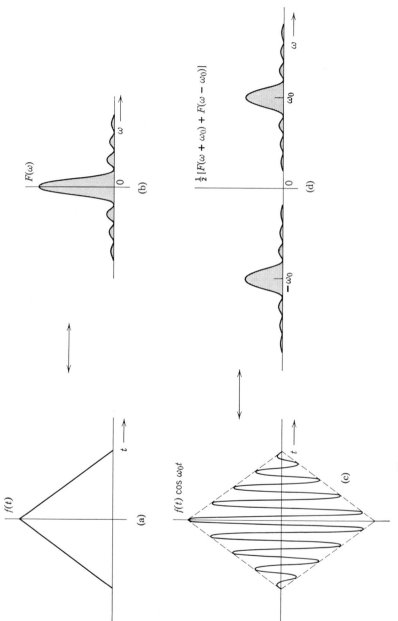

Figure 4.27   Effect of modulation on the frequency spectrum.

The theorem states that a shift of ω_0 in the frequency domain is equivalent to multiplication by $e^{j\omega_0 t}$ in the time domain. Note the dual nature between the time-shift and the frequency-shift theorems. It is evident that multiplication by a factor $e^{j\omega_0 t}$ translates the whole frequency spectrum $F(\omega)$ by an amount ω_0. Hence this theorem is also known as the *frequency-translation theorem*.

In communication systems it is often desirable to translate the frequency spectrum. This is usually accomplished by multiplying a signal $f(t)$ by a sinusoidal signal. This process is known as modulation. Since a sinusoidal signal of frequency ω_0 can be expressed as the sum of exponentials, it is evident that multiplication of a signal $f(t)$ by a sinusoidal signal (modulation) will translate the whole frequency spectrum. This can be easily shown by observing the identity:

$$f(t) \cos \omega_0 t = \tfrac{1}{2}[f(t)e^{j\omega_0 t} + f(t)e^{-j\omega_0 t}]$$

Using the frequency-shift theorem, it therefore follows that if

$$f(t) \leftrightarrow F(\omega)$$

then

$$f(t) \cos \omega_0 t \leftrightarrow \tfrac{1}{2}[F(\omega + \omega_0) + F(\omega - \omega_0)] \qquad (4.54)$$

Similarly it can be shown that

$$f(t) \sin \omega_0 t \leftrightarrow \frac{j}{2}[F(\omega + \omega_0) - F(\omega - \omega_0)]$$

Thus, the process of modulation translates the frequency spectrum by the amount $\pm \omega_0$. This is a very useful result in communication theory. An example of frequency translation caused by modulation is shown in Fig. 4.27. This result is also known as the *modulation theorem*.

6. Time Differentiation and Integration

If

$$f(t) \leftrightarrow F(\omega)$$

then[3]

$$\frac{df}{dt} \leftrightarrow (j\omega)F(\omega) \qquad (4.55)$$

and

$$\int_{-\infty}^{t} f(\tau)\, d\tau \leftrightarrow \frac{1}{j\omega} F(\omega) \qquad (4.56)$$

---

[3] Equation 4.55 does not guarantee the existence of the transform of df/dt. It merely says that if that transform exists it is given by $j\omega F(\omega)$.

provided[4] that $F(\omega)/\omega$ is bounded at $\omega = 0$. This is equivalent to saying that $F(0) = 0$ or

$$\int_{-\infty}^{\infty} f(t)\, dt = 0$$

Proof.

$$f(t) = \frac{1}{2\pi} \int_{-\infty}^{\infty} F(\omega)e^{j\omega t}\, d\omega$$

Therefore

$$\frac{df}{dt} = \frac{1}{2\pi} \frac{d}{dt} \int_{-\infty}^{\infty} F(\omega)e^{j\omega t}\, d\omega$$

Changing the order of differentiation and integration, we get

$$\frac{df}{dt} = \frac{1}{2\pi} \int_{-\infty}^{\infty} j\omega F(\omega)e^{j\omega t}\, d\omega$$

It is now evident from the above equation that

$$\frac{df}{dt} \leftrightarrow j\omega F(\omega)$$

In a similar way the result can be extended to the nth derivative.

$$\frac{d^n f}{dt^n} \leftrightarrow (j\omega)^n F(\omega) \qquad\qquad (4.57)$$

Now consider the function:

$$\varphi(t) = \int_{-\infty}^{t} f(\tau)\, d\tau$$

Then

$$\frac{d\varphi}{dt}(t) = f(t)$$

Hence, if

$$\varphi(t) \leftrightarrow \Phi(\omega)$$

then

$$f(t) \leftrightarrow j\omega \Phi(\omega)$$

that is,

$$F(\omega) = j\omega \Phi(\omega)$$

Therefore

$$\Phi(\omega) = \frac{1}{j\omega} F(\omega)$$

and thus

$$\int_{-\infty}^{t} f(\tau)\, d\tau \leftrightarrow \frac{1}{j\omega} F(\omega)$$

[4] If this condition is not satisfied, then Eq. 4.56 is modified. See Problem 16 at the end of the chapter.

Note that this result is valid only if $\Phi(\omega)$ exists, that is, if $\varphi(t)$ is absolutely integrable. This is possible only if

$$\lim_{t\to\infty} \varphi(t) = 0$$

That is,

$$\int_{-\infty}^{\infty} f(t)\, dt = 0$$

This is equivalent to the condition that $F(0) = 0$ since

$$\int_{-\infty}^{\infty} f(t)\, dt = F(\omega)\big|_{\omega=0}$$

The time-differentiation and time-integration theorems as expressed in Eqs. 4.55 and 4.56 are also obvious intuitively. The Fourier transform actually expresses a function $f(t)$ in terms of a continuous sum of exponential functions of the form $e^{j\omega t}$. The derivative of $f(t)$ is therefore equal to the continuous sum of the derivatives of the individual exponential components. But the derivative of an exponential function $e^{j\omega t}$ is equal to $j\omega e^{j\omega t}$. Therefore, the process of differentiation of $f(t)$ is equivalent to multiplication by $j\omega$ of each exponential component. Hence

$$\frac{df}{dt} \longleftrightarrow j\omega F(\omega)$$

A similar argument applies to the integration.

We conclude that differentiation in the time domain is equivalent to multiplication by $j\omega$ in the frequency domain, and that integration in the time domain is equivalent to division by $j\omega$ in the frequency domain. The time-differentiation theorem proves convenient in deriving the Fourier transform of some piecewise continuous functions. This is illustrated by the next example.

Example 4.4

Evaluate the Fourier transform of a trapezoidal function $f(t)$ shown in Fig. 4.28. We differentiate this function twice to obtain a sequence of impulses. The transform of the impulses is readily found. It is evident from Fig. 4.28 that

$$\frac{d^2 f}{dt^2} = \frac{A}{(b-a)}[\delta(t+b) - \delta(t+a) - \delta(t-a) + \delta(t-b)] \qquad (4.58)$$

The Fourier transform of a unit impulse is 1. Therefore, using the time-shift theorem, we have

$$\delta(t - t_0) \longleftrightarrow e^{-j\omega t_0}$$

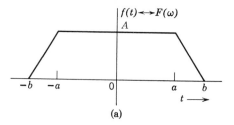

(a)

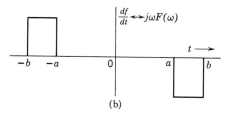

(b)

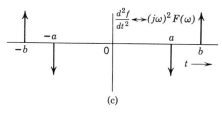

(c)

Figure 4.28

Using this result and the time-differentiation theorem, the transform of Eq. 4.58 can now be readily written as

$$(j\omega)^2 F(\omega) = \frac{A}{(b-a)}[e^{j\omega b} - e^{j\omega a} - e^{-j\omega a} + e^{-j\omega b}]$$

from which we get

$$F(\omega) = \frac{2A}{(b-a)}\left(\frac{\cos a\omega - \cos b\omega}{\omega^2}\right)$$

This problem suggests a numerical method of obtaining a Fourier transform of a function $f(t)$. Any function $f(t)$ may be approximated by straight-line segments as shown in Fig. 4.29. The approximation can be improved as much as desired by increasing the number of segments. The second derivative of the approximated function yields a train of impulses whose Fourier transform can be readily found. The transform $F(\omega)$ of the desired function is merely $1/(j\omega)^2$ times the transform of the second derivative.

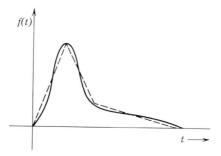

Figure 4.29   Approximation of a function with straight-line segments.

7. Frequency Differentiation

If

$$f(t) \longleftrightarrow F(\omega) \tag{4.59}$$

Then

$$-jtf(t) \longleftrightarrow \frac{dF}{d\omega} \tag{4.60}$$

Proof.

$$F(\omega) = \int_{-\infty}^{\infty} f(t)e^{-j\omega t}\, dt$$

Therefore

$$\frac{dF}{d\omega} = \frac{d}{d\omega}\int_{-\infty}^{\infty} f(t)e^{-j\omega t}\, dt$$

Changing the order of differentiation and integration, we get

$$\frac{dF}{d\omega} = \int_{-\infty}^{\infty} -jtf(t)e^{-j\omega t}\, dt$$

It is evident from the above equation that

$$-jtf(t) \longleftrightarrow \frac{dF}{d\omega}$$

The extension of this result to higher derivatives of $F(\omega)$ yields

$$(-jt)^n f(t) = \frac{d^n F}{d\omega^n}$$

We therefore conclude that differentiation in the frequency domain is equivalent to multiplication by $-jt$ in the time domain.

   Frequency Integration.   It can be shown that within an additive constant, $\int F(\omega)\, d\omega$ is a Fourier transform of $f(t)/(-jt)$, that is,

$$\frac{1}{-jt}f(t) \longleftrightarrow \int F(\omega)\, d\omega$$

within an additive constant (see Problem 22 at the end of the chapter).

8. The Convolution Theorem

The convolution theorem is perhaps one of the most powerful tools in frequency analysis. It permits the easy derivation of many important results, and will be used often in this text.

Given two functions $f_1(t)$ and $f_2(t)$, we form the integral

$$f(t) = \int_{-\infty}^{\infty} f_1(\tau) f_2(t - \tau)\, d\tau \tag{4.61}$$

This integral defines the convolution of functions $f_1(t)$ and $f_2(t)$. The convolution integral (Eq. 4.61) is also expressed symbolically as

$$f(t) = f_1(t) * f_2(t) \tag{4.62}$$

The physical significance and the graphical interpretation of convolution will be considered later in Chapter 10. Here we shall merely state and prove the theorem. Again, as usual, we have two theorems: time convolution and frequency convolution.

Time-Convolution Theorem. If

$$f_1(t) \leftrightarrow F_1(\omega)$$

and

$$f_2(t) \leftrightarrow F_2(\omega)$$

then

$$\int_{-\infty}^{\infty} f_1(\tau) f_2(t - \tau)\, d\tau \leftrightarrow F_1(\omega) F_2(\omega) \tag{4.63}$$

that is,

$$f_1(t) * f_2(t) \leftrightarrow F_1(\omega) F_2(\omega) \tag{4.64}$$

Proof

$$\mathscr{F}[f_1(t) * f_2(t)] = \int_{-\infty}^{\infty} e^{-j\omega t} \left[\int_{-\infty}^{\infty} f_1(\tau) f_2(t - \tau)\, d\tau \right] dt$$

$$= \int_{-\infty}^{\infty} f_1(\tau) \left[\int_{-\infty}^{\infty} e^{-j\omega t} f_2(t - \tau)\, dt \right] d\tau$$

From the time-shifting theorem (Eq. 4.52), it is evident that the integral inside the bracket, on the right-hand side, is equal to $F_2(\omega)e^{-j\omega\tau}$. Hence

$$\mathscr{F}[f_1(t) * f_2(t)] = \int_{-\infty}^{\infty} f_1(\tau) e^{-j\omega\tau} F_2(\omega)\, d\tau$$

$$= F_1(\omega) F_2(\omega)$$

Frequency Convolution. If

$$f_1(t) \leftrightarrow F_1(\omega)$$

and

$$f_2(t) \leftrightarrow F_2(\omega)$$

then

$$f_1(t)f_2(t) \longleftrightarrow \frac{1}{2\pi} \int_{-\infty}^{\infty} F_1(u)F_2(\omega - u)\, du \qquad (4.65)$$

that is

$$f_1(t)f_2(t) \longleftrightarrow \frac{1}{2\pi} [F_1(\omega) * F_2(\omega)] \qquad (4.66)$$

This theorem can be proved in exactly the same way as the time-convolution theorem because of the symmetry in the direct and inverse Fourier transform.

TABLE 4.2

Operation	$f(t)$	$F(\omega)$
1. Scaling	$f(at)$	$\dfrac{1}{|a|}F\left(\dfrac{\omega}{a}\right)$
2. Time shifting	$f(t - t_0)$	$F(\omega)e^{-j\omega t_0}$
3. Frequency shifting	$f(t)e^{j\omega_0 t}$	$F(\omega - \omega_0)$
4. Time differentiation	$\dfrac{d^n f}{dt^n}$	$(j\omega)^n F(\omega)$
5. Frequency differentiation	$(-jt)^n f(t)$	$\dfrac{d^n F}{d\omega^n}$
6. Time integration	$\displaystyle\int_{-\infty}^{t} f(\tau)\, d\tau$	$\dfrac{1}{(j\omega)}F(\omega)$
7. Time convolution	$f_1(t) * f_2(t)$	$F_1(\omega)F_2(\omega)$
8. Frequency convolution	$f_1(t)f_2(t)$	$\dfrac{1}{2\pi}[F_1(\omega) * F_2(\omega)]$

We therefore conclude that the convolution of two functions in the time domain is equivalent to multiplication of their spectra in the frequency domain and that multiplication of two functions in the time domain is equivalent to convolution of their spectra in the frequency domain.

Table 4.2 shows some of the important properties of the Fourier transform. Note the symmetry and correspondence between the time and the frequency domains.

4.9 ENERGY DENSITY SPECTRUM

For a periodic function we have seen that the power in a signal can be associated with the power contained in each discrete frequency component.

The same result can be extended to nonperiodic functions. For nonperiodic signals, the energy of the signal over the entire interval $(-\infty, \infty)$ is usually finite, and the average power (that is, energy per second) tends to be zero. A more useful concept for a nonperiodic signal is energy E, defined as

$$E = \int_{-\infty}^{\infty} f^2(t) \, dt \qquad (4.67)$$

If $F(\omega)$ is the Fourier transform of $f(t)$,

$$f(t) = \frac{1}{2\pi} \int_{-\infty}^{\infty} F(\omega) e^{j\omega t} \, d\omega$$

and the energy E of $f(t)$ is given by

$$E = \int_{-\infty}^{\infty} f^2(t) \, dt = \int_{-\infty}^{\infty} f(t) \left[\frac{1}{2\pi} \int_{-\infty}^{\infty} F(\omega) e^{j\omega t} \, d\omega \right] dt$$

Interchanging the order of integration on the right-hand side, we get

$$E = \int_{-\infty}^{\infty} f^2(t) \, dt = \frac{1}{2\pi} \int_{-\infty}^{\infty} F(\omega) \left[\int_{-\infty}^{\infty} f(t) e^{j\omega t} \, dt \right] d\omega$$

The inner integral on the right-hand side is obviously $F(-\omega)$. Hence we have

$$\int_{-\infty}^{\infty} f^2(t) \, dt = \frac{1}{2\pi} \int_{-\infty}^{\infty} F(\omega) F(-\omega) \, d\omega \qquad (4.68)$$

We have already proved (see Eq. 4.14) that for a real $f(t)$:

$$F(\omega) = F^*(-\omega)$$

Hence

$$F(\omega) F(-\omega) = |F(\omega)|^2 \qquad (4.69)$$

and

$$\int_{-\infty}^{\infty} f^2(t) \, dt = \frac{1}{2\pi} \int_{-\infty}^{\infty} |F(\omega)|^2 \, d\omega \qquad (4.70)$$

It is evident from Eq. 4.69 that $|F(\omega)|^2$ is a real even function of ω. Equation 4.70 states that the energy of a signal is given by $1/2\pi$ times the area under the $|F(\omega)|^2$ curve.[5]

Functions $F(\omega)$ and $|F(\omega)|^2$ for a gate function are shown in Fig. 4.30. Since $|F(\omega)|^2$ is an even function, it is symmetrical about the vertical axis passing through the origin. By analogy with periodic functions, we

---

[5] Equation 4.70, which corresponds to Parseval's theorem (Eq. 3.125) for nonperiodic functions, is called Rayleigh's theorem and was first used by Lord Rayleigh in his study of blackbody radiation. This theorem is also referred to as Parseval's theorem of Plancherel's theorem.

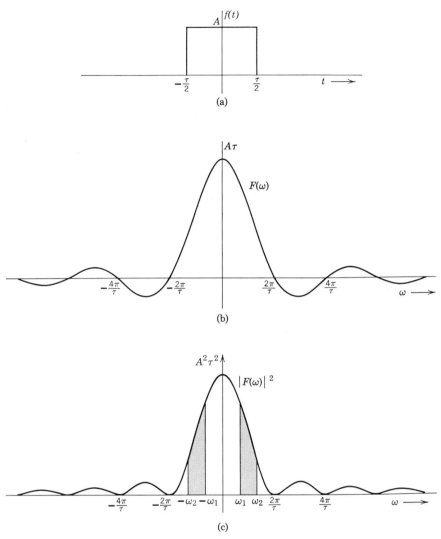

Figure 4.30 (a) $f(t)$. (b) The spectral density function. (c) The energy density spectrum.

associate energy with each frequency component. The energy spectrum, however, is continuous and the energy associated with any one particular frequency is zero. But there is a finite energy associated with any finite band of frequencies. The energy contained in the frequency components within a band of frequencies (ω_1, ω_2) is given by $1/2\pi$ times the area of $|F(\omega)|^2$ under the band (ω_1, ω_2). However, there is also a band of negative frequencies $(-\omega_1, -\omega_2)$ which also has exactly the same amount of energy as that in (ω_1, ω_2). We also know from the analogy of periodic signals that the energy in both of these bands contributes to the energy of the components lying in the frequency band (ω_1, ω_2). Hence it follows that the energy contained in the frequency band (ω_1, ω_2) is given by

$$E = 2 \frac{1}{2\pi} \int_{\omega_1}^{\omega_2} |F(\omega)|^2 \, d\omega = \frac{1}{\pi} \int_{\omega_1}^{\omega_2} |F(\omega)|^2 \, d\omega$$

Note that the quantity $(1/\pi)|F(j\omega)|^2$ represents energy per unit bandwidth and hence represents energy density. We define energy density $S(\omega)$ as

$$S(\omega) = \frac{1}{\pi} |F(j\omega)|^2 \tag{4.71}$$

If ΔE is the energy associated with components of frequencies lying in the interval (ω_1, ω_2), then

$$\Delta E = \int_{\omega_1}^{\omega_2} S(\omega) \, d\omega$$

and

$$E = \int_0^\infty S(\omega) \, d\omega \tag{4.72}$$

PROBLEMS

1. Show that the Fourier transform of $f(t)$ may also be expressed as

$$\mathscr{F}[f(t)] = F(\omega) = \int_{-\infty}^\infty f(t) \cos \omega t \, dt - j \int_{-\infty}^\infty f(t) \sin \omega t \, dt$$

Further, show that if $f(t)$ is an even function of t, then

$$F(\omega) = 2 \int_0^\infty f(t) \cos \omega t \, dt$$

and if $f(t)$ is an odd function of t, then

$$F(\omega) = -2j \int_0^\infty f(t) \sin \omega t \, dt$$

Hence, prove the following:

If $f(t)$ is a	then $F(\omega)$ is a
real and even function of t	real and even function of ω
real and odd	imaginary and odd
imaginary and even	imaginary and even
complex and even	complex and even
complex and odd	complex and odd

2. Find the Fourier transform of sgn t (pronounced signum t), where

$$\text{sgn } (t) = \begin{cases} -1 & \text{for} \quad t < 0 \\ 1 & \text{for} \quad t > 0 \end{cases}$$

(a) From the above result and from the fact that $1 \leftrightarrow 2\pi\, \delta(\omega)$, derive the Fourier transform of a unit step function.

Hint.

$$\text{sgn}\,(t) \;=\; \lim_{a\to 0}\,[e^{-at}u(t) \;-\; e^{at}u(-t)]$$

(b) From the knowledge of the Fourier transform of $u(t)$ and the modulation theorem (frequency-translation theorem), derive Eqs. 4.36 and 4.37.

3. Find the Fourier transforms of the functions shown in Figs. P-4.7, 3.18a, P-3.10, P-3.14, P-5.6b, P-5.6c and 10.5a.

4. Determine the functions $f(t)$ whose Fourier transforms are shown in Fig. P-4.4.

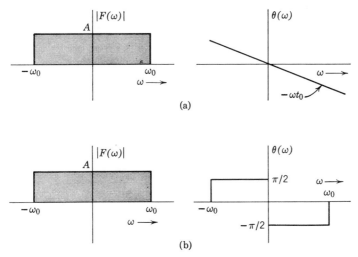

Figure P-4.4

5. Find the function $f(t)$ whose Fourier transforms are shown in Fig. P-4.5. (*Hint.* Use the modulation theorem.)

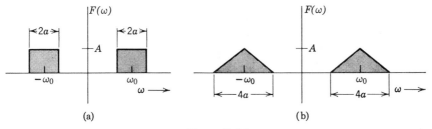

Figure P-4.5

6. Find the Fourier transform of the functions shown in Fig. P-4.6, using the modulation theorem. Sketch the spectral-density function in each case.

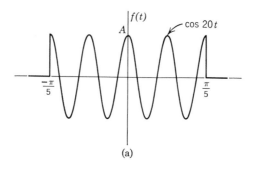

(a)

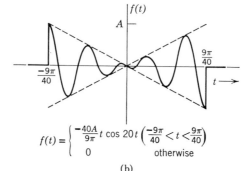

$$f(t) = \begin{cases} \dfrac{-40A}{9\pi} t \cos 20t \left(\dfrac{-9\pi}{40} < t < \dfrac{9\pi}{40}\right) \\ 0 \qquad\qquad \text{otherwise} \end{cases}$$

(b)

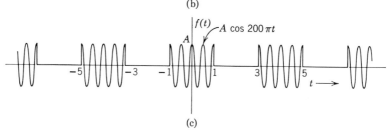

(c)

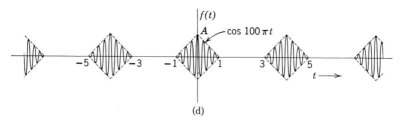

(d)

Figure P-4.6

7. Find the Fourier transforms of the functions shown in Fig. P-4.7 by using the time-differentiation property, the time-shifting property and transform Table 4.1B.

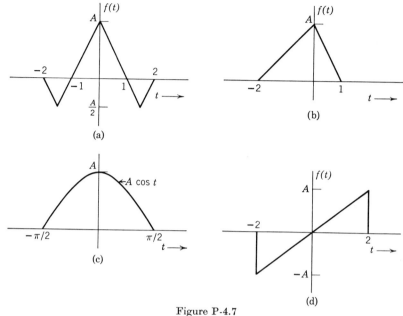

Figure P-4.7

8. Prove the dual of the modulation theorem; that is, if

$$f(t) \longleftrightarrow F(\omega)$$

then

$$f(t + T) + f(t - T) \longleftrightarrow 2 \cos (\omega T) F(\omega)$$

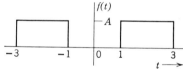 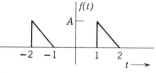

Figure P-4.8

Using this theorem, derive $F(\omega)$ for the functions shown in Fig. P-4.8.

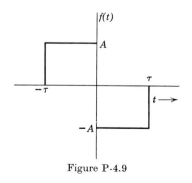

Figure P-4.9

9. Find the Fourier transform of a function shown in Fig. P-4.9 by:

(a) Straightforward integration.
(b) Using only the time-integration property and transform Table 4.1B.
(c) Using only the time-differentiation property, the time-shifting property, and transform Table 4.1B.
(d) Using only the time-shifting property and transform Table 4.1B.

10. The nth moment m_n of a function $f(t)$ is defined by

$$m_n = \int_{-\infty}^{\infty} t^n f(t) \, dt$$

Using the frequency-differentiation theorem, show that

$$m_n = (j)^n \frac{d^n F(0)}{d\omega^n}$$

Using this result, show that Taylor's series expansion of $F(\omega)$ can be expressed as

$$F(\omega) = m_0 - jm_1\omega - \frac{m_2\omega^2}{2!} + \frac{jm_3\omega^3}{3!} + \frac{m_4\omega^4}{4!} + \cdots$$

$$= \sum_{n=0}^{\infty} (-j)^n m_n \frac{\omega^n}{n!}$$

Determine the various moments of a gate function and, using the above equation, find its Fourier transform.

11. Show that if

$$f(t) \longleftrightarrow F(\omega)$$

then

$$|F(\omega)| \leqslant \int_{-\infty}^{\infty} |f(t)| \, dt$$

$$|F(\omega)| \leqslant \frac{1}{|\omega|} \int_{-\infty}^{\infty} \left| \frac{df}{dt} \right| dt$$

$$|F(\omega)| \leqslant \frac{1}{\omega^2} \int_{-\infty}^{\infty} \left| \frac{d^2 f}{dt^2} \right| dt$$

These inequalities determine the upper bounds of $|F(\omega)|$.

12. Show that if $f(t)$ is a solution of the differential equation:

$$\frac{d^2 x}{dt^2} - t^2 x(t) = \alpha x(t)$$

then its Fourier transform is also a solution of the same equation.

13. Prove that

$$\delta(t) = \frac{1}{2\pi} \int_{-\infty}^{\infty} e^{j\omega t} \, d\omega$$

and, hence, show that

$$\delta(t) = \frac{1}{\pi} \int_{0}^{\infty} \cos \omega t \, d\omega$$

(*Hint.* Evaluate the integral over the interval $(-\tau/2, \tau/2)$ and in the limit let $\tau \to \infty$.)

14. Find the Fourier transforms of the following functions:

(a) $\quad f(t) = \begin{cases} \dfrac{1}{\tau}\left[1 - \dfrac{|t|}{\tau}\right] & |t| < \tau \\ 0 & \text{otherwise} \end{cases}$

(c) $\quad f(t) = \dfrac{1}{\tau} e^{(-t/\tau)} u(t)$

(b) $\quad f(t) = \dfrac{1}{2\tau} e^{-|t|/\tau}$

(d) $\quad f(t) = \dfrac{1}{\tau} e^{(t/\tau)} u(-t)$

Each of these functions approaches a unit impulse function as τ approaches zero. Show that the Fourier transform of each of these functions approaches 1 as $\tau \to 0$.

15. Show that the sequence of a function $Sa^2(kt)$ yields an impulse function as $k \to \infty$. In particular, show that

$$\delta(t) = \lim_{k \to \infty} \frac{k}{\pi} Sa^2(kt)$$

Hint.

$$\int_{-\infty}^{\infty} Sa^2(x)\, dx = \pi$$

16. The time-integration theorem (Eq. 4.56) holds only if $\int_{-\infty}^{\infty} f(t)\, dt = 0$. If this condition is not satisfied, then show that

$$\int_{-\infty}^{t} f(\tau)\, d\tau \to \pi F(\omega)\, \delta(\omega) + \frac{1}{j\omega} F(\omega)$$

Hint. Express $\int_{-\infty}^{t} f(\tau)\, d\tau$ as a convolution of $f(t)$ and $u(t)$.

17. Let the function $f(t)$, shown in Fig. 4.1, have a Fourier transform $F(\omega)$.

(a) Show that the Fourier transform of the periodic function $f_T(t)$, formed by repetition of $f(t)$ every T seconds as shown in Fig. 4.2, is given by

$$f_T(t) \longleftrightarrow \frac{2\pi}{T} F(\omega)\, \delta_{\omega_0}(\omega), \qquad \left(\omega_0 = \frac{2\pi}{T} \right)$$

[*Hint.* Expand $f_T(t)$ by the Fourier series and note that the nth coefficient F_n of this series is $\frac{1}{T} F(\omega)|_{\omega=n\omega_0}$; or express $f_T(t)$ as a convolution of $f(t)$ and $\delta_T(t)$].

(b) Sketch the Fourier transform of a gate function $G_\tau(t)$ for $\tau = \frac{1}{20}$. Using the result in (a), sketch the Fourier transform of a periodic gate function repeating every $\frac{1}{4}$ seconds.

Compare these results with those obtained in Example 4.1 in the text.

18. Let the function $f(t)$, shown in Fig. 4.1, have a Fourier transform $F(\omega)$. Form a new function as shown in Fig. 4.2 but with n pulses only, spaced T seconds apart. The new function $f_n(t)$ thus formed exists in the interval $(-nT/2 < t < nT/2)$ and is zero outside this interval. Show that

$$f_n(t) \longleftrightarrow F(\omega) \frac{\sin(n\omega T/2)}{\sin(\omega T/2)}$$

Sketch the function $[\sin(n\omega T/2)]/[\sin(\omega T/2)]$ for $n = 15$. Show that as $n \to \infty$, this function tends to a sequence of impulse functions; that is,

$$\lim_{n \to \infty} \frac{\sin(n\omega T/2)}{\sin(\omega T/2)} = \omega_0\, \delta_{\omega_0}(\omega)$$

where

$$\omega_0 = \frac{2\pi}{T}$$

Hint. Use

$$\sum_{k=-m}^{m} e^{jkx} = \frac{\sin(nx/2)}{\sin(x/2)}, \qquad n = 2m + 1$$

19. A function $h(t)$ is given so that it is zero for all $t < 0$ (this function is called a causal function). $H(\omega)$ is the Fourier transform of $h(t)$. If $R(\omega)$ and $X(\omega)$ are the real and imaginary parts respectively of $H(\omega)$, and if $h(t)$ contains no impulse function at the origin, then show that

$$R(\omega) = \frac{1}{\pi} \int_{-\infty}^{\infty} \frac{X(y)}{\omega - y} \, dy$$

and

$$X(\omega) = \frac{1}{\pi} \int_{-\infty}^{\infty} \frac{R(y)}{\omega - y} \, dy$$

This pair of equations defines the Hilbert transform. Modify this result if $h(t)$ is a negative time function, that is, $h(t) = 0$, for all $t > 0$.

Hint. Express $h(t)$ in terms of even and odd components $h_e(t)$ and $h_0(t)$ (see Problem 15 in Chapter 3).

It follows from the results of Problem 1 that

$$h_e(t) \longleftrightarrow R(\omega) \quad \text{and} \quad h_0(t) \longleftrightarrow X(\omega)$$

Also note that for a causal function $h(t)$

$$h_e(t) = h_0(t) \operatorname{sgn} t$$

and

$$h_0(t) = h_e(t) \operatorname{sgn} t$$

Now use the result of Problem 2 and the convolution theorem.

20. Derive Parseval's theorem (Eq. 4.70) from the time convolution theorem.

Hint. If

$$f(t) \longleftrightarrow F(\omega)$$

then

$$f(-t) \longleftrightarrow F(-\omega)$$

and

$$f(t) * f(-t) \longleftrightarrow F(\omega) F(-\omega)$$

21. Show that

$$\frac{d^n \, \delta(t)}{dt^n} \longleftrightarrow (j\omega)^n$$

$$t^n \longleftrightarrow 2\pi j^n \frac{d^n \, \delta(\omega)}{d\omega^n}$$

22. Prove the frequency integration theorem. In particular, show that if

$$G(\omega) = \int F(\omega) \, d\omega$$

then, within an additive constant, $G(\omega)$ is a Fourier transform of $f(t)/(-jt)$.

23. For real signals $f(t)$ and $g(t)$, show that

$$\int_a^b f^2(t) \, dt \int_a^b g^2(t) \, dt \geqslant \left[\int_a^b f(t)g(t) \, dt \right]^2$$

This is known as the *Schwartz inequality.*

Hint. Observe that

$$\int_a^b [f(t) + xg(t)]^2 \, dt > 0$$

for the real value of x. If

$$a = \int_a^b f^2(t) \, dt, \; b = \int_c^b f(t)g(t) \, dt \quad \text{and} \quad c = \int_a^b g^2(t) \, dt$$

then

$$cx^2 + 2bx + a > 0$$

and hence the Schwartz inequality follows.

24. Prove that the uncertainty principle for any signal $f(t)$ which vanishes at $t = \infty$, is faster than the function $1/\sqrt{t}$. This principle states that the width of $f(t)$ multiplied by the width of $F(\omega)$ is always greater than or equal to $\sqrt{\pi E/2}$ where E is the energy of $f(t)$ and the width W_x of any function $x(t)$ is defined as

$$W_x{}^2 = \int_{-\infty}^{\infty} t^2 \, |x(t)|^2 \, dt$$

Hint. Observe that W_F, the width of $F(\omega)$, is given by $W_F{}^2 = 2\pi \int_{-\infty}^{\infty} [f'(t)]^2 \, dt$.

Now, use the Schwartz inequality to show that

$$W_f W_F \geqslant \sqrt{\pi E/2}$$

25. Show that the inequality in the uncertainty principle becomes an equality only for a gaussian signal

$$f(t) = Ke^{-\alpha t^2}$$

Hint. Observe that the Schwartz inequality in Problem 23 becomes an equality only if $f(t)$ is proportional to $g(t)$.

chapter 5

Signal Representation
by Generalized Exponentials:
The Bilateral Laplace Transform

As we have seen, the Fourier transform is a tool which allows us to represent an arbitrary function $f(t)$ by a continuous sum of exponential functions of the form $e^{j\omega t}$. The frequencies of these exponential functions are therefore restricted to the $j\omega$ axis in the complex frequency plane. In general, however, it is desirable to represent a function $f(t)$ by a continuous sum of exponentials of the form e^{st} where $s = \sigma + j\omega$. We therefore need to extend the results derived for the special case of $s = j\omega$ to the one for $s = \sigma + j\omega$. It is indeed possible (as will be shown now) to express a function $f(t)$ as a continuous sum of generalized exponential functions with complex frequencies.

$$\left. \begin{aligned} f(t) &= \frac{1}{2\pi j} \int_{\sigma - j\infty}^{\sigma + j\infty} F(s)e^{st}\, ds \\ \text{where } F(s) &= \int_{-\infty}^{\infty} f(t)e^{-st}\, dt \end{aligned} \right\} \tag{5.1}$$

and

$$s = \sigma + j\omega$$

5.1 GENERALIZATION OF FREQUENCY: THE COMPLEX FOURIER TRANSFORM

The generalization of frequency can be accomplished conveniently by making a slight change in our notation. If

$$f(t) \leftrightarrow F(\omega)$$

then

$$F(\omega) = \int_{-\infty}^{\infty} f(t)e^{-j\omega t} dt \qquad (5.2)$$

and

$$f(t) = \frac{1}{2\pi} \int_{-\infty}^{\infty} F(\omega)e^{j\omega t} d\omega \qquad (5.3)$$

Note that in Eqs. 5.2 and 5.3 the variable ω always appears with j, and hence the integral can also be written as a function of $j\omega$. Thus, we may just as well have expressed the Fourier transform as a function $j\omega$ instead of ω. For the purpose of generalization of frequency, the notation of $j\omega$ proves more convenient than that of ω. Hence we shall express the pair of Eqs. 5.2 and 5.3 as

$$F(j\omega) = \int_{-\infty}^{\infty} f(t)e^{-j\omega t} dt \qquad (5.4)$$

and

$$f(t) = \frac{1}{2\pi} \int_{-\infty}^{\infty} F(j\omega)e^{j\omega t} d\omega \qquad (5.5)$$

As a result of this usage, $F(\omega)$ and $F(j\omega)$ represent identical functions [the Fourier transform of $f(t)$]. This fact should be kept in mind throughout the rest of this book.

Let a function $\varphi(t)$ be defined as

$$\varphi(t) = f(t)e^{-\sigma t}$$

where σ is a real constant. Then

$$\mathscr{F}[\varphi(t)] = \int_{-\infty}^{\infty} f(t)e^{-\sigma t}e^{-j\omega t} dt$$

$$= \int_{-\infty}^{\infty} f(t)e^{-(\sigma+j\omega)t} dt \qquad (5.6a)$$

It is evident from Eq. 5.4 that the above integral is $F(\sigma + j\omega)$. Thus

$$\mathscr{F}[\varphi(t)] = F(\sigma + j\omega) \qquad (5.6b)$$

Hence

$$\varphi(t) = \frac{1}{2\pi} \int_{-\infty}^{\infty} F(\sigma + j\omega)e^{j\omega t} d\omega \qquad (5.7)$$

Substituting $\varphi(t) = f(t)e^{-\sigma t}$ in Eq. 5.7, we obtain

$$f(t)e^{-\sigma t} = \frac{1}{2\pi} \int_{-\infty}^{\infty} F(\sigma + j\omega)e^{j\omega t} d\omega$$

Therefore

$$f(t) = \frac{1}{2\pi} \int_{-\infty}^{\infty} F(\sigma + j\omega)e^{(\sigma+j\omega)t} d\omega \qquad (5.8)$$

The quantity $(\sigma + j\omega)$ is the complex frequency s and $d\omega = (1/j)\, ds$. The limits of integration for $\omega = -\infty$ to ∞ become $(\sigma - j\infty)$ to $(\sigma + j\infty)$ for variable s. Hence the Equation 5.8 becomes

$$f(t) = \frac{1}{2\pi j} \int_{\sigma-j\infty}^{\sigma+j\infty} F(s)e^{st}\, ds \qquad (5.9)$$

We also have from Eqs. 5.6a and 5.6b:

$$F(s) = \int_{-\infty}^{\infty} f(t)e^{-st}\, dt \qquad (5.10)$$

Equation 5.9 expresses $f(t)$ as a continuous sum of exponentials of complex frequency $s = \sigma + j\omega$. Note that the Fourier transform is just a special case of this, and can be obtained by letting $\sigma = 0$, that is, $s = j\omega$ in Eqs. 5.9 and 5.10. The pair of Eqs. 5.9 and 5.10 is called the *complex Fourier transform pair* or *the bilateral Laplace transform pair*.[1] It should be mentioned here that some authors use $\omega + j\sigma$ instead of $\sigma + j\omega$ as the generalized frequency variable.

The complex Fourier transform (or the bilateral Laplace transform) will be denoted symbolically as

$$F(s) = \mathscr{F}_c[f(t)]$$

and

$$f(t) = \mathscr{F}_c^{-1}[F(s)]$$

Note that the complex transform $F(s)$ of $f(t)$ can be found by substituting s for $j\omega$ in its Fourier transform. The Fourier transform discussed thus far $(s = j\omega)$ is also sometimes called an ordinary Fourier transform in contrast to a complex Fourier transform $(s = \sigma + j\omega)$.

As an example, consider the function $e^{-at}u(t)$. The Fourier transform of this function is given by (Table 4.1B):

$$\mathscr{F}[e^{-at}u(t)] = \frac{1}{a + j\omega} \qquad (5.11)$$

The complex Fourier transform of $e^{-at}u(t)$ may be evaluated directly from Eq. 5.10 or may be found by replacing $j\omega$ by s in Eq. 5.11.[2] Thus

$$\mathscr{F}_c[e^{-at}u(t)] = \frac{1}{a + s}$$

---

[1] This is also known as a two-sided Laplace transform pair.

[2] A note of caution is in order here. The complex Fourier transform can be found from an ordinary Fourier transform by replacing $j\omega$ by s only for absolutely integrable functions. This procedure cannot be applied for those functions whose Fourier transform exists in the limit. For these functions we should evaluate the transform directly by using Eq. 5.10.

5.2 EXISTENCE OF THE COMPLEX FOURIER TRANSFORM

From Eq. 5.10, it is evident that the complex Fourier transform of $f(t)$ exists if

$$\int_{-\infty}^{\infty} f(t)e^{-st}\, dt \tag{5.12}$$

is finite. But

$$|f(t)e^{-st}| = |f(t)|\, e^{-\sigma t}$$

Therefore the existence of the complex Fourier transform is guaranteed if

$$\int_{-\infty}^{\infty} |f(t)|\, e^{-\sigma t}\, dt \tag{5.13}$$

is finite. If there exists a real positive finite number M, so that for some real α and β:

$$|f(t)| \leqslant \begin{cases} Me^{\alpha t} & \text{for } t > 0 \\ Me^{\beta t} & \text{for } t < 0 \end{cases} \tag{5.14}$$

then the condition of Eq. 5.13 is satisfied for a value of σ greater than α but less than β; that is, the integral of Eq. 5.13 converges absolutely in the region:

$$\beta > \sigma > \alpha \tag{5.15}$$

This may be easily shown by breaking the integral of Eq. 5.12 into two parts:

$$F(s) = \int_{-\infty}^{0} f(t)e^{-st}\, dt + \int_{0}^{\infty} f(t)e^{-st}\, dt$$

The use of the inequality of Eq. 5.14 yields

$$F(s) \leqslant \int_{-\infty}^{0} Me^{(\beta-s)t}\, dt + \int_{0}^{\infty} Me^{(\alpha-s)t}\, dt$$

$$\leqslant M \left\{ \frac{1}{\beta - s}\, e^{(\beta-s)t} \Big|_{-\infty}^{0} + \frac{1}{\alpha - s}\, e^{(\alpha-s)t} \Big|_{0}^{\infty} \right\}$$

It is obvious that the first integral will converge for $\text{Re } s < \beta$ and the second integral will converge for $\text{Re } s > \alpha$. The two regions are shown in Fig. 5.1. The region where both integrals converge absolutely is the common region given by

$$\beta > \sigma > \alpha$$

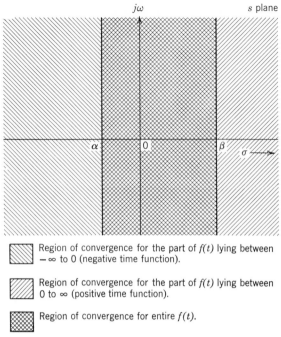

Region of convergence for the part of $f(t)$ lying between $-\infty$ to 0 (negative time function).

Region of convergence for the part of $f(t)$ lying between 0 to ∞ (positive time function).

Region of convergence for entire $f(t)$.

Figure 5.1

The region of absolute convergence for various time functions is shown in Fig. 5.2 by shaded areas.

It is obvious that for all values of s lying in the region of convergence, $F(s)$ is finite. Consequently, any singularities of $F(s)$ [poles of $F(s)$] must lie outside the region of convergence. If $f(t)$ is an entirely positive time function, that is, if $f(t)$ exists in the interval $(0, \infty)$ only, then it is obvious from Fig. 5.1 that the poles of $F(s)$ must lie to the left of the region of convergence. Similarly, if $f(t)$ is an entirely negative time function, that is, if $f(t)$ exists in the interval $(-\infty, 0)$ only, then the poles of $F(s)$ must lie to the right of the region of convergence. For a general $f(t)$, which exists in the interval $(-\infty, \infty)$, $F(s)$ may have several poles, some lying on the left and some lying to the right of the region of convergence. It is now evident that the poles to left of the region arise due to the positive time part of $f(t)$ and those to the right of the region arise due to the negative time part of $f(t)$. This fact is of crucial importance in finding the inverse transform.

Note that an ordinary Fourier transform does not exist for the functions shown in Figs. 5.2c and 5.2f, whereas a complex Fourier transform does exist as these functions satisfy Eq. 5.14 in the regions of convergence shown in those figures. This is because there is an additional convergence

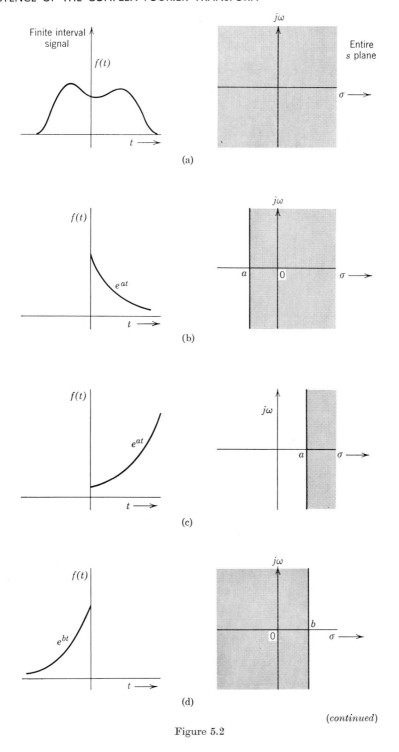

(a)

(b)

(c)

(d)

(continued)

Figure 5.2

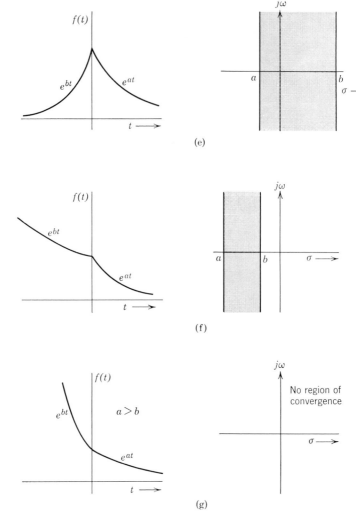

Figure 5.2 *(Concluded)*

factor in the complex Fourier transform. For ordinary Fourier transforms
the existence of a transform is assured if

$$\int_{-\infty}^{\infty} |f(t)|\, dt < \infty$$

On the other hand, for complex transforms the existence of a transform is
assured if

$$\int_{-\infty}^{\infty} |f(t)|\, e^{-\sigma t}\, dt < \infty$$

The factor $e^{-\sigma t}$ is known as the *convergence factor*. We are free to choose the value of σ which will make the integral absolutely convergent. The complex Fourier transform, therefore, covers a broader class of functions than does the ordinary Fourier transform. As mentioned earlier, the ordinary Fourier transform is a special case of the complex Fourier transform where $\sigma = 0$ or the convergence factor is unity.

The shaded regions shown in Fig. 5.2 are the regions of convergence. The ordinary Fourier transform is a special case, and its region of convergence is the imaginary axis where $s = j\omega$. If the region of convergence for any function $f(t)$ includes the imaginary axis $s = j\omega$, then the ordinary Fourier transform for $f(t)$ exists and can be obtained by substituting $s = j\omega$ in $F(s)$. For the functions shown in Figs. 5.2a, 5.2b, 5.2d, and 5.2e, the region of convergence includes the imaginary axis and, therefore, these functions have ordinary Fourier transforms. If, however, the region of convergence does not include the imaginary axis, the function fails to satisfy the condition of absolute integrability, and the function does not possess the ordinary Fourier transform. (It does, however, have a complex Fourier transform in the region of convergence.) The functions shown in Figs. 5.2c and 5.2f are such cases.

5.3 NONUNIQUENESS OF COMPLEX FOURIER TRANSFORMS

Whenever a complex transform is given, the region of convergence must also be specified in order to have a unique inverse transform. If the region of convergence is not specified, the inverse transform is not unique. Consider, for example,

$$f_1(t) = e^{at}u(t)$$

and

$$f_2(t) = -e^{at}u(-t)$$

The two functions are shown in Fig. 5.3. The complex Fourier transforms

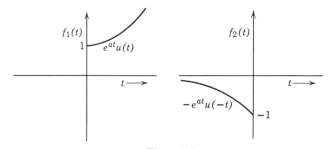

Figure 5.3

of these functions are $F_1(s)$ and $F_2(s)$, given by

$$F_1(s) = \int_{-\infty}^{\infty} e^{at} u(t) e^{-st}\, dt = \int_0^{\infty} e^{at} e^{-st}\, dt$$

$$= \frac{-1}{s-a} e^{-(s-a)t} \Big|_0^{\infty}$$

$$= \frac{1}{s-a} \qquad \text{for} \quad \sigma > a$$

$$F_2(s) = \int_{-\infty}^{\infty} -e^{at} u(-t) e^{-st}\, dt = \int_{-\infty}^0 -e^{at} e^{-st}\, dt$$

$$= \frac{1}{s-a} e^{-(s-a)t} \Big|_{-\infty}^0$$

$$= \frac{1}{s-a} \qquad \text{for} \quad \sigma < a$$

It follows that the complex Fourier transform of both $f_1(t)$ and $f_2(t)$ is the same, namely, $1/(s-a)$. The regions of convergence are different, however, for the two functions. If the region of convergence is specified along with the transform, then the function is uniquely specified. We, therefore, conclude that the inverse transform of any $F(s)$ cannot be determined uniquely unless the region of convergence is specified.[3] This topic will be treated later in sec. 5.15.

5.4 CAUSAL FUNCTIONS AND UNILATERAL FREQUENCY TRANSFORMS

Thus far we have assumed that a general time function $f(t)$ exists in the entire interval $(-\infty < t < \infty)$. In practice, however, there is a large class of functions which start at some finite time, say $t = 0$, and have zero value for $t < 0$. Such functions are called causal functions.[4] Henceforth, we shall call a function causal if it is zero for negative values of t.

$$f(t) = 0, \qquad t < 0$$

For all of the physical systems, if the driving function is zero for the negative values of t, the response must also be zero for the negative values

[3] For more discussion of the bilateral Laplace transform, see B. Van der Pol and H. Bremmer, *Operational Calculus*, Cambridge University Press, New York, 1955.

[4] A Papoulis, *The Fourier Integral and Its Applications*, page 13, McGraw-Hill, New York, 1962.

of t, since the system cannot anticipate the driving function. It therefore follows that for physical systems the response function of the causal excitation function must also be a causal function.

Most of the analysis problems, in practice, involve causal functions. A system is generally excited at some finite time $t = 0$. We are, therefore, interested in the time interval $0 < t < \infty$ instead of the entire interval $-\infty < t < \infty$. The causal functions effect a great deal of simplification in the frequency transformation. When the frequency transforms are specialized for causal functions, they are called unilateral transforms (also known as single-sided or right-handed transforms). The complex Fourier transform (the bilateral Laplace transform), when specialized for causal functions, is known as the unilateral Laplace transform. It is also known as the single-sided or right-handed Laplace transform. Henceforth, we shall refer to this transform simply as the Laplace transform.

For causal functions, the transform equations (5.9 and 5.10) reduce to

$$F(s) = \int_0^\infty f(t)e^{-st}\, dt \qquad (5.16)$$

$$f(t) = \frac{1}{2\pi j}\int_{\sigma-j\infty}^{\sigma+j\infty} F(s)e^{st}\, ds \qquad (5.17)$$

Equations 5.16 and 5.17 form a Laplace transform pair. Equation 5.16 represents the direct Laplace transform of $f(t)$, and Eq. 5.17 forms the inverse Laplace transform of $F(s)$. Symbolically, this pair is written as

$$F(s) = \mathscr{L}[f(t)]$$

$$f(t) = \mathscr{L}^{-1}[F(s)]$$

The lower limit of integration in Eq. 5.16 is 0. If $f(t)$ contains an impulse function or its derivatives at the origin, $f(t)$ is undefined at $t = 0$. To make sure that the impulse or its higher derivatives are included, we must choose the lower limit of 0^-. If the lower limit is chosen as 0^+, the impulse and its derivatives that are present, if any, at the origin will be ignored. Hence, in general, the lower limit should be taken as 0^-. Henceforth the lower limit in the integral of Eq. 5.16 will be tacitly assumed to be 0^-. Observe that

$$F(s) = \mathscr{L}\{\mathscr{L}^{-1}[F(s)]\}$$
and
$$f(t) = \mathscr{L}^{-1}\{\mathscr{L}[f(t)]\}$$

5.5 EXISTENCE OF THE LAPLACE TRANSFORM

For the Laplace transform to exist, the first condition is that the integral in Eq. 5.16 must exist. That is,

$$\int_0^\infty f(t)e^{-st}\, dt$$

must be finite. This integral will be finite, provided that

$$\int_0^\infty |f(t)|\, e^{-\sigma t}\, dt < \infty \qquad (5.18)$$

For a function $f(t)$, if real positive finite numbers M and α exist so that

$$|f(t)| < Me^{\alpha t} \qquad (5.19)$$

for all positive t, $f(t)$ is said to be an exponential-order function or an E-function. The inequality Eq. 5.18 is always satisfied for an exponential-order function. This can be easily verified by substituting the inequality Eq. 5.19 in the inequality Eq. 5.18. The integral

$$\int_0^\infty |f(t)|\, e^{-\sigma t}\, dt < \int_0^\infty Me^{\alpha t}\, e^{-\sigma t}\, dt = \int_0^\infty Me^{(\alpha-\sigma)t}\, dt$$

$$= \frac{M}{\alpha - \sigma}\, e^{(\alpha-\sigma)t}\Big|_0^\infty$$

$$= \frac{M}{\sigma - \alpha} \qquad \text{if } \sigma > \alpha$$

Thus, by choosing $\sigma > \alpha$, the integral can be made absolutely convergent.

The exponential-order function may be defined alternatively as follows: a function $f(t)$ is of exponential order if there exists a real positive number α such that

$$\lim_{t \to \infty} [e^{-\alpha t} f(t)] = 0 \qquad (5.20)$$

It can be easily shown that if $f(t)$ satisfies the condition of Eq. 5.20, then

$$\int_0^\infty |f(t)|\, e^{-\sigma t}\, dt$$

is finite for $\sigma > \alpha$. The region of convergence is, therefore, given by

$$\infty > \sigma > \alpha \qquad (5.21)$$

This condition is similar to that derived for the bilateral Laplace transform except that β is replaced by ∞ in this case. This is quite logical, since Eq. 5.14 is satisfied for $\beta = \infty$ when $f(t)$ is a causal function. The

Laplace transform converges for values of s given by

$$\text{Re } s = \sigma > \alpha$$

where α satisfies the condition of Eq. 5.20.

The minimum value of α that satisfies the condition of Eq. 5.20 is known as the abscissa of absolute convergence for a given $f(t)$.

As an example, consider a unit step function $u(t)$. For this function:

$$\lim_{t \to \infty} u(t)e^{-\alpha t} = 0$$

for any value of $\alpha > 0$. Hence the region of convergence of the Laplace transform of $u(t)$ is given by $\sigma > 0$. Similarly, it can be shown that the region of convergence for a function $e^{-at}u(t)$ is $\sigma > a$.

The usefulness of the frequency-analysis technique depends upon whether or not all of the functions encountered in practice possess a Laplace transform. It can be stated here affirmatively that every physically possible signal is Laplace-transformable. Saying that a signal should be of an exponential order is another way of saying that $f(t)$ should not grow more rapidly than $Me^{\alpha t}$ for any positive real M and α. There are some functions that do grow faster than $Me^{\alpha t}$; for example, e^{t^2} or t^t are such functions, which do not possess Laplace transforms. But such functions are of no practical significance. Even these functions possess a Laplace transform in the limit. This is done by assuming that a nontransformable function, say e^{t^2}, exists for the interval $0 < t < T$ and is zero for $t > T$. We can make T as large as we desire. The Laplace transform exists as long as T is finite, no matter how large it may be. Thus, instead of dealing with the nontransformable function over the interval $0 < t < \infty$, we truncate the function at $t = T$, making T very large and assuming zero value for the function for $t > T$. This is much closer to reality than one may think, since all of the driving functions, in practice, are going to be switched off at some time T. The Laplace transform of every truncated function (or function in the limit) exists, since every piecewise continuous function which is zero for $t > T$ is an exponential-order function.

5.6 INTERPRETATION OF THE LAPLACE TRANSFORM

The ordinary Fourier transform is a tool for expressing a function $f(t)$ as a continuous sum of exponential functions of frequencies lying along the $j\omega$ axis.

$$f(t) = \frac{1}{2\pi} \int_{-\infty}^{\infty} F(j\omega)e^{j\omega t} \, d\omega$$

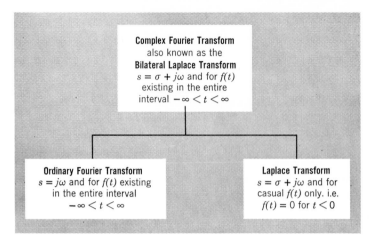

Figure 5.4   The ordinary Fourier transform and the Laplace transform as special cases of the complex Fourier transform.

Generalization of the ordinary Fourier transform leads to the complex Fourier transform by means of which it is possible to express a function $f(t)$ as a continuous sum of exponential functions of complex frequencies.

$$f(t) = \frac{1}{2\pi j} \int_{\sigma-j\infty}^{\sigma+j\infty} F(s)e^{st}\,ds$$

The above expression represents $f(t)$ as a continuous sum of exponential functions whose frequencies lie along the path $\sigma + j\omega$ for $\omega = -\infty$ to ∞. An ordinary Fourier transform is just a special case of the complex Fourier transform when $\sigma = 0$ or $s = j\omega$. The Laplace transform is really a complex Fourier transform, but it deals only with causal functions, that is, those functions which have zero value for $t < 0$. Hence the Laplace transform is also a special case of the complex Fourier transform. The relationship between various transforms is shown in Fig. 5.4. The Laplace transform therefore expresses a causal function $f(t)$ as a continuous sum of exponentials of complex frequencies. This point will now be illustrated by an example.

Consider a function $e^{-at}u(t)$. We shall now express this function as a continuous sum of exponential functions of complex frequencies by means of the Laplace transform.

$$e^{-at}u(t) = \frac{1}{2\pi j} \int_{\sigma-j\infty}^{\sigma+j\infty} F(s)e^{st}\,ds$$

where

$$F(s) = \int_0^\infty e^{-at}u(t)e^{-st}\,dt$$

$$= \frac{-1}{s+a}e^{-(s+a)t}\Big|_0^\infty$$

$$= \frac{-1}{s+a}e^{-(\sigma+j\omega+a)t}\Big|_0^\infty$$

$$= \frac{1}{s+a} \qquad \text{if} \qquad (\sigma+a) > 0 \tag{5.22}$$

$$\text{i.e., if } \sigma > -a$$

Note that if $(\sigma + a) < 0$, then the value of the above integral goes to infinity and the transform does not exist. Hence the region of convergence is given by Re $s > -a$. The region in the s plane where Re $s > -a$ is shown in Fig. 5.5. We can thus express the function $e^{-at}u(t)$ as a continuous sum of complex exponentials.

$$e^{-at}u(t) = \frac{1}{2\pi j}\int_{\sigma-j\infty}^{\sigma+j\infty}\frac{1}{s+a}e^{st}\,ds \tag{5.23}$$

The function $1/(s + a)$ represents the relative amplitudes of the frequency components. The integral represents the continuous summation of exponential functions whose frequencies lie along the path $\sigma + j\omega$ from

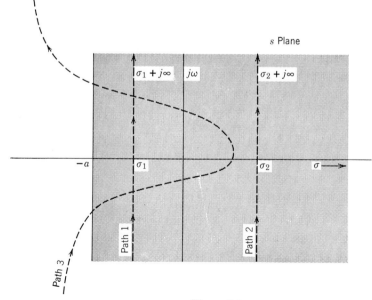

Figure 5.5

$\omega = -\infty$ to $\omega = \infty$. How shall we choose this path? From the above discussion, it may appear that the path should lie in the region of convergence. This conclusion, however, needs some qualifications. It is sufficient to choose the entire path of integration in the region of convergence (Paths 1 and 2 in Fig. 5.5). However, it is not necessary that the entire path should lie in the region of convergence. It can be shown from the properties of analytic functions that all that is required is that the path of integration should lie to the right[5] of the singularity points (poles) of $F(s)$. In the present case the singularity is at $s = -a$, and any path to the right of $s = -a$ (Path 3, for example) is permissible. It is evident that there are infinite possible paths of integration of which three are shown in Fig. 5.5. The choice of Path 1 is equivalent to expressing $f(t)$ as a continuous sum of exponentially decaying sinusoids, since all the frequencies on this path lie in LHP. On the other hand, Path 2 lies entirely in RHP and hence this choice yields the representation of $f(t)$ as a continuous sum of exponentially growing sinusoids. Path 3 lies both in LHP and RHP and hence corresponds to the representation of $f(t)$ as a continuous sum of exponentially growing and decaying sinusoids. The integral on the right-hand side of Eq. 5.23 yields the same result, namely $e^{-at}u(t)$ when integrated along any of these paths.

Note that we may just as well have chosen the path along the $j\omega$ axis. The choice of this path is equivalent to expressing $f(t)$ as a continuous sum of exponentials of the form $e^{j\omega t}$ (along the $j\omega$ axis). This is exactly what a Fourier transform accomplishes. Hence the special case when $s = j\omega$ reduces the Laplace transform to a Fourier transform. It is important to observe that there is a lower bound on the value of σ (in this case $-a$), but there is no upper bound. We can choose σ as high as we wish (as long as it is greater than the lower bound σ_m). Thus a signal can always be expressed as a continuous sum of exponentially growing sinusoids. Moreover, we may choose these sinusoids to grow as rapidly as we wish.

One more important point needs clearing up here. All of the frequency transforms discussed thus far express a function as a continuous sum of exponential functions which exist in the entire interval ($-\infty < t < \infty$).

---

[5] In the bilateral Laplace transform, the poles of $F(s)$ lie on both sides of the strip of convergence. The poles to the left and right sides of the strip of convergence correspond to positive and negative time functions, respectively (see Section 5.2). In such a case, $F(s)$ is separated into two parts: $F^+(s)$ and $F^-(s)$, corresponding to positive and negative time functions. The path of integration for a positive time function lies to the right of the poles of $F^+(s)$ and the path of integration for a negative time function lies to the left of the poles of $F^-(s)$.

Obviously any path which lies entirely inside the strip of convergence is a path of integration allowable for both $F^+(S)$ and $F^-(S)$.

The Laplace transform therefore expresses a causal function [$f(t) = 0$, $t < 0$] as a continuous sum of eternal exponential functions (existing for $-\infty < t < \infty$). This may appear rather surprising since $f(t)$ is zero for negative values of t. It just so happens, however, that all these eternal exponential components add in such a way as to yield a zero value for $t < 0$ and yield the desired function $f(t)$ for $t > 0$. To reiterate: the Laplace transform is a tool by means of which we can express a causal function as a continuous sum of eternal exponential functions of complex frequencies. The continuous sum is expressed by the integral.

$$f(t) = \frac{1}{2\pi j} \int_{\sigma-j\infty}^{\sigma+j\infty} F(s)e^{st}\, ds$$

The function $F(s)$ represents the relative amplitude of the component of frequency s.

5.7 UNIQUENESS OF THE LAPLACE TRANSFORM

For a complex Fourier transform, that is, a bilateral Laplace transform, it was demonstrated that the inverse transform of a function $F(s)$ is not unique unless the region of convergence is specified. There is an ambiguity in the inverse transform if the region of convergence is unspecified. The inverse transform may be a function $f_1(t)$ existing only for the positive values of t and being zero for the negative values of t, or it may be a function $f_2(t)$ existing only for the negative values of t and being zero for the positive values of t. In the case of the unilateral transform, on the other hand, all functions exist only for the positive values of t and are zero for the negative values of t. Hence, there is no ambiguity in the inverse transform even if the region of convergence is not specified. For this reason, we shall, in the future, avoid any mention of the region of convergence in the case of Laplace transforms. It therefore follows that the inverse Laplace transform is unique.

The inverse transform is obtained by evaluating the complex integral in Eq. 5.17. The evaluation of such an integral requires a familiarity with the functions of complex variables in general and calculus of the residues in particular.[6] The integration is performed along a path from ($\sigma - j\infty$) to ($\sigma + j\infty$). Fortunately, however, the need for complex integration is obviated by using tables of the Laplace transforms. Standard tables of the Laplace transforms are available which list the direct and inverse

[6] See, for instance, S. Goldman, *Transformation Calculus and Electrical Transients*, Chapter 7, Prentice-Hall, Englewood Cliffs, N.J., 1949.

transforms of a large number of functions required in practice. One column lists the function $f(t)$ and the other column gives the corresponding $F(s)$. The inverse transform of a function $F(s)$ can therefore be found directly from these tables, thus obviating the need for complex integration. Similarly, the direct transform $F(s)$ of a function $f(t)$ can be found. A table of transforms for a large number of useful functions is given in Appendix A.

5.8 TRANSFORMS OF SOME USEFUL FUNCTIONS

Let us find the Laplace transforms of some functions that are commonly encountered in practice. The exponential function starting at $t = 0$ is a very important one.

$$f(t) = e^{-at}u(t)$$
$$F(s) = \mathcal{L}[f(t)] = \int_0^\infty e^{-at}u(t)e^{-st}\,dt$$
$$= \int_0^\infty e^{-at}e^{-st}\,dt$$
$$= \int_0^\infty e^{-(s+a)t}\,dt$$
$$= \frac{1}{s+a}$$

Therefore

$$\mathcal{L}\left[e^{-at}u(t)\right] = \frac{1}{s+a} \tag{5.24}$$

$$\mathcal{L}^{-1}\left[\frac{1}{s+a}\right] = e^{-at}u(t) \tag{5.25}$$

Equation 5.25 also implies that

$$e^{-at}u(t) = \frac{1}{2\pi j}\int_{\sigma-j\infty}^{\sigma+j\infty}\frac{1}{s+a}e^{st}\,ds$$

A unit step function is a special case of $e^{-at}u(t)$ obtained by letting a go to zero. From Eqs. 5.24 and 5.25 we can write

$$\mathcal{L}[u(t)] = \frac{1}{s} \tag{5.26}$$

$$\mathcal{L}^{-1}\left[\frac{1}{s}\right] = u(t) \tag{5.27}$$

A sinusoidal function can be written as the sum of two exponential functions.

$$\sin \omega_0 t = \frac{e^{j\omega_0 t} - e^{-j\omega_0 t}}{2j}$$

$$\mathscr{L}[\sin (\omega_0 t)u(t)] = \int_0^\infty \frac{e^{j\omega_0 t} - e^{-j\omega_0 t}}{2j} e^{-st} dt$$

$$= \int_0^\infty \frac{e^{-(s-j\omega_0)t} - e^{-(s+j\omega_0)t}}{2j}$$

$$= \frac{1}{2j}\left(\frac{1}{s - j\omega_0} - \frac{1}{s + j\omega_0}\right)$$

$$= \frac{\omega_0}{(s^2 + \omega_0^2)}$$

that is,

$$\mathscr{L}[\sin (\omega_0 t)u(t)] = \frac{\omega_0}{(s^2 + \omega_0^2)} \tag{5.28}$$

$$\mathscr{L}^{-1}\left[\frac{\omega_0}{s^2 + \omega_0^2}\right] = \sin (\omega_0 t)u(t) \tag{5.29}$$

Similarly

$$\mathscr{L}[\cos (\omega_0 t)u(t)] = \frac{s}{s^2 + \omega_0^2} \tag{5.30}$$

$$\mathscr{L}^{-1}\left[\frac{s}{s^2 + \omega_0^2}\right] = \cos (\omega_0 t)u(t) \tag{5.31}$$

Note that Eqs. 5.29 and 5.31 imply that

$$\sin (\omega_0 t)u(t) = \frac{1}{2\pi j} \int_{\sigma-j\infty}^{\sigma+j\infty} \frac{\omega_0}{(s^2 + \omega_0^2)} e^{st} ds$$

and

$$\cos (\omega_0 t)u(t) = \frac{1}{2\pi j} \int_{\sigma-j\infty}^{\sigma+j\infty} \frac{s}{(s^2 + \omega_0^2)} e^{st} ds$$

Table 5.1 tabulates the direct and inverse transforms of a number of functions (a more complete table of transforms is given in Appendix A). Note that the use of $u(t)$ in $f(t)u(t)$ is somewhat redundant for the Laplace transform since, by the very definition of this transform, it is understood that only the positive time component of $f(t)$ is used. Nevertheless, this usage avoids unnecessary confusion. Moreover, it allows us to write the unified expression for both the bilateral Laplace transform and the (unilateral) Laplace transform. Thus

$$\mathscr{F}_c[f(t)u(t)] = \mathscr{L}[f(t)u(t)] = F(s)$$

However

$$\mathscr{F}_c[f(t)] \neq \mathscr{L}[f(t)]$$

TABLE 5.I

Table of the Laplace Transforms

$f(t) = \mathscr{L}^{-1}[F(s)]$	$F(s) = \mathscr{L}[f(t)]$
1. $u(t)$	$\dfrac{1}{s}$
2. $tu(t)$	$\dfrac{1}{s^2}$
3. $t^n u(t)$	$\dfrac{n!}{s^{n+1}}$
4. $e^{at}u(t)$	$\dfrac{1}{s-a}$
5. $te^{at}u(t)$	$\dfrac{1}{(s-a)^2}$
6. $t^n e^{at}u(t)$	$\dfrac{n!}{(s-a)^{n+1}}$
7. $\sin(\omega_0 t)u(t)$	$\dfrac{\omega_0}{(s^2 + \omega_0{}^2)}$
8. $\cos(\omega_0 t)u(t)$	$\dfrac{s}{(s^2 + \omega_0{}^2)}$
9. $e^{-at}\sin(\omega_0 t)u(t)$	$\dfrac{\omega_0}{(s+a)^2 + \omega_0{}^2}$
10. $e^{-at}\cos(\omega_0 t)u(t)$	$\dfrac{s+a}{(s+a)^2 + \omega_0{}^2}$
11. $\sinh at\, u(t)$	$\dfrac{a}{(s^2 - a^2)}$
12. $\cosh at\, u(t)$	$\dfrac{s}{(s^2 - a^2)}$
13. $\delta(t)$	1

5.9 SOME REMARKS ON THE FOURIER AND THE LAPLACE TRANSFORMS

Since the Fourier transform is a special case of the Laplace transform under the condition $s = j\omega$, the former can be obtained from the latter merely by substituting[7] $s = j\omega$. As an example, consider the function $e^{-at}u(t)$.

$$\mathcal{L}[e^{-at}u(t)] = \frac{1}{s + a}$$

The Fourier transform of this function can be obtained merely by letting $s = j\omega$ in the above expression.

$$\mathcal{F}[e^{-at}u(t)] = \frac{1}{j\omega + a}$$

This is the correct result as seen from Table 4.1B. The result, of course, applies only for positive values of a. If a is negative, the function is not absolutely integrable, and hence its Fourier transform does not exist. This can also be seen from the region of convergence of the Laplace transform. We have shown that (see Fig. 5.5) the region of convergence of $e^{-at}u(t)$ is given by Re $s > -a$. If a is positive, the convergence region includes the $j\omega$ axis (as shown in Fig. 5.5). If, however, a is negative, the convergence region does not contain the $j\omega$ axis, and hence the Fourier transform does not exist.

We must, however, be cautious in deriving the Fourier transform from the Laplace transform by substituting $j\omega$ for s in the latter for the case of those functions whose Fourier transforms exist in the limit. Consider, for example, a unit step function $u(t)$. We have

$$\mathcal{L}[u(t)] = \frac{1}{s}$$

To obtain the Fourier transform of $u(t)$, if we substitute $j\omega$ for s, we obtain

$$\mathcal{F}[u(t)] = \frac{1}{j\omega}$$

This result is not incorrect. But the function $1/j\omega$ is infinite at $\omega = 0$ and hence is undefined. We shall now show that this infinity is actually an impulse function of strength π at the origin.

To start with, we shall define $u(t)$ as a limiting case of the function $e^{-at}u(t)$ as a is made zero. Thus

$$u(t) = \lim_{a \to 0} [e^{-at}u(t)]$$

and

$$\mathcal{L}[u(t)] = \lim_{a \to 0} \frac{1}{s + a} \tag{5.32}$$

[7] This is, of course, true only if the region of convergence of the Laplace transform includes the $j\omega$ axis. If the region does not contain the $j\omega$ axis, the function $f(t)$ is not absolutely integrable, and hence its Fourier transform does not exist.

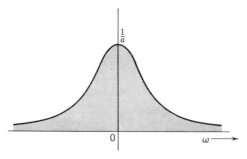

Figure 5.6

The Fourier transform of $u(t)$ is obtained by letting $s = j\omega$ and $a \to 0$ in Eq. 5.32. Therefore

$$\mathscr{F}[u(t)] = \lim_{a \to 0} \frac{1}{j\omega + a} \tag{5.33}$$

$$= \lim_{a \to 0} \frac{a - j\omega}{a^2 + \omega^2}$$

$$= \lim_{a \to 0} \left[\frac{a}{a^2 + \omega^2} \right] + \lim_{a \to 0} \left[\frac{\omega}{j(a^2 + \omega^2)} \right]$$

$$= \lim_{a \to 0} \left[\frac{a}{a^2 + \omega^2} \right] + \frac{1}{j\omega} \tag{5.34}$$

Note that we cannot substitute $a = 0$ in the first term $[a/(a^2 + \omega^2)]$ because that makes the term indeterminate at $\omega = 0$. The function $a/(a^2 + \omega^2)$ is plotted in Fig. 5.6. As a is made smaller and smaller, the function becomes more and more peaked at $\omega = 0$, and becomes narrower. The area under the curve, however, is independent of a. It can be readily shown that

$$\int_{-\infty}^{\infty} \frac{a}{(a^2 + \omega^2)} \, d\omega = \pi$$

As a is made zero, the function is zero everywhere except at $\omega = 0$ where it is infinite. But the area under the curve is still π. It is therefore obvious that the function $[a/(a^2 + \omega^2)]$ represents an impulse of strength π at $\omega = 0$ when $a = 0$. Therefore, from Eq. 5.34,

$$\mathscr{F}[u(t)] = \pi\delta(\omega) + \frac{1}{j\omega}$$

which is the correct result as seen from Table 4.1B. Similar procedures may be applied to such functions as $\cos(\omega_0 t)u(t)$, $\sin(\omega_0 t)u(t)$, etc.

5.10 SOME PROPERTIES OF THE LAPLACE TRANSFORM

Since the Laplace transform is merely a generalization of the Fourier transform, we expect it to possess properties similar to those of the Fourier transform with the variable s replacing $j\omega$. This indeed is the case. The reader may prove the following properties by methods similar to those used for the Fourier transform. We shall use an arrow with one half of the tip to symbolize the Laplace transform pair. Thus the symbol

$$f(t) \rightharpoonup F(s)$$

means that $F(s)$ is the Laplace transform of $f(t)$, and $f(t)$ is the inverse Laplace transform of $F(s)$. If

$$f(t) \rightharpoonup F(s)$$

then the following properties hold true.

1. Scaling Property. For $a > 0$

$$f(at) \rightharpoonup \frac{1}{a} F\left(\frac{s}{a}\right) \tag{5.35}$$

2. Time-Shifting Property. For $t_0 > 0$

$$f(t - t_0) \rightharpoonup F(s)e^{-st_0} \tag{5.36}$$

3. Frequency-Shifting Property.

$$f(t)e^{s_0 t} \rightharpoonup F(s - s_0) \tag{5.37}$$

4. Frequency-Differentiation Property.

$$(-t)^n f(t) \rightharpoonup \frac{d^n F}{ds^n} \tag{5.38}$$

5. Linearity Property. If

$$f_1(t) \rightharpoonup F_1(s) \qquad \text{and} \quad f_2(t) \rightharpoonup F_2(s)$$

then

$$a_1 f_1(t) + a_2 f_2(t) \rightharpoonup a_1 F_1(s) + a_2 F_2(s) \tag{5.39}$$

6. Time Convolution.

$$f_1(t) * f_2(t) \rightharpoonup F_1(s) F_2(s) \tag{5.40}$$

7. Frequency Convolution.

$$f_1(t) f_2(t) \rightharpoonup \frac{1}{2\pi j} [F_1(s) * F_2(s)] \tag{5.41}$$

where

$$F_1(s) * F_2(s) = \int_{\sigma - j\infty}^{\sigma + j\infty} F_1(\lambda) F_2(s - \lambda)\, d\lambda$$

and the path of integration $(\sigma + j\omega)$ lies inside the region of convergence of the $\mathscr{L}[f_1(t)f_2(t)]$.

All of the above properties also apply to the bilateral Laplace transform provided that such a transform exists. When these properties are applied to the bilateral Laplace transform, there is an additional consideration regarding the region of convergence. For the frequency-shifting property, for example, the strip of convergence of $F(s - s_0)$ is the same as that for $F(s)$ but shifted to the right by Re s_0. For the time-convolution theorem, the strip of convergence is given by the region of convergence for $F_1(s)F_2(s)$. It is easily seen that this region is given by

$$\max (\alpha_1, \alpha_2) < \sigma < \min (\beta_1, \beta_2);$$

where the strip of convergence of $F_1(s)$ is $\alpha_1 < \sigma < \beta_1$ and that for $F_2(s)$ is $\alpha_2 < \sigma < \beta_2$. Similarly, for the frequency-convolution theorem, the region of convergence is given by the strip of convergence for $f_1(t)f_2(t)$. It can be shown that this region is given by $\alpha_2 + \sigma_1 < \sigma < \beta_2 + \sigma_1$ where $\alpha_1 < \sigma_1 < \beta_1$.

In addition, the scaling property holds true for positive as well as negative values of a for the bilateral Laplace transform. Also the time-shifting property holds true of positive as well as negative values of t_0.

As mentioned before in Chapter 4, the convolution theorem is one of the most powerful tools in frequency-analysis techniques as applied to linear-system analysis and communication theory. A complete treatment of this topic will be postponed until Chapter 10.

8. Time-Differentiation Property. If

$$f(t) \rightarrow F(s)$$

then

$$\frac{df}{dt} \rightarrow [sF(s) - f(0^-)] \tag{5.42}$$

In general,

$$\frac{d^n f}{dt^n} \rightarrow [s^n F(s) - s^{n-1}f(0^-) - s^{n-2}f'(0^-) - \cdots - f^{(n-1)}(0^-)] \tag{5.43}$$

This property may be proved as follows. By definition

$$\mathscr{L}\left[\frac{df}{dt}\right] = \int_{0^-}^{\infty} \frac{df}{dt} e^{-st} dt$$

Integration by part of the right-hand side yields

$$\mathscr{L}\left[\frac{df}{dt}\right] = f(t)e^{-st}\Big|_{0^-}^{\infty} + s\int_{0^-}^{\infty} f(t)e^{-st} dt \tag{5.44}$$

The quantity $f(t)e^{-st}$ goes to zero at $t = \infty$. This follows from the fact that s lies in the region of convergence where $f(t)e^{-st}$ goes to zero at $t = \infty$ (see Eq. 5.20 and the discussion on the region of convergence). Hence Eq. 5.44 becomes

$$\mathscr{L}\left[\frac{df}{dt}\right] = -f(0^-) + sF(s)$$
$$= sF(s) - f(0^-)$$

The extension of this result to the nth derivative yields Eq. 5.43.

Note that if the function $f(t)$ is causal, then

$$f(t) = 0, \qquad (t < 0)$$

Hence

$$f(0^-), f'(0^-), \dots, f^{(n-1)}(0^-)$$

are all zero, and the time-differentiation property becomes

$$\frac{df}{dt} \longrightarrow sF(s) \tag{5.45}$$

and

$$\frac{d^n f}{dt^n} \longrightarrow s^n F(s) \tag{5.46}$$

In view of this result we may wonder why we retain the terms such as $f(0^-)$, $f'(0^-)$, $\dots$, etc., in Eqs. 5.42 and 5.43. The reason for this apparent redundancy will become obvious when we study the frequency analysis of linear systems (Chapter 6). There are many instances where certain signals in the system are noncausal although the driving function is applied at $t = 0$. This arises because of the possibility of initial energy storages in the systems.

9. Time-Integration Property. If

$$f(t) \longrightarrow F(s)$$

then

$$\int_0^t f(t)\, dt \longrightarrow \frac{F(s)}{s} \tag{5.47}$$

Proof. By definition

$$\mathscr{L}\left\{\int_0^t f(t)\, dt\right\} = \int_0^\infty \left[\int_0^t f(t)\, dt\right] e^{-st}\, dt \tag{5.48}$$

Integrating by parts, we get

$$\mathscr{L}\left[\int_0^t f(t)\, dt\right] = \left[\frac{-e^{-st}}{s} \int_0^t f(t)\, dt\right]_0^\infty + \frac{1}{s} \int_0^\infty f(t)e^{-st}\, dt \tag{5.49}$$

If $f(t)$ is an exponential-order function, then it can be shown that its integral is also an exponential-order function. Hence it follows that the term $e^{-st} \int_0^t f(t)\, dt$ at $t = \infty$ is zero for values of s lying in the region of convergence of $\int f(t)\, dt$. Also the integral term is zero at $t = 0$. Hence the first term on the right-hand side of Eq. 5.49 is zero, and we get

$$\mathcal{L}\left[\int_0^t f(t)\, dt\right] \to \frac{F(s)}{s}$$

For an indefinite integral the result is modified as follows:

$$\int f(t)\, dt \to \frac{F(s)}{s} + \frac{f^{(-1)}(0^-)}{s} \tag{5.50}$$

where

$$f^{(-1)}(0^-) = \int f(t)\, dt\,\Big|_{t=0^-}$$

Proof. The indefinite integral is used to mean $\int_{-\infty}^t f(\tau)\, d\tau$. Hence

$$\int f(t)\, dt = \int_0^t f(t)\, dt + f^{(-1)}(0^-)u(t) \tag{5.51}$$

Taking the Laplace transform of both sides, we get

$$\mathcal{L}\left[\int f(t)\, dt\right] = \frac{F(s)}{s} + \frac{f^{-1}(0^-)}{s}$$

The result can be generalized to higher integrals. Note that for causal functions:

$$f(t) = 0, \qquad t < 0$$

and consequently $f^{(-1)}(0^-)$, $f^{(-2)}(0^-)$, $\ldots$, $f^{(-n)}(0^-)$ are all zero. Hence Eq. 5.50 reduces to

$$\int f(t)\, dt \to \frac{F(s)}{s} \tag{5.52}$$

10. Frequency-Integration Property. If

$$f(t) \to F(s) \tag{5.53}$$

then

$$\frac{f(t)}{t} \to \int_s^\infty F(s)\, ds \tag{5.54}$$

Proof. By definition

$$\int_s^\infty F(s)\,ds = \int_s^\infty \int_0^\infty f(t)e^{-st}\,dt\,ds$$

$$= \int_0^\infty \int_s^\infty f(t)e^{-st}\,ds\,dt$$

$$= \int_0^\infty \frac{-f(t)}{t} e^{-st}\Big|_s^\infty dt$$

$$= \int_0^\infty \frac{f(t)}{t} e^{-st}\,dt$$

$$= \mathscr{L}\!\left[\frac{f(t)}{t}\right]$$

5.11 CORRESPONDENCE BETWEEN THE TIME AND THE FREQUENCY DOMAINS

It was pointed out in Chapter 4 that there is a correspondence and a measure of symmetry between the time and the frequency domains. This correspondence holds true for real as well as complex frequencies, as is evident from Table 5.2. Differentiation in the time domain is reflected as multiplication by s in the frequency domain, and differentiation in the frequency domain is equivalent to multiplication by $-t$ in the time domain. Integration in the time domain is equivalent to division by s in the frequency domain and integration in the frequency domain corresponds to division by t in the time domain. Compression in the time domain is reflected as expansion in the frequency domain, and vice versa. The shift of t_0 in the time domain is equivalent to multiplication by e^{-st_0} (phase shift) in the frequency domain, and the shift of s_0 in the frequency domain is equivalent to multiplication by $e^{s_0 t}$ in the time domain. Convolution in the time domain corresponds to multiplication in the frequency domain, and vice versa.

Most of these results are intuitively evident. They were shown to be plausible purely by qualitative arguments in Chapter 4. The arguments used for the Fourier transform also apply here for the Laplace transform. For example, we can argue that the Laplace transform expresses a function $f(t)$ as a continuous sum of exponentials of complex frequencies. The derivative of $f(t)$ is therefore equal to the continuous sum of the derivative

TABLE 5.2

Some Properties of the Laplace Transform

Operation	Time domain	Frequency domain
Addition	$a_1 f_1(t) + a_2 f_2(t)$	$a_1 F_1(s) + a_2 F_2(s)$
Time differentiation	$\dfrac{df}{dt}$	$s F(s) - f(0^-)$
Time integration	$\displaystyle\int f(t)\,dt$	$\dfrac{F(s)}{s} + \dfrac{f^{(-1)}(0^-)}{s}$
Frequency differentiation	$-tf(t)$	$\dfrac{dF}{ds}$
Frequency integration	$f(t)/t$	$\displaystyle\int_s^\infty f(s)\,ds$
Time shift $t_0 > 0$	$f(t - t_0)$	$F(s)\,e^{-s t_0}$
Frequency shift	$f(t)e^{s_0 t}$	$F(s - s_0)$
Scaling $a > 0$	(at)	$\dfrac{1}{a} F\left(\dfrac{s}{a}\right)$
Time convolution	$f_1(t) * f_2(t)$	$F_1(s) F_2(s)$
Frequency convolution	$f_1(t) f_2(t)$	$\dfrac{1}{2\pi j}[F_1(s) * F_2(s)]$

of the individual exponential function. Since the derivative of e^{st} is se^{st}, it follows that

$$\frac{df}{dt} \longrightarrow s F(s)$$

See Chapter 4 for more discussion on this point.

Example 5.1

Find

$$\mathscr{L}^{-1}\left(\ln\frac{s+a}{s+b}\right).$$

Let

$$F(s) = \ln\frac{s+a}{s+b}$$

$$= \ln(s+a) - \ln(s+b)$$

$$\frac{dF}{ds} = \frac{1}{s+a} - \frac{1}{s+b}$$

From Table 5.1 it is evident that

$$(e^{-at} - e^{-bt})\,u(t) \longrightarrow \frac{dF}{ds}$$

Using frequency-differentiation property (Eq. 5.38), we get

$$f(t) = \frac{1}{t} (e^{-bt} - e^{-at}) u(t)$$

Example 5.2

Find

$$\mathcal{L}^{-1} s \ln \left(\frac{s + a}{s + b} \right).$$

We have

$$\frac{1}{t} (e^{-bt} - e^{-at}) u(t) \longrightarrow \ln \left(\frac{s + a}{s + b} \right)$$

Using time-differentiation property (Eq. 5.42), we get

$$\frac{d}{dt} \left[\frac{1}{t} (e^{-bt} - e^{-at}) u(t) \right] \longrightarrow s \ln \left(\frac{s + a}{s + b} \right)$$

Note that $f(0^-) = 0$. Similarly

$$\int_0^t \left[\frac{1}{t} (e^{-bt} - e^{-at}) \right] dt \longrightarrow \frac{1}{s} \ln \left(\frac{s + a}{s + b} \right)$$

Example 5.3

Find

$$\mathcal{L} \left[\frac{\sin \omega t}{t} \right] u(t).$$

From Table 5.1 and frequency-integration property (Eq. 5.54), we get

$$\mathcal{L} \left[\frac{\sin \omega t}{t} \right] = \int_s^\infty \frac{\omega}{s^2 + \omega^2} ds \qquad (5.55)$$

$$= \tan^{-1} \left(\frac{s}{\omega} \right) \Big|_s^\infty$$

$$= \frac{\pi}{2} - \tan^{-1} \left(\frac{s}{\omega} \right)$$

$$= \cot^{-1} \left(\frac{s}{\omega} \right)$$

5.12 APPROXIMATION TECHNIQUES

Often a function $f(t)$, whose Laplace transform is to be determined, is known only graphically. In such cases the transform can be evaluated by properly approximating the function. Here we shall describe some approximation techniques.

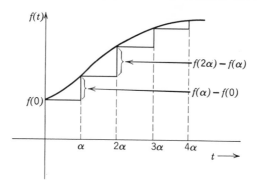

Figure 5.7

I. Staircase Approximation

A given function is approximated by a staircase function as shown in Fig. 5.7. The steps are spaced α seconds apart. It is not necessary to space the steps uniformly. One may choose the spacing suitable for a given function. For the sake of simplicity we shall assume here uniform spacing. Note that the approximation may be improved as much as desired by making α small.

The staircase approximation of $f(t)$ will be denoted by $f_a(t)$. It is obvious from Fig. 5.7 that $f_a(t)$ can be expressed as a sum of step functions as follows.

$$(t) = f(0)u(t) + [f(\alpha) - f(0)]u(t - \alpha) + [f(2\alpha) - f(\alpha)]u(t - 2\alpha)$$
$$+ \cdots \quad (5.56)$$

The Laplace transform of Eq. 5.56 can be obtained easily with the help of time-shifting property (Eq. 5.36) as follows.

$$F_a(s) = \frac{1}{s} \{f(0) + [f(\alpha) - f(0)]e^{-s\alpha} + [f(2\alpha) - f(\alpha)]e^{-2s\alpha} + \cdots\}$$

$$= \frac{(1 - e^{-s\alpha})}{s} [f(0) + f(\alpha)e^{-s\alpha} + f(2\alpha)e^{-2s\alpha} + \cdots + \cdots]$$

$$= \frac{(1 - e^{-s\alpha})}{s} \sum_n f(n\alpha)e^{-ns\alpha} \quad (5.57)$$

For higher accuracy, α should be chosen small. If α is small enough, so that

$$s\alpha \to 0,$$

then

$$e^{-s\alpha} = 1 - s\alpha + \frac{(s\alpha)^2}{2!} + \cdots$$

$$\simeq 1 - s\alpha$$

and

$$1 - e^{-s\alpha} \simeq s\alpha$$

Equation 5.57 can now be written as

$$F_a(s) \simeq \alpha \sum_n f(n\alpha)e^{-ns\alpha} \qquad (5.58)$$

2. Straight-Line Segment Approximation

Here a function is approximated by straight-line segments as shown in Fig. 5.8. The second derivative of the approximated function $f_a(t)$ yields a train of impulses as shown in Fig. 5.8. It is obvious that

$$f_a''(t) = a_0\,\delta(t) + a_1\,\delta(t - \alpha_1) + a_2\,\delta(t - \alpha_2) + a_3\,\delta(t - \alpha_3) \qquad (5.59)$$

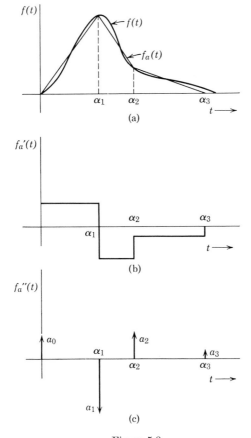

Figure 5.8

The Laplace transform of $f_a''(t)$ is s^2 times the transform of $f_a(t)$. The transform of both sides of Eq. 5.59 yields

$$s^2 F_a(s) = a_0 + a_1 e^{-s\alpha_1} + a_2 e^{-s\alpha_2} + a_3 e^{-s\alpha_3}$$

Hence

$$F_a(s) = \frac{1}{s^2}(a_0 + a_1 e^{-s\alpha_1} + a_2 e^{-s\alpha_2} + a_3 e^{-s\alpha_3})$$

In general

$$F_a(s) = \frac{1}{s^2} \sum_n a_n e^{-s\alpha_n} \tag{5.60}$$

3. Higher Order Approximation

It is also possible to approximate $f(t)$ by a sequence of parabolic curves, cubic curves, or curves of higher powers of t. If $f(t)$ is approximated by a sequence of curves of the nth power of t, then the approximated function has to be differentiated $n + 1$ times to obtain the sequence of impulses.[8] The transform of this sequence of impulses is $s^{n+1} F_a(s)$. The accuracy of approximation can be improved by differentiating $f(t)$ first and then approximating the derivative of $f(t)$ by various sequences as discussed above.

There are a number of other methods available for the evaluation of $F(s)$ from $f(t)$. For a detailed discussion on the various methods, see I. M. Horowitz.[9] In these approximations the factor e^{-ks} may, however, prove a little awkward to deal with, since each term represents a function delayed by a certain amount in the time domain. The addition of such a large number of functions that are delayed by various amounts is very laborious.

The difficulty associated with exponential functions is sometimes avoided by approximating an exponential function by a rational algebraic function.

$$e^{-ks} \simeq \frac{a_0 + a_1 s + a_2 s^2 + \cdots + a_m s^m}{b_0 + b_1 s + b_2 s^2 + \cdots + b_n s^n} \tag{5.61}$$

This is also known as the Padé approximation. The accuracy of approximation can be improved by choosing m and n sufficiently large. The values of coefficients a's and b's for various values of m and n can be found from standard Padé tables.[10]

---

[8] E. A. Guillemin, "Computational Techniques which Simplify the Correlation Between Steady State and Transient Response of Filters and Other Networks," *Proc. National Electronics Conference*, 1953, Vol. 9, 1954.

[9] I. M. Horowitz, *Synthesis of Feedback Systems*, Academic Press, New York, 1963, pp. 658–708.

[10] D. F. Tuttle, Jr., *Network Synthesis*, Wiley, New York, 1958, pp. 760–782.

Note that the Padé approximation becomes better and better with larger numbers of terms in the numerator and the denominator of Eq. 5.61. For a given number of terms the approximation becomes better for smaller values of s. Thus, if we are interested only in low frequencies, a fairly good approximation may be obtained only with a few terms.

A Padé table (see Table 5.3) may be constructed by expanding the function in Taylor series about the origin.

$$e^x = 1 + x + \frac{x^2}{2!} + \frac{x^3}{3!} + \frac{x^4}{4!} + \cdots + \cdots . \qquad (5.62)$$

Suppose we want to approximate e^x as

$$e^x \simeq \frac{a_0 + a_1 x}{1 + b_1 x}$$

By long division this may be expressed as

$$e^x = a_0 + (a_1 - a_0 b_1)x - b_1(a_1 - a_0 b_1)x^2 + \cdots \qquad (5.63)$$

Equating Eq. 5.62 with Eq. 5.63, we get

$$a_0 = 1, \qquad a_1 = \tfrac{1}{2}, \qquad \text{and} \quad b_1 = -\tfrac{1}{2}$$

Thus

$$e^x \simeq \frac{1 + \dfrac{x}{2}}{1 - \dfrac{x}{2}}$$

The higher order approximations may be obtained in a similar manner.

5.13 CAUSAL PERIODIC SIGNALS

A causal periodic signal of period T repeats itself every T seconds starting at $t = 0$. Therefore, such a function can be represented as a sum of the function in the first T seconds (the first cycle) and this same function delayed by T, $2T$, $3T$, $\ldots$, seconds. If we designate the first cycle of $f(t)$ as $f_0(t)$, then (see Fig. 5.9):

$$f(t) = f_0(t) + f_0(t - T) + f_0(t - 2T) + \cdots + f_0(t - nT) + \cdots \qquad (5.64)$$

Let

$$\mathscr{L}[f_0(t)] = F_0(s), \qquad \text{and} \quad \mathscr{L}[f(t)] = F(s)$$

TABLE 5.3

The Padé Table for e^x, Approximated at the Origin

	$m = 0$	$m = 1$	$m = 2$	$m = 3$	$m = 4$
$n = 0$	$\dfrac{1}{1}$	$\dfrac{1+x}{1}$	$\dfrac{1+x+\frac{1}{2}x^2}{1}$	$\dfrac{1+x+\frac{1}{2}x^2+\frac{1}{6}x^3}{1}$	$\dfrac{1+x+\frac{1}{2}x^2+\frac{1}{6}x^3+\frac{1}{24}x^4}{1}$
$n = 1$	$\dfrac{1}{1-x}$	$\dfrac{1+\frac{1}{2}x}{1-\frac{1}{2}x}$	$\dfrac{1+\frac{2}{3}x+\frac{1}{6}x^2}{1-\frac{1}{3}x}$	$\dfrac{1+\frac{3}{4}x+\frac{1}{4}x^2+\frac{1}{24}x^3}{1-\frac{1}{4}x}$	$\dfrac{1+\frac{4}{5}x+\frac{3}{10}x^2+\frac{1}{15}x^3+\frac{1}{120}x^4}{1-\frac{1}{5}x}$
$n = 2$	$\dfrac{1}{1-x+\frac{x^2}{2!}}$	$\dfrac{1+\frac{1}{3}x}{1-\frac{2}{3}x+\frac{1}{6}x^2}$	$\dfrac{1+\frac{1}{2}x+\frac{1}{12}x^2}{1-\frac{1}{2}x+\frac{1}{12}x^2}$	$\dfrac{1+\frac{3}{5}x+\frac{3}{20}x^2+\frac{1}{60}x^3}{1-\frac{2}{5}x+\frac{1}{20}x^2}$	$\dfrac{1+\frac{2}{3}x+\frac{1}{5}x^2+\frac{1}{30}x^3+\frac{1}{360}x^4}{1-\frac{1}{3}x+\frac{1}{30}x^2}$
$n = 3$	$\dfrac{1}{1-x+\frac{x^2}{2!}-\frac{x^3}{3!}}$	$\dfrac{1+\frac{1}{4}x}{1-\frac{3}{4}x+\frac{1}{4}x^2-\frac{1}{24}x^3}$	$\dfrac{1+\frac{2}{5}x+\frac{1}{20}x^2}{1-\frac{3}{5}x+\frac{3}{20}x^2-\frac{1}{60}x^3}$	$\dfrac{1+\frac{1}{2}x+\frac{1}{10}x^2+\frac{1}{120}x^3}{1-\frac{1}{2}x+\frac{1}{10}x^2-\frac{1}{120}x^3}$	$\dfrac{1+\frac{4}{7}x+\frac{1}{7}x^2+\frac{2}{105}x^3+\frac{1}{840}x^4}{1-\frac{3}{7}x+\frac{1}{14}x^2-\frac{1}{210}x^3}$
$n = 4$	$\dfrac{1}{1-x+\frac{x^2}{2!}-\frac{x^3}{3!}+\frac{x^4}{4!}}$	$\dfrac{1+\frac{1}{5}x}{1-\frac{4}{5}x+\frac{3}{10}x^2-\frac{1}{15}x^3+\frac{1}{120}x^4}$	$\dfrac{1+\frac{1}{3}x+\frac{1}{30}x^2}{1-\frac{2}{3}x+\frac{1}{5}x^2-\frac{1}{30}x^3+\frac{1}{360}x^4}$	$\dfrac{1+\frac{3}{7}x+\frac{1}{14}x^2+\frac{1}{210}x^3}{1-\frac{4}{7}x+\frac{1}{7}x^2-\frac{2}{105}x^3+\frac{1}{840}x^4}$	$\dfrac{1+\frac{1}{2}x+\frac{3}{28}x^2+\frac{1}{84}x^3+\frac{1}{1680}x^4}{1-\frac{1}{2}x+\frac{3}{28}x^2-\frac{1}{84}x^3+\frac{1}{1680}x^4}$

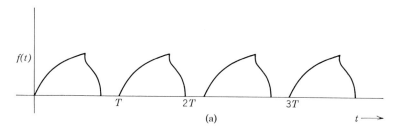

(a)

$t \longrightarrow$

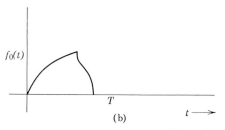

(b)

$t \longrightarrow$

Figure 5.9

Taking the transform of both sides of Eq. 5.64 and using the time-shift property, we get

$$F(s) = F_0(s) + F_0(s)e^{-sT} + F_0(s)e^{-2sT} + \cdots + F_0(s)e^{-nsT} + \cdots$$

$$\cdots + \cdots$$

$$= F_0(s)[1 + e^{-sT} + e^{-2sT} + e^{-3sT} + \cdots + e^{-nsT} + \cdots + \cdots]$$

$$= \frac{F_0(s)}{1 - e^{-sT}} \tag{5.65}$$

Example 5.4

A rectified half sine wave (Fig. 5.10) is a causal periodic function with period T equal to $2\pi/\omega$. We shall identify the first cycle of $f(t)$ as $f_0(t)$. Then

$$f_0(t) = \begin{cases} A \sin \omega t & \left(0 < t < \dfrac{\pi}{\omega}\right) \\[2mm] 0 & \left(t > \dfrac{\pi}{\omega}\right) \end{cases}$$

$$F_0(s) = \mathcal{L}[f_0(t)] = \int_0^{\pi/\omega} A \sin (\omega t)e^{-st}\, dt$$

$$= \frac{A}{2j} \int_0^{\pi/\omega} [e^{(j\omega - s)t} - e^{-(j\omega + s)t}]\, dt$$

$$= \frac{\omega(1 + e^{-\pi s/\omega})}{s^2 + \omega^2}$$

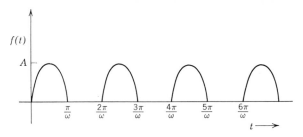

Figure 5.10

The function $f_0(t)$ repeats itself every $2\pi/\omega$ seconds to yield the rectified half sine wave. Therefore

$$F(s) = \frac{F_0(s)}{1 - e^{(-2\pi/\omega)s}}$$

$$= \frac{\omega}{(s^2 + \omega^2)} \frac{(1 + e^{-\pi s/\omega})}{(1 - e^{-2\pi s/\omega})} = \frac{\omega}{s^2 + \omega^2} \frac{1}{1 - e^{-\pi s/\omega}}$$

Example 5.5

Determine the Laplace transform of the rectangular pulses of width t_0, repeating with periodicity T (Fig. 5.11).

$$f_0(t) = Au(t) - Au(t - t_0)$$

$$F_0(s) = \frac{A}{s} - \frac{A}{s} e^{-st_0}$$

$$= \frac{A}{s}(1 - e^{-st_0})$$

The desired transform $F(s)$ is given by

$$F(s) = \frac{F_0(s)}{1 - e^{-sT}}$$

$$= \frac{A}{s}\left[\frac{1 - e^{-st_0}}{1 - e^{-sT}}\right] \tag{5.66}$$

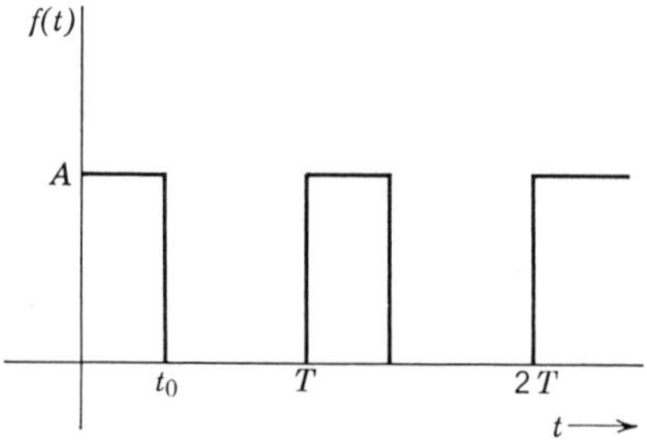

Figure 5.11

5.14 THE INITIAL- AND FINAL-VALUE THEOREM

If the transform $F(s)$ of an unknown function $f(t)$ is known, then it is possible to determine the initial and final value of $f(t)$, that is, the values of $f(t)$ at $t = 0^+$ and $t = \infty$. With the help of the initial- and final-value theorem, this can be done without having to find the inverse transform of $F(s)$.

I. The Initial-Value Theorem

If $f(t)$ and its first derivative are Laplace-transformable, then the initial value of $f(t)$ is given by

$$f(0^+) = \lim_{s \to \infty} [sF(s)] \tag{5.67}$$

Proof. Consider the transform of the derivative of $f(t)$. From Eq. 5.42,

$$sF(s) - f(0^-) = \int_{0^-}^{\infty} \frac{df}{dt} e^{-st}\, dt$$

$$= \int_{0^-}^{0^+} \frac{df}{dt} e^{-st}\, dt + \int_{0^+}^{\infty} \frac{df}{dt} e^{-st}\, dt$$

In general, there may be a jump discontinuity in $f(t)$ at $t = 0$. In such a case, the derivative of $f(t)$ at $t = 0$ is an impulse of strength equal to the discontinuity. Thus

$$\frac{df}{dt}(0) = [f(0^+) - f(0^-)]\, \delta(t) \quad \text{and} \quad e^{-st}(0) = 1$$

Therefore

$$sF(s) - f(0^-) = \int_{0^-}^{0^+} [f(0^+) - f(0^-)]\, \delta(t)\, dt + \int_{0^+}^{\infty} \frac{df}{dt} e^{-st}\, dt$$

$$= f(0^+) - f(0^-) + \int_{0^+}^{\infty} \frac{df}{dt} e^{-st}\, dt$$

Therefore

$$sF(s) = f(0^+) + \int_{0^+}^{\infty} \frac{df}{dt} e^{-st}\, dt \tag{5.68}$$

Now, if we let $s \to \infty$ in Eq. 5.68, the integral on the right-hand side vanishes, and we have

$$\lim_{s \to \infty} [sF(s)] = f(0^+)$$

Note that the left-hand side of the above equation may exist without the existence of $f(0^+)$. Therefore this theorem should be applied only when $f(0^+)$ exists.

2. The Final-Value Theorem

If $f(t)$ and its first derivative are Laplace-transformable, then

$$\lim_{s \to 0} [sF(s)] = f(\infty) \tag{5.69}$$

Proof. Again, let us consider the transform of the derivative of $f(t)$. Consider Eq. 5.68.

$$sF(s) = f(0^+) + \int_{0^+}^{\infty} \frac{df}{dt} e^{-st} \, dt \tag{5.70}$$

Now, if we let $s \to 0$ in Eq. 5.70, we get

$$\lim_{s \to 0} [sF(s)] = f(0^+) + \int_{0^+}^{\infty} \frac{df}{dt} \, dt$$

$$= f(0^+) + f(t) \Big|_{0^+}^{\infty} = f(0^+) + f(\infty) - f(0^+)$$

$$= f(\infty)$$

Therefore

$$f(\infty) = \lim_{s \to 0} [sF(s)]$$

Here, again, the right-hand side of the above equation may exist without the existence of $f(\infty)$. Hence, it is important to know that $f(\infty)$ exists before applying this theorem.

5.15 EVALUATION OF BILATERAL TRANSFORMS FROM UNILATERAL TRANSFORMS

We shall now show that any bilateral transform can be expressed as a sum of two unilateral transforms. It is, therefore, possible to evaluate bilateral transforms from the tables of unilateral transforms.

Consider a function $f(t)$ shown in Fig. 5.12a. We can separate $f(t)$ into two component functions $f_1(t)$ and $f_2(t)$ representing a positive time component and a negative time component respectively of $f(t)$ as shown in Figs. 5.12b and 5.12c. In other words,

$$f_1(t) = f(t)u(t)$$

and

$$f_2(t) = f(t)u(-t)$$

The bilateral Laplace transform of $f(t)$ is given by

$$\mathscr{F}_c[f(t)] = \int_{-\infty}^{\infty} f(t)e^{-st} \, dt$$

$$= \int_{-\infty}^{0} f_2(t)e^{-st} \, dt + \int_{0}^{\infty} f_1(t)e^{-st} \, dt$$

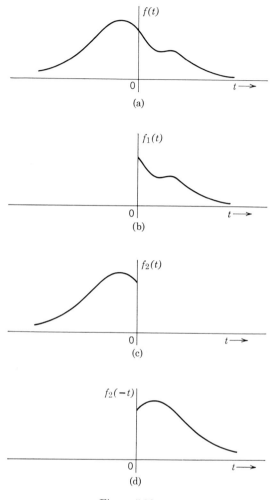

Figure 5.12

Changing the dummy variable t in the first integral to $-t$, we get

$$\mathscr{F}_c[f(t)] = \int_0^\infty f_2(-t)e^{st}\, dt + \int_0^\infty f_1(t)e^{-st}\, dt$$

$$= F_2(-s) + F_1(s) \tag{5.71}$$

where

$$F_1(s) = \mathscr{L}[f_1(t)] \tag{5.72}$$

$$F_2(s) = \mathscr{L}[f_2(-t)]$$

Function $f_2(-t)$ is a mirror image of $f_2(t)$ about the vertical axis $t = 0$ as shown in Fig. 5.12d. Hence the contribution due to the negative time function may be found as follows.

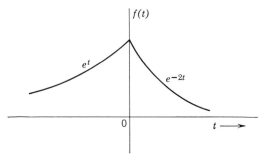

Figure 5.13

(1) Take the reflection (mirror image) of the negative time function about the $t = 0$ axis and find its unilateral Laplace transform.

(2) Replace s by $-s$ in the transform obtained in (1). This gives the contribution to the transform due to the negative time function.

The procedure is illustrated by the following example.

Example 5.6

Find the bilateral Laplace transform of $f(t)$ given by

$$f(t) = e^{-2t}u(t) + e^{t}u(-t)$$

This function is shown in Fig. 5.13. It is evident that

$$f_1(t) = e^{-2t}u(t)$$
$$f_2(t) = e^{t}u(-t)$$

and

$$f_2(-t) = e^{-t}u(t)$$

Hence

$$F_1(s) = \mathscr{L}[f_1(t)] = \frac{1}{s+2}$$

$$F_2(s) = \mathscr{L}[f_2(-t)] = \frac{1}{s+1}$$

Therefore

$$\mathscr{F}_c[f(t)] = F_1(s) + F_2(-s) = \frac{1}{s+2} + \frac{1}{-s+1} = \frac{-3}{(s+2)(s-1)}$$

Note that the region of convergence is given by $-2 < \sigma < 1$ (see Section 5.2).

Example 5.7

Find the inverse transform of $F(s)$ given by

$$F(s) = \frac{s}{(s+2)(s+1)} \qquad (-2 < \sigma < -1)$$

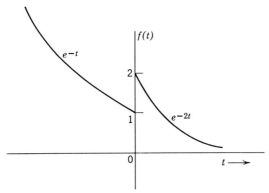

Figure 5.14

$F(s)$ may be expanded by partial fractions (see Section 6.3) as

$$F(s) = \frac{2}{s+2} - \frac{1}{s+1}$$

Since the pole at $s = -2$ lies to the left of the strip of convergence, the term $2/(s+2)$ represents the positive time function (see Section 5.2). Similarly, the term $-1/(s+1)$ represents the negative time function since the pole at $s = -1$ lies to the right of the strip of convergence. Hence

$$F_1(s) = \frac{2}{s+2} \quad \text{and} \quad f_1(t) = 2e^{-2t}u(t)$$

$$F_2(-s) = -\frac{1}{s+1} \quad \text{and} \quad F_2(s) = \frac{1}{s-1}$$

Therefore

$$f_2(-t) = \mathcal{L}^{-1}[F_2(s)] = e^t u(t)$$

and

$$f_2(t) = e^{-t}u(-t)$$

Thus

$$f(t) = f_1(t) + f_2(t)$$
$$= 2e^{-2t}u(t) + e^{-t}u(-t)$$

The function $f(t)$ is shown in Fig. 5.14.

PROBLEMS

1. Find the region of convergence of the bilateral Laplace transform of the following functions.

(a) $e^{tu(t)}$

(b) $e^{-tu(t)}$

(c) e^t

(d) $\dfrac{1}{1+t^2}$

(e) $\dfrac{1}{1+e^t}$

(f) $\dfrac{1}{1+|t^3|}$

(g) e^{-at^2}

2. Find the region of convergence of the Laplace transform of the following functions.

(a) $\sin \omega_0 t u(t)$

(c) $\dfrac{1}{1 + t^2} u(t)$

(b) $te^{-at}u(t)$

(d) $\dfrac{1}{1 + e^t} u(t)$

3. Find the Laplace transforms of the following functions.

(a) $u(t) - u(t - 1)$

(h) $t^2 e^{-t}u(t - \tau)$

(b) $t \sin (\omega t)u(t)$

(i) $(t - \tau) \sin \omega(t - \tau)$

(c) $\dfrac{1 - \cos at}{t} u(t)$

(j) $\sin \omega_1 t \cos \omega_2 t u(t)$

(d) $t^2 e^{-at}u(t)$

(k) $e^{-t} \displaystyle\int_0^t t \sin \omega t \, dt$

(e) $\sin \omega(t - \tau)u(t - \tau)$

(l) $\dfrac{e^{-at} \sin (\omega t)u(t)}{t}$

(f) $\sin (\omega t)u(t - \tau)$

(m) $\dfrac{e^{-t} - 1}{t} u(t)$

(g) $\sin \omega(t - \tau)u(t)$

(n) $te^{-at} \cos (\omega t)u(t)$

4. Time-shifting property (Eq. 5.36) is somewhat modified for negative t_0. Show that for $t_0 < 0$:

$$\mathscr{L}[f(t - t_0)] = e^{-st_0}\left[F(s) - \int_0^{-t_0} f(t)e^{-st} \, dt\right]$$

5. Find the inverse Laplace transforms of the following functions.

(a) $\dfrac{s}{(s + a)^2}$

(e) $\dfrac{e^{-(s-1)}}{(s - 1)^2 + 4}$

(b) $\dfrac{s^2}{(s + a)^2 + b^2}$

(f) $\ln \left(\dfrac{s + 1}{s + 2}\right)$

(c) $\dfrac{se^{-s}}{s + a}$

(g) $s \ln \left(\dfrac{s + 1}{s + 2}\right)$

(d) $\dfrac{e^{-s} + e^{-2s}}{(s + 1)(s + 2)}$

(h) $\dfrac{1}{s} \ln \left(\dfrac{s + 1}{s + 2}\right)$

Caution: The derivative of $f(t)u(t)$ yields an impulse $f(0^+)\delta(t)$ at the origin.

6. Find the Laplace transforms of the functions shown in Fig. P-5.6.

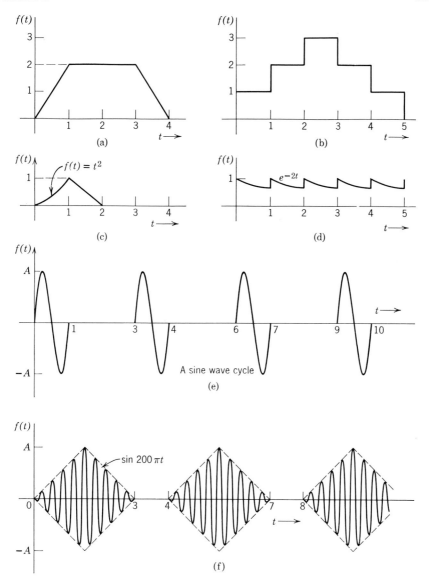

Figure P-5.6

7. Given that

$$e^{at}u(t) \longrightarrow \frac{1}{s-a}$$

construct the entire Table 5.1 from the above equation and the properties of the Laplace transform listed in Table 5.2.

8. A certain function $f(t)$ is known to have a transform:

$$F(s) = \frac{6s^2 + 8s - 5}{s(2s^2 + 6s + 5)}$$

Find $f(0^+)$ and $f(\infty)$.

9. Find the (bilateral) Laplace transform and the region of its absolute convergence for the following functions. Sketch each of the functions.

(a) $e^{-|t|}$

(b) $e^{-|t|} \cos t$

(c) $e^t u(t) + e^{2t} u(-t)$

(d) $\cos \omega_0 t u(t) + e^t u(-t)$

(e) $e^{-t u(t)}$

(f) $e^t u(-t)$

10. Find $f(t)$ whose bilateral Laplace transform $F(s)$ is given as follows.

(a) $\dfrac{1}{s + 2} + \dfrac{1}{s + 3}$, $(-3 < \sigma < -2)$

(b) $\dfrac{1}{s - 2} + \dfrac{1}{s - 3}$, $(2 < \sigma < 3)$

(c) $\dfrac{1}{s + 1} + \dfrac{1}{s + 3} + \dfrac{1}{s - 5}$, $(-1 < \sigma < 5)$

11. Find the inverse transform of $F(s)$, if:

(a) $F(s) = \dfrac{1}{s + 1} + \dfrac{1}{s + 2}$, $(-2 < \sigma < -1)$

(b) $F(s) = \dfrac{1}{s + 1} + \dfrac{1}{s + 2}$, $(\sigma > -1)$

(c) $F(s) = \dfrac{1}{s + 1} + \dfrac{1}{s + 2}$, $(\sigma < -2)$

12. If $f(t)$ is absolutely integrable, then show that the poles of $F(s)$ must lie in LHP if $f(t)$ is the positive time function and in RHP if $f(t)$ is the negative time function.

chapter 6

Frequency Analysis
of Linear Systems

6.1 INTRODUCTION

In Chapter 2 the concept of frequency analysis of linear systems was outlined. This method, based upon the concept of superposition, holds true by virtue of the linearity property of the system. The response to an eternal exponential function e^{st} ($-\infty < t < \infty$) was shown to be $H(s)e^{st}$. In Chapter 5 it was shown that any signal $f(t)$ can be expressed as a continuous sum of eternal exponential functions. Hence the response of a system to a driving function $f(t)$ will be a continuous sum of the responses of the system to individual exponential components. This approach has been discussed at length in Chapter 2. We shall briefly review these concepts.

If a linear time-invariant system is excited by an exponential signal e^{st} at time $t = 0$, then its response consists of two components: a transient component, which is characteristic of the system, and a steady-state component $H(s)e^{st}$, where $H(s)$ is the transfer function of the system. In stable systems the transient component decays with time. The steady-state component $H(s)e^{st}$ may or may not decay with time depending upon the value of s, the complex frequency. If s is such that the magnitude of e^{st} decays at a rate slower than that of the transient component, then after a long time the transient component would become negligible compared to the steady-state component $H(s)e^{st}$. The steady-state component dominates the response and hence the response of the system will be given entirely by the steady-state component $H(s)e^{st}$ after a sufficiently long time. If the frequency s is such that the magnitude of e^{st} decays at a rate slower than that of the transient component, then the signal e^{st} is said to satisfy the *dominance condition* for the system.

Assume that a signal e^{st} satisfies the dominance condition and that the system is excited by this driving function e^{st} at time $t = -\infty$. Then, at any finite time, it would seem that the excitation was applied at an infinitely remote time in the past. Hence the transient component would become negligible compared to the steady-state component, and the response would consist entirely of the steady-state term $H(s)e^{st}$. We therefore conclude that the complete response of a linear time-invariant system to an eternal exponential signal e^{st} is given by $H(s)e^{st}$. It is important to remember that this statement applies to an eternal or an everlasting exponential signal e^{st} $(-\infty < t < \infty)$ which satisfies the dominance condition.

If the driving function is given by a sum of eternal exponential functions satisfying the dominance condition

$$f(t) = C_1 e^{s_1 t} + C_2 e^{s_2 t} + \cdots + C_n e^{s_n t} \tag{6.1}$$

then, by the principle of superposition, $r(t)$, the response of the system— will be the sum of the responses of the system to the individual components.

$$r(t) = C_1 H(s_1)e^{s_1 t} + C_2 H(s_2)e^{s_2 t} + \cdots + C_n H(s_n)e^{s_n t} \tag{6.2}$$

If a driving function $f(t)$ is expressed as a continuous sum of eternal exponential functions, then the response will be given by a continuous sum of the responses of the system to the individual components. The frequency transforms discussed thus far (Fourier and Laplace) can express any function $f(t)$ as a continuous sum of eternal exponential functions.

$$f(t) = \frac{1}{2\pi j} \int_{\sigma-j\infty}^{\sigma+j\infty} F(s)e^{st} \, ds \tag{6.3}$$

If the values of s are chosen so that the dominance condition is satisfied, then the response $r(t)$ of the system will be given by[1]

$$r(t) = \frac{1}{2\pi j} \int_{\sigma-j\infty}^{\sigma+j\infty} H(s)F(s)e^{st} \, ds \tag{6.4}$$

---

[1] This relation can also be proved rigorously as follows. It is shown in Chapter 10 that

$$r(t) = h(t) * f(t)$$

where

$$h(t) = \mathscr{L}^{-1}[H(s)]$$

Hence, from the time convolution theorem, it follows that $r(t) = \mathscr{L}^{-1}[H(s)F(s)]$. This is the same result as that in Eq. 6.4.

We have thus obtained the response of a system to a driving function in terms of the integral in Eq. 6.4. What has been gained by this procedure? Actually, the integral in Eq. 6.4 represents integration in the complex plane and requires familiarity with the functions of complex variables in general and the calculus of residues in particular. It appears that we may have traded one difficulty for another. We seem to have avoided the need for solving simultaneous integrodifferential equations at the cost of evaluating a complex integral. Fortunately, however, in most of the problems encountered in practice, the evaluation of the integral in Eq. 6.4 can be avoided through the use of standard tables of transforms. This can be easily seen when we write Eq. 6.4 as an inverse Laplace transform.

$$r(t) = \mathscr{L}^{-1}[H(s)F(s)] \tag{6.5}$$

If $f(t)$ is a noncausal function, then we must use the bilateral Laplace transform (see Section 6.16). Once $H(s)F(s)$ is known, its inverse transform can be readily found from the standard tables of Laplace transforms similar to Table 5.1.

Example 6.1

Consider a simple $R\text{-}C$ circuit, shown in Fig. 6.1, and driven by a unit step function $u(t)$ applied across terminals aa'. The output voltage $v_o(t)$ across the terminals bb' is to be determined.

It is evident that the transfer function of this network which relates the voltage across terminals bb' to the voltage across aa', is given by

$$H(s) = \frac{1}{1 + 1/s} = \frac{s}{s + 1}$$

The driving function $f(t) = u(t)$. The Laplace transform of $u(t)$, as seen from Table 5.1, is $1/s$. Therefore

$$F(s) = \mathscr{L}[f(t)] = \frac{1}{s}$$

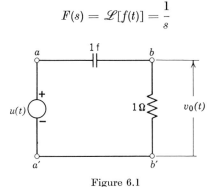

Figure 6.1

The response function $v_0(t)$, as given by Eq. 6.5, is

$$v_0(t) = \mathcal{L}^{-1}[H(s)F(s)]$$

$$v_0(t) = \mathcal{L}^{-1}\left[\frac{s}{s+1}\frac{1}{s}\right]$$

$$= \mathcal{L}^{-1}\left[\frac{1}{s+1}\right]$$

Referring to Table 5.1, we note that the inverse Laplace transform of $1/(s+1)$ is $e^{-t}u(t)$. Hence

$$v_0(t) = \mathcal{L}^{-1}\left[\frac{1}{s+1}\right] = e^{-t}u(t)$$

The principles of frequency analysis of linear systems may be expressed succinctly as follows.

(1) The response of a linear time-invariant system to an eternal exponential[2] signal e^{st} is given by $H(s)e^{st}$.

$$e^{st} \rightarrow H(s)e^{st}$$

(2) By means of frequency transforms, every driving function $f(t)$ can be expressed as a continuous sum of exponential functions.

$$f(t) = \frac{1}{2\pi j}\int_{\sigma-j\infty}^{\sigma+j\infty} F(s)e^{st}\,ds \tag{6.6}$$

(3) By virtue of linearity, the principle of superposition applies, and the response $r(t)$ is given by a continuous sum of the responses of the system to individual components.

$$r(t) = \frac{1}{2\pi j}\int_{\sigma-j\infty}^{\sigma+j\infty} H(s)F(s)e^{st}\,ds \tag{6.7}$$

The procedure for analyzing any linear system can be written down in simple steps. Let $f(t)$ and $r(t)$ be the driving function and the response function, respectively.

(1) Evaluate $H(s)$, the transfer function of the system, relating the response variable to the driving variable. (This is discussed in Chapter 2.)

(2) Find $F(s)$, the Laplace transform of $f(t)$, from the table of transforms (Table 5.1).

$$F(s) = \mathcal{L}[f(t)]$$

(3) The response $r(t)$ is given by the inverse transform of $H(s)F(s)$.

$$r(t) = \mathcal{L}^{-1}[H(s)F(s)]$$

From the table of transforms, find the inverse transform of $H(s)F(s)$. This is the desired response $r(t)$.

The procedure is represented graphically in Fig. 6.2.

---

[2] It is assumed that these exponentials satisfy the dominance condition for the system. We shall presently show that this is always possible.

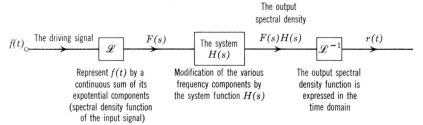

Figure 6.2

Example 6.2

Find the current $i(t)$ in a series R-L-C circuit (Fig. 6.3) when a voltage of 100 volts is switched on across the terminals aa' at $t = 0$.

Step 1. The transfer function $H(s)$, relating the current $i(t)$ to the voltage across terminals aa', is obviously given by an admittance of the circuit across terminals aa'.

$$H(s) = \frac{1}{2 + s + 1/0.2s}$$

$$= \frac{s}{s^2 + 2s + 5}$$

Step 2. The driving function $f(t)$ is given by $100u(t)$. From Table 5.1,

$$F(s) = \mathscr{L}[100u(t)] = \frac{100}{s}$$

Step 3. The desired response is the current $i(t)$ given by

$$i(t) = \mathscr{L}^{-1}[H(s)F(s)]$$

$$= \mathscr{L}^{-1}\left[\frac{100}{s^2 + 2s + 5}\right]$$

$$= \mathscr{L}^{-1}\left[\frac{100}{(s + 1)^2 + 4}\right]$$

From Table 5.1, pair 9, we obtain

$$i(t) = 50e^{-t}\sin 2t$$

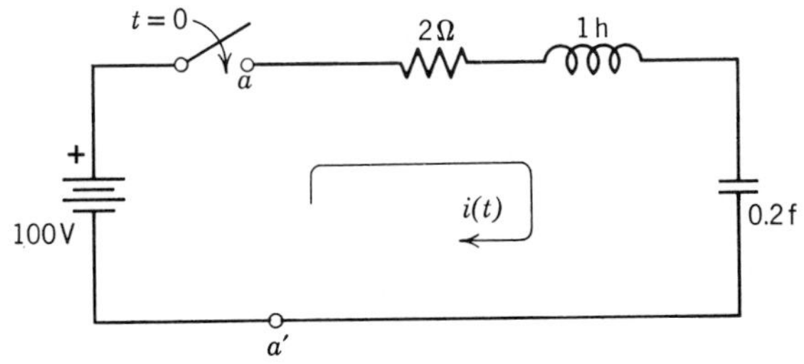

Figure 6.3

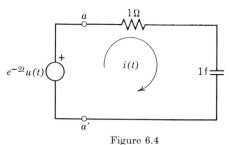

Figure 6.4

Example 6.3

Find the current $i(t)$ in a series R-C circuit, shown in Fig. 6.4, if a voltage $e^{-2t}u(t)$ is applied across terminals aa'.

The transfer function $H(s)$, relating $i(t)$ to the voltage across aa', is given by

$$H(s) = \frac{1}{1 + 1/s} = \frac{s}{s + 1}$$

From Table 5.1, we have

$$F(s) = \mathcal{L}[e^{-2t}u(t)] = \frac{1}{s + 2}$$

Therefore

$$i(t) = \mathcal{L}^{-1}[H(s)F(s)]$$

$$= \mathcal{L}^{-1}\left[\frac{s}{(s + 1)(s + 2)}\right]$$

$$= \mathcal{L}^{-1}\left[\frac{2}{s + 2} - \frac{1}{s + 1}\right]$$

$$= [2e^{-2t} - e^{-t}]u(t)$$

6.2 THE DOMINANCE CONDITION

The response of a linear time-invariant system to an eternal exponential function e^{st} is $H(s)e^{st}$, provided that the exponential e^{st} satisfies the dominance condition for the system. In other words, the statement holds true only for those values of s for which the magnitude of e^{st} decays at a smaller rate than that of the transient component. The method of the Laplace transform evidently holds true if a signal $f(t)$ is expressed as a continuous sum of eternal exponential functions e^{st} which decay at a rate smaller than that of the transient component. At this point we recall the discussion about the region of convergence of the Laplace transform in the s plane (Section 5.6). It was shown that a causal function $f(t)$ can be expressed as a continuous sum of exponential functions in infinitely different ways, depending upon the choice of our path in this region. Moreover, we found that there was a lower limit on the value of σ (Re s), but there was no upper limit. We can therefore choose σ as high as we wish (as long as it is larger than the lower limit σ_{min}). The higher value of σ thus makes the signals $e^{st} = e^{\sigma t}e^{j\omega t}$ grow at a faster rate. Therefore, we can always express $f(t)$ as a continuous sum of exponential functions which can grow at any rate we desire by a proper choice of the path. The dominance condition requires that the magnitudes of exponentials decay at a rate slower than the transient component (or grow at a rate faster than the transient component) of the system. It is evident that this can always be done by choosing σ large enough.[3]

Note that for stable systems the transient component decays with time. Hence the exponentials $e^{j\omega t}$, which have constant magnitudes, also satisfy the dominance condition. It is therefore evident that the Fourier transform can be used to analyze stable systems.

As an example, consider the R-C circuit in Example 6.3 (Fig. 6.4). The transfer function $H(j\omega)$ is given by

$$H(j\omega) = \frac{1}{1 + 1/j\omega} = \frac{j\omega}{1 + j\omega}$$

The Fourier transform of $f(t)$ is found from Table 4.1B.

$$F(j\omega) = \mathscr{F}[e^{-2t}u(t)] = \frac{1}{j\omega + 2}$$

Therefore

$$r(t) = \mathscr{F}^{-1}[H(j\omega)F(j\omega)]$$

$$= \mathscr{F}^{-1}\left[\frac{j\omega}{(j\omega + 2)(j\omega + 1)}\right]$$

$$= \mathscr{F}^{-1}\left[\frac{2}{j\omega + 2} - \frac{1}{j\omega + 1}\right]$$

Using Table 4.1B, we obtain

$$r(t) = [2e^{-2t} - e^{-t}]u(t)$$

This is, of course, the same result as obtained before. We can therefore use the Fourier transform to analyze any linear stable system. In this case, all that we are doing is replacing the variable s by $j\omega$. Hence there is really very little point in using the Fourier transform. The Laplace

---

[3] One can show from the properties of analytic functions that this condition is sufficient but not necessary. All that is required is that the function $f(t)$ should be expressed as a continuous sum of exponentials of frequencies lying to the right of the singularity points (poles) of $H(s)$. However, it was seen in Chapter 5 (Section 5.6) that a function $f(t)$ can be expressed as a continuous sum of exponentials of frequencies lying along any path restricted to the right of the poles of $F(s)$. Hence it follows that in the analysis of a linear system with a transfer function $H(s)$, $f(t)$ must be expressed as a continuous sum of exponentials of frequencies lying along a path to the right of poles of $H(s)$ and $F(s)$ both, that is, to the right of poles of $F(s)H(s)$.

transform, as we saw, is a more general form and the Fourier transform is just a special case obtained by letting $s = j\omega (\sigma = 0)$. Moreover, the Fourier transform cannot be used to analyze unstable systems because by definition the unstable system has a transient component which grows with time. The exponentials $e^{j\omega t}$ used in the Fourier transform have constant magnitudes, and hence do not satisfy the dominance condition.[4] For these reasons the Laplace transform is almost universally adopted for the analysis of linear systems.

Example 6.4

Find the currents $i_1(t)$ and $i_2(t)$ in the network shown in Fig. 6.5a. The switch is closed at time $t = 0$. The driving function $f(t)$ is $10u(t)$.

Step 1. Let $H_1(s)$ and $H_2(s)$ be the transfer functions relating $i_1(t)$ and $i_2(t)$, respectively, to the voltage across the input terminals. The transfer functions can be found by using the techniques described in Chapter 2. The two loop equations are (Fig. 6.5b):

$$V = \left(1 + \frac{s}{2} + \frac{1}{s}\right)I_1 - \frac{1}{s}I_2$$

$$0 = -\frac{1}{s}I_1 + \left(1 + \frac{s}{2} + \frac{1}{s}\right)I_2$$

Using Cramer's rule,

$$I_1 = \frac{\begin{vmatrix} V & -\dfrac{1}{s} \\[2ex] 0 & \dfrac{s^2 + 2s + 2}{2s} \end{vmatrix}}{\begin{vmatrix} \dfrac{s^2 + 2s + 2}{2s} & -\dfrac{1}{s} \\[2ex] -\dfrac{1}{s} & \dfrac{s^2 + 2s + 2}{2s} \end{vmatrix}}$$

$$= \frac{(2s^2 + 4s + 4)V}{s^3 + 4s^2 + 8s + 8}$$

The transfer function $H_1(s)$, by definition, is given by

$$H_1(s) = \frac{I_1}{V} = \frac{2s^2 + 4s + 4}{s^3 + 4s^2 + 8s + 8}$$

$$= \frac{2s^2 + 4s + 4}{(s + 2)(s^2 + 2s + 4)} \tag{6.8}$$

[4] The frequency-analysis method may be used even if the dominance condition is not satisfied. In such cases the transient component must be determined separately. The method becomes rather involved. See, for instance, E. A. Guillemin, *Theory of Linear Physical Systems*, Wiley, New York, 1963.

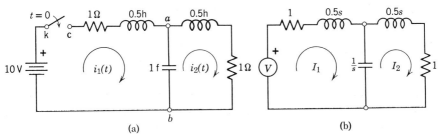

Figure 6.5

Step 2. The driving function $f(t)$ is $10u(t)$. Therefore

$$F(s) = \frac{10}{s}$$

Step 3. The required current $i_1(t)$ is given by

$$i_1(t) = \mathscr{L}^{-1}\left[\frac{10}{s}\ \frac{2s^2 + 4s + 4}{(s+2)(s^2 + 2s + 4)}\right] \tag{6.9}$$

The inverse transform of the above function is not listed in Table 4.1B. Such an expression, however, can be separated into simpler components known as *partial fractions* (to be discussed in the next Section). The above equation can be rearranged into its partial fractions as

$$i_1(t) = \mathscr{L}^{-1}\left[\frac{5}{s} - \frac{5}{s+2} + \frac{10}{(s+1)^2 + 3}\right]$$

The inverse transform of each term now can be found from Table 5.1.

$$i_1(t) = [5 - 5e^{-2t} + \frac{10}{\sqrt{3}}\ e^{-t} \sin \sqrt{3}\ t]u(t) \tag{6.10}$$

Similarly, we find

$$H_2(s) = \frac{4}{(s+2)(s^2 + 2s + 4)} \tag{6.11}$$

$$i_2(t) = \mathscr{L}^{-1}\left[\frac{10}{s}\ \frac{4}{(s+2)(s^2 + 2s + 4)}\right]$$

$$= \mathscr{L}^{-1}\left[\frac{5}{s} - \frac{5}{s+2} - \frac{10}{(s+2)^2 + 3}\right]$$

Again, from Table 5.1, we get

$$i_2(t) = [5 - 5e^{-2t} - \frac{10}{\sqrt{3}}\ e^{-t} \sin \sqrt{3}\ t]\ u(t) \tag{6.12}$$

It will be observed that the inverse transform of

$$\frac{10}{s}\ \frac{4}{(s+2)(s^2 + 2s + 4)}$$

was obtained by separating it into several parts as

$$\frac{40}{s(s+2)(s^2+2s+4)} = \frac{5}{s} - \frac{5}{s+2} - \frac{10}{s^2+2s+4} \tag{6.13}$$

This process is known as partial-fraction expansion. We have to use partial-fraction expansion often in order to find the inverse transform. For this reason we shall study this topic in detail.

6.3 PARTIAL-FRACTION EXPANSION

It was shown in Chapter 2 that the transfer function of linear-lumped networks is a ratio of polynomials in s. Such functions are known as rational algebraic fractions. If $F(s)$, the transform of $f(t)$, is also a rational algebraic fraction, then the transform of the response function is $F(s)H(s)$ and is also a rational algebraic fraction. For most driving functions used in practice (for example, a unit step function, a ramp function, an exponential or sinusoidal function, etc.), the transforms are rational algebraic fractions. Hence, this type of function is often encountered in transform theory.[5] The inverse transform of such functions can be accomplished by separation into several parts, as was done in previous examples.

Let us consider a typical rational algebraic fraction.

$$F(s) = \frac{a_n s^n + a_{n-1}s^{n-1} + \cdots + a_1 s + a_0}{s^m + b_{m-1}s^{m-1} + \cdots + b_1 s + b_0} \tag{6.14}$$

$$= \frac{N(s)}{D(s)} \tag{6.15}$$

There are two possibilities in regard to the relative magnitudes of n and m: (1) $n \geqslant m$, and (2) $n < m$. The function is known as an improper fraction if $n \geqslant m$, and a proper fraction if $n < m$. If the fraction is improper, then it can always be separated into a sum of polynomials in s of the order $(n-m)$ and a proper fraction. Consider, for example, the function $F(s)$.

$$F(s) = \frac{2s^4 + 3s^3 + s^2 + 2s}{s^2 + 4s + 3}$$

---

[5] It should be emphasized here that the transfer function is a rational algebraic fraction for the case of lumped systems alone. For distributed systems, the transfer functions may be irrational functions.

This is an improper fraction and can be expressed as

$$F(s) = \underbrace{(2s^2 - 5s + 15)}_{\substack{\text{polynomial in} \\ \text{positive powers of } s}} - \underbrace{\frac{(43s + 45)}{s^2 + 4s + 3}}_{\text{proper fraction}} \tag{6.16}$$

We have, therefore, represented an improper fraction as a sum of polynomials in positive powers of s and a proper fraction. The inverse transforms of polynomials in positive powers of s are singularity functions (such as impulse functions and their derivatives) and will be discussed later in this chapter. Here we shall restrict the functions $F(s)$ to a proper fraction. Let $s_1, s_2, s_3, \ldots, s_m$ be the roots of the denominator polynomial $D(s) = 0$ in Eq. 6.15.

$$F(s) = \frac{a_n s^n + a_{n-1} s^{n-1} + \cdots + a_1 s + a_0}{(s - s_1)(s - s_2) \cdots (s - s_m)} \tag{6.17}$$

We shall now consider various possibilities regarding the nature of roots $s_1, s_2, \ldots, s_m$.

Case I. All Roots Simple (No Multiple Roots)

Consider, first, the case where all the roots $s_1, s_2, \ldots, s_m$ are distinct (that is, no two roots are identical). Equation 6.17 may be written as

$$F(s) = \frac{N(s)}{(s - s_1)(s - s_2) \cdots (s - s_m)} \tag{6.18}$$

$F(s)$ can be written as the sum of m partial fractions.

$$F(s) = \frac{c_1}{s - s_1} + \frac{c_2}{s - s_2} + \cdots + \frac{c_m}{s - s_m} \tag{6.19}$$

We desire to find the values of the various constants c_r. These constants are also known as residues. Thus, c_r is the residue of the pole at $s = s_r$. Multiplying both sides of Eq. 6.19 by $(s - s_r)$, we get

$$F(s)(s - s_r) = \frac{c_1(s - s_r)}{s - s_1} + \frac{c_2(s - s_r)}{s - s_2} + \cdots + c_r$$

$$+ \frac{c_{r+1}(s - s_r)}{s - s_{r+1}} + \cdots + \frac{c_m(s - s_r)}{s - s_m} \tag{6.20}$$

If we let $s = s_r$ in Eq. 6.20, we observe that all the terms, except c_r, vanish. Also note that the left-hand side does not vanish, even though

$s = s_r$, because the factor $(s - s_r)$ in $D(s)$ cancels with the factor $(s - s_r)$. Thus

$$F(s)(s - s_r)\big|_{s=s_r} = c_r \qquad (6.21)$$

Substituting Eq. 6.18 in Eqs. 6.21, we get

$$\frac{N(s)}{(s - s_1)(s - s_2) \cdots (s - s_{r-1})(s - s_{r+1}) \cdots (s - s_m)}\bigg|_{s=s_r} = c_r \qquad (6.22)$$

There is an alternate method of evaluating c_r. This method is based upon the observation that

$$\frac{D(s)}{s - s_r}\bigg|_{s=s_r} = \frac{d}{ds}[D(s)]\bigg|_{s=s_r} \qquad (6.23)$$

This can be verified as shown below.

$$\frac{d}{ds}[D(s)] = \frac{d}{ds}\left[\frac{D(s)}{s - s_r}(s - s_r)\right]$$

$$= (s - s_r)\frac{d}{ds}\left[\frac{D(s)}{s - s_r}\right] + \frac{D(s)}{s - s_r}$$

Therefore

$$\frac{d}{ds}[D(s)]\bigg|_{s=s_r} = \frac{D(s)}{s - s_r}\bigg|_{s=s_r} \qquad (6.24)$$

Note that $d/ds[D(s)/(s - s_r)]$ is finite at $s = s_r$ because the factor $(s - s_r)$ in the denominator is canceled by the same factor in the numerator. Substituting Eq. 6.24 in Eq. 6.21,

$$c_r = \frac{N(s)}{\dfrac{d}{ds}[D(s)]}\bigg|_{s=s_r}$$

$$= \frac{N(s)}{D'(s)}\bigg|_{s=s_r} \qquad (6.25)$$

where we denote $d/ds[D(s)] = D'(s)$. Now $F(s)$ can be written as the sum of m partial fractions as

$$F(s) = \frac{c_1}{s - s_1} + \frac{c_2}{s - s_2} + \cdots + \frac{c_r}{s - s_r} + \cdots \frac{c_m}{s - s_m} \qquad (6.26)$$

The inverse transform of each partial fraction in Eq. 6.26 can be readily evaluated. From Table 5.1, we have

$$\mathscr{L}^{-1}\left(\frac{c}{s - s_k}\right) = ce^{s_k t}u(t)$$

Thus

$$[\mathscr{L}^{-1}F(s)] = \left(c_1 e^{s_1 t} + c_2 e^{s_2 t} + \cdots + c_r e^{s_r t} + \cdots + c_m e^{s_m t}\right) u(t)$$

$$= \sum_{r=1}^{m} c_r e^{s_r t} u(t) \tag{6.27}$$

$$= \sum_{r=1}^{m} [F(s)(s - s_r)]\Big|_{s=s_r} e^{s_r t} u(t) \tag{6.28}$$

$$= \sum_{r=1}^{m} \frac{N(s)}{D'(s)}\Big|_{s=s_r} e^{s_r t} u(t)$$

Example 6.5

(1) Find $\mathscr{L}^{-1}\left[\dfrac{3s + 10}{s^2 + 7s + 12}\right]$.

$$F(s) = \frac{N(s)}{D(s)} = \frac{3s + 10}{s^2 + 7s + 12}$$

$$= \frac{3s + 10}{(s + 3)(s + 4)}$$

$$= \frac{c_1}{s + 3} + \frac{c_2}{s + 4}$$

$$c_1 = F(s)(s + 3)\big|_{s=-3} = 1$$

Similarly

$$c_2 = F(s)(s + 4)\big|_{s=-4} = 2$$

Thus

$$F(s) = \frac{1}{s + 3} + \frac{2}{s + 4}$$

and

$$\mathscr{L}^{-1}[F(s)] = (e^{-3t} + 2e^{-4t})u(t)$$

The values of c_1 and c_2 may be alternately evaluated by using the formula

$$c_r = \frac{N(s)}{D'(s)}\Big|_{s=s_r}$$

In this problem,

$$D(s) = s^2 + 7s + 12$$

$$D'(s) = 2s + 7$$

$$c_1 = \frac{N(s)}{D'(s)}\Big|_{s=-3} = 1$$

$$c_2 = \frac{3s + 10}{2s + 7}\Big|_{s=-4} = 2$$

Example 6.6

Find $\mathscr{L}^{-1}\left[\dfrac{2s + 9}{s^2 + 4s + 29}\right]$

$$F(s) = \frac{2s + 9}{s^2 + 4s + 29}$$

$$= \frac{2s + 9}{(s + 2 + j5)(s + 2 - j5)}$$

$$= \frac{c_1}{s + 2 + j5} + \frac{c_2}{s + 2 - j5}$$

$$c_1 = \frac{2s + 9}{s + 2 - j5}\bigg|_{s=-2-j5} = \frac{2 + j1}{2}$$

$$c_2 = \frac{2s + 9}{s + 2 + j5}\bigg|_{s=-2+j5} = \frac{2 - j1}{2}$$

Thus

$$F(s) = \frac{2 + j1}{2(s + 2 + j5)} + \frac{2 - j1}{2(s + 2 - j5)}$$

$$\mathscr{L}^{-1}[F(s)] = \left[\frac{(2 + j1)}{2} e^{-(2+j5)t} + \frac{(2 - j1)}{2} e^{-(2-j5)t}\right] u(t)$$

$$= \frac{e^{-2t}}{2}[2(e^{-j5t} + e^{j5t}) - j(e^{j5t} - e^{-j5t})]u(t)$$

$$= e^{-2t}[2 \cos 5t + \sin 5t]u(t)$$

Note that the residues c_1 and c_2 of complex conjugate roots are also complex conjugates.

In cases where complex conjugate roots occur, as in the above problem, there is a more convenient method of evaluating the inverse transform. This is based on the observation (Table 5.1):

$$\mathscr{L}^{-1}\left[\frac{s + a}{(s + a)^2 + \omega^2}\right] = e^{-at} \cos \omega t\, u(t)$$

and

$$\mathscr{L}^{-1}\left[\frac{\omega}{(s + a)^2 + \omega^2}\right] = e^{-at} \sin \omega t\, u(t)$$

Thus, whenever complex conjugate roots occur, instead of separating them into two separate roots, it is generally more convenient to manipulate them in a way suggested by the above equations. This can be illustrated by $F(s)$ in Example 6.6. We can express $F(s)$ as

$$F(s) = \frac{2(s + 2)}{(s + 2)^2 + (5)^2} + \frac{5}{(s + 2)^2 + (5)^2}$$

Now the inverse transform may be written directly.

Example 6.7

Find the inverse transform of $F(s)$ given by

$$F(s) = \frac{5s^3 + 32s^2 + 122s + 60}{s(s + 3)[(s + 2)^2 + 16]}$$

Note that there are two complex conjugate roots. $F(s)$ can be separated into its partial fractions by a straightforward evaluation of the constants. Here, again, short cuts may be applied. The evaluation of residues at complex conjugate poles and subsequently taking the inverse transform is rather cumbersome and prone to errors. In this case, we shall evaluate the residues at the two roots $s = 0$ and $s = -3$ only. The composite residue at the complex conjugate poles may be found by subtracting the two partial fractions from $F(s)$. Thus

$$F(s) = \frac{c_1}{s} + \frac{c_2}{s + 3} + \frac{c(s)}{(s + 2)^2 + 16} \tag{6.29}$$

$$c_1 = \left. \frac{5s^3 + 32s^2 + 122s + 60}{(s + 3)[(s + 2)^2 + 16]} \right|_{s=0} = 1$$

$$c_2 = \left. \frac{5s^3 + 32s^2 + 122s + 60}{s[(s + 2)^2 + 16]} \right|_{s=-3} = 3$$

Now

$$\frac{c(s)}{(s + 2)^2 + 16} = F(s) - \frac{c_1}{s} - \frac{c_2}{s + 3}$$

$$= \frac{5s^3 + 32s^2 + 122s + 60}{s(s + 3)[(s + 2)^2 + 16]} - \frac{1}{s} - \frac{3}{s + 3}$$

$$= \frac{s + 10}{(s + 2)^2 + 16}$$

Thus

$$F(s) = \frac{1}{s} + \frac{3}{s + 3} + \frac{s + 10}{(s + 2)^2 + 16}$$

$$= \frac{1}{s} + \frac{3}{s + 3} + \frac{s + 2}{(s + 2)^2 + 16} + \frac{8}{(s + 2)^2 + 16}$$

and

$$\mathcal{L}^{-1}[F(s)] = [1 + 3e^{-3t} + e^{-2t}(\cos 4t + 2 \sin 4t)]u(t)$$

To verify the labor saved by this short cut, the student should try to work out this problem by the direct method of evaluating all of the residues.

Case 2. Multiple Order Roots

Thus far, we have considered the case of the simple roots of $D(s) = 0$; that is, all the roots were distinct. If two or more of these m roots

coincide, the situation is somewhat different. Let us assume that there
are n coincident roots at $s = s_0$.

$$F(s) = \frac{N(s)}{D(s)} = \frac{N(s)}{(s - s_0)^n D_1(s)} \tag{6.30}$$

where $D_1(s)$ has only simple roots.

From Eq. 6.30, we have

$$F(s)(s - s_0)^n = \frac{N(s)}{D_1(s)} \tag{6.31}$$

For convenience, we shall introduce a new variable p, given by

$$p = (s - s_0) \tag{6.32}$$

Substituting Eq. 6.32 in Eq. 6.31, we have

$$F(p + s_0)p^n = \frac{N(p + s_0)}{D_1(p + s_0)} \tag{6.33}$$

Dividing the numerator $N(p + s_0)$ by the denominator $D_1(p + s_0)$
with both polynomials written in ascending powers of p, we obtain

$$F(p + s_0)p^n = k_0 + k_1 p + \cdots + k_{n-1}p^{n-1} + \frac{\phi(p)p^n}{D_1(p + s_0)} \tag{6.34}$$

Hence

$$F(p + s_0) = \frac{k_0}{p^n} + \frac{k_1}{p^{n-1}} + \cdots + \frac{k_{n-1}}{p} + \frac{\phi(p)}{D_1(p + s_0)}$$

and

$$F(s) = \frac{k_0}{(s - s_0)^n} + \frac{k_1}{(s - s_0)^{n-1}} + \cdots + \frac{k_{n-1}}{(s - s_0)} + \frac{\phi(p)}{D_1(s)} \tag{6.35}$$

Note that

$$D_1(s) = 0$$

has simple roots, and hence the last term on the right-hand side of Eq.
6.35 can be expanded by the partial-fraction techniques discussed
previously. It is therefore obvious from Eq. 6.35 that nth order roots
can be expanded into n partial fractions. The inverse transform of each
of the fractions in Eq. 6.35 can be found from Table 5.1.

Alternately the coefficients $k_0, k_1, \ldots, k_{n-1}$ can be found by formulating
the function $(s - s_0)^n F(s)$ and differentiating it j times and set $s = s_0$.
This yields

$$k_j = \frac{1}{j!} \frac{d^j}{ds^j} \left[F(s)(s - s_0)^n \right] \Bigg|_{s=s_0}, \quad j = 0, 1, \ldots, (n-1) \tag{6.36}$$

Example 6.8

Find

$$\mathscr{L}^{-1}\left[\frac{4s^3 + 16s^2 + 23s + 13}{(s+1)^3(s+2)}\right].$$

$$F(s)(s+1)^3 = \frac{4s^3 + 16s^2 + 23s + 13}{s+2} \tag{6.37}$$

Substituting $p = s + 1$, we have

$$F(s)p^3 = \frac{4p^3 + 4p^2 + 3p + 2}{p+1}$$

We now divide the numerator by the denominator with both polynomials in ascending powers of p.

$$
\begin{array}{r}
2 + p + 3p^2 \\
1 + p\ )\overline{2 + 3p + 4p^2 + 4p^3} \\
2 + 2p \\
\hline
p + 4p^2 + 4p^3 \\
p + p^2 \\
\hline
3p^2 + 4p^3 \\
3p^2 + 3p^3 \\
\hline
p^3
\end{array}
$$

Thus

$$F(s)p^3 = 2 + p + 3p^2 + \frac{p^3}{p+1}$$

and

$$F(s) = \frac{2}{p^3} + \frac{1}{p^2} + \frac{3}{p} + \frac{1}{p+1}$$

$$= \frac{2}{(s+1)^3} + \frac{1}{(s+1)^2} + \frac{3}{(s+1)} + \frac{1}{(s+2)}$$

The inverse transform of each term can now be found from Table 5.1.

$$\mathscr{L}^{-1}[F(s)] = [t^2e^{-t} + te^{-t} + 3e^{-t} + e^{-2t}]u(t)$$
$$= [(t^2 + t + 3)e^{-t} + e^{-2t}]u(t)$$

We may obtain the same result by using alternate Eq. 6.36.

Example 6.9

The network in Fig. 6.6 is excited by a voltage source e^{-t}. The switch is closed at $t = 0$. Let us find the current $i(t)$.

$$f(t) = e^{-t}u(t)$$

$$F(s) = \frac{1}{s+1}$$

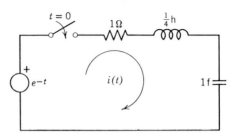

Figure 6.6

The transfer function is

$$H(s) = \frac{1}{Z(s)} = \frac{1}{1 + s/4 + 1/s}$$

$$= \frac{4s}{s^2 + 4s + 4}$$

The current $i(t)$ is given by

$$i(t) = \mathscr{L}^{-1}\left[\frac{1}{s + 1}\frac{4s}{s^2 + 4s + 4}\right]$$

$$= \mathscr{L}^{-1}\left[\frac{4s}{(s + 1)(s + 2)^2}\right]$$

$$= \mathscr{L}^{-1}\left[\frac{k_0}{(s + 2)^2} + \frac{k_1}{(s + 2)} + \frac{k_2}{s + 1}\right]$$

Here we shall use Eq. 6.36 to evaluate coefficients k_0 and k_1.

$$k_0 = \left.\frac{4s}{s + 1}\right|_{s=-2} = 8$$

$$k_1 = \left.\frac{d}{ds}\left(\frac{4s}{s + 1}\right)\right|_{s=-2} = 4$$

$$k_2 = \left.\frac{4s}{(s + 2)^2}\right|_{s=-1} = -4$$

$$i(t) = \mathscr{L}^{-1}\left[\frac{8}{(s + 2)^2} + \frac{4}{(s + 2)} - \frac{4}{(s + 1)}\right]$$

$$= [(8t + 4)e^{-2t} - 4e^{-t}]u(t)$$

A Note on Evaluating the Roots of a Polynomial

In the discussion of partial fractions we have assumed that the denominator polynomial $D(s)$ was either given in a factored form or could be easily factored. The polynomial can be factored if we can find the roots of $D(s) = 0$. If $s_1, s_2, \ldots, s_m$ are the roots of $D(s) = 0$, then

$$D(s) = (s - s_1)(s - s_2) \cdots (s - s_m)$$

Thus, the crucial problem is that of finding the roots of a polynomial. It is possible to find the roots of second- and even third- and fourth-order polynomials analytically. No analytical methods are available to solve the higher order polynomials. But there are a large number of numerical methods such as Graffe root-squaring, and Bairstow and Lin's methods.[6] The task of finding the roots of polynomials is not peculiar to the transform method but is inherent in the solution of integro-differential equations with constant coefficients, regardless of the analytical method employed in such a solution. Thus, the analysis of any but the simplest linear systems entails the evaluation of the roots of higher order polynomials and, therefore, it is desirable that the student acquaint himself with some of these numerical methods of evaluating the roots of a polynomial.

6.4 REPRESENTATION OF A SYSTEM IN THE FREQUENCY DOMAIN

Thus far, we have represented the systems in the time domain from which the frequency-domain relationships have been written. For example, in the network of Fig. 6.6 the driving voltage $e^{-t}u(t)$ and the current $i(t)$ are time-domain representations. For efficient use of the frequency-domain technique, we must be able to represent the system directly in the frequency domain. All of the signals as well as the elements of the system should be represented in the frequency domain. The frequency-domain representation of signals is achieved by writing their transforms. We shall now consider the frequency-domain representation of the elements of the system.

Let $Z(s)$ be the impedance of the element under consideration. Then, for a driving voltage Ve^{st}, the current through the element is Ie^{st}, given by

$$Ve^{st} = Z(s)Ie^{st}.$$

[6] F. Hildebrand, *Introduction to Numerical Analysis*, McGraw-Hill, New York, 1956.

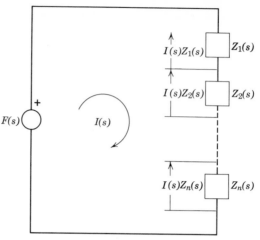

Figure 6.7

Now let the voltage across the element be an arbitrary function $f(t)$ and the consequent current be $i(t)$. If $F(s)$ and $I(s)$ are the transforms of $f(t)$ and $i(t)$, respectively, then

$$F(s) = Z(s)I(s).$$

If there should be n elements with impedances $Z_1(s)$, $Z_2(s)$, ..., $Z_n(s)$ in series, then the total impedance of the system is given by

$$Z = Z_1 + Z_2 + \cdots + Z_n$$

and

$$F(s) = ZI(s)$$
$$= (Z_1 + Z_2 + \cdots)I(s)$$

This fact may be expressed by representing a network in the frequency domain as shown in Fig. 6.7. The voltages and currents are replaced by their respective transforms and the elements are represented by their impedances. Kirchhoff's voltage law can now be applied directly to this frequency-domain representation. In a similar way, it can be shown that Kirchhoff's current law also holds true for networks represented in the frequency domain.

The network elements should be represented by their functional representation in the frequency domain. This means that they may either be represented by their impedances or admittances and Kirchhoff's equations may be written accordingly. When an element is represented by its impedance $Z(s)$, it is understood that the frequency-domain ratio of voltage to current associated with the element is $Z(s)$. Similarly, if an element is represented by its admittance, $Y(s)$, the corresponding current-to-voltage ratio in the frequency domain associated with the element is $Y(s)$.

The frequency-domain representation of the network shown in Fig. 6.6 is illustrated in Fig. 6.8. Note that the switch which closes at $t = 0$ in Fig. 6.6 is not shown in the frequency-domain representation. This is because the driving function $1/(s + 1)$ is the frequency-domain representation of the time function $e^{-t}u(t)$ and implies that the driving function is zero for $t < 0$. It is therefore superfluous to show a switch in the frequency-domain representation. Kirchhoff's voltage equation may be written directly for this network:

$$\frac{1}{s+1} = \left(1 + \frac{s}{4} + \frac{1}{s}\right)I(s)$$

$$= \frac{s^2 + 4s + 4}{4s}I(s)$$

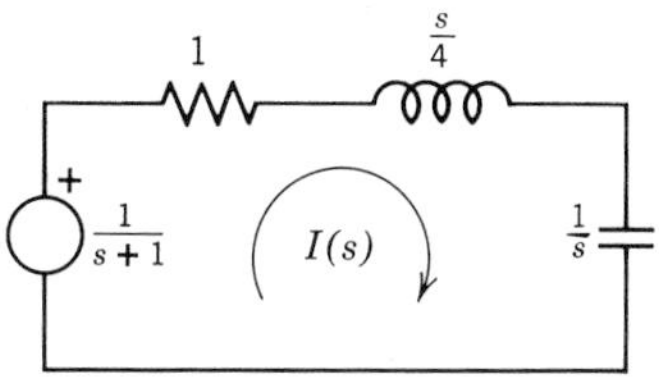

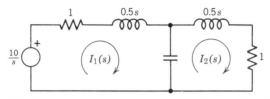

Figure 6.8   Frequency-domain representation of the network of Fig. 6.6.

Expanding $I(s)$ in partial fractions we get

$$I(s) = \frac{4}{s+2} + \frac{8}{(s+2)^2} - \frac{4}{s+1}$$

$$i(t) = \mathscr{L}^{-1}[I(s)] = [(4 + 8t)e^{-2t} - 4e^{-t}]u(t)$$

Similarly, the network in Fig. 6.5a is represented in the frequency domain in Fig. 6.9. For this network, Kirchhoff's laws may be applied to two loops:

$$\frac{10}{s} = \left(1 + 0.5s + \frac{1}{s}\right)I_1 - \frac{1}{s}(I_2)$$

$$0 = \frac{-1}{s}I_1 + \left(1 + 0.5s + \frac{1}{s}\right)I_2$$

The application of Cramer's rule to these equations yields $I_1(s)$ and $I_2(s)$, as found in Example 6.4.

Figure 6.9   Frequency-domain representation of network in Fig. 6.5a.

6.5 TRANSFORM OF A UNIT IMPULSE FUNCTION

The Laplace transform of a unit impulse function can be found in the usual manner.

$$\mathscr{L}[\delta(t)] = \int_0^\infty \delta(t)e^{-st}\, dt$$

Note that the function $\delta(t)$ is not defined at $t = 0$. Hence the lower limit should be taken as $t = 0^-$. It should be pointed out that the lower limit of $t = 0^+$ is incorrect because $\delta(t)$ exists only at $t = 0$ and is zero for all values of $t \neq 0$. Hence the function $\delta(t)e^{-st} = 0$ for $t > 0^+$, and the lower limit of 0^+ would give $\mathscr{L}[\delta(t)] = 0$. Therefore, we must choose the lower limit as 0^-. This choice will assure that the point $t = 0$ is included in our consideration.

Using the sampling property (Eq. 4.29) of the impulse function, it is evident that the above integral will be given by unity. Therefore

$$\mathscr{L}[\delta(t)] = 1 \tag{6.38}$$

It follows from this result and the time-differentiation property that[7]

$$\mathscr{L}\frac{d}{dt}[\delta(t)] = s$$

and

$$\mathscr{L}\frac{d^n}{dt^n}[\delta(t)] = s^n$$

Example 6.10

Let us consider the circuit shown in Fig. 6.10. Voltage V_0 is applied across an ideal capacitor C at time $t = 0$. We shall find the current $i(t)$.

$$v(t) = V_0 u(t)$$

and

$$V(s) = \mathscr{L}[V_0 u(t)] = \frac{V_0}{s}$$

The transfer function in this case is the admittance of the capacitor.

Figure 6.10

$$I(s) = Y(s)V(s)$$
$$= Cs\,\frac{V_0}{s}$$
$$= CV_0$$
$$i(t) = \mathscr{L}^{-1}[I(s)] = \mathscr{L}^{-1}(CV_0)$$
$$= CV_0\,\delta(t)$$

[7] For further discussion of higher derivatives of impulse functions, see E. A. Guillemin, *Mathematics of Circuit Analysis*, pp. 541–544, Wiley, New York, 1949.

Therefore, the current is an impulse of strength CV_0. The result can be verified intuitively. As soon as the voltage is applied, the capacitor must reach this voltage instantaneously; that is, a charge of CV_0 must flow in the capacitor instantaneously. This would need an infinite current for zero time. This may be written as

$$\text{charge } Q = \int_{0^-}^{0^+} i \, dt = CV_0$$

This is possible only if the current is an impulse of strength CV_0.

Example 6.11

A voltage E is applied to a circuit as shown in Fig. 6.11 at time $t = 0$. Let us find the current $i(t)$. The impedance $Z(s)$ of the circuit is given by

$$Z(s) = \frac{1}{C_1 s + 1/R} + \frac{1}{C_2 s}$$

$$= \frac{(C_1 + C_2)Rs + 1}{C_2 s(C_1 Rs + 1)}$$

and

$$I(s) = \frac{EC_2(C_1 Rs + 1)}{(C_1 + C_2)Rs + 1}$$

$$= EC_2 \left[\frac{C_1}{C_1 + C_2} + \frac{C_2/(C_1 + C_2)}{(C_1 + C_2)Rs + 1} \right]$$

Therefore

$$i(t) = \mathscr{L}^{-1}[I(s)] = \frac{EC_2 C_1}{C_1 + C_2} \delta(t) + \frac{EC_2}{(C_1 + C_2)^2 R} e^{[-t/(C_1 + C_2)R]} u(t)$$

Intuitively, one would expect impulse functions in the solution of the above problem. Initially, capacitances C_1 and C_2 both act as short circuits and the series combination of C_1 and C_2 must charge instantaneously at $t = 0$ to a voltage E. This is possible only through a current impulse of strength $(EC_1 C_2)/(C_1 + C_2)$. Capacitor C_1 will at time $t = 0^+$ charge to a voltage

$$E_{C_1} = \frac{1}{C_1} \int_{0^-}^{0^+} \frac{EC_1 C_2}{C_1 + C_2} \delta(t) \, dt$$

$$= \frac{EC_2}{C_1 + C_2} \tag{6.39}$$

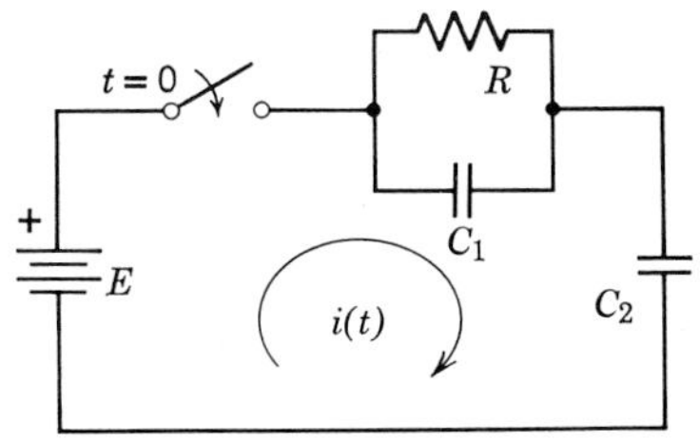

Figure 6.11

and, similarly, the capacitor C_2 charges at $t = 0^+$ to a voltage

$$E_{C2} = \frac{EC_1}{C_1 + C_2} \tag{6.40}$$

Impulse functions are also expected whenever sudden changes in the currents through inductive elements are involved.

Example 6.12

A unit impulse voltage is applied across an $R\text{-}C$ circuit as shown in Fig. 6.12. Find the current $i(t)$ through the circuit.

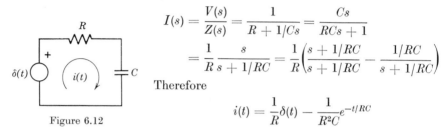

$$I(s) = \frac{V(s)}{Z(s)} = \frac{1}{R + 1/Cs} = \frac{Cs}{RCs + 1}$$

$$= \frac{1}{R}\frac{s}{s + 1/RC} = \frac{1}{R}\left(\frac{s + 1/RC}{s + 1/RC} - \frac{1/RC}{s + 1/RC}\right)$$

Therefore

$$i(t) = \frac{1}{R}\delta(t) - \frac{1}{R^2C}e^{-t/RC}$$

Figure 6.12

6.6 SYSTEMS WITH INITIAL CONDITIONS

In all of the examples of analysis thus far, it has been implicitly assumed that the systems were initially de-energized at the time of application of the driving function. In practice, however, energy is often initially stored in the elements of the system before the application of the driving function. For example, there may be an initial charge stored on a capacitor (energy stored in the electric field) or a current flowing through an inductor (energy stored in the magnetic field). In a mechanical system, this energy may be stored in the form of an initial displacement of a spring or an initial velocity of a mass.

We shall show here that the initial-energy storage in a system can be replaced by driving functions of constant strength applied at the appropriate points in the system. Therefore, the system with initial-energy storage is equivalent to an initially de-energized system with multiple driving functions. The desired response of the system is that due to an externally applied driving function and that due to the equivalent driving functions arising from initial energy storage.

In electrical systems, the energy is stored either in the form of a charge on a capacitor or a current flowing through an inductor. Let us consider each case separately. Let a certain capacitor in the system have an initial charge $q(0)$ coulombs at $t = 0^-$ (Fig. 6.13a). One can easily show that this capacitor is equivalent to a capacitor C with a zero initial

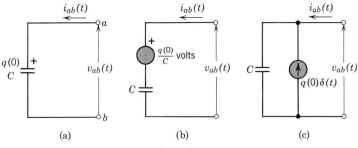

Figure 6.13

charge in series with an ideal voltage source $q(0)/C$ volts (Fig. 6.13b).
Note that $q(0)/C$ is also the initial voltage on the capacitor; that is,
$q(0)/C = v_{ab}(0)$. Alternately, it can also be represented by a capacitor
without an initial charge in parallel with an ideal current source $q(0)\,\delta(t)$
(Fig. 6.13c). We shall now show that the terminal voltage and current
relationships of all three arrangements are identical, and hence they are
mutually equivalent. The current $i_{ab}(t)$ is a causal function and hence is
zero for $t < 0$. For Fig. 6.13a, if $q(t)$ represents the charge on the
capacitor, then

$$v_{ab}(t) = \frac{1}{C}\,q(t)$$

$$= \frac{1}{C}\left[q(0) + \int_0^t i_{ab}\,dt\right] \qquad (6.41\mathrm{a})$$

For Fig. 6.13b,

$$v_{ab}(t) = \frac{q(0)}{C} + \frac{1}{C}\int_0^t i_{ab}\,dt$$

$$= \frac{1}{C}\left[q(0) + \int_0^t i_{ab}\,dt\right] \qquad (6.41\mathrm{b})$$

For Fig. 6.13c,

$$v_{ab}(t) = \frac{1}{C}\int_0^t [i_{ab} + q(0)\,\delta(t)]\,dt$$

$$= \frac{1}{C}\int_0^t i_{ab}\,dt + \frac{q(0)}{C}\int_0^t \delta(t)\,dt$$

$$= \frac{1}{C}\left[q(0) + \int_0^t i_{ab}\,dt\right] \qquad (6.41\mathrm{c})$$

Since the current $i_{ab}(t)$ is finite, the lower limit in the integral in Eq. 6.41c
has been changed to 0 from 0^-. It is obvious that the relationship
between terminal voltage and current is identical for all three circuits,
and hence they are equivalent. Since we specify that the problem starts
at $t = 0$, the voltage source in Fig. 6.13b is taken as $[q(0)/C]u(t)$.

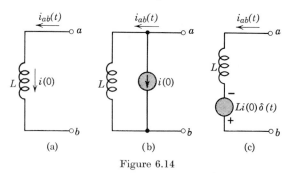

Figure 6.14

In a similar way, we can find an equivalent circuit for an inductor with initial magnetic energy stored due to an initial current flowing through it at time $t = 0^-$. The equivalent circuits in this case are shown in Fig. 6.14. Figure 6.14a shows an inductor L which has an initial current $i(0)$ flowing at $t = 0^-$. Figures 6.14b and 6.14c show the equivalent circuits for this situation. The terminal voltage and current relationship for the circuit in Fig. 6.14a is given by

$$i_{ab} = \frac{1}{L}\int_{-\infty}^{t} v_{ab}(t)\, dt$$

$$= \frac{1}{L}\int_{-\infty}^{0-} v_{ab}(t)\, dt + \frac{1}{L}\int_{0-}^{t} v_{ab}(t)\, dt$$

The first integral above represents the value of i_{ab} at $t = 0$. Hence

$$i_{ab}(t) = \frac{1}{L}\left[i(0) + \int_{0-}^{t} v_{ab}(t)\, dt\right] \tag{6.42}$$

The reader can easily verify that the terminal voltage and current relationship for the other two arrangements (Figs. 6.14b and 6.14c) are also given by Eq. 6.42.

Since we specify that the problem starts at $t = 0$, the current source in Fig. 6.14b is written as $i(0)u(t)$.

We now have a method of taking into account the initial-energy storage in the system. This fact can be accounted for by additional equivalent sources (constant voltage or constant current) at the appropriate locations in the system. The problem essentially reduces to that of a system with multiple driving functions. We shall illustrate the application of initial-condition generators by a few examples.

Example 6.13

Let us consider the same network of Fig. 6.3 with the same driving voltage except that there is an initial charge of 10 coulombs on the capacitor. The initially charged capacitor will be replaced with an uncharged capacitor of 0.2

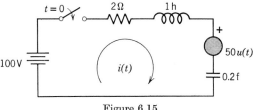

Figure 6.15

farads in series with a voltage source $[10/0.2]\ u(t)$, that is, $50u(t)$ as shown in Fig. 6.15. The total driving function now is

$$f(t) = 100u(t) - 50u(t)$$
$$= 50u(t)$$

and

$$F(s) = \frac{50}{s}$$

The transfer function $H(s)$, with respect to current $i(t)$, is the same as before.

$$H(s) = \frac{s}{s^2 + 2s + 5}$$

and the response $i(t)$ is given by

$$i(t) = \mathscr{L}^{-1}\left(\frac{50}{s}\ \frac{s}{s^2 + 2s + 5}\right)$$
$$= \mathscr{L}^{-1}\left[\frac{50}{(s+1)^2 + 4}\right]$$
$$= 25e^{-t} \sin 2tu(t)$$

Example 6.14

A circuit shown in Fig. 6.16a is in the steady state at time $t = 0$ with the switch in position 1. At this moment, the switch is thrown to position 2. Find the various currents in the circuit.

Since the steady state is reached before switching occurred, the current through the inductor must be $40/(5 + 1 + 4)$; that is, 4 amp and the voltage across the capacitor must be 16 volts. At the time of switching at $t = 0$, we have a situation of energy storage both in the inductor and the capacitor. We draw an equivalent circuit valid for $t > 0$ with the initial-condition generators as shown in Fig. 6.16b. In this figure, the capacitor with initial voltage of 16 volts is replaced by an uncharged capacitor in series with a voltage source of 16 volts. Similarly, an inductor with initial current of 4 amp is replaced by an inductor with zero initial current in series with an impulsive voltage source $Li(0)\ \delta(t) = 8\ \delta(t)$ volts. This particular form of equivalent circuits for initial-energy storage proves convenient here, since we are using loop analysis. In circuits where node analysis is employed, it is more convenient to choose

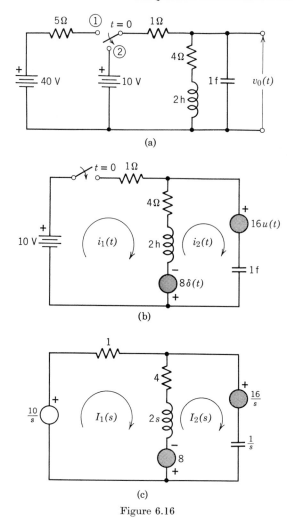

Figure 6.16

alternate forms with a current source in parallel with the energy storing element. The equivalent circuit in the frequency domain is shown in Fig. 6.16c. Note that

$$\mathscr{L}[8\,\delta(t)] = 8 \quad\text{and}\quad \mathscr{L}[16u(t)] = \frac{16}{s}$$

Let $I_1(s)$ and $I_2(s)$ be the two mesh currents, as shown in Fig. 6.16c. The loop equations are

$$\frac{10}{s} = (1 + 4 + 2s)I_1(s) - 8 - (4 + 2s)I_2(s)$$

$$0 = 8 + \frac{16}{s} - (4 + 2s)I_1(s) + \left(4 + 2s + \frac{1}{s}\right)I_2(s)$$

The equations can be rearranged as

$$\frac{(10 + 8s)}{s} = (5 + 2s)I_1 - (4 + 2s)I_2$$

$$-\frac{(16 + 8s)}{s} = -(4 + 2s)I_1 + \frac{(2s^2 + 4s + 1)}{s} I_2(s)$$

The application of Cramer's rule to these equations yields

$$I_1(s) = \frac{\begin{vmatrix} \dfrac{(8s + 10)}{s} & -(2s + 4) \\[2mm] \dfrac{-(16 + 8s)}{s} & \dfrac{(2s^2 + 4s + 1)}{s} \end{vmatrix}}{\begin{vmatrix} (2s + 5) & -(2s + 4) \\[2mm] -(2s + 4) & \dfrac{(2s^2 + 4s + 1)}{s} \end{vmatrix}}$$

$$= \frac{-(12s^2 + 16s - 10)}{s(2s^2 + 6s + 5)}$$

$$= \frac{-(6s^2 + 8s - 5)}{s[(s + \frac{3}{2})^2 + \frac{1}{4}]}$$

Separating into partial fractions,

$$I_1(s) = \frac{2}{s} - \frac{8(s + \frac{3}{2})}{(s + \frac{3}{2})^2 + \frac{1}{4}} - \frac{2}{(s + \frac{3}{2})^2 + \frac{1}{4}}$$

The current $i_1(t)$ is the inverse transform of $I_1(s)$.

$$i_1(t) = \mathscr{L}^{-1}[I_1(s)] = \left[2 - 8e^{-3t/2} \cos \frac{t}{2} - 4e^{-3t/2} \sin \frac{t}{2} \right] u(t)$$

Similarly

$$I_2(s) = \frac{-20(s + 2)}{2s^2 + 6s + 5} = \frac{-10(s + \frac{3}{2})}{(s + \frac{3}{2})^2 + \frac{1}{4}} - \frac{5}{(s + \frac{3}{2})^2 + \frac{1}{4}}$$

and

$$i_2(t) = \left[-10e^{-3t/2} \cos \frac{t}{2} - 10e^{-3t/2} \sin \frac{t}{2} \right] u(t)$$

6.7 TRANSFORM ANALYSIS OF LINEAR SYSTEMS

It is possible to analyze a linear system by using the Laplace transform without having to evaluate the transfer function. The solution is obtained by transforming directly the integrodifferential equations of the system. This method leads to a slightly different point of view of the Laplace transform. In the frequency-analysis method, (discussed thus far) the transform of a signal is viewed as an expression of various frequency contents in the signal, and the transfer function represents the response of the system to various frequency components. In transform analysis, on the other hand, the Laplace transform is viewed as an operation which transforms the integrodifferential equations into algebraic equations (transformation from the t domain to the s domain). The solution of the resultant algebraic equations is the transform of the desired time-domain solution. This will be demonstrated by analyzing the network in Example 6.2 (Fig. 6.3). This problem has been solved previously by the frequency-analysis approach. We shall again analyze it, using the transform-analysis approach. The integrodifferential equation for this network is

$$2i(t) + \frac{di}{dt} + 5\int i(t)\, dt = 100u(t) \tag{6.43}$$

The above equation will now be transformed into an algebraic equation by taking the Laplace transforms of both sides of this equation. Let

$$\mathscr{L}[i(t)] = I(s) \tag{6.44}$$

Then

$$\mathscr{L}\left[\frac{di}{dt}\right] = sI(s) - i(0^-) \tag{6.45a}$$

and

$$\mathscr{L}\left[\int i(t)\, dt\right] = \frac{I(s)}{s} + \frac{i^{(-1)}(0^-).}{s} \tag{6.45b}$$

Since the circuit is initially de-energized, $i(0^-)$ and $i^{(-1)}(0^-)$ are both zero, and we have

$$\mathscr{L}\left[\frac{di}{dt}\right] = sI(s); \qquad \mathscr{L}\left[\int i(t)\, dt\right] = \frac{I(s)}{s} \tag{6.46}$$

Taking the Laplace transform of Eq. 6.43 and using Eqs. 6.44 and 6.46, we get

$$\left(2 + s + \frac{5}{s}\right)I(s) = \frac{100}{s}$$

and

$$I(s) = \frac{100}{s^2 + 2s + 5}$$

Therefore

$$i(t) = \mathscr{L}^{-1}[I(s)] = 50e^{-t}\sin(2t)u(t)$$

This is, of course, the same result as that obtained in Example 6.2.

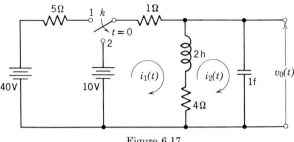

Figure 6.17

In the transform approach, the initial storage of energy can be auto-matically taken into account by such terms as $i(0^-)$ and $i^{(-1)}(0^-)$. We shall illustrate this point by analyzing the network in Example 6.14 (Fig. 6.16a). This network is shown in Fig. 6.17. The switch k is in position 1 for a long time before $t = 0$, when it is moved to position 2. The integro-differential equations of the network in this situation are given by the two loop equations:

$$5i_1(t) + 2\frac{di_1}{dt} - 4i_2(t) - 2\frac{di_2}{dt} = 10u(t)$$

$$-4i_1(t) - 2\frac{di_1}{dt} + 4i_2 + 2\frac{di_2}{dt} + \int i_2(t)\, dt = 0 \qquad (6.47)$$

If

$$\mathcal{L}[i_1(t)] = I_1(s); \qquad \mathcal{L}[i_2(t)] = I_2(s) \qquad (6.48)$$

then

$$\mathcal{L}\left[\frac{di_1}{dt}\right] = sI_1(s) - i_1(0^-); \qquad \mathcal{L}\left[\frac{di_2}{dt}\right] = sI_2(s) - i_2(0^-) \qquad (6.49)$$

and

$$\mathcal{L}\left[\int i_2(t)\, dt\right] = \frac{I_2(s)}{s} + \frac{i_2^{(-1)}(0^-)}{s} \qquad (6.50)$$

Note that before the switch is moved to position 2, at time $t = 0$, the value of the current i_1 was the value of the steady-state current circulating in loop 1 when the switch was in position 1. This current is $40/(5 + 1 + 4) = 4$ amp. Therefore, $i_1(0^-) = 4$. Since there is a capaci-tor in series in loop 2, there can be no current in that loop at time $t = 0^-$. Thus $i_2(0^-) = 0$. However, there was a voltage across the capacitor at time $t = 0^-$ given by $40 - 4(5 + 1) = 16$ volts. That is,

$$\int_{-\infty}^{0^-} i_2\, dt = 16$$

or

$$i_2^{(-1)}(0^-) = 16$$

Equation 6.49 may now be written as

$$\mathscr{L}\left(\frac{di_1}{dt}\right) = sI_1(s) - 4; \qquad \mathscr{L}\left(\frac{di_2}{dt}\right) = sI_2(s) \tag{6.51}$$

Equation 6.50 becomes

$$\mathscr{L}\left[\int i_2(t)\, dt\right] = \frac{I_2(s)}{s} + \frac{16}{s} \tag{6.52}$$

Taking the Laplace transforms of the set of Eqs. 6.47 and substituting Eqs. 6.48, 6.51, and 6.52:

$$(5 + 2s)I_1(s) - 8 - (4 + 2s)I_2(s) = \frac{10}{s}$$

$$\tag{6.53}$$

$$-(4 + 2s)I_1(s) + 8 + \left(4 + 2s + \frac{1}{s}\right)I_2(s) + \frac{16}{s} = 0$$

Using Cramer's rule, we get

$$I_1(s) = \frac{-(12s^2 + 16s - 10)}{s(2s^2 + 6s + 5)}$$

and

$$I_2(s) = \frac{-20(s + 2)}{2s^2 + 6s + 5}$$

Separating $I_1(s)$ and $I_2(s)$ into partial fractions, and taking the inverse transform, we get

$$i_1(t) = \left[2 - 8e^{-3t/2}\cos\frac{t}{2} - 4e^{-3t/2}\sin\frac{t}{2}\right]u(t)$$

and

$$i_2(t) = \left[-10e^{-3t/2}\cos\frac{t}{2} - 10e^{-3t/2}\sin\frac{t}{2}\right]u(t)$$

This is the correct result as seen from the solution of Example 6.14.

It will be noticed that the concept of the transfer function is the heart of the frequency-analysis approach. On the other hand, the transfer function was not even considered in the transform approach. In the former, the transfer function $H(s)$ of the system is determined, and the response $r(t)$ is the inverse transform of $H(s)F(s)$ where $F(s)$ is the transform of the driving function $f(t)$. For the transform-analysis approach, however, the integrodifferential equations characterizing the system are determined. These equations are now transformed into algebraic equations in the s domain by the Laplace transform. The solution of these equations in the s domain yields $R(s)$. The inverse transform of $R(s)$ is the desired response $r(t)$. The concept of a transfer function is therefore not required in the transform approach. One can, however, as a matter of convenience, define the transfer function as the ratio of the transform of the response $r(t)$ to the transform of the driving function $f(t)$. Thus

$$H(s) = \frac{\mathscr{L}[r(t)]}{\mathscr{L}[f(t)]}$$

The distinction between the two approaches (the frequency-analysis approach and the transform approach) should be clearly understood. The frequency-analysis approach is based upon classical dynamics which has been the basis of the circuit theory. A given driving function is expressed as a continuous sum of eternal exponential signals. The response to such an eternal exponential signal e^{st} consists entirely of the steady-state response $H(s)e^{st}$. Hence the response of the system is given by a continuous sum of the responses to various exponential components.

On the other hand, the transform approach views the Laplace transform as a machine which simplifies the solution of integrodifferential equations characterizing the system. There is no physical significance attached to any quantity. All one has to do is to feed these integrodifferential equations to a Laplace machine which yields the products (algebraic equations in the s domain) which are easier to handle. The solutions of these simplified equations are then fed back to the inverse Laplace machine to get the desired solutions. Hence the transform approach is a nonphysical abstract approach. Guillemin calls it a "black-box" approach, which gives little insight into the operation of the system.

Traditionally, the transform approach has been used in the analysis of linear systems. The frequency-analysis approach is relatively of recent origin.[8] This approach gives the physical viewpoint of frequency transforms which heretofore had been treated as abstract operations (in transform approach). It makes the whole frequency-domain behavior very meaningful.

6.8 THE IMPULSE RESPONSE OF A LINEAR SYSTEM

The transform of a unit impulse is unity. Hence the response of a system to a unit impulse function will be given by $\mathscr{L}^{-1}[H(s)]$ where $H(s)$ is the transfer function of the system. We shall designate the unit impulse response of a system by $h(t)$. Thus

$$h(t) = \mathscr{L}^{-1}[H(s)]$$

and   (6.54)

$$H(s) = \mathscr{L}[h(t)]$$

[8] E. A. Guillemin, *Theory of Linear Physical Systems*, Wiley, New York, 1963.

This is a significant result. *The unit impulse response of a system is the inverse Laplace transform of its transfer function.*

For a lumped-linear system, the transfer function $H(s)$ is a rational algebraic fraction.

$$H(s) = \frac{N(s)}{D(s)} = \frac{N(s)}{(s - p_1)(s - p_2) \cdots (s - p_n)}$$

Expanding $H(s)$ into partial fractions, we get

$$H(s) = \frac{a_1}{s - p_1} + \frac{a_2}{s - p_2} + \cdots + \frac{a_n}{s - p_n}$$

and[9]

$$h(t) = \mathscr{L}^{-1}[H(s)] = a_1 e^{p_1 t} + a_2 e^{p_2 t} + \cdots a_n e^{p_n t} \tag{6.55}$$

The terms $p_1, p_2, \ldots, p_n$ are the poles of the transfer function and are known as the *natural frequencies* of the system. This designation will become clear in Chapter 7. We therefore conclude that *the impulse response of a system consists of a linear combination of signals of the natural frequencies of the system.*

6.9 THE TRANSIENT AND THE STEADY-STATE RESPONSE OF A SYSTEM

The complete response of a system to any driving function consists of two components: the transient and the steady-state response. It was indicated in Chapter 1 that the nature of the transient component is characteristic of the system, whereas the nature of the steady-state component depends upon the system and the driving function. These concepts can be clearly illustrated in the frequency domain.

Let us apply a driving function $f(t)$ to a system with the transfer function $H(s)$, and let $r(t)$ be the response of the system. If $F(s)$ and $R(s)$ are the Laplace transforms of $f(t)$ and $r(t)$ respectively, then for an initially de-energized system,

$$R(s) = H(s)F(s)$$

Let

$$H(s) = \frac{N_1(s)}{D_1(s)} = \frac{N_1(s)}{(s - p_1)(s - p_2) \cdots (s - p_n)} \tag{6.56}$$

---

[9] The response $h(t)$ contains impulse functions and its higher derivatives if the order of $N(s)$ is equal to or greater than $D(s)$.

and[10]

$$F(s) = \frac{N_2(s)}{D_2(s)}$$

$$= \frac{N_2(s)}{(s - s_1)(s - s_2) \cdots (s - s_m)} \quad (6.57)$$

Then

$$R(s) = \frac{N_1(s)N_2(s)}{(s - p_1)(s - p_2) \cdots (s - p_n)(s - s_1)(s - s_2) \cdots (s - s_m)}$$

$$(6.58)$$

Expanding the right-hand side into partial fractions,

$$R(s) = \frac{C_1}{s - p_1} + \frac{C_2}{s - p_2} + \cdots + \frac{C_n}{s - p_n}$$

$$+ \frac{K_1}{s - s_1} + \frac{K_2}{s - s_2} + \cdots + \frac{K_m}{s - s_m} \quad (6.59)$$

Taking the inverse transform of both sides of Eq. 6.59, we have

$$r(t) = C_1 e^{p_1 t} + C_2 e^{p_2 t} + \cdots + C_n e^{p_n t} + K_1 e^{s_1 t} + K_2 e^{s_2 t} + \cdots + K_m e^{s_m t}$$

$$(6.60)$$

$$= \underbrace{\sum_i C_i e^{p_i t}}_{\substack{\text{The transient} \\ \text{component}}} + \underbrace{\sum_j K_j e^{s_j t}}_{\substack{\text{The steady-} \\ \text{state component}}} \quad (6.61)$$

Observe that the response consists of two components. The first component is formed by exponentials of frequencies $p_1, p_2, \ldots, p_n$ which are characteristic of the system. This component is called the source-free component or the transient component. The second component arises due to the driving function or the source and is called the component due to source or the steady-state component.[11] Note that the transient component consists of a linear combination of signals of the natural frequencies of the system. For this reason the transient component is also sometimes referred to as the *natural response* of a system. In general, any signal which is a linear combination of signals of natural frequencies of a system is referred to as the natural response of the system. Note that the unit impulse response $h(t)$ (Eq. 6.55) is also a natural response of the system.

[10] Here we have implicitly assumed that $F(s)$ is a rational algebraic fraction. In general, this may not be true. This assumption, however, will suffice to indicate our line of reasoning.

[11] Presently no standard definitions of the transient and the steady-state components are prevalent, and different authors define these terms differently. The reader should, therefore, be careful in interpreting these terms in different books.

In this text the terms source-free response, transient response, and natural response will be used interchangeably. Similarly, the terms response due to source, steady-state response, and forced response will mean one and the same thing. To summarize; the two components of the response are referred to as follows.

(a) Source-free response and the response due to source,
(b) Natural response and the forced response,
(c) Transient response and the steady-state response.

Sometimes these components are also referred to by complimentary function and the particular integral. This choice, however, is not very popular among engineers.

Example 6.15

A voltage $100 \cos 5t$ is applied to terminals aa' of the network shown in Fig. 6.18. Find the output voltage $v_o(t)$.

Solution. The transfer function $H(s)$ relating the output voltage $v_o(t)$ to the input voltage across terminals aa' can be found in the usual way. The transfer function $H(s)$ is found to be

$$H(s) = \frac{4}{3s^2 + 11s + 4}$$

$$= \frac{1.33}{(s + 0.41)(s + 3.26)}$$

The Laplace transform of the driving function is given by

$$F(s) = \mathcal{L}[100 \cos (5t)u(t)] = \frac{100s}{s^2 + 25}$$

Hence, if $V_o(s)$ is the Laplace transform of the output voltage $v_o(t)$, we have

$$V_o(s) = \frac{133s}{(s + 0.41)(s + 3.26)(s^2 + 25)}$$

The right-hand side may be separated into partial fractions:

$$V_o(s) = \frac{4.24}{s + 3.26} - \frac{0.76}{s + 0.41} - \frac{(3.48s - 13.6)}{s^2 + 25}$$

$$= \underbrace{\frac{4.24}{s + 3.26} - \frac{0.76}{s + 0.41}}_{\text{transient component}} - \underbrace{\frac{3.48s}{s^2 + 25} + \frac{13.6}{s^2 + 25}}_{\text{steady-state component}}$$

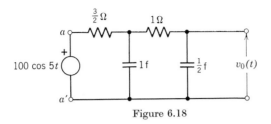

Figure 6.18

Hence $v_o(t)$ is given by

$$v_o(t) = \mathscr{L}^{-1}[V_o(s)] = \underbrace{4.24e^{-3.26t} - 0.76e^{-0.41t}}_{\text{transient component}}$$

$$\underbrace{-\ 3.48 \cos 5t + 2.72 \sin 5t}_{\text{steady-state component}}$$

Note that the steady-state component can also be obtained by using the method described in Chapter 2. It was shown that the steady-state response of a system to a sinusoidal signal of angular frequency ω has a magnitude of $|H(j\omega)|$ and is shifted in phase by $\underline{/H(j\omega)}$. In this case,

$$H(j\omega) = \frac{4}{-3\omega^2 + 11j\omega + 4}$$

For a signal of angular frequency $\omega = 5$,

$$H(j5) = \frac{4}{-75 + j55 + 4}$$

$$= \frac{4}{-71 + j55}$$

$$= 4.45 \times 10^{-2} \qquad \underline{/-142°}$$

Hence the steady-state response of the system to a signal $100 \cos 5t$ is given by

$$4.45 \cos (5t - 142°)$$

$$= -3.48 \cos 5t + 2.72 \sin 5t$$

This is the same result as obtained before.

6.10 RESPONSE OF A LINEAR SYSTEM TO CAUSAL PERIODIC NONSINUSOIDAL SIGNALS

The response of a linear system to a semi-infinite periodic driving function (causal periodic function) can be found conveniently by using the Laplace transform. The Laplace transform of a causal periodic function was determined in Chapter 5 (Eq. 5.65). Let the transform of such a periodic driving function $f(t)$ with period T be given by $F_0(s)/(1 - e^{-Ts})$.

If $R(s)$ is the transform of the desired response $r(t)$ of the system, then

$$R(s) = \frac{H(s)F_0(s)}{1 - e^{-Ts}} \qquad (6.62)$$

Let $H(s)$, the transfer function of the system, be given by

$$H(s) = \frac{N(s)}{D(s)} = \frac{N(s)}{(s - p_1)(s - p_2) \cdots (s - p_n)} \qquad (6.63)$$

Substituting Eq. 6.63 in Eq. 6.62, we get

$$R(s) = \frac{N(s)F_0(s)}{(s - p_1)(s - p_2) \cdots (s - p_n)(1 - e^{-Ts})} \qquad (6.64)$$

Expanding the right-hand side of Eq. 6.64 into partial fractions,

$$R(s) = \underbrace{\frac{C_1}{s - p_1} + \frac{C_2}{s - p_2} + \cdots + \frac{C_n}{s - p_n}}_{\text{transient terms}} + \underbrace{\frac{\Phi(s)}{1 - e^{-Ts}}}_{\substack{\text{steady-state} \\ \text{term}}} \qquad (6.65)$$

$R(s)$ has been separated into two components. The first part, consisting of all of the natural frequencies of the system, is a transient component, and the second part is the steady-state component which is a periodic function. The periodic nature of the steady-state component is evident from the factor[12] $1/(1 - e^{-Ts})$. This procedure is demonstrated here by an example.

Example 6.16

A periodic voltage $v_1(t)$, as shown in Fig. 6.19a, is applied to the R-C circuit shown in Fig. 6.19b. Let us find the output voltage $v_o(t)$.

The transfer function $H(s)$ is given by

$$H(s) = \frac{1/s}{1 + 1/s}$$

Therefore

$$H(s) = \frac{1}{s + 1}$$

---

[12] If $\phi(t)$ is the inverse transform of $\Phi(s)$ in Eq. 6.65, then $\Phi(s)/(1 - e^{-sT})$ represents $\phi(t)$ repeated every T seconds. If $\Phi(s)/(1 - e^{-sT})$ were to represent a steady-state component, then it is necessary that $\phi(t)$ must exist only in the region ($0 < t < T$) and should be zero everywhere outside this region. It can be proved that this condition is always fulfilled for linear lumped parameter systems. See, for instance, W. R. LePage, *Complex Variables and the Laplace Transform for Engineers*, pp. 438–443, McGraw-Hill, New York, 1961. See also S. Seshu and N. Balabanian, *Linear Network Analysis*, pp. 168–183, Wiley, New York, 1959.

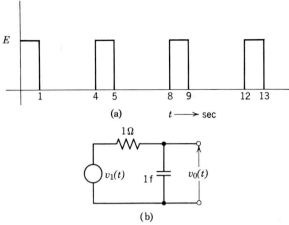

(a)

(b)

Figure 6.19

If
$$\mathcal{L}[v_1(t)] = V_1(s)$$
and
$$\mathcal{L}[v_o(t)] = V_o(s)$$

Then from Eq. 5.66,
$$V_1(s) = \frac{E(1 - e^{-s})}{s(1 - e^{-4s})}$$

and
$$\begin{aligned} V_o(s) &= H(s)V_1(s) \\ &= \frac{E(1 - e^{-s})}{s(s + 1)(1 - e^{-4s})} \end{aligned} \tag{6.66}$$

We shall separate $V_o(s)$ into its transient and steady-state components. There is only one pole of $H(s)$, that is, $s = -1$.

$$V_o(s) = \frac{C_1}{s + 1} + \frac{\Phi(s)}{(1 - e^{-4s})} \tag{6.67}$$

C_1 is the residue at pole $s = -1$, and may be found from
$$\begin{aligned} C_1 &= (s + 1)V_o(s)\big|_{s=-1} \\ &= -E\frac{(1 - e)}{(1 - e^4)} = -0.032E \end{aligned} \tag{6.68}$$

$$V_o(s) = \underbrace{\frac{-0.032E}{s + 1}}_{\substack{\text{transient} \\ \text{component}}} + \underbrace{\frac{\Phi(s)}{(1 - e^{-4s})}}_{\substack{\text{steady-state} \\ \text{component}}} \tag{6.69}$$

From Eq. 6.69, $\Phi(s)$ is found to be
$$\Phi(s) = \frac{E(1 - e^{-s})}{s(s + 1)} + \frac{0.032E(1 - e^{-4s})}{s + 1} \tag{6.70}$$

The output voltage $v_o(t)$ has the steady-state components $v_{tr}(t)$ and $v_{ss}(t)$, respectively.

$$v_o(t) = v_{tr}(t) + v_{ss}(t) \tag{6.71}$$

The transient and the steady-state components are given by the inverse transforms of the first and the second term, respectively, on the right-hand side of Eq. 6.69.

$$v_{tr}(t) = \mathcal{L}^{-1}\left[\frac{-0.032E}{s+1}\right] \tag{6.72}$$

$$= -0.032Ee^{-t}u(t) \tag{6.73}$$

and

$$v_{ss}(t) = \mathcal{L}^{-1}\left[\frac{\Phi(s)}{1 - e^{-4}}\right] \tag{6.74}$$

The steady-state component of a linear system to a periodic driving function must also be a periodic function. The Laplace transform of the steady-state component over the first cycle $(0 < t < 4)$ is obviously $\Phi(s)$. We shall now find the inverse transform of $\Phi(s)$.

$$v_{ss}(t) = \mathcal{L}^{-1}[\Phi(s)], \qquad (0 < t < 4) \tag{6.75}$$

The distinction between Eqs. 6.74 and 6.75 must be properly understood. Equation 6.74 represents $v_{ss}(t)$ over the entire interval $(0 < t < \infty)$, whereas Eq. 6.75 represents $v_{ss}(t)$ only over the first period $(0 < t < 4)$.

Substituting Eq. 6.70 in Eq. 6.75, we get

$$v_{ss}(t) = \mathcal{L}^{-1}\left[\frac{E(1 - e^{-s})}{s(s+1)} + \frac{0.032E(1 - e^{-4s})}{s+1}\right] \tag{6.76}$$

$$= \mathcal{L}^{-1}\left\{E\left[\left(\frac{1}{s} - \frac{1}{s+1}\right) - e^{-s}\left(\frac{1}{s} - \frac{1}{s+1}\right) + 0.032\left(\frac{1}{s+1} - \frac{e^{-4s}}{s+1}\right)\right]\right\} \tag{6.77}$$

The terms e^{-s}, e^{-4s} represent the delay of 1 and 4 seconds, respectively. Thus

$$v_{ss}(t) = E\{[1 - e^{-t}]u(t) - [1 - e^{-(t-1)}]u(t-1)$$
$$+ 0.032[e^{-t}u(t) - e^{-(t-4)}u(t-4)]\} \tag{6.78}$$

Note that in the interval $0 < t < 1$, the terms multiplied by $u(t-1)$ and $u(t-4)$ have no influence, and hence in this interval, $v_{ss}(t)$ reduces to

$$v_{ss}(t) = E(1 - 0.968e^{-t}), \qquad (0 < t < 1) \tag{6.79}$$

Also in the interval $1 < t < 4$, the term multiplied by $u(t-4)$ has no influence and the terms $u(t)$ and $u(t-1)$ both are unity, and cancel each other. Therefore

$$v_{ss}(t) = E[-e^{-t} + e^{-(t-1)} + 0.032e^{-t}]$$
$$= 1.75Ee^{-t}, \qquad (1 < t < 4) \tag{6.80}$$

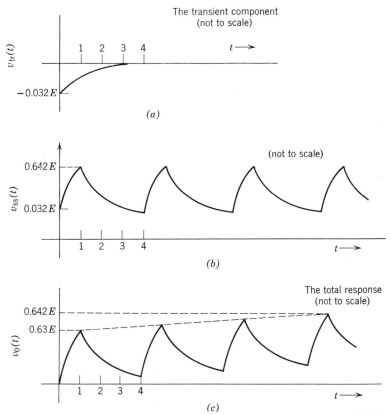

Figure 6.20 (a) The transient component. (b) The steady-state component. (c) The total response.

Since the steady-state solution repeats after every 4 seconds, there is no need to evaluate it for the remaining time interval. It can be easily determined for any value of t from Eqs. 6.79 and 6.80. Thus

$$v_{ss}(t) = \begin{cases} E[1 - 0.968e^{-(t-4n)}], & (4n < t < 4n + 1) & (6.81) \\ 1.75Ee^{-(t-4n)}, & (4n + 1) < t < 4(n + 1) & (6.82) \end{cases}$$

The various waveshapes are shown in Fig. 6.20.

An Alternate Approach

A convenient solution to the above problem may be found alternatively by recognizing the fact that the response has the transient and the steady-state components and that the steady-state component is a periodic function. Because of the periodic nature of the steady-state component, it is necessary to evaluate it only during the first period.

The transient component can be easily found by the method discussed before. The total response of the network during the first period can also be evaluated from simple circuit considerations. The steady-state component during the first period can be found by subtracting the transient component from the total response of the network during the first period. The procedure will be illustrated by applying it to the problem in Fig. 6.19.

The total response v_t during the first interval can be evaluated by inspection. At $t = 0$, a constant voltage E is applied to a series R-C network. The output voltage across the capacitor during the interval $(0 < t < 1)$ is given by

$$v_t = E(1 - e^{-t}), \qquad (0 < t < 1) \tag{6.83}$$

At $t = 1^-$, the output voltage is

$$v_t(1^-) = E(1 - e^{-1})$$

$$= E\left(\frac{e - 1}{e}\right) = 0.63E \tag{6.84}$$

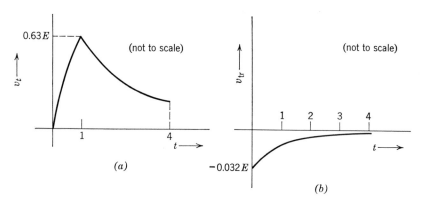

(a)

(b)

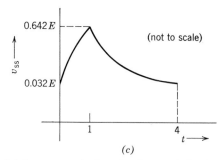

(c)

Figure 6.21 (a) The total response during the first period. (b) The transient response. (c) The steady-state component during the first period.

At $t = 1$, the applied voltage suddenly drops to zero and the capacitor discharges through the resistor. The initial voltage on the capacitor is $0.63E$. The output voltage now is given by

$$v_t = 0.63Ee^{-(t-1)}$$
$$= 1.72Ee^{-t}, \qquad (1 < t < 4) \qquad (6.85)$$

Therefore, the total response during the first period is given by

$$v_t = \begin{cases} E(1 - e^{-t}), & (0 < t < 1) \\ 1.72Ee^{-t}, & (1 < t < 4) \end{cases} \qquad (6.86)$$

The transient component of the response can be easily found by partial-fraction expansion as shown in Eq. 6.73.

$$v_{\text{tr}} = -0.032Ee^{-t} \qquad (6.87)$$

The steady-state component of the response during the first period can now be easily found by subtracting Eq. 6.87 from Eq. 6.86. Thus, the steady-state component v_{ss} during the first period is given by

$$v_{\text{ss}}(t) = E(1 - 0.968e^{-t}), \qquad (0 < t < 1)$$
$$= 1.753Ee^{-t}, \qquad (1 < t < 4) \qquad (6.88)$$

This is the same result as obtained previously. The various waveforms are shown in Fig. 6.21.

6.11 THE FILTER CHARACTERISTIC OF LINEAR SYSTEMS

For a given system, an input signal $f(t)$ gives rise to a response signal $r(t)$. The system therefore processes the signal $f(t)$ in a way that is characteristic of the system. The spectral density function of the input signal is given by $F(s)$; whereas the spectral density function of the response is given by $F(s)H(s)$. The system therefore modifies the spectral density function of the input signal. It is evident that the system acts as a kind of filter to various frequency components. Some frequency components are boosted in strength, some are attenuated, and some may remain unaffected. Similarly, each frequency component suffers a different amount of phase shift in the process of transmission. The system therefore modifies the spectral density function according to its filter characteristics. The modification is carried out according to the transfer function $H(s)$, which represents the response of the system to various frequency components. Therefore, $H(s)$ acts as a weighting function to different frequencies. The resultant response has the spectral density

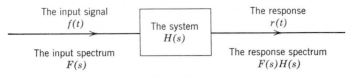

Figure 6.22

$F(s)H(s)$ (Fig. 6.22). The filtering process of a system can be conveniently visualized in terms of real frequencies $s = j\omega$. The input signal has a spectral density $F(j\omega)$ and the system response is given by $H(j\omega)$. The spectral density of the response is evidently $F(j\omega)H(j\omega)$.

Consider a simple R-C network shown in Fig. 6.23. A square pulse shown in the Fig. 6.23a is applied at the input terminals aa' of this network. The response is the output voltage $v_o(t)$ observed across the output terminals of this network. The spectral density function of the input signal (rectangular pulse) is shown in Fig. 6.23c. The transfer function $H(s)$ of the network, relating the output voltage to the input voltage, is obviously $1/(s + 1)$. Hence $H(j\omega) = 1/(j\omega + 1)$. The

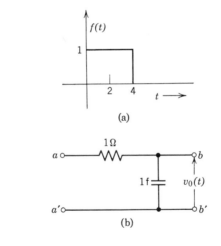

(a)

(b)

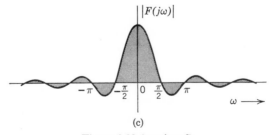

(c)

Figure 6.23 (*continued*)

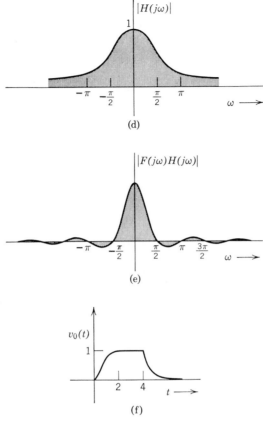

(d)

(e)

(f)

Figure 6.23 (*concluded*)

magnitude plot $|H(j\omega)|$ of the network filter characteristics is shown in Fig. 6.23d. For the time being, we shall ignore the phase characteristics. Observe that this network attenuates high frequencies and allows lower frequencies to pass with a relatively small attenuation. This network is therefore the simplest form of a low-pass filter. The high frequency components in the input spectrum suffer severe attenuation compared to the low frequency components. The spectral density function of the response is the product of $F(j\omega)$ and $H(j\omega)$. The magnitude $|F(j\omega)H(j\omega)|$ of the response spectral density function is shown in Fig. 6.23e. A comparison of Figs. 6.23c and 6.23e show clearly the attenuation of high frequency components caused by the network. The response function $v_o(t)$ is obviously a distorted replica of the input signal, the distortion being caused by the fact that the network does not allow equal access to the transmission of all the frequency components of the input signal. In particular, the high frequency components suffer most. This is manifested in the rising and falling characteristic of the response voltage. The input signal rises sharply at $t = 0$. The sharp rise means a rapid change, implying very high frequency components. Since the network does not allow the high frequency components, the output voltage cannot change at a rapid rate and hence it rises and falls sluggishly compared to the input signal.

6.12 DISTORTIONLESS TRANSMISSION

The preceding discussion immediately suggests the requirement to be met by a system in order to allow the distortionless transmission of a signal. A system must attenuate all of the frequency components equally; that is, $H(j\omega)$ should have constant magnitude for all frequencies. Even this requirement is not sufficient to guarantee the distortionless transmission. The phase shift of each component must also satisfy certain relationships. Thus far, we have ignored the effect of phase shift. It is conceivable that even if all of the frequency components of a signal are transmitted through the system with equal attenuation, but if they acquire different phase shifts in the process of transmission, they may add up to an entirely different signal. We shall now investigate the requirement of the relative phase shifts of various components for a distortionless transmission.

For a distortionless transmission, we require that the response be an exact replica of the input signal. This replica may, of course, have a different magnitude. The important thing is the waveform and not its relative magnitude. In general, there may also be some time delay associated with this replica. We may therefore say that a signal $f(t)$ is transmitted without distortion if the response is $kf(t - t_0)$. It is evident that the response is the exact replica of the input with a magnitude k times the original signal and delayed by t_0 seconds. If $F(s)$ is the transform of $f(t)$, then from the time shifting theorem,

$$\mathcal{L}[kf(t - t_0)] = kF(s)e^{-st_0}$$

We now have

$$F(s)H(s) = kF(s)e^{-st_0}$$

Therefore

$$H(s) = ke^{-st_0} \tag{6.89}$$

Therefore, to achieve distortionless transmission through a system, the transfer function of the system must be of the form shown in Eq. 6.89. For real frequencies $s = j\omega$,

$$H(j\omega) = ke^{-j\omega t_0} \tag{6.90}$$

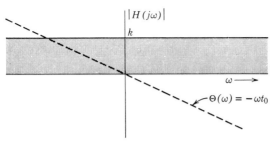

Figure 6.24   The magnitude and phase characteristic of a distortionless transmission system.

It is evident that $|H(j\omega)|$, the magnitude of the transfer function, is k, and that it is constant for all values of ω. The phase shift for a component of frequency ω should be ωt_0. In other words, the phase shift should be proportional to frequency. Strictly speaking,

$$\theta(\omega) = n\pi - \omega t_0 \qquad (n \text{ integral})$$

since the addition of excess phase shift of $n\pi$ radians may, at most, change the sign of the signal.

Bandwidth of a System

The constancy of the magnitude $H(j\omega)$ in a system is usually specified by its bandwidth. The bandwidth of a system is arbitrarily defined as the interval of frequencies over which the magnitude $|H(j\omega)|$ remains within $1/\sqrt{2}$ times (within 3 db) its value at the midband. The bandwidth of a system whose $|H(j\omega)|$ plot is shown in Fig. 6.25 has a bandwidth of $\omega_2 - \omega_1$.

For distortionless transmission, we obviously need a system with infinite bandwidth. Due to physical limitations, it is impossible to construct a system with infinite bandwidth. Actually, a satisfactory distortionless transmission can be achieved by systems with finite but fairly large bandwidths. For any physical signal, the energy content decreases with frequency. Hence it is only necessary to construct a

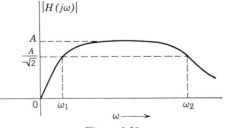

Figure 6.25

system which will transmit the frequency components which contain most of the energy of the signal. Attenuation of extremely high frequency components would tend to introduce very little distortion, since those components carry very little energy.

6.13 THE ENERGY DENSITY SPECTRUM OF THE INPUT AND THE OUTPUT SIGNALS

If a signal has a spectral density function $F(j\omega)$, then it was shown (Eq. 4.71) that the energy density spectrum:

$$S(\omega) = \frac{1}{\pi} |F(j\omega)|^2$$

The energy spectral density function of the response will be given by

$$\frac{1}{\pi} |F(j\omega)H(j\omega)|^2 = \frac{1}{\pi} |F(j\omega)|^2 |H(j\omega)|^2.$$

It is obvious that the ratio of the energy density spectra of the output signal and the input signal is given by $|H(j\omega)|^2$. Note that the ratio is independent of the phase characteristics of the network.

6.14 IDEAL FILTERS

An ideal low-pass filter transmits, without any distortion, all of the signals of frequencies below a certain frequency (w/2) radian/second. The signals of frequencies above (w/2) radian/second are completely attenuated (Fig. 6.26a). The frequency response (magnitude characteristic) of a low-pass filter is thus a gate function $G_w(\omega)$. The corresponding phase function for distortionless transmission is $-\omega t_0$. The transfer function of such a filter is evidently given by

$$H(j\omega) = |H(j\omega)|\, e^{j\theta(\omega)}$$
$$= G_w(\omega)e^{-j\omega t_0}$$

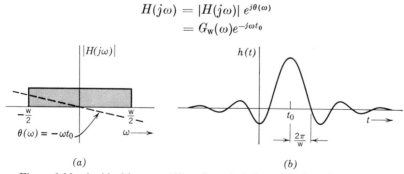

(a)   (b)

Figure 6.26   An ideal low-pass filter characteristic and its impulse response.

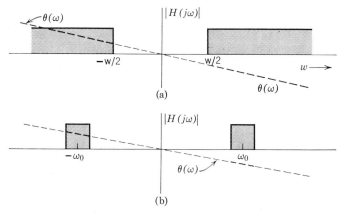

Figure 6.27   Ideal high-pass and bandpass filter characteristics.

The unit impulse response $h(t)$ of this filter can be found by taking the inverse Fourier transform of $H(j\omega)$.

$$h(t) = \mathscr{L}^{-1}[H(j\omega)]$$
$$= \mathscr{L}^{-1}[G_w(\omega)e^{-j\omega t_0}]$$

Using pair 12 in Table 4.1B and time-shifting property, we get

$$h(t) = \frac{w}{2\pi} Sa\left[\frac{w(t - t_0)}{2}\right]$$

A glance at Fig. 6.26b shows that the impulse response exists for negative values of t. This is certainly a strange result in view of the fact that the

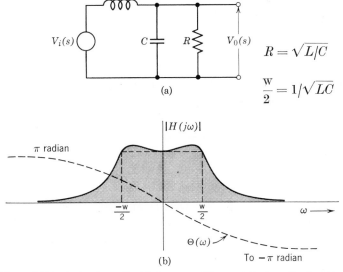

$$R = \sqrt{L/C}$$

$$\frac{w}{2} = 1/\sqrt{LC}$$

Figure 6.28   A simple realizable low-pass filter and its transfer function.

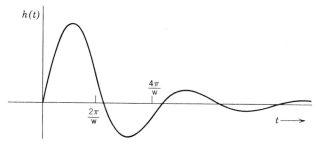

Figure 6.29   Impulse response of the low-pass filter shown in Fig. 6.28a.

driving function (unit impulse) was applied at $t = 0$. The response therefore appears even before the driving function is applied. Unfortunately it is not possible in practice to build such a circuit with crystal ball properties. Hence we must conclude that although an ideal low-pass filter is very desirable, it is physically not realizable. One can similarly show that other ideal filters (such as the ideal high-pass or band-pass filters shown in Fig. 6.27) are also unrealizable.

In practice we are satisfied with filters having characteristics close to those of an ideal filter. A simple low-pass filter and its magnitude and phase characteristics are shown in Fig. 6.28. Compare the magnitude and phase characteristics of this filter with that of an ideal filter. The impulse response is very similar to that of an ideal filter except that it is a causal function.

We now wonder whether there is any test which can distinguish the physically realizable characteristic from an unrealizable one. Such a test is provided by the Paley-Wiener criterion to be discussed in the next section.

6.15   CAUSALITY AND PHYSICAL REALIZABILITY: THE PALEY-WIENER CRITERION

Physical realizability is defined in the literature in different ways. Here, we shall use the least restrictive definition which will distinguish the systems that are physically possible from those that are not. It is intuitively evident that a physically realizable system cannot have a response before the driving function is applied. This is known as the *causality condition*. This condition may also be expressed alternatively. A unit impulse response $h(t)$ of a physically realizable system must be causal $[h(t) = 0;\ t < 0]$. This is the time-domain criterion of physical realizability. In the frequency domain, this criterion implies that a necessary and sufficient condition for a magnitude function $|H(j\omega)|$ to be physically realizable is that[13]

$$\int_{-\infty}^{\infty} \frac{|\ln |H(j\omega)| |}{1 + \omega^2} \, d\omega < \infty \qquad (6.91)$$

The magnitude function $|H(j\omega)|$ must, however, be square-integrable before the Paley-Wiener criterion is valid,[14] that is,

$$\int_{-\infty}^{\infty} |H(j\omega)|^2 \, d\omega < \infty$$

A system whose magnitude function violates the Paley-Weiner criterion (Eq. 6.91) has a noncausal impulse response, that is, the response exists forever in the past, prior to the application of the driving function.

We can draw some significant conclusions from the Paley-Wiener criterion. It is evident that the magnitude function $|H(j\omega)|$ may be zero at some discrete frequencies, but it cannot be zero over a finite band of frequencies since this will cause the integral in Eq. 6.91 to become infinity. It is therefore evident that the ideal filters shown in Figs. 6.26 and 6.27 are not physically realizable. We can conclude from Eq. 6.91 that the amplitude function cannot fall off to zero faster than a function of exponential order. Thus

$$|H(j\omega)| = ke^{-\alpha|\omega|}$$

is permissible. But the gaussian error curve

$$|H(j\omega)| = ke^{-\alpha\omega^2}$$

is not realizable, since it violates Eq. 6.91. In short, a realizable magnitude characteristic cannot have too great a total attenuation. It is interesting to note that although the ideal filter characteristics shown in Figs. 6.26

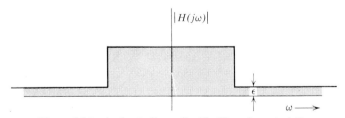

Figure 6.30   A physically realizable filter characteristic.

[13] Raymond E. A. C. Paley and Norbert Wiener, *Fourier Transforms in the Complex Domain*, American Mathematical Society Colloquium Publication 19, New York, 1934.

[14] If the magnitude of function $H(j\omega)$ satisfies the Paley-Wiener criterion (Eq. 6.91), it does not follow that the system is physically realizable. It merely says that a suitable phase function $\theta(\omega)$ may be associated with $|H(j\omega)|$, so that the resulting transfer function is physically realizable.

and 6.27 are not realizable, it is possible to approach these characteristics as closely as desired. Thus the low-pass filter characteristics shown in Fig. 6.30 is physically realizable for arbitrarily small value of ε. The reader can verify that this characteristic does not violate the Paley-Wiener criterion.

6.16 RESPONSE OF LINEAR SYSTEMS TO NONCAUSAL SIGNALS

To obtain the response of a system to a noncausal driving function, we must use the bilateral Laplace transform (complex Fourier transform). This is illustrated here by an example.

Example 6.17

Find the current $i(t)$ for the $R\text{-}C$ circuit shown in Fig. 6.31 if the driving voltage $f(t)$ is given by

$$f(t) = e^t u(t) + e^{2t} u(-t)$$

The transfer function $H(s)$ of the circuit is given by

$$H(s) = \frac{s}{s+1}$$

Note that since $h(t)$ is a causal function, the region of convergence of $H(s)$ is $\sigma > -1$. The bilateral Laplace transform of $f(t)$ is given by

$$F(s) = \frac{1}{s-1} - \frac{1}{s-2} = \frac{-1}{(s-1)(s-2)}$$

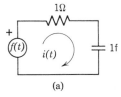

(a)

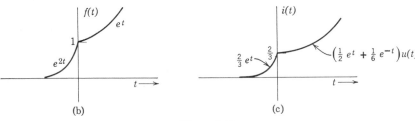

(b)   (c)

Figure 6.31

Note that the region of convergence of $F(s)$ is

$$1 < \sigma < 2$$

The response $i(t)$ is the inverse transform of $F(s)H(s)$

$$i(t) = \mathscr{F}_c^{-1}\left[\frac{-s}{(s+1)(s-1)(s-2)}\right]$$

$$= \mathscr{F}_c^{-1}\left[\frac{1}{6}\frac{1}{s+1} + \frac{1}{2}\frac{1}{s-1} - \frac{2}{3}\frac{1}{s-2}\right]$$

The region of convergence of $F(s)H(s)$ is the region of convergence common to both $F(s)$ and $H(s)$. This is obviously $1 < \sigma < 2$. The poles $s = \pm 1$ lie to the left of the region of convergence and hence represent positive time functions; the pole $s = 2$ lies to the right of the region of convergence and thus represents the negative time function. Hence

$$i(t) = \tfrac{1}{6}e^{-t}u(t) + \tfrac{1}{2}e^{t}u(t) + \tfrac{2}{3}e^{2t}u(-t)$$

In this example, if

$$f(t) = e^{-4t}u(t) + e^{-2t}u(-t)$$

then the region of convergence of $F(s)$ is $-4 < \sigma < -2$. Note that now no region of convergence exists for $F(s)H(s)$, since there is no region of convergence common to both $F(s)$ and $H(s)$. In such a case the response $i(t)$ goes to infinity. This is because the signal cannot satisfy the dominance condition for the system. It is not possible to express the signal as a continuous sum of exponentials which decay at a rate slower than the transient response of the system (also see Problem 14 at the end of Chapter 10). In order that the response of a system be finite, both the positive and negative time components of $f(t)$ must satisfy the dominance condition for the system separately. As we have seen, it is always possible to satisfy the dominance condition by a positive time function (a causal function). It is therefore necessary to test only for the negative time component. In the above example, the transient component is proportional to e^{-t}; the negative time component of $f(t)$ is $e^{-2t}u(-t)$, which has a region of convergence $\sigma < -2$ and obviously does not satisfy the dominance condition.

There are situations where the negative time component of $f(t)$ does satisfy the dominance condition, but the bilateral transform of $f(t)$ may not exist because the positive and negative time components of $f(t)$ do not have a common region of convergence. Consider, for example,

$$f(t) = e^{2t}u(t) + e^{t}u(-t)$$

The negative time component has a region of convergence $\sigma < 1$ and satisfies the dominance condition for the circuit in Fig. 6.31. But the region of convergence of the positive time component is $\sigma > 2$, and hence there is no region of convergence common to both components and consequently the bilateral Laplace transform of $f(t)$ does not exist. In such a case the response must be evaluated for each time component separately. The desired response is the sum of two responses [see Problems 26(d) and 26(e)].

PROBLEMS

1. Find the output voltage $v(t)$ of a network shown in Fig. P-6.1 when the voltage applied to the terminals ab is given by $te^{-t}u(t)$.

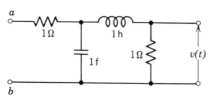

Figure P-6.1

2. Find currents $i_1(t)$ and $i_2(t)$ in an inductively coupled circuit shown in Fig. P-6.2.

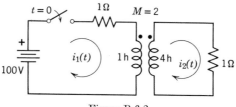

Figure P-6.2

3. A voltage $v(t)$ is applied across the terminals ab of a parallel resonant circuit shown in Fig. P-6.3. It is given that $\omega_0{}^2 = 1/LC$. Find the current $i(t)$ if $v(t)$ is given by the following.

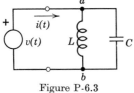

Figure P-6.3

(a) $A \cos(\omega_0 t)u(t)$.

(b) $A \sin(\omega_0 t)u(t)$.

Explain the results qualitatively.

4. Find the inverse Laplace transform of the following functions.

(a) $\dfrac{(s+1)^2}{s^2 - s - 6}$

(b) $\dfrac{K}{s^2(s+2)}$

(c) $\dfrac{s}{(s+1)(s^2 + 2s + 2)}$

(d) $\dfrac{s+2}{s(s+1)^2}$

(e) $\dfrac{1}{(s+1)(s+2)^4}$

(f) $\dfrac{s+1}{(s+2)(s^2 + 4s + 5)^2}$

(g) $\dfrac{2s+3}{(s+1)^2(s^2 + 2s + 5)^2}$

(h) $\dfrac{s+1}{s(s+2)^2(s^2 + 2s + 5)}$

5. Derive Eq. 6.36.

6. An equivalent circuit of a vacuum tube amplifier is shown in Fig. P-6.6.

(a) Find the transfer function $H(s)$ relating the output voltage to the input voltage, and determine the bandwidth of voltage gain.

(b) Find and sketch the output voltage $v_0(t)$ when a unit step voltage is applied at the input terminals gk.

(c) If the rise time is defined as the time required for the respones in a to rise from 10 to 90% of its final value, show that the bandwidth (rps) multiplied by the rise time is a constant, independent of the tube parameters. Show that this constant is 2.2.

(d) Show that the product of the d-c gain $[H(0)]$ and the bandwidth found in (b) is equal to g_m/C_{pk}.

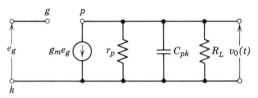

Figure P-6.6

7. Find the currents $i_1(t)$ and $i_2(t)$ for the network shown in Fig. 6.5a (Example 6.4), assuming that the capacitor is initially charged to 10 volts (terminal a being positive).

8. Assume the network shown in Fig. 6.5a (Example 6.4) to be in steady state. Now the terminals ab are suddenly shorted. Find and sketch currents $i_1(t)$ and $i_2(t)$.

9. Assume the network shown in Fig. 6.5a (Example 6.4) to be in steady state. Now the switch k is opened instantaneously and, at the same time, the terminal c is connected to the terminal b. Find the currents $i_1(t)$ and $i_2(t)$.

10. The switch s in the network of Fig. P-6.10 is in position a initially, and the network is de-energized. At time $t = 0$, the switch is connected to position b, and at time $t = 1$ seconds the switch is connected to position c from b. Find the output voltage $v_0(t)$.

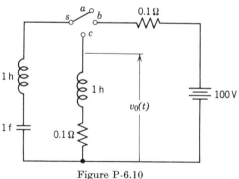

Figure P-6.10

11. Find the Laplace transform of a rectangular pulse shown in Fig. P-6.11. As a is made smaller, the pulse becomes narrower but increases in height in such a way that the area remains constant. In the limit as $a \to 0$, the pulse tends to an impulse function. Find the transform of an impulse function as a limiting case of this pulse.

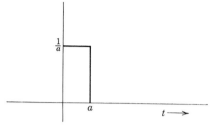

Figure P-6.11

12. Solve Problems 1, 2, 3, 7, 8, 9, and 10 using the transform-analysis approach described in Section 6.7.

13. A network is excited by 100 V at $t = 0$ as shown in Fig. P-6.13. The capacitor C_1 is initially charged to 10 V. Find the output voltage $e_0(t)$ using the frequency-analysis approach and the transform-analysis approach.

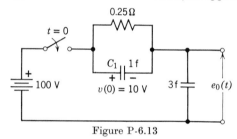

Figure P-6.13

14. A periodic voltage $e_1(t)$ shown in Fig. P-6.14a is applied to a series R-L circuit as shown in Fig. P-6.14b. Find the output voltage $e_0(t)$.

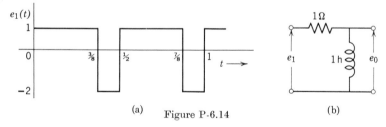

(a)   Figure P-6.14   (b)

15. A periodic voltage $e_1(t)$ shown in Fig. P-6.15a is applied to a series R-L-C circuit as shown in Fig. P-6.15b. Find the output voltage $e_0(t)$.

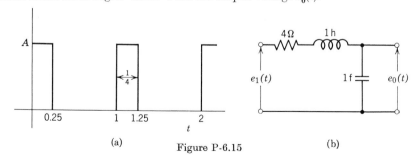

(a)   Figure P-6.15   (b)

16. A resistive network formed by two resistors R_1 and R_2 is used as an attenuator to reduce the voltage applied at terminals ab by a factor $R_2/(R_1 + R_2)$. Resistors R_1 and R_2 have stray capacitances across them of magnitude C_1 and C_2, respectively, as shown in Fig. P-6.16. What should be the relationship between R's and C's in order to have a distortionless attenuation?

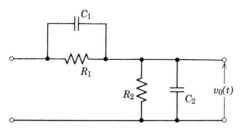

Figure P-6.16

17. The transfer function of an ideal low-pass filter is given by

$$H(j\omega) = kG_\mathrm{w}(\omega)e^{-j\omega t_0}$$

Evaluate the unit step response of this filter. *Hint.* Express your answer in terms of the sine integral function $Si(t)$ defined by

$$Si(t) = \int_0^t Sa(x)\,dx$$

18. The transfer function of an ideal bandpass filter is given by

$$H(j\omega) = k[G_\mathrm{w}(\omega - \omega_0) + G_\mathrm{w}(\omega + \omega_0)]e^{-j\omega t_0}$$

(a) Sketch the magnitude and phase function of this transfer function.
(b) Evaluate the impulse response of this filter.
(c) Sketch this response and state whether the filter is physically realizable.

19. A signal $f(t) = (2\pi/w)\delta(t) - Sa(wt/2)$ is applied at the input terminals of the filter in Problem 17. Find the response. Comment on your results.

20. (a) Find the transfer function of the lattice network shown in Fig. P-6.20.
(b) Sketch the magnitude and phase characteristics of $H(j\omega)$.
(c) Can this network be used to transmit signals without distortion? What are the limitations?

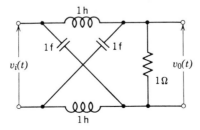

Figure P-6.20

(d) What is the input admittance?

(e) Can you form a delay line using a large number of such sections in cascade? What are the limitations? Find the amount of delay obtained by using n sections in cascade.

(f) For one lattice section (as shown in Fig. P-6.20), find the output voltage $v_0(t)$, when the input voltage $v_i(t)$ is given by $e^t u(-t)$. Sketch the input and output voltages. (*Hint.* Use the Fourier transform or the bilateral Laplace Transform, and do not be surprised at the result.)

21. Assume a signal $f(t)$ to be bandlimited; that is, the spectral density function $F(j\omega)$ has no frequency component beyond a certain frequency $w/2$. In other words, $F(j\omega) = 0$ for $\omega > w/2$. Such a signal can be amplified without distortion by an amplifier whose transfer function $H(j\omega)$ has an ideal low-pass filter characteristic.

$$H(j\omega) = kG_{\text{w}}(\omega)e^{-j\omega t_0}$$

Deviation of either magnitude or phase characteristic from that given in this equation introduces what is known as paired echo type of distortion. Assume that the phase characteristic of such an amplifier is ideal; that is, $\theta(\omega) = -\omega t_0$ but the magnitude characteristic drops at higher frequencies as shown in Fig. P-6.21. This may be expressed as

$$|H(j\omega)| = k(1 + \alpha \cos \omega T)G_{\text{w}}(\omega)$$

Find the output of the amplifier when a pulse signal $f(t)$ bandlimited to $w/2$ rps is applied at the input. (*Hint.* Use the dual of the modulation theorem.)

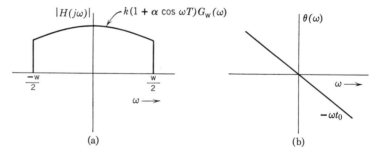

Figure P-6.21

22. In the amplifier discussed in Problem 21, assume that the magnitude characteristic of the amplifier is ideal; that is, $|H(j\omega)| = kG_{\text{w}}(\omega)$ but the phase characteristic is nonideal (Fig. P-6.22), and is given by

$$\theta(\omega) = -\omega t_0 + \alpha \sin \omega T$$

Find the output of the amplifier when the same bandlimited pulse signal $f(t)$ is applied at the input. (*Hint.* Assume α and T to be very small, and expand $e^{j\alpha \sin \omega T}$ by the first two terms of the Taylor series

$$e^{(j\alpha \sin \omega T)} \simeq 1 + j\alpha \sin \omega T$$

$$= 1 + \frac{\alpha}{2}(e^{j\omega T} - e^{-j\omega T})$$

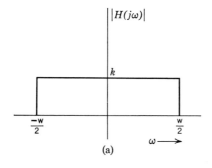

(a)

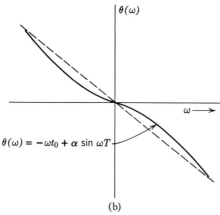

$\theta(\omega) = -\omega t_0 + \alpha \sin \omega T$

(b)

Figure P-6.22

23. Using the initial- and final-value theorems (Eqs. 5.67 and 5.69), find the initial and final values of the currents $i_1(t)$ and $i_2(t)$ in Example 6.4 from the knowledge of the transform of $i_1(t)$ and $i_2(t)$. Check the result with the values obtained from the inverse transforms of $I_1(s)$ and $I_2(s)$.

24. Solve the following equations using the Laplace transform.

(a) $\dfrac{dy}{dx} + 2y + 3 = 0$ given that $y(0^-) = 2$

(b) $\dfrac{d^2y}{dx^2} + 3\dfrac{dy}{dx} + 2y + 2\delta(x) = 0$ if $y(0^-) = 1$ and $y'(0^-) = 2$

(c) $\dfrac{d^2y}{dx^2} + 4y + 2 \sin 4x = 0$ if $y(1) = 1$ and $y(2) = 3$

(d) $\dfrac{d^2y}{dx^2} + 4\dfrac{dy}{dx} + 4y - 2e^{-2x} = 0$ ·if $y(1) = 2, y'(1) = 5$

(e) $\dfrac{d^3y}{dx^3} + 5\dfrac{d^2y}{dx^2} + 8\dfrac{dy}{dx} + 4y - e^{-x} = 0$ if $y(0^-) = y'(0^-) = 0$

                                             and $y''(0^-) = 1$

(f) $\dfrac{d^4y}{dx^4} + 4\dfrac{d^3y}{dx^3} + 8\dfrac{d^2y}{dx^2} + 8\dfrac{dy}{dx} + 3y + e^{-x} = 0$

     if $y(0^-) = y'(0^-) = y''(0^-) = y'''(0^-) = 0$

25. Solve the following simultaneous differential equations for y_1 and y_2.

(a) $\dfrac{d^2 y_1}{dx^2} + 2 \dfrac{dy_2}{dx} + 2y_1 - 2y_2 = 10u(x)$

$\dfrac{d^2 y_2}{dx^2} + 2 \dfrac{dy_2}{dx} + 2y_2 - 2y_1 = 0$

given

$$y_1(0^-) = y_2(0^-) = y_1{}'(0^-) = y_2{}'(0^-) = 0$$

(b) $\dfrac{d^2 y_1}{dx^2} + \dfrac{dy_1}{dx} + y_1 - y_2 = u(x) - u(x - 2)$

$\dfrac{dy_2}{dx} + y_2 - y_1 = 0$

given

$$y_1(0^-) = y_1{}'(0^-) = y_2(0^-) = 0$$

26. Find the output voltage $v(t)$ of the network shown in Fig. P-6.1 when the voltage applied to the terminals ab is given by

(a) $f(t) = e^{-|t|/2}$
(b) $f(t) = e^t u(t) + e^{2t} u(-t)$
(c) $f(t) = e^{-t/2} u(t) + e^{-t/4} u(-t)$
(d) $f(t) = e^{2t} u(t) + e^t u(-t)$
(e) $f(t) = e^{-t/4} u(t) + e^{-t/2} u(-t)$
(f) $f(t) = e^{-3t} u(t) + e^{-2t} u(-t)$

chapter 7

The Natural Response
and the Stability of a System

The response of a system to any driving function consists of two components: the transient and the steady-state component. The transient component consists of a linear combination of signals of natural frequencies (poles of the transfer function) of the system. The nature of this component is therefore characteristic of the system and is also known as the natural response. In this chapter we shall investigate the physical significance of the natural response and its relation to the system stability.

If $p_1, p_2, \ldots, p_n$ are the natural frequencies of a system, then the natural response is given by

$$r_n(t) = C_1 e^{p_1 t} + C_2 e^{p_2 t} + \cdots + C_n e^{p_n t} \tag{7.1}$$

where $C_1, C_2, \ldots, C_n$ are arbitrary constants.

7.1 UNIQUENESS OF THE NATURAL FREQUENCIES OF A SYSTEM

By definition, natural frequencies are the poles of the transfer function $H(s)$ of the system. However, the transfer function of a system is not unique. It depends upon the position where the response is observed and the position where the driving function is applied. In short, the transfer function depends upon what is being considered as the response and the driving function. This nonuniqueness of the transfer function leads us directly to a disturbing question. Since the natural frequencies of a system are the poles of the transfer function, and since the transfer function is not unique, does this mean that a given system has a different set of natural frequencies associated with each transfer function? Fortunately, the answer is no! There is only one set of natural frequencies of a system, irrespective of what is being considered as the response and the driving function.[1] This implies that poles of any transfer function of a given system must be identical. This is indeed true! A system may have any number of transfer functions, but their poles must be identical. This will be shown for a general network with n meshes (n independent loops).

We shall represent this network directly in the frequency domain. Let $I_1(s)$, $I_2(s)$, $\ldots$, $I_n(s)$ be the n mesh currents. Let $V(s)$ be the transform of the driving voltage in mesh 1, as shown in Fig. 7.1. Further, let Z_{11}, Z_{12}, $\ldots$, Z_{nn} be the total mesh impedances for meshes 1, 2, 3, $\ldots$, n, respectively, and let Z_{mn} be the transfer impedance between mesh m and n.

The n mesh equations may now be written as

$$\left.\begin{aligned}
V(s) &= Z_{11}(s)I_1(s) + Z_{12}(s)I_2(s) + \cdots + Z_{1n}(s)I_n(s) \\
0 &= Z_{21}(s)I_1(s) + Z_{22}(s)I_2(s) + \cdots + Z_{2n}(s)I_n(s) \\
0 &= Z_{n1}(s)I_1(s) + Z_{n2}(s)I_2(s) + \cdots + Z_{nn}(s)I_n(s)
\end{aligned}\right\} \quad (7.2)$$

I_j, the current in jth mesh, may be found from the set of Eqs. 7.2 by using Cramer's rule.

$$I_j(s) = \frac{\begin{vmatrix} Z_{11} & Z_{12} & \cdots & Z_{1,j-1} & V(s) & Z_{1,j+1} & \cdots & Z_{1n} \\ Z_{21} & Z_{22} & \cdots & Z_{2,j-1} & 0 & Z_{2,j+1} & \cdots & Z_{2n} \\ \cdots & \cdots & \cdots & \cdots & \cdots & \cdots & \cdots & \cdots \\ Z_{n1} & Z_{n2} & \cdots & Z_{n,j-1} & 0 & Z_{n,j+1} & \cdots & Z_{nn} \end{vmatrix}}{\begin{vmatrix} Z_{11} & Z_{12} & \cdots & Z_{1n} \\ Z_{21} & Z_{22} & \cdots & Z_{2n} \\ \cdots & \cdots & \cdots & \cdots \\ Z_{n1} & Z_{n2} & \cdots & Z_{nn} \end{vmatrix}} \quad (7.3)$$

Hence

$$I_j(s) = \frac{\Delta_{1j} V(s)}{\Delta_z(s)} \quad (7.4)$$

where Δ_{1j} is the cofactor of $V(s)$ in the numerator determinant in Eq. 7.3,

[1] This statement will be slightly modified later for some degenerate systems.

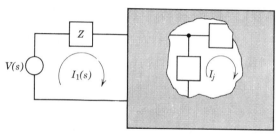

Figure 7.1

and Δ_z is the denominator determinant. If we consider I_j as the response, then the transfer function H_j is given by the ratio of I_j to $V(s)$.

$$H_j(s) = \frac{I_j(s)}{V(s)} = \frac{\Delta_{1j}(s)}{\Delta_z(s)} \tag{7.5}$$

Note that the natural frequencies of this network are poles of $H_j(s)$. From Eq. 7.5, it is obvious that the poles of $H_j(s)$ are zeros of $\Delta_z(s)$. There is a possibility of some zeros of $\Delta_z(s)$ being canceled by zeros[2] of $\Delta_{1j}(s)$ in Eq. 7.5. Such a situation occurs in what are known as degenerate systems (see Problems 2 and 3 at the end of this chapter). For a non-degenerate system, the poles of all possible transfer functions are the same [zeros of $\Delta_z(s)$], whereas for a degenerate case some of the poles (natural frequencies) may be missing in some transfer functions due to the cancellation process mentioned above. We shall tacitly assume in the rest of our discussion that the system under consideration is a nondegenerate one unless otherwise specified.

Note that zeros of $\Delta_z(s)$ are independent of the choice of the mesh current considered as the response. It is therefore evident that the natural frequencies of the network are independent of the choice of the response function.[3] Thus, $\Delta_z(s)$ is a very important determinant known as the characteristic determinant of the system, and the Eq. $\Delta_z(s) = 0$ is known as the characteristic equation of the system. The natural frequencies of any system are the roots of

$$\Delta_z(s) = 0$$

[2] The impedance $Z_{mn}(s)$ is, in general, of the form $(R + Ls + 1/Cs)$, and hence the denominators of both Δ_{1j} and Δ_z consist of a single term s^p and s^q, respectively, where $q > p$. Hence the denominator of Δ_{1j} does not add any new natural frequencies.

[3] We have derived this result for a case where any of the mesh currents is considered as the response; it may be readily extended to the voltage across any terminals being considered as the response.

7.2 EVALUATION OF THE NATURAL FREQUENCIES OF A NETWORK

We have proved that the natural frequencies of a network are independent of the choice of the response and the driving function. Alternatively, it can be stated that in general the poles of all the possible transfer functions of a given system are the same. Although we have shown this result only for networks, it also holds true for any linear system in general.

It is now easy to find the natural frequencies of any network in the light of the above discussion. Let us consider the impedance seen by the generator $V(s)$ in Fig. 7.1. This impedance Z_1 is given by

$$Z_1(s) = \frac{V(s)}{I_1(s)}$$

From Eq. 7.4, we have

$$I_1(s) = \frac{\Delta_{11}(s)V(s)}{\Delta_z(s)}$$

and

$$Z_1 = \frac{V(s)}{I_1(s)} = \frac{\Delta_z(s)}{\Delta_{11}(s)}$$

Since the natural frequencies of the network are the roots of the equation:

$$\Delta_z(s) = 0,$$

it follows that the natural frequencies are also zeros of the impedance $Z_1(s)$. That is, the natural frequencies are the roots of the equation

$$Z_1(s) = 0.$$

Evidently, the impedance Z_1 is zero for the signals of the natural frequencies of the system. This result can be generalized for any mesh. We may just as well have found the impedance Z_r in the rth mesh (Fig. 7.2).

$$Z_r = \frac{\Delta_z(s)}{\Delta_{rr}(s)}$$

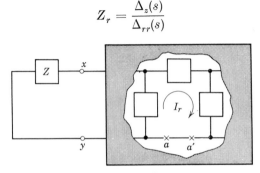

Figure 7.2

Thus the zeros of $Z_r(s) = 0$ are the natural frequencies of the network. To find $Z_r(s)$, we need to break the rth mesh at aa' and find the impedance seen across the terminals aa'. Indeed, the above result may be generalized for the impedance seen by breaking at any point in the network.

We therefore conclude that *the natural frequencies of any network are the zeros of the impedance seen by breaking at any point in the network.* This is a very significant result. It follows that the network offers zero impedance to signals of its own natural frequencies. In other words, a signal of any natural frequency of the system can be sustained by the system without a driving function. Evidently the natural response, which is composed of the signals of all of the natural frequencies of a system, must be sustained by the system without a driving function or source. Hence this response is the source-free response. We therefore conclude that the natural response (also known as the transient or the source-free response) can be sustained by the system itself, without a driving function.

As an example, consider a simple *R-L* circuit driven by a voltage source as shown in Fig. 7.3. If we consider $i(t)$ as the response, then the transfer function of the network is

$$H(s) = \frac{1}{R + Ls}$$

and the network has one natural frequency

$$s = -R/L$$

The natural response of the system is $Ae^{-Rt/L}$ and, from the above discussion, it follows that this current can be sustained by the system without a driving function. This is indeed true, and can be easily verified by finding the voltage $v(t)$ required to sustain this current. From Fig. 7.3, we have

$$v(t) = Ri(t) + L\frac{di}{dt}$$

If

$$i(t) = Ae^{-Rt/L}$$

then

$$v(t) = RAe^{-Rt/L} + LA(-R/L)e^{-Rt/L} = 0$$

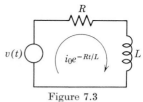

Figure 7.3

It is evident that the current $Ae^{-R/Lt}$ can be sustained by the system without a driving function.[4]

---

[4] Although a system sustains the natural response without a source, it does not mean that the natural response does not dissipate energy. Actually the system exhibits the natural response without a driving source only when there is some initial energy stored in the system. This stored energy is dissipated in the natural response.

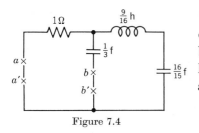

Figure 7.4

The natural frequencies of a network can be found from the impedance seen by breaking at any point in the network. We have shown that the natural frequencies are the zeros of such an impedance function.

Example 7.1

Find the natural frequencies of the network shown in Fig. 7.4. The natural frequencies of this network may be found by investigating the impedance seen by breaking at any convenient point. First, we shall break at aa'. The impedance $Z_{aa'}$ seen across these terminals, is given by

$$Z_{aa'} = 1 + \cfrac{1}{\cfrac{s}{3} + \cfrac{1}{9s/16 + 15/16s}}$$

$$= 1 + \frac{3(9s^2 + 15)}{9s^3 + 63s}$$

$$= \frac{9s^3 + 27s^2 + 63s + 45}{9s^3 + 63s}$$

$$= \frac{s^3 + 3s^2 + 7s + 5}{s^3 + 7s}$$

$$= \frac{(s + 1)(s^2 + 2s + 5)}{s(s^2 + 7)}$$

The impedance $Z_{aa'}$ goes to zero at frequencies

$$s = -1, \qquad (-1 + j2), \qquad \text{and} \qquad (-1 - j2)$$

Hence, these are the natural frequencies of this network. Instead of breaking at aa', we may just as well have broken at bb'. The impedance $Z_{bb'}$, seen across bb', is

$$Z_{bb'} = \cfrac{1}{\cfrac{1}{3}s} + \cfrac{1}{1 + \cfrac{1}{9s/16 + 15/16s}}$$

$$= \frac{3}{s} + \frac{9s^2 + 15}{9s^2 + 16s + 15}$$

$$= \frac{9s^3 + 27s^2 + 63s + 45}{s(9s^2 + 16s + 15)}$$

$$= \frac{9(s + 1)(s + 1 + j2)(s + 1 - j2)}{s(9s^2 + 16s + 15)}$$

Clearly, $Z_{bb'}$ goes to zero at frequencies

$$s = -1, \qquad (-1 + j2), \qquad \text{and} \qquad (-1 - j2)$$

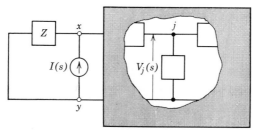

Figure 7.5

Hence these are the natural frequencies of the network. We will get the same results by breaking at any other point in the network.

It is also possible to find the natural frequencies of a network by investigating the admittance seen across any two nodes of the network.

Consider the general network shown in Fig. 7.1 Instead of connecting a voltage source in the mesh as shown in Fig. 7.1, we shall connect a current source $I(s)$ across nodes xy as shown in Fig. 7.5. Let the voltage at node j be $V_j(s)$. If there are m independent nodes for this network, we may write the node equations for the system:

$$
\left.
\begin{aligned}
I(s) &= Y_{11}(s)V_1(s) + Y_{12}(s)V_2(s) + \cdots + Y_{1m}(s)V_m(s) \\
0 &= Y_{21}(s)V_1(s) + Y_{22}(s)V_2(s) + \cdots + Y_{2m}(s)V_m(s) \\
0 &= Y_{m1}(s)V_1(s) + Y_{m2}(s)V_2(s) + \cdots + Y_{mm}(s)V_m(s)
\end{aligned}
\right\}
\qquad (7.6)
$$

Using Cramer's rule,

$$
V_j(s) = \frac{
\begin{vmatrix}
Y_{11} & Y_{12} & \cdots & Y_{1,j-1} & I(s) & Y_{1,j+1} & \cdots & Y_{1m} \\
Y_{12} & Y_{22} & \cdots & Y_{2,j-1} & 0 & Y_{2,j+1} & \cdots & Y_{2m} \\
\cdots & & & & & & & \cdots \\
Y_{m1} & Y_{m2} & \cdots & Y_{m,j-1} & 0 & Y_{m,j+1} & \cdots & Y_{mm}
\end{vmatrix}
}{
\begin{vmatrix}
Y_{11} & Y_{12} & \cdots & Y_{1m} \\
Y_{21} & Y_{22} & \cdots & Y_{2m} \\
Y_{m1} & Y_{m2} & \cdots & Y_{mm}
\end{vmatrix}
}
\qquad (7.7)
$$

Therefore

$$
V_j(s) = \frac{\Delta_{1j}I(s)}{\Delta_y(s)}
\qquad (7.8)
$$

where Δ_{1j} is of the cofactor of $I(s)$ in the numerator determinant of Eq. 7.7 and $\Delta_y(s)$ is the denominator determinant. Now let $H_j(s)$ be the transfer function defined as

$$
H_j(s) = \frac{V_j(s)}{I(s)}
\qquad (7.9)
$$

From Eq. 7.8 it follows that

$$H_j(s) = \frac{\Delta_{1j}(s)}{\Delta_y(s)} \tag{7.10}$$

The natural frequencies of the network are poles of $H_j(s)$. From Eq. 7.11 it is evident that the natural frequencies of the network are zeros of $\Delta_y(s)$.

The admittance seen across nodes xy is given by

$$Y(s) = \frac{I(s)}{V_1(s)} = \frac{\Delta_y(s)}{\Delta_{11}(s)} \tag{7.11}$$

The natural frequencies are the zeros of $\Delta_y(s)$. From Eq. 7.11 it is obvious that the zeros of $\Delta_y(s)$ are also the zeros of $Y(s)$. Therefore, the zeros of the admittance $Y(s)$ are the natural frequencies of the network. This result can be generalized for any node pair in the network. Thus *the natural frequencies of the network are given by the zero of the admittance seen across any node pair of the network.*[5]

This result can also be derived from the previous result that the natural frequencies of a network are the zeros of the impedance seen by breaking at any point in the network. Consider the network shown in Fig. 7.6a. Let s_1 be the natural frequency of this network. Then the impedance $Z_{aa'}(s_1)$ at frequency s_1, seen by breaking at aa', must be zero.

$$Z_{aa'}(s_1) = Z(s_1) + Z_i(s_1) = 0 \tag{7.12}$$

where Z_i is the impedance of the rest of the system seen across the node pair xy as shown in Fig. 7.6a. Therefore, the node pair xy has an impedance Z on the left and an impedance Z_i on the right as shown in Fig. 7.6b. The net impedance across the node pair xy is therefore a parallel combination of impedance Z and Z_i. The net admittance $Y_{xy}(s)$ across the node pair xy is therefore

$$Y_{xy}(s) = \frac{1}{Z} + \frac{1}{Z_i} = \frac{Z + Z_i}{ZZ_i}$$

However, from Eq. 7.12, it follows that

$$Y_{xy}(s_1) = \frac{Z(s_1) + Z_i(s_1)}{Z(s_1)Z_i(s_1)} = 0 \tag{7.13}$$

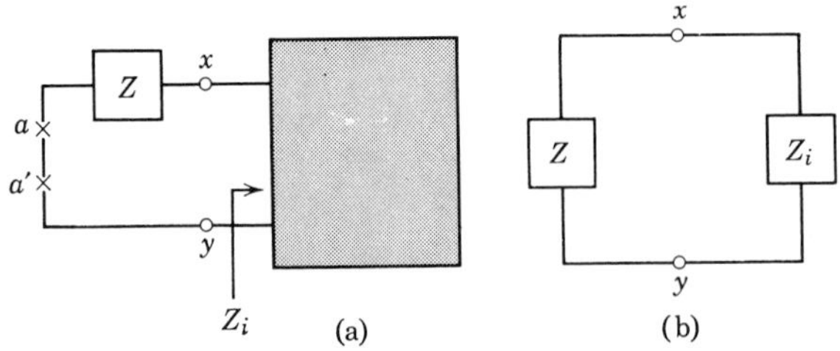

Figure 7.6

[5] Here, again, a possibility of the degenerate case exists.

Therefore, the admittance seen across any node pair of a network is zero at the natural frequencies. Conversely, the natural frequencies of a network are zeros of the admittance function seen across any node pair of the network.

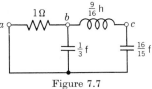

Figure 7.7

Example 7.2

We shall again consider the network in Fig. 7.4. The natural frequencies of this network will now be found by investigating the admittance seen across any node pair of the network. The admittance $Y_{ab}(s)$ across the node pair ab (Fig. 7.7) is given by

$$Y_{ab}(s) = 1 + \frac{1}{3}s + \frac{1}{9s/16 + 15/16s}$$

$$= 1 + \frac{s}{3} + \frac{16s}{9s^2 + 15}$$

$$= \frac{3s^3 + 9s^2 + 21s + 15}{9s^2 + 15}$$

$$= \frac{s^3 + 3s^2 + 7s + 5}{3s^2 + 5}$$

$$= \frac{(s+1)(s+1+j2)(s+1-j2)}{3s^2 + 5}$$

It is evident that $Y_{ab}(s)$ goes to zero at frequencies

$$s = -1, \qquad (-1+j2), \qquad \text{and} \quad (-1-j2).$$

Hence these are the natural frequencies of the network. This is, of course, the same result as that obtained in Example 7.1. We shall now find the admittance Y_{bc} across the node pair bc. From Fig. 7.7 the admittance Y_{bc} is given by

$$Y_{bc}(s) = \frac{16}{9s} + \frac{1}{\dfrac{15}{16s} + \dfrac{1}{1 + s/3}}$$

$$= \frac{16}{9s} + \frac{16s(s+3)}{63s + 45}$$

$$= 16\,\frac{s^3 + 3s^2 + 7s + 5}{9s(7s + 5)}$$

$$= \frac{16}{9s}\,\frac{(s+1)(s+1+j2)(s+1-j2)}{(7s + 5)}$$

The natural frequencies are given by

$$s = -1, \qquad (-1+j2), \qquad \text{and} \quad (-1-j2).$$

Thus we arrive at the same result as before.

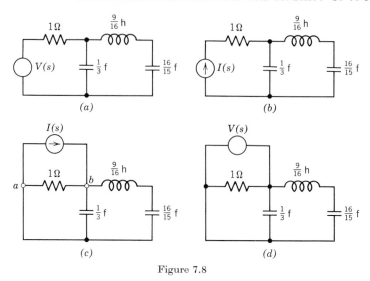

Figure 7.8

The natural frequencies of any network may be found by either of the following means.

(a) The poles of any transfer function of the network.
(b) The zeros of the impedances seen by breaking at any point in the network.
(c) The zeros of the admittance seen across any node pair of the network.

A word of caution is in order at this point. When we are finding the natural frequencies of any network, all of the sources (generators) must be replaced by their impedances. An ideal voltage source is replaced by a zero resistance (short circuit) and an ideal current source is replaced by an infinite resistance (open circuit). The same network will have different natural frequencies if it is driven by a voltage source across two terminals and a current source across the same terminals. Consider again, for example, the network in Fig. 7.4. If this network is driven by an ideal voltage source, as shown in Fig. 7.8a, its natural frequencies are those found earlier [that is, $s = -1, (-1 \pm j2)$]. If, however, we insert an ideal current source at aa, as shown in Fig. 7.8b, the entire network has been changed since a current source has an infinite impedance. However, an ideal current source may be connected across any node pair without changing the network since the current source has an infinite impedance. The natural frequencies of the network excited by the current source, as shown in Fig. 7.8c, are again $(-1, -1, \pm j2)$. However, the connection of a voltage source across a node pair short-circuits the impedance between the node pair. The natural frequencies of a network excited as shown in Fig. 7.8d will not be $-1, (-1 \pm j2)$. Therefore, when we say that the natural frequencies of a network are the poles of any of its transfer functions, we must make sure that the driving functions for which these transfer functions are evaluated are such that they do not change the nature of the original network. It is left as an exercise for the student to show that the natural frequencies of the networks excited as shown in Figs. 7.8a and 7.8c are

$$s = -1 \quad \text{and} \quad (-1 \pm j2).$$

and the natural frequencies for the network in Fig. 7.8b and 7.8d are different.

We stated previously that the system offers zero resistance to signals of natural frequencies. This statement may appear to be contradicted by the fact that the admittance seen across any node pair of a network at natural frequencies is zero. Zero admittance implies infinite impedance. This apparent contradiction is resolved easily when we define clearly what we mean by resistance. We used the word resistance in the sense of an obstacle. If we have a voltage source and the current through the element is considered as the response, then high impedance is an obstacle, since it yields a lower response (current) to a given driving function (voltage). On the other hand, if the driving function is a current source and the response is the voltage across the element, then the lower impedance (higher admittance) is an obstacle, since it yields a lower response (voltage) to a given driving function (current). Therefore, for a current source, zero admittance (infinite resistance) is zero obstacle. When we find the admittance across any node pair, we connect a current source across the node pair and find the resultant voltage across that node pair. If the admittance is zero, we shall have the highest voltage response (infinite voltage) for a given value of current. This is very similar to having a voltage source connected across the terminals which represent zero impedance. The response in this case is the current, and is infinity. Thus, the zero admittance across any node pair of a network and the zero impedance seen by breaking at any point in the network are analogous phenomena, and take place for signals of the natural frequencies of the network. This may be easily seen by considering an L-C circuit as shown in Fig. 7.9. The natural frequency of this network is given by

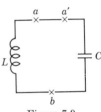

Figure 7.9

$$\pm j \frac{1}{\sqrt{LC}}$$

At this frequency the impedance seen by breaking at aa' is zero. On the other hand, the admittance seen across the node pair ab at this frequency is zero (infinite impedance).

7.3 PHYSICAL SIGNIFICANCE OF THE NATURAL RESPONSE

From the above discussion, it is evident that each system has a preference for certain frequencies. It is very interesting to seek the reasoning behind this. If a stable system is disturbed from its equilibrium state, its response must eventually vanish after the disturbing agency is removed. Immediately after the disturbance is removed, there is no driving function and the system is on its own. During this period, the system must exhibit a response without the benefit of an external driving force. In other words, the system is restricted to only such type of responses as will be sustained by the system without a driving force. As shown in previous sections, every system can sustain some form of response without the need of a driving function.

If a pendulum, for example, is disturbed from the equilibrium position, it exhibits an oscillatory response of decaying amplitude. This is evidently the natural response of a pendulum since it is executed without any external force. Similarly when a mass spring and damper system is disturbed from the rest position and then left to itself, it will return to its rest position through its natural response which may be oscillatory (with exponentially decaying amplitude) or nonoscillatory (monotonically decaying exponential). Thus every system has a natural response which is characteristic of the system. This characteristic response is sustained by the system without any external driving function.[6]

Each system has a number of natural frequencies depending upon the nature of the system. In general, the number of natural frequencies of a system are equal to the number of independent energy storages in the system.[7] The natural frequencies are so designated because these are the frequencies that are most natural to the system. The system offers no obstacle to signals of these frequencies. The phenomenon of resonance arises from this very same effect. As seen before, the system offers the least resistance to signals of the natural frequencies. Hence, the response of the system to the driving functions which possess the natural frequencies is very high. For a resonant L-C circuit, for example, a sinusoidal voltage of the resonance frequency will give rise to an infinite current response. For a series R-L-C circuit, the natural frequencies are complex, and any sinusoidal voltage of frequency close to the complex natural frequency will give rise to a relatively high value of current. We may, therefore, conclude that every system responds readily to signals of the natural frequencies and to those in the neighborhood of the natural frequencies.

[6] Although the natural response is executed without an external force or an external driving function, it does not mean that the natural response dissipates no energy. Actually the initial disturbance in a system is equivalent to storing some energy in the system. This stored energy is dissipated in the natural response executed by the system while returning to its equilibrium position.

[7] The number of independent energy storages in a system are not necessarily equal to the number of energy-storing elements, since the energies stored in various elements may be related. See, for instance, E. A. Guillemin, *Theory of Linear Physical Systems*, pp. 181–189, Wiley, New York, 1963.

The response of the system decreases to signals of frequencies far removed from the natural frequencies.

The phenomenon of the natural frequencies is also helpful in understanding the transient and steady-state components of the response. The response of a system to any driving function has two components: a source-free component (also known as the transient component) and a component due to source (also known as the steady-state component). The component of the response due to source is independent of initial conditions. Thus, no matter what the initial conditions are, the response due to source remains unaltered. But it is intuitively evident that the total response must differ with different initial conditions. If the response due to source does not lend itself to adjustment to the varying initial conditions, we must seek an extra component of response which will vary in such a way as to take into account all of the possible initial conditions. This extra component, however, is not due to the source and therefore must be sustained by the system without any source. We have just seen that a system can sustain such an extra component without any source if this component is composed of the natural frequencies of the system. It, therefore, follows that the source-free component or the transient component of the response is composed of signals having the natural frequencies of the system. The amplitudes of the signals of various natural frequencies adjust in such a way as to satisfy the given initial conditions. This point of view may also be expressed in a slightly different way. In the absence of impulsive sources the initial energy stored in the energy-storing elements cannot change instantaneously. The application of a source may demand the distribution of energy in the elements in a manner different from the initial conditions of the system. Since instantaneous changes in the stored energy are not possible, there must exist an extra component in the response which will allow the system to change gradually from one state to the other. Moreover, this component is not due to the source and therefore must be sustained by the system without any source and hence must be composed of signals of the natural frequencies of the system. Consider, for example, the network shown in Fig. 7.10a. The switch has been in position a for a long time, and the steady-state conditions have been established before $t = 0$. The output voltage $e_0(t)$ is 10 volts. Now the switch is suddenly changed to position b at $t = 0$. It is evident that the new steady-state output voltage $e_0(t)$ will now be 20 volts. The capacitor, however, is incapable of instantaneous change in voltage, and hence the transition from 10 to 20 volts across the capacitor must be gradual. This is accomplished with the help of an extra component in the response. This extra component

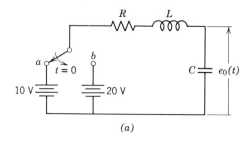

(a)

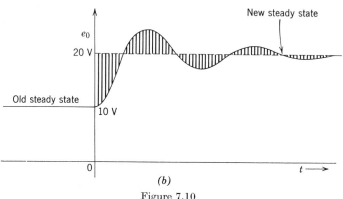

(b)

Figure 7.10

evidently must be sustained by the system without any external source, and hence is composed of the natural frequencies of the system. Figure 7.10*b* illustrates how the transition from the old steady state to the new steady state is accomplished gradually through the natural response (transient response) shown hatched in Fig. 7.10*b*. The amplitudes of the signals of the various natural frequencies adjust in such a way as to satisfy the given initial conditions.

7.4 STABILITY OF A SYSTEM

Thus far we have used the term stable system without a precise definition. The reader is, no doubt, acquainted with the intuitive concept of stability, which can be illustrated by a cone. If a cone, standing on its base, is disturbed slightly, it will eventually return to its equilibrium position (original position) after the source of disturbance is removed. The cone is said to be in stable equilibrium. On the other hand, if it stands on its apex, then the slightest disturbance will cause the cone to move farther and farther away from its equilibrium position, even after the source of disturbance is removed. In this case the cone is said to be in unstable equilibrium.

For a physical system the concept of stability has similar connotations to those described above. *We define a system as unstable if a disturbance applied to it in the equilibrium state produces a response that grows without limit, even after the source of disturbance is removed.* The source of disturbance is some driving function applied to the system. We can now find the stability criterion in terms of the natural frequencies of a system. The response of a system when the source of disturbance is removed must be a source-free or a natural response. As shown before, this response is composed of signals of the natural frequencies of the system. If p_1, $p_2, \ldots, p_n$ are the natural frequencies of the system, then the natural response $r_n(t)$ is given by

$$r_n(t) = C_1 e^{p_1 t} + C_2 e^{p_2 t} + \cdots + C_n e^{p_n t} \tag{7.14}$$

It follows from the definition that a system is unstable if its natural response grows without limit. From Eq. 7.14 it is evident that this is possible if any of the natural frequencies of the system lie in RHP. If, on the other hand, all of the natural frequencies lie in LHP, or along the $j\omega$ axis, the natural response is bounded, and hence the system is stable. Note that the system is unstable even if only one of its natural frequencies lies in RHP. Another special case of interest is that of the multiple natural frequencies [multiple poles of $H(s)$] on the $j\omega$ axis. Such a system is also an unstable system. This can be easily shown by considering a transfer function $H(s)$ with a second-order pole on the $j\omega$ axis.

$$H(s) = \frac{k}{(s + j\omega_0)^2 (s - j\omega_0)^2}$$

Expanding into partial fractions, we get

$$H(s) = \frac{C_1}{s + j\omega_0} + \frac{C_1{}^*}{s - j\omega_0} + \frac{C_2}{(s + j\omega_0)^2} + \frac{C_2{}^*}{(s - j\omega_0)^2}$$

It is evident from Table 5.1 that the natural response of such a system will be of the form

$$r_n(t) = a \cos(\omega_0 t + \theta) + bt \cos(\omega_0 t + \varphi)$$

The natural response contains a term $t \cos(\omega_0 + \varphi)$ which grows without limit. Hence a transfer function with multiple poles along the $j\omega$ axis represents an unstable system.

We therefore conclude that *a system is stable if and only if all of its natural frequencies (poles of the transfer function) lie in LHP, and the natural frequencies along $j\omega$ axis, if any, are simple.* Thus, in the frequency domain the criterion for testing the stability of a system is based upon the location in the complex frequency plane of the natural frequencies (poles of the transfer function) of the system. This criterion is used in many forms to test the stability of a system. A large number of analytical and graphical tests, based upon this criterion, are presently available for examining the stability of a system.

7.5 THE NATURAL FREQUENCIES OF PASSIVE SYSTEMS

A passive system is a system composed entirely of passive elements. The passive system cannot contain a source of power. Since the system does not contain any source of energy, it cannot have a response which grows without limit after the disturbance is removed, as this will imply an increase in the stored and the dissipated energy in the system. It therefore, follows that all passive systems must necessarily be stable; that is, the natural frequencies of passive systems must lie in LHP. If the system is composed of idealized energy-storing elements only (without any dissipative elements), the natural frequencies of the system lie on the $j\omega$ axis. The response of such systems will not vanish after the disturbance is removed, but may have a constant amplitude or may oscillate about the equilibrium state with a constant amplitude. Idealized L-C circuits or mass spring systems are examples of this case. In practice, however, idealized energy-storing elements do not exist. There is always a certain amount of dissipation involved in each practical element, and hence for all practical passive systems the natural frequencies always lie in the LHP. Hence, in a passive physical system, the transient component of the response (or the natural response) always decays with time. A rigorous proof showing that all passive systems are necessarily stable is based upon a study of power and energy relations in passive systems.[8]

A system containing active elements can be made unstable. For example, a network containing active elements such as transistors, vacuum tubes, etc. may become unstable under certain conditions.

7.6 SYSTEMS CONTAINING ACTIVE ELEMENTS

In contrast to passive elements such as resistors, inductors, and capacitors, there are active elements like vacuum tubes and transistors.

---

[8] For proof pertaining to passive networks, see H. W. Bode, *Network Analysis and Feedback Amplifier Design*, pp. 132–134, Van Nostrand, New York, 1945.

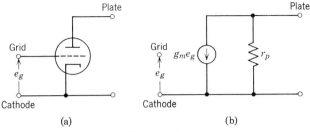

Figure 7.11

Almost all active elements are nonlinear but can be approximated by linear models for small signals. All the analysis techniques studied thus far apply to systems containing linear elements whether passive or active.

We shall define[9] an element as passive if, under all conditions imposed by its environment (values for terminal voltages and currents in electrical systems), it absorbs more energy from the environment than it can supply. For an active element it is possible to find an environment for which the element supplies more energy than it absorbs from the environment.

A somewhat loose definition of active elements, which is commonly used in the literature, is that an active element is one which contains sources of energy. Although this definition is somewhat misleading, most of the active elements are characterized in light of this definition. Consider, for example, a vacuum triode which can be represented by an idealized linear equivalent circuit at low frequencies as shown in Fig. 7.11b. Note that the equivalent circuit contains a current source which is proportional to the voltage between the grid and cathode terminals (e_g). Such a source

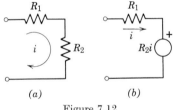

Figure 7.12

is called a controlled source. Hence, sometimes an active element is defined as one containing a controlled source. This definition is misleading, since even passive elements can be represented by an equivalent circuit containing controlled sources. An ordinary resistive circuit in Fig. 7.12a, for example, is equivalent to the one shown in Fig. 7.12b which contains a controlled source. In this case the resistor R_2 can be represented by a voltage source proportional to the current in branch R_1. Similarly, a mutual inductive coupling can be represented by a controlled voltage

[9] For a quantitative definition of these elements in terms of positive-definiteness of a loss function of the element, see E. A. Guillemin, *Theory of Linear Physical Systems*, Chapter 6, Wiley, New York, 1963; see also L. de Pian, *Linear Active Network Theory*, Chapter 6, Prentice-Hall, Englewood Cliffs, N.J., 1962.

source in one branch, proportional to the time derivative of a current in another branch.[10]

Since active elements can deliver positive energy under favorable conditions, it may be possible to make systems containing active elements unstable. This indeed is the case. As an example we shall consider, in a later section, the stability of a tuned vacuum tube amplifier (Fig. 7.13a), and show that such an amplifier can be made unstable under certain conditions.

7.7 TESTING FOR STABILITY

The basic test criterion for the stability of any system depends upon the location of the poles of $H(s)$, the transfer function of the system. If

$$H(s) = \frac{N(s)}{D(s)} \tag{7.15}$$

then the poles of $H(s)$ are zeros of the denominator polynomial $D(s)$. Therefore, an inspection of the roots of $D(s) = 0$ reveals the nature of the transients as well as the information about the stability of the system.

If, however, we are interested in investigating only the stability of the system, it is only necessary to know whether any of the roots of $D(s) = 0$ lie in RHP without any need to know the actual values of these roots. There are a number of methods available to provide this information without having to find the actual roots of $D(s) = 0$.

One of the tests which provides the necessary but not the sufficient condition for all of the roots of a polynomial equation

$$D(s) = a_0 s^n + a_1 s^{n-1} + \cdots + a_{n-1} s + a_n = 0 \tag{7.16}$$

to lie in LHP is that all the coefficients $a_0, a_1, \ldots, a_n$ must be non-zero and have the same sign. If $a_0 > 0$, then the coefficients of $D(s)$ must satisfy

$$a_1 > 0, \qquad a_2 > 0, \qquad \ldots, \qquad a_n > 0 \tag{7.17}$$

Let us consider the denominator polynomial $D(s)$ of the transfer function. For a linear lumped system under consideration, this is a rational algebraic function with real coefficients.

$$D(s) = a_0 s^n + a_1 s^{n-1} + \cdots + a_{n-1} s + a_n \tag{7.18}$$

This polynomial has n zeros $s_1, s_2, \ldots, s_n$. The zeros may be real or complex with positive or negative real parts.

---

[10] For a complete discussion, see E. A. Guillemin, cited in reference 9.

Equation 7.18 may be written in terms of its zeros as

$$D(s) = a_0(s - s_1)(s - s_2) \cdots (s - s_n) \qquad (7.19)$$

Expanding Eq. 7.19 and equating it with Eq. 7.18 we find that

$$\frac{a_1}{a_0} = -(s_1 + s_2 + \cdots + s_n)$$

$$\frac{a_2}{a_0} = (s_1 s_2 + s_1 s_3 + \cdots + s_2 s_3 + s_2 s_4 + \cdots + s_{n-1} s_n) \qquad (7.20)$$

$$\cdots\cdots\cdots\cdots\cdots\cdots\cdots\cdots\cdots\cdots\cdots\cdots\cdots\cdots\cdots\cdots\cdots\cdots$$

$$\frac{a_n}{a_0} = (-1)^n s_1 s_2 \cdots s_n$$

From the set of Eqs. 7.20, we can draw the following important conclusions.

(1) If all of the coefficients $a_0, a_1, \ldots, a_n$ are positive real, then the complex zeros, if any, must occur in conjugate pairs.

(2) If all of the zeros $s_1, s_2, \ldots, s_n$ are real and negative and if $a_0 > 0$, then it is evident from Eq. 7.20 that all of the coefficients $a_0, a_1, \ldots, a_n$ must be positive real. Similarly, one may establish that if some of the zeros are in the form of complex conjugate pairs with negative real parts, then all of the coefficients must be positive.[11] It is thus obvious that for all of the zeros to lie in LHP, a necessary (but not sufficient) condition is that (a) all of the coefficients must be positive, and (b) all the coefficients should be nonzero. To express this succinctly: a necessary condition for all of the zeros to have negative real parts (to lie in LHP) is that the coefficients of the polynomial $D(s)$ satisfy:[12]

$$a_0 > 0, \qquad a_1 > 0, \qquad \ldots, \qquad a_n > 0 \qquad (7.21)$$

The above conclusion provides only the necessary condition for stability. A system satisfying these conditions need not be stable. Consider

$$D(s) = s^3 + 4s^2 - 3s + 2 \qquad (7.22)$$

In this case, all of the coefficients of $D(s)$ do not have the same signs, and therefore it represents an unstable system.

---

[11] W. Kaplan, *Operational Methods for Linear Systems*, Addison-Wesley, Reading, Mass.
[12] The conclusion obviously applies if all of the roots are nonzero negative, that is,

$$a_0 < 0, \qquad a_1 < 0, \qquad \ldots, \qquad a_n < 0$$

The significant point here is that they should all be nonzero and have the same sign.

Similarly, a polynomial

$$D(s) = 2s^3 + 7s + 9 \qquad (7.23)$$

represents an unstable system because one of the coefficients a_2 is zero. On the other hand, a polynomial

$$D(s) = 3s^3 + s^2 + 2s + 8 \qquad (7.24)$$

also represents an unstable system, since it may be factored as

$$D(s) = (s^2 - s + 2)(3s + 4) \qquad (7.25)$$

The term $(s^2 - s + 2)$ represents the zeros in RHP.

Although, in general, the condition of Eq. 7.21 is necessary but not sufficient to guarantee the location in LHP of the zeros, one can easily show that for the first- and second-order equations, it serves as a necessary as well as a sufficient condition.

The Routh-Hurwitz Criterion for Stability

The condition $a_0 > 0, a_1 > 0, \ldots, a_n > 0$ provides a necessary but not a sufficient condition for the roots of $D(s) = 0$ to lie in LHP. There are additional conditions, due to Routh, to ensure that the real parts of the roots are negative. This test is known as the *Routh-Hurwitz criterion*, Using this test, it is possible to find out exactly the number of roots of a polynomial lying in LHP and RHP without having to evaluate the actual roots. This test is used in many different forms. The "array form" of the test is particularly useful to us, since it reveals not only whether the system is stable or unstable but also the exact number of roots lying in LHP and RHP. The proof of this criterion is rather involved.[13] The test procedure will be presented below without proof.

For the nth-order equation with real coefficients,

$$D(s) = a_0 s^n + a_1 s^{n-1} + \cdots + a_{n-1} s + a_n = 0 \qquad (7.26)$$

The location of the roots in the complex s plane is determined by the following procedure. Arrange the coefficients of this equation in two rows as follows:

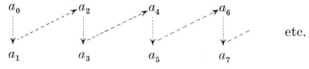

[13] See, for example, E. A. Guillemin, *The Mathematics of Circuit Analysis*, Chap. VI, Wiley, New York, 1949.

Then, complete the following array (shown here for the sixth-order system):

$$
\begin{array}{cccc}
a_0 & a_2 & a_4 & a_6 \\
a_1 & a_3 & a_5 & 0 \\
b_1 & b_2 & b_3 & 0 \\
c_1 & c_2 & 0 & 0 \\
d_1 & d_2 & 0 & 0 \\
e_1 & 0 & 0 & 0 \\
f_1 & 0 & 0 & 0 \\
0 & 0 & 0 & 0
\end{array}
\qquad (7.27)
$$

where the coefficients b, c, d, e, f, and g are formed as follows:

$$
b_1 = \begin{array}{cc} a_0 & a_2 \\ a_1 & a_3 \end{array} = \frac{a_1 a_2 - a_0 a_3}{a_1},
$$

$$
b_2 = \begin{array}{cc} a_0 & a_4 \\ a_1 & a_5 \end{array} = \frac{a_1 a_4 - a_0 a_5}{a_1},
$$

$$
c_1 = \begin{array}{cc} a_1 & a_3 \\ b_1 & b_2 \end{array} = \frac{b_1 a_3 - a_1 b_2}{b_1},
$$

$$
d_1 = \begin{array}{cc} b_1 & b_2 \\ c_1 & c_2 \end{array} = \frac{c_1 b_2 - b_1 c_2}{c_1}, \qquad \text{etc.}
$$

In general, any new element is formed from the two elements immediately above the element, but from the first column, and the two elements above it but in the column to the immediate right of the element. All these coefficients form a determinant line structure, and if we designate α_{jk} as the element in the jth row and kth column, then

$$
\alpha_{jk} = \frac{\alpha_{(j-1),1}\, \alpha_{(j-2),(k+1)} - \alpha_{(j-2),1}\, \alpha_{(j-1),(k+1)}}{\alpha_{(j-1,1)}} \qquad (7.28)
$$

We continue forming such elements until the last row has all zero elements. In the process, the coefficients in any row may be multiplied or divided by a positive number without altering the result. Such operation often simplifies the numerical work of finding the coefficients of succeeding rows.

If all of the terms in the first column (that is, a_0, a_1, b_1, . . . , etc.) are of the same sign, all of the roots of the equation lie in LHP. If there are changes in the sign of the elements in the first column, the total number of changes in sign represents the number of roots in RHP.

Let us consider the polynomial:

$$D(s) = 2s^4 + s^3 + 12s^2 + 8s + 2$$

We form the test array according to the rules stated above:

2	12	2
1	8	0
$\dfrac{12 - 16}{1} = -4$	$\dfrac{2 - 0}{1} = 2$	0
$\dfrac{-32 - 2}{-4} = 8.5$	0	0
$\dfrac{17}{8.5}$	0	0
0	0	0

Note that there are two sign changes in the first column, from $+1$ to -4 and from -4 to $+8.5$. Hence, there are two zeros in RHP and the remaining two zeros must be in LHP. The system is therefore unstable.

There are certain cases which require special handling. The first case is one in which the first-column term of any row vanishes, but the remaining terms in this row are not all zero. Under these conditions the first column element in the next row becomes indeterminate. Consider the example:

$$D(s) = s^5 + 2s^4 + 2s^3 + 4s^2 + s + 1 = 0 \qquad (7.29)$$

The required array is

1	2	1
2	4	1
0	1/2	0
$-1/0$		

(7.30)

Here, $b_1 = 0$ and $c_1 = -1/0$, which is indeterminate. We cannot proceed further. There are various ways of handling this situation.[14] One of them is to replace the zero in the first column by an arbitrarily small number δ

[14] See, for instance, M. F. Gardner and J. L. Barnes, *Transients in Linear Systems*, pp. 198–199. Wiley, New York, 1942.

and proceed as usual. The terms in δ^2 shall be neglected unless there is an uncertainty regarding the relative magnitudes of the derived coefficients. It will be found that the total number of sign changes in the first column is independent of the sign of δ.

Using this procedure we continue the array of Eq. 7.30 as

$$
\begin{array}{ccc}
1 & 2 & 1 \\[2mm]
2 & 4 & 1 \\[2mm]
\delta & 1/2 & 0 \\[2mm]
(4 - 1/\delta) & 1 & 0 \\[2mm]
\left(\dfrac{1}{2} - \dfrac{\delta^2}{4\delta - 1}\right) & 0 & 0
\end{array}
\qquad (7.31)
$$

We shall neglect the term $\delta^2/(4\delta - 1)$ and also

$$
4 - \frac{1}{\delta} \simeq -\frac{1}{\delta}
$$

since

$$
\delta \ll 1
$$

The array thus can be rewritten as

$$
\begin{array}{ccc}
1 & 2 & 1 \\[2mm]
2 & 4 & 1 \\[2mm]
\delta & 1/2 & 0 \\[2mm]
-1/\delta & 1 & 0 \\[2mm]
1/2 & 0 & 0
\end{array}
\qquad (7.32)
$$

Observe that there are, in all, two sign changes in the first column whether δ is assumed positive or negative. The fifth-order polynomial $D(s)$ therefore has two zeros in RHP and the remaining three zeros are in LHP.

Another simple way of handling this situation is to invert the order of the coefficients.[15] Thus, instead of starting the array as shown in Eq. 7.27, we start as follows:

$$
\begin{array}{cccc}
a_6 & a_4 & a_2 & a_0 \\[2mm]
a_5 & a_3 & a_1 & \\[2mm]
b_1 & b_2 & b_3 &
\end{array}
\qquad (7.33)
$$

[15] See Problem 7 at the end of the chapter.

For the polynomial in Eq. 7.29, the inverted array is as follows:

$$
\begin{array}{ccc}
1 & 4 & 2 \\
1 & 2 & 1 \\
2 & 1 & 0 \\
3/2 & 1 & 0 \\
-1/3 & 0 & 0 \\
1 & 0 & 0
\end{array}
\tag{7.34}
$$

We have the same result as before. There is a total of two sign changes. Therefore, $D(s)$ has two roots in RHP and three roots in LHP.

A second exception to the standard procedure occurs when all of the coefficients in any of the derived rows vanish. This situation occurs when the corresponding elements in two consecutive rows of an equal number of elements are proportional. This happens when two diametrically opposite roots, equidistant from the origin, are present; that is, two roots $\sigma_r + j\omega_r$ and $-\sigma_r - j\omega_r$ are present. In this case we may complete the array by replacing the row containing zeros by the coefficients of the derivative of the auxiliary polynomial whose coefficients are the numbers in the last nonvanishing row.[16]

The auxiliary equation occurs only in even powers. If all of the elements in the jth row vanish, then the highest power of the auxiliary equation is $(n - j + 2)$. The roots of the auxiliary equation are the zeros of the original polynomial. Consider

$$
D(s) = s^4 + 3s^3 + 4s^2 + 6s + 4 = 0
\tag{7.35}
$$

The R-H array is

$$
\begin{array}{ccc}
1 & 4 & 4 \\
3 & 6 & 0 \\
2 & 4 & 0 \\
0 & 0 & 0
\end{array}
\tag{7.36}
$$

All of the elements of the fourth row vanish $(j = 4)$, and therefore the highest order of the auxiliary equation is

$$
n - j + 2 = 4 - 4 + 2 = 2.
$$

Also, the auxiliary equation is formed by using the elements in the last nonvanishing row (third row) and contains only the even powers of s. The auxiliary equation is therefore

$$
2s^2 + 4
$$

[16] M. F. Gardner and J. L. Barnes, cited in reference 14.

The derivative of the auxiliary equation is $4s$. Therefore, we should replace the fourth row with element 4. The new modified array is now as follows:

$$
\begin{array}{ccc}
1 & 4 & 4 \\
3 & 6 & 0 \\
2 & 4 & 0 \\
4 & 0 & 0 \\
4 & 0 & 0
\end{array}
\tag{7.37}
$$

The roots of the equation

$$2s^2 + 4 = 0$$

are also the roots of $D(s) = 0$. And $s = \pm j\sqrt{2}$ are the roots of $D(s) = 0$. From the array of Eq. 7.37, it is clear that the remaining two roots lie in LHP and the system is stable.

The array test discussed above is one form of the Routh-Hurwitz criterion. There are other forms available. A notable one among them is the Lienard-Chipart test criterion.[17] The array form of the test, however, yields more information.

Example 7.3

We shall now investigate the stability of a vacuum tube tuned amplifier, illustrated in Fig. 7.13a. It will be shown that this circuit can become unstable under certain conditions. The vacuum triode is replaced by its equivalent circuit in Fig. 7.13b.

In order to investigate the stability of this amplifier, we shall find the admittance $Y(s)$, seen at the input terminals gk. From the discussion in Section 7.2, it follows that the natural frequencies of the circuit are zeros of the admittance $Y(s)$. Node equations will be used to analyze the circuit.

There are two independent nodes, g and p, and the voltages at these nodes with respect to the datum node k are E_g and E_p, respectively. Note that there is a controlled current source in the equivalent circuit of a triode of the magnitude $g_m E_g$. The node equations are

$$I(s) = \left(C_1 s + \frac{1}{L_1 s} + C_f s\right) E_g - C_f s E_p$$

$$0 = g_m E_g - C_f s E_g + \left(C_2 s + \frac{1}{L_2 s} + g_p + C_f s\right) E_p$$

---

[17] See, for instance, F. R. Gantmacher, Applications of the Theory of Matrices, Interscience, New York, 1959; L. Zadeh and C. Desoer, *Linear System Theory*, pp. 419–420, McGraw-Hill, New York, 1963.

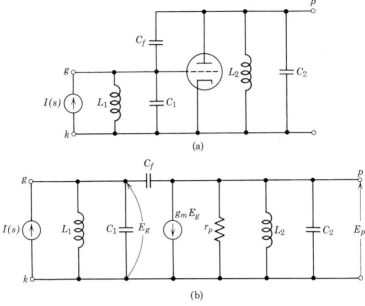

Figure 7.13

Using Cramer's rule,

$$E_g(s) = \frac{\begin{vmatrix} I(s) & -C_f s \\[2mm] 0 & (C_2 + C_f)s + g_p + \dfrac{1}{L_2 s} \end{vmatrix}}{\begin{vmatrix} (C_1 + C_f)s + \dfrac{1}{L_1 s} & -C_f s \\[2mm] g_m - C_f s & (C_2 + C_f)s + g_p + \dfrac{1}{L_2 s} \end{vmatrix}}$$

$$= \frac{[(C_2 + C_f)L_2 s^2 + L_2 g_p s + 1]I(s)}{L_2 s \, \Delta_y(s)}$$

where

$$\Delta_y(s) = \frac{1}{L_1 L_2 s^2} [s^4 L_1 L_2 (C_1 C_2 + C_1 C_f + C_2 C_f) + s^3 L_1 L_2 (g_m C_f + g_p C_1 + g_p C_f)$$

$$+ s^2 (L_1 C_1 + L_2 C_2 + L_1 C_f + L_2 C_f) + s g_p L_2 + 1]$$

The determinant $\Delta_y(s)$ is the characteristic determinant, and the zero of $\Delta_y(s)$ are the natural frequencies of the circuit. [These are also the zeros of the input admittance $Y(s) = I(s)/E_g(s)$.] Hence, to investigate the stability of this circuit, we must test the zeros of $\Delta_y(s)$ by the Routh-Hurwitz criterion. The *R-H* test array applied to the bracketed polynomial in the above equation is shown below.

$$
\begin{array}{ccc}
a_0 & a_2 & a_4 \\
a_1 & a_3 & 0 \\
b_1 & b_2 & 0 \\
c_1 & 0 & 0 \\
b_2 & 0 & 0
\end{array}
$$

where

$$a_0 = L_1L_2(C_1C_2 + C_1C_f + C_2C_f)$$
$$a_1 = L_1L_2(g_mC_f + g_pC_1 + g_pC_f)$$
$$a_2 = L_1C_1 + L_2C_2 + L_1C_f + L_2C_f$$
$$a_3 = L_2g_p$$
$$a_4 = b_2 = 1$$
$$b_1 = \frac{L_1L_2}{a_1}[g_mC_f(L_1C_1 + L_2C_2 + L_1C_f + L_2C_f) + L_1g_p(C_1 + C_f)^2 + L_2C_f{}^2g_p]$$
$$c_1 = \frac{L_1L_2{}^2C_f}{a_1b_1}[g_p{}^2L_2C_f + g_mg_p(L_2C_2 + L_2C_f - L_1C_1 - L_1C_f) - g_m{}^2L_1C_f]$$

An examination of the first column of the array reveals that only the coefficient c_1 may have a negative sign, in which case there will be two roots in RHP. Assuming, for simplicity, that $L_1 = L_2$, then the system is stable if

$$g_m{}^2 < \frac{g_mg_p}{C_f}(C_2 - C_1) + g_p{}^2 \tag{7.38}$$

If we define the amplification factor μ as

$$\mu = g_m/g_p \tag{7.39}$$

then the condition of Eq. 7.38 reduces to

$$\mu^2 < \frac{\mu}{C_f}(C_2 - C_1) + 1 \tag{7.40}$$

The amplifier will be unstable if

$$\mu^2 > \frac{\mu}{C_f}(C_2 - C_1) + 1 \tag{7.41}$$

7.8 SOME COMMENTS ON THE TRANSIENT, STEADY-STATE RESPONSE AND THE STABILITY OF A SYSTEM

For stable systems the transient component decays with time, and hence the steady-state component dominates the response.[16] After

---

[16] If some of the natural frequencies lie on the $j\omega$ axis, the transient component will not vanish but will have a constant amplitude.

sufficient time has elapsed, the response consists entirely of the steady-state component. On the other hand, for unstable systems the transient component grows with time without limit and dominates the response. In fact, after a short time, the steady-state component is completely drowned in a very large transient component. Theoretically, the transient component grows without limit. In practice, however, this does not happen. If this component becomes too large it may destroy the system. But, in almost all practical cases, the growing amplitude of this component causes the changes in the parameters of the system in such a way as to reduce the instability of the system. The changes in the parameters are such as to shift the natural frequencies in the right half plane onto the $j\omega$ axis. The transient component, under these circumstances, grows to a certain value and then settles down to a constant amplitude. This is precisely what happens in electronic oscillators and signal generators. These circuits are intentionally made unstable to generate the desired frequency. In the beginning, the transient component grows exponentially with time, but soon the amplitude of oscillation stabilizes through the mechanism described above. The output signal of a typical oscillator is shown in Fig. 7.14.

In vacuum tubes the amplification factor μ (Eq. 7.39) generally decreases with the signal amplitude. In the tuned triode amplifier discussed in the previous section, if condition of Eq. 7.41 is satisfied, the amplifier becomes unstable and gives rise to oscillations whose amplitude grows exponentially. As the amplitude grows, μ decreases continuously until the inequality of Eq. 7.41 is barely satisfied. In this condition, the natural frequencies which were previously in RHP are brought to the marginal position (on the $j\omega$ axis). The amplitude of the oscillation now stabilizes to a constant value.

It must be clearly understood that the steady-state component of an unstable system is always finite. The transient component, however, grows with time and swamps out the steady-state component. The situation is exactly the opposite of that in the stable system.

The next question is: What happens to an unstable system if it is not excited? Theoretically, if an unstable system is not disturbed from its equilibrium state, there will be no response. On the other hand, a disturbance, no matter how small, will start a transient in the system which will eventually grow with time without limit. In practice, it is impossible to shield any system from the disturbances of nature. For example, in electrical circuits, there is always a random noise voltage present across every element. Similarly, every element is picking up signals by various processes of induction from an electromagnetic field caused by external

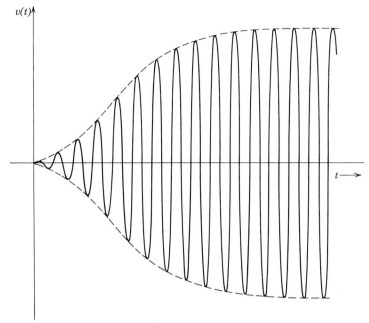

Figure 7.14

sources which are always present in space. Thus a slight disturbance from these natural phenomena can start the transient, which eventually grows to a very large value. Therefore, unstable systems do not need any deliberate excitation to exhibit their growing transient. In electronic oscillators, for example, the oscillations start without any external deliberate attempt to disturb the system. A small noise voltage, which is always present in a circuit, is enough to start such oscillations.

From the above discussion it is evident that an unstable system is useless as an amplifier or processor of any signal, since the response of such a system to these signals will be drowned or swamped out by the transient component. Therefore, any system used to process signals in any manner must be a stable system. Unstable systems, however, are not always liabilities. They can be conveniently used to generate signals of various frequencies. The transients of the system are the signals of the natural frequencies of the system. Hence, if we set the natural frequencies of a system on the $j\omega$ axis at a frequency $\pm j\omega_0$, then it will generate a transient which will be a sinusoidal signal of frequency ω_0. This is the principle of signal generation in electronic oscillators. Actually, the natural frequencies of an oscillator are located in RHP but close to the $j\omega$ axis. The transient of such an oscillator will be an exponentially growing sinusoid. As the amplitude grows with time, the parameters of the active elements in the circuit change in such a way as to cause the natural frequencies to shift onto the $j\omega$ axis. At this point the amplitude of the transient becomes constant (see Fig. 7.14). Nonsinusoidal oscillations may be obtained by placing the natural frequencies on the real axis (σ axis) in RHP.

7.9 FEEDBACK

Thus far we have viewed a system as a processor of the input signal (or the driving function). Techniques have been developed to evaluate the response (the output) of the system from the knowledge of the driving function (the input) and the system itself. Assume that we have a system which yields the desired output for a certain input. In practice, however, system characteristics do not remain constant over a period. This may be due to the aging of the components, to change in the environment in which the system is operating, or to the replacement of some components. For a given input, the output of the system will also change over a period. This is a very undesirable situation in many cases. One solution, which takes into account the variations of the system characteristics, is to adjust our input so that the output remains constant. This solution, however, would be possible only if the variations in the system characteristics and the environment were known precisely beforehand. The variations that we are talking about are unpredictable, and hence the preprogrammed compensation applied to the input is not possible. In such circumstances, feedback systems provide the proper solution.

In feedback systems the output of the system is monitored and compared with the desired output. Then the input to the system is continuously adjusted so as to make the difference between the actual output and the desired output zero. We thus have a system where the input is not constant but depends upon the information fed back from the output.

All automatic control systems use the feedback mechanism. A household heating system with a thermostatic control is a familiar example of the feedback system. The thermostat is set at a certain temperature. The thermometer reads the temperature of the room and if the temperature falls below the set temperature, the thermostat is activated and opens the valve in the furnace. The room is now heated until the set temperature is reached. Under these conditions, there is no difference between the desired and the actual temperature of the room. The thermostat is deactivated and the valve in the furnace closes. Here, the thermostat acts as a monitoring device which compares the desired and the actual temperature of the room and if there is any error in the two temperatures,

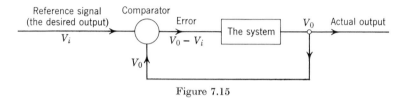

Figure 7.15

it activates the system (or adjusts the input to the system) in such a way as to make the error zero.

From these examples, we observe that in a feedback system the input to the system is the difference between the desired output and the actual output. We may thus say that the system is actuated by the error between the two outputs. A feedback system must therefore consist of a comparator. This may be simply a device which can add or subtract two signals. The desired output is some standard reference signal. The actual output is compared with the standard reference signal and the output of the comparator is fed to the system. The system representation of feedback is shown in Fig. 7.15. The system has a path from the input to the output and another path back from the output to the input. These two paths form a closed loop, and hence feedback systems are also sometimes referred to as *closed-loop* systems.

We shall now consider an example of an automatic control system, used to regulate the angular velocity of a gasoline engine despite load variations. This can be accomplished in a manner shown in Fig. 7.16. In this system, the throttle of the engine is actuated by an electric motor which, in turn, is actuated by the error signal. A tachometer on the engine shaft yields a voltage proportional to the actual rpm of the engine. This voltage is compared to a standard voltage (fixed reference voltage for a desired rpm). If the output voltage of the tachometer is less than the reference voltage, the error signal actuates the motor which, in turn, positions the throttle causing the increase in the actual rpm of the engine. When the actual rpm is greater than the desired rpm, the error signal is of opposite sign and actuates the motor and the throttle valve in the opposite direction to cause the reduction in actual rpm. The feedback system, therefore, tends

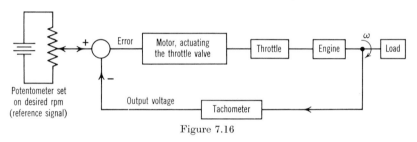

Figure 7.16

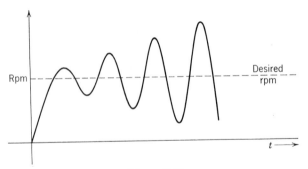

Figure 7.17

to maintain a constant speed regardless of the variation of the load on the engine.

Closed-loop systems, with all their advantages, are, however, susceptible to instability. If there is too much feedback, a system may try to over-correct itself, which causes the error in the opposite direction. This, in turn, will cause another overcorrection, now in an exactly opposite direction. The process of overcorrection from one direction to the other about the equilibrium position continues building up progressively in amplitude—causing an instability in the system. In the example of the gasoline engine, if the actual rpm is below the desired rpm, the error signal may be large enough to overcompensate, and the actual rpm now is higher than the desired rpm. This will now cause an error in the opposite direction and may overcompensate, reducing the actual rpm by a larger magnitude. The process of successive buildup of the oscillations is shown in Fig. 7.17.

Sometimes a term, servomechanism, is used for an automatic control system. The term servomechanism, however, implies only such feedback systems as are concerned with the automatic positioning of an object. Systems such as the aircraft auto pilot, gunfire control, missile control, rudder control on ships, remote control of valves, power steering on automobiles, and control of machine tools are familiar examples of servomechanisms.

7.10 STABILITY OF FEEDBACK SYSTEMS

The stability of a feedback system can be investigated through the natural frequencies of the system. Consider a feedback system represented by a block diagram in Fig. 7.18. A block with the transfer function $G(s)$ represents the forward transmission path, whereas a block with the transfer function $H(s)$ represents the feedback path. The comparator is replaced by a circle. The plus and minus signs indicate that the output of the comparator is the difference between the input signal $V_i(s)$ and the feedback signal. Note that the signal which is fed back to the comparator is $V_o(s)H(s)$. It therefore follows that

$$E(s) = V_i(s) - V_o(s)H(s) \qquad (7.42)$$

But

$$V_o(s) = E(s)G(s). \qquad (7.43)$$

Eliminating $E(s)$ from Eqs. 7.42 and 7.43, we get

$$\frac{V_o(s)}{V_i(s)} = T(s) = \frac{G(s)}{1 + G(s)H(s)} \qquad (7.44)$$

where $T(s)$ represents the transfer function of the feedback system. The natural frequencies of this system are poles of $T(s)$. It is evident from Eq. 7.44 that the natural frequencies of the feedback system are the zeros of the quantity $1 + G(s)H(s)$. This quantity plays an important role in the feedback theory, and is called the return difference with respect to $G(s)$. If there is no feedback in the system then $H(s) = 0$ and

$$T(s) = G(s).$$

The presence of feedback modifies the transfer function from $G(s)$ to $G(s)/[1 + G(s)H(s)]$. It is therefore evident that the quantity $1 + GH$ is a measure of feedback. We shall designate this quantity (the return difference with respect to G) by $F_G(s)$.

$$F_G(s) = 1 + G(s)H(s)$$

The quantity $G(s)H(s)$ is known as the *open-loop transfer function*. If the feedback system is opened by breaking the feedback loop at the comparator (Fig. 7.18), the transfer function of this open-loop system will be $G(s)H(s)$. The natural frequencies of the feedback system (closed-loop system) are the zeros of $1 + G(s)H(s)$. It is therefore evident that the stability of a closed-loop system can be determined from the knowledge of its open-loop transfer function $G(s)H(s)$.

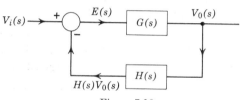

Figure 7.18

Example 7.4

Investigate the stability of a closed-loop system whose open-loop transfer function is given by

$$G(s)H(s) = \frac{K}{s(s+1)(s+2)}$$

The return difference $F_G(s)$ is given by

$$F_G(s) = 1 + G(s)H(s) = 1 + \frac{K}{s(s+1)(s+2)}$$

$$= \frac{s^3 + 3s^2 + 2s + K}{s(s+1)(s+2)}$$

To investigate the location of zeros of $F_G(s)$, we apply the Routh-Hurwitz test to the numerator polynomial of $F_G(s)$. The required Routh-Hurwitz test array is given below:

1	2
3	K
$(6-K)/3$	0
K	0
0	0

It can be easily seen from this array that there will be sign changes in the first column if $K > 6$ or $K < 0$. Hence, the closed-loop system is stable if $0 < K < 6$.

The Routh-Hurwitz test provides a quick check on the stability of a feedback system from the knowledge of its open-loop transfer function. The test, however, yields only information regarding the stability and nothing else. It does not give a clear indication about the system performance and does not provide the designer with any clue about effecting improvements in the performance. For this purpose, either the root-locus method or the graphical method, provided by the Nyquist plot, proves greatly superior. These methods not only determine the stability of the system but also indicate the system performance and give a clue to the accomplishment of desirable improvements in the system. Now we shall briefly discuss these methods.

Root-Locus Method

This method, developed by W. R. Evans,[19] indicates the poles of the closed-loop system from the knowledge of the open-loop transfer function. Knowledge of the poles of a closed-loop system clearly gives an indication of stability. The method provides the locus of poles of a closed-loop system as the gain constant K of the open-loop transfer function assumes

[19] W. R. Evans "Graphical Analysis of Control Systems," *Trans. AIEE*, **67**, 547–551 (1948).

various values. Consider, for example,

$$G(s)H(s) = \frac{K}{s(s+1)} \tag{7.45}$$

The poles of the corresponding closed-loop system are the roots of the equation:

$$1 + GH = 0$$

or

$$1 + \frac{K}{s(s+1)} = 0$$

that is,

$$s(s+1) + K = 0$$

or

$$s^2 + s + K = 0 \tag{7.46}$$

The roots of Eq. 7.46 are given by

$$p_1, p_2 = -\frac{1}{2} \pm \sqrt{\frac{1}{4} - K}$$

For $K < \frac{1}{4}$, the roots p_1, p_2 are real. For $K > \frac{1}{4}$, the roots become complex conjugate. For all values $0 < K < \infty$, the poles lie in LHP. The locus of the roots of Eq. 7.46 as K varies from 0 to ∞ is shown in Fig. 7.19. When $K = 0$, the roots are -1 and 0; as K increases, both roots move toward $-\frac{1}{2}$; and when $K = \frac{1}{4}$, both roots coincide at $-\frac{1}{2}$. As K is increased beyond $\frac{1}{4}$, the roots become a complex conjugate pair, and the locus takes off vertically at $-\frac{1}{2}$. One branch goes vertically up, and

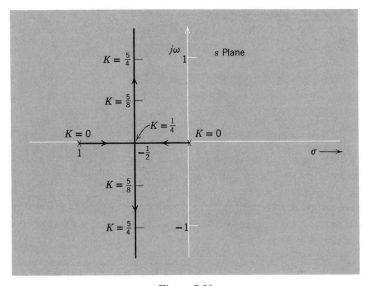

Figure 7.19

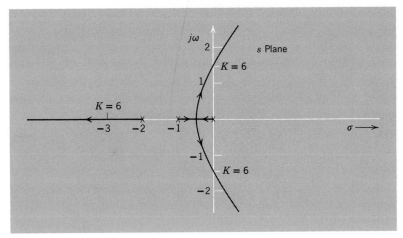

Figure 7.20

the other goes down. The points on the locus for various values of K are marked.

We shall consider another open-loop transfer function:

$$GH = \frac{K}{s(s+1)(s+2)} \tag{7.47}$$

We have tested this function before, by using the Routh-Hurwitz criterion, and found that the closed-loop system is stable for $K < 6$ and becomes unstable for $K > 6$. The root locus for this function is shown in Fig. 7.20.

The poles of the closed-loop system are zeros of the equation,

$$1 + \frac{K}{s(s+1)(s+2)} = 0 \tag{7.48}$$

or the poles of the closed-loop system are roots of

$$s(s+1)(s+2) + K = 0 \tag{7.49}$$

As K is varied from 0 to ∞, the roots of Eq. 7.49 move along the paths indicated in Fig. 7.20. Note that the poles of the closed-loop system lie in RHP for $K > 6$.

Evans has developed a large number of graphical aids and special techniques which facilitate the construction of root loci. With the help of these techniques, the root loci can be sketched approximately with very little work, even for complex functions that contain a large number of poles and zeros.[20]

---

[20] See, for example, J. G. Truxal, *Automatic Feedback Control System Synthesis*. pp. 223–250, McGraw-Hill, New York, 1955; E. Grabbe, S. Ramo, and D. Wooldridge, *Handbook of Automation Computation and Control*, pp. 21–46 to 21–72, Wiley, New York, 1958.

Next we shall consider the Nyquist test for stability. This test criterion employs the plot of $G(j\omega)H(j\omega)$ for values of ω in the interval $-\infty < \omega < \infty$. In order to prove the Nyquist criterion of stability, it is necessary to understand complex mapping.

Complex Mapping

The reader is familiar with the mapping of the functions of real variables. Mapping is a visual or graphical representation of the relationship between two variables which are related by a certain function. Thus, when we say y is a function of x and represent the relation as,

$$y = f(x) \tag{7.50}$$

we mean that for every value of x there exists a corresponding value of y, and these values are related by Eq. 7.50. This relationship is represented graphically in Fig. 7.21. The graph is just a visual means of representing Eq. 7.50 or of showing the values of y for the corresponding values of x. The graphical or visual representation is quite simple for two real variables x and y. If, however, the two variables under consideration are complex, say s and W, then such a representation is not so easy. Each complex variable contains two variables within itself: the real variable and the imaginary variable. Thus

$$\begin{aligned} s &= \sigma + j\omega \\ W &= u + jv \end{aligned} \tag{7.51}$$

There are, in all, four variables, and a simple graphical representation in two- or even three-dimensional space is not possible. We overcome this difficulty by defining two planes: the s plane and the W plane. Each plane has two dimensions, and hence we obtain the required four dimensions to represent four variables. Let us write the functional representation:

$$W = f(s) \tag{7.52a}$$

or

$$u + jv = f(\sigma + j\omega) \tag{7.52b}$$

Equation 7.52a expresses the fact that for every value of s there is a corresponding value of W related through Eq. 7.52a. This information can be represented graphically on two planes: s and W planes. We represent a certain point s_1 in the s plane and a corresponding point W_1 in the W plane. Thus the point W_1 in the W plane is a sort of image of point s_1 in the s plane, and W_1 and s_1 are related by Eq. 7.52.

$$W_1 = f(s_1) \tag{7.53}$$

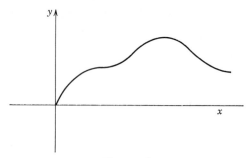

Figure 7.21

Let us consider a simple function:

$$W = s^2 \tag{7.54}$$

Then

$$u + jv = (\sigma + j\omega)^2 \tag{7.55}$$

$$= \sigma^2 - \omega^2 + j2\sigma\omega \tag{7.56}$$

It can be seen from Eq. 7.56 that for every value of s there is a corresponding value of W. If, for example,

$$s = 2 + j3$$

then

$$W = (2 + j3)^2$$

$$= -5 + j12$$

Similarly, for different values of s, we get different values of W. If we consider a closed curve C_s in the s plane, each point on this curve has an image in the W plane, and thus the whole curve C_s in the s plane maps into another closed curve C_W in the W plane, provided that W is a continuous function of s along C_s. Thus, C_W is an image of C_s, as shown in Fig. 7.22. The points A, B, C, D, E, F, and G on C_s map into points A', B', C', D', E', F', and G' on C_W in the W plane.

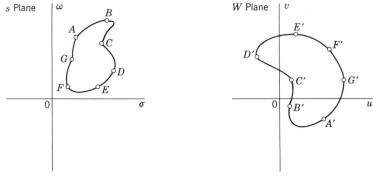

Figure 7.22

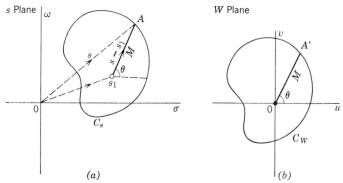

Figure 7.23

Now, consider the transformation:

$$W = (s - s_1) \tag{7.57}$$

We shall map the image in the W plane of a closed curve C_s in the s plane enclosing the point s_1 (Fig. 7.23a). This is done by computing the values of W for various values of s for points lying along C_s. The quantity $s - s_1$ is complex, in general, and can be conveniently visualized graphically in Fig. 7.23a. For a point A on C_s, for example, $s - s_1$ is represented by a phasor joining the point s_1 to point A. If we designate

$$s - s_1 = M e^{j\theta}$$

then, for each point along C_s, there is a certain value for M (magnitude of $s - s_1$) and θ (phase of $s - s_1$). We now map a point of magnitude M and argument θ in the W plane. This point A' in the W plane is the image of A in the s plane. As we move along the entire contour C_s in the s plane, θ goes through a net variation of 2π radians. Obviously the image in the W plane of a closed curve C_s in the s plane is also a closed curve C_W which encloses the origin of the W plane once. Note that if we move along C_s in a clockwise direction, angle θ decreases, and hence the image C_W is also traversed in a clockwise direction.

Consider, now, another transformation:

$$W = \frac{1}{s - s_1} \tag{7.58}$$

$$= \frac{1}{M e^{j\theta}} = \frac{1}{M} e^{-j\theta}$$

Note that the magnitude of W is now $1/M$ and the argument is $-\theta$. Hence, by the previous argument, it follows that as we traverse the close curve C_s once, in counterclockwise direction, the phase of W goes through a net variation of -2π radians. In other words, C_W encloses the origin in the W plane, but the corresponding direction of traverse is clockwise.

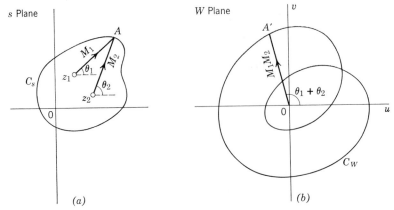

Figure 7.24

Next, consider the transformation:

$$W = (s - z_1)(s - z_2) \tag{7.59}$$

We shall assume that C_s encloses z_1 and z_2 (Fig. 7.24). We can interpret $s - z_1$ and $s - z_2$ as before. If

$$s - z_1 = M_1 e^{j\theta_1} \quad \text{and} \quad s - z_2 = M_2 e^{j\theta_2}$$

then

$$W = M_1 M_2 e^{j(\theta_1 + \theta_2)}$$

Note that as we move along C_s in a counterclockwise direction once, the angles θ_1 and θ_2 each go through a variation of 2π radians. The argument of W goes through a change of 4π radians. Hence, C_W encloses the origin in the W plane twice in a counterclockwise direction.

Now, consider a general transformation:

$$W = \frac{(s - z_1)(s - z_2) \cdots (s - z_m)}{(s - p_1)(s - p_2) \cdots (s - p_n)} \tag{7.60}$$

If

$$s - z_k = M_k e^{j\theta_k}$$

and

$$s - p_l = N_l e^{j\varphi_l}$$

then

$$W = \frac{M_1 M_2 \cdots M_m}{N_1 N_2 \cdots N_n} e^{j(\theta_1 + \theta_2 + \cdots + \theta_m - \varphi_1 - \varphi_2 - \cdots - \varphi_n)}$$

As before, we shall assume that C_s encloses all of the m zeros and n poles. As we traverse along C_s in a counterclockwise direction, each of the angles θ_k and φ_l goes through a variation of 2π radians. Hence the net variation of an argument of W is $2\pi(m - n)$, where m and n are the numbers of zeros and poles respectively of W enclosed by C_s. Thus, C_W encloses the origin in the W plane $m - n$ times, in a counterclockwise direction. If $m - n$ is negative, the enclosure is in a clockwise direction.

This discussion may be summarized by the following conclusion. *A closed curve C_s in the s plane enclosing m zeros and n poles of $W(s)$ maps into a closed curve C_W in the W plane encircling the origin of the W plane $m - n$ times, in the same direction as that of C_s. If $m - n$ is negative, then the encirclement is in the opposite direction.* Suppose $m = 2$ and $n = 5$, then C_W will encircle the origin in the W plane three times in the direction opposite to that of C_s.

Graphical Criterion for Stability in Feedback Systems (the Nyquist Criterion)

We shall again consider a simple feedback system shown in Fig. 7.18. The transfer function $T(s)$ is given by

$$T(s) = \frac{G(s)}{1 + G(s)H(s)}$$

To investigate the stability of this system, it is sufficient to know whether $T(s)$ has any poles in RHP. Since the poles of $T(s)$ are zeros of $1 + G(s)H(s)$, we need to know whether $1 + GH$ has any zeros in RHP. If the function $1 + GH$ has m zeros and n poles in RHP, then the image of a closed curve C_s in the s plane, which encloses all poles and zeros of $1 + GH$, will encircle the origin of the $1 + GH$ plane $m - n$ times, in the same direction as that of C_s. It is evident that if we draw the image of C_s in the GH plane instead of in the $1 + GH$ plane, then the corresponding image of C_s will enclose the point -1, $m - n$ times in the same direction as that of C_s. (This is because a map of any curve in the GH plane will be the same as that in the $1 + GH$ plane except that it will be shifted by -1.)

Note that the curve C_s must enclose all poles and zeros of $G(s)H(s)$ in RHP. This means that C_s must enclose all RHP. A suitable curve C_s, which will enclose all RHP, is shown in Fig. 7.25. The curve encloses the region inside a semicircle of radius R as shown in Fig. 7.25. The radius R is made arbitrarily large to enclose all RHP. In the limit, $R = \infty$. The curve C_s thus consists of the entire $j\omega$ axis, and a semicircle of radius $R = \infty$. To map this curve on the $G(s)H(s)$ plane, we need to know the values of $G(s)H(s)$ along the $j\omega$ axis and along the semicircle. Along the $j\omega$ axis, $G(s)H(s)$ is given by $G(j\omega)H(j\omega)$, and along the semicircular path GH is given by $G(\infty)H(\infty)$. In all the cases observed in practice,

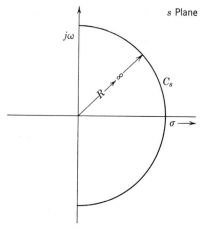

Figure 7.25

$G(\infty)H(\infty)$ is either zero or a constant given by $G(j\omega)H(j\omega)$ at $\omega = \infty$. Thus, in mapping the C_s curve in the GH plane, we need to know $GH(j\omega)$, that is, the steady-state frequency response of the open-loop transfer function.

As an illustration, let us consider the function:

$$GH = \frac{1}{s+1} \tag{7.61a}$$

$$GH(j\omega) = \frac{1}{j\omega + 1} = \frac{1}{\sqrt{\omega^2 + 1}} e^{-j \tan^{-1} \omega} \tag{7.61b}$$

and

$$GH(\infty) = 0.$$

Thus the entire semicircle of radius $R = \infty$ in the s plane maps into one point, that is, $GH = 0$. The values of GH along the $j\omega$ axis are given by Eq. 7.61b. We may find the values of GH for various values of ω in the manner shown in Table 7.1. Observe that from Eq. 7.61b it follows that

$$G(-j\omega)H(-j\omega) = \frac{1}{\sqrt{\omega^2 + 1}} e^{j \tan^{-1} \omega}$$

Thus

$$G(-j\omega)H(-j\omega) = G^*(j\omega)H^*(j\omega)$$

Indeed, for a transfer function $H(j\omega)$ of a linear physical network,

$$H(-j\omega) = H^*(j\omega) \tag{7.62}$$

To prove this, we observe that $H(j\omega)$ is the Fourier transform of a real function of time $h(t)$ (an impulse response of the system). It was shown in

Chapter 4 that if $H(j\omega)$ is a Fourier transform of a real function of time, then (Eq. 4.14):

$$H(-j\omega) = H^*(j\omega)$$

Note that, for any physical linear system, $h(t)$ is a real function of time, and Eq. 7.62 holds true for all physical linear systems. Now, since $G(j\omega)H(j\omega)$ is the transfer function of a physical system, it follows that

$$G(-j\omega)H(-j\omega) = G^*(j\omega)H^*(j\omega) \tag{7.63}$$

Therefore, in mapping the contour in the s plane from $s = -j\infty$ to $+j\infty$ along the $j\omega$ axis, it is necessary to map GH only for $\omega = 0$ to ∞. As a result of Eq. 7.63, the map of GH for the negative $j\omega$ axis ($s = -j0$

TABLE 7.1

ω	$|GH| = \dfrac{1}{\sqrt{\omega^2 + 1}}$	$\underline{/GH} = \tan^{-1}\omega$ (degrees)
0	1	0
1	0.707	−45
2	0.447	−63
3	0.316	−70.5
5	0.196	−78.7
10	0.099	−84.33
100	0.01	−89.4
1000	0.001	−89.95
10,000	0.0001	−90
∞	0	−90

to $-j\infty$) will be the mirror image about the horizontal axis of the map for the positive $j\omega$ axis. Therefore, the image of C_s in the GH plane can be plotted from the knowledge of $GH(j\omega)$ for all values of ω in the range $0 < \omega < \infty$. The values of $GH(j\omega)$ can be conveniently obtained from logarithmic plots[21] (Bode plots).

The curve C_s and its image in the GH plane are shown in Fig. 7.26. Note that the map of C_s in the GH plane is merely a polar plot of $GH(j\omega)$ for ω lying in the region $-\infty < \omega < \infty$. Hence, the image of C_s can be plotted directly from the knowledge of the steady-state frequency response of the open-loop transfer function.

It is obvious that the direction of mapping of C_s and C_W are the same, that is, clockwise. The image of C_s in GH does not encircle the critical point -1. Hence the difference between the number of zeros and the

[21] See, for instance, C. J. Savant, *Control System Design*, McGraw-Hill, New York, 1964.

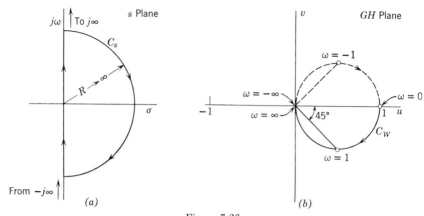

Figure 7.26

number of poles, $m - n$, for the function $1 + GH$ is zero in RHP of the s plane.

Note that if the open-loop transfer function GH represents a stable system, then $1 + GH$ cannot have any poles in RHP. This can be easily shown. Let

$$GH = \frac{N(s)}{D(s)}$$

Then

$$1 + GH = \frac{N(s) + D(s)}{D(s)} \qquad (7.64)$$

Since, by assumption, the open-loop transfer represents a stable system, $D(s)$ cannot have zeros in RHP. But zeros of $D(s)$ are also the poles of $1 + GH$ (Eq. 7.64). Hence it follows that $1 + GH$ cannot have poles in RHP. This means that $n = 0$ and the number of encirclements of the critical point -1 in the GH plane by the image of C_s is equal to m; that is, the number of zeros of $1 + GH$ enclosed in C_s. For the example considered above,

$$m - n = 0$$

and since

$$n = 0, \qquad m = 0.$$

The function $1 + GH$ has no zeros in RHP, and hence the closed-loop system represented by the open-loop transfer function GH is stable (Eq. 7.61a).

The example given here could have been easily solved by analytical means. For example,

$$GH = \frac{1}{s + 1}$$

and

$$1 + GH = 1 + \frac{1}{s + 1}$$

$$= \frac{s + 2}{s + 1}$$

Thus, $1 + GH$ has no zeros in RHP, and the closed-loop system is stable. If the stability of the closed-loop system, from the knowledge of the open-loop transfer function, can be evaluated so conveniently by analytical means, why do we then use the cumbersome graphical method of plotting the image of C_s in the GH plane? The answer is that, in practice, very often the analytical description of the open-loop transfer function is not available. Under these conditions, we determine experimentally the steady-state frequency response $GH(j\omega)$ of the open-loop system for all values of ω. This information can be conveniently represented in a polar form in a GH plane, and the number of encirclements of the critical point -1 by this plot determines the stability of the closed-loop system which will result from this open-loop system. The graphical test proves valuable even if the analytical description of the open-loop system were available. The graphical test not only gives information regarding the stability of the closed-loop system, but also indicates clearly the method of improvements in the design for the required specifications.

We have shown above that if the open-loop transfer function represents a stable system, then the quantity $1 + GH$ has no poles in RHP, and the total number of encirclements of the critical point -1 in the GH plane, by the image of contour C_s (Fig. 7.26a), is equal to the number of zeros of $1 + GH$ in RHP. If a closed-loop system is stable, then $1 + GH$ should have no zeros in RHP. We are now ready to state the Nyquist criterion for stability.

We shall first state the general Nyquist criterion. *If a closed-loop system has m zeros and n poles in RHP, then the polar plot of the $GH(j\omega)$, the steady-state frequency response of the open-loop transfer function, as ω varies from $-\infty$ to $+\infty$ encircles the critical point -1, $m - n$ times in the clockwise direction.*

In practice, however, all of the open-loop systems (with very few exceptions) are stable, and hence $n = 0$. In this case, the Nyquist stability criterion is considerably simplified and the number of encirclements of point -1 by the plot of $GH(j\omega)$ is equal to the number of zeros of $1 + GH$. *Hence, for a stable open-loop transfer function, the closed-loop system will be stable if the point -1 is not encircled by the polar plot of $GH(j\omega)$ for $-\infty < \omega < \infty$.* This is Nyquist's abbreviated criterion for stability of a closed-loop system and applies to systems with stable open-loop transfer functions.

At times the plot may be rather complicated and the number of en-circlements of the point -1 may not be obvious. In such cases, it may become necessary to trace out the net change in the angle subtended by $GH(j\omega)$ at point -1 as ω varies from $-\infty$ to $+\infty$. This may be easily done by actually drawing a vector from point -1 to $GH(j\omega)$ and moving the end of this vector along $GH(j\omega)$ from $\omega = -\infty$ to ∞ and noting the net angle generated by this vector at the point -1. Two such cases are shown in Fig. 7.27.

The case of the open-loop transfer function containing poles on the $j\omega$ axis needs special handling. We must choose C_s so that no pole of $W(s)$ lies along its path, since $W = \infty$ at the pole. We must therefore make detours around the poles, if any, existing along the $j\omega$ axis.

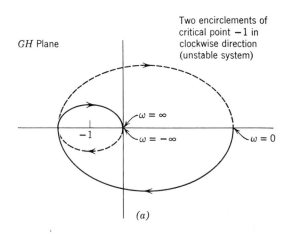

(a)

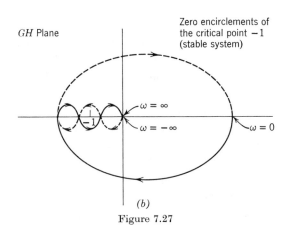

(b)

Figure 7.27

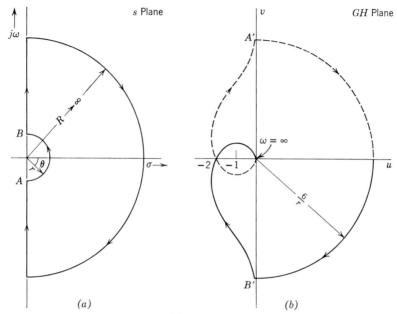

Figure 7.28

Consider the function $G(s)H(s)$ from Example 7.4.

$$GH = \frac{K}{s(s+1)(s+2)}$$

We shall consider the specific case of $K = 12$ and determine, using the Nyquist criterion, whether this open-loop transfer function represents a stable closed-loop system.

$$G(j\omega)H(j\omega) = \frac{12}{j\omega(j\omega+1)(j\omega+2)}$$

Note that there is a pole on the $j\omega$ axis at $\omega = 0$. Hence we shall make a small semicircular detour along C_s at $\omega = 0$ (Fig. 7.28a). Along the semicircular detour,

$$s = re^{j\theta} \tag{7.65}$$

where θ varies from $-\pi/2$ to $\pi/2$ radians. The function $G(s)H(s)$ along the detour is given by

$$GH = \frac{12}{re^{j\theta}(re^{j\theta}+1)(re^{j\theta}+2)} \tag{7.66}$$

The radius of the detour is arbitrarily small. If we let $r \to 0$ in Eq. 7.66, we get

$$GH = \frac{12}{re^{j\theta}(1)(2)} = \frac{6}{r}e^{-j\theta}$$

As θ varies from $-\pi/2$ to $\pi/2$ radians along the detour, the corresponding map of GH traces out a semicircle of radius $6/r$ in the GH plane with the angle varying from $\pi/2$ to $-\pi/2$. The entire map of C_s in the GH plane is shown in Fig. 7.28b. Let us find the frequency ω_c where this map of GH intersects the negative real axis in the GH plane. At this point,

$$\arg\,(GH) = -\pi$$

$$\arg\,(GH) = \arg \frac{12}{j\omega_c(j\omega_c + 1)(j\omega_c + 2)}$$

$$= -\frac{\pi}{2} - \tan^{-1} \omega_c - \tan^{-1}(\omega_c/2)$$

or

$$-\pi = -\frac{\pi}{2} - [\tan^{-1} \omega_c + \tan^{-1}(\omega_c/2)]$$

But

$$\tan^{-1} A + \tan^{-1} B = \tan^{-1} \frac{AB}{1 - AB}$$

Therefore

$$-\frac{\pi}{2} = -\tan^{-1} \frac{(\omega_c^2/2)}{(1 - \omega_c^2/2)}$$

or

$$\frac{\pi}{2} = \tan^{-1} \left[\frac{\omega_c^2}{(2 - \omega_c^2)} \right]$$

or

$$\tan\,(\pi/2) = \frac{\omega_c^2}{2 - \omega_c^2}$$

This gives

$$\omega_c = \pm\sqrt{2}$$

The magnitude of GH at $\omega_c = \pm\sqrt{2}$ is

$$|GH(j\sqrt{2})| = \left| \frac{12}{j\sqrt{2}(j\sqrt{2} + 1)(j\sqrt{2} + 2)} \right|$$

$$= \frac{12}{\sqrt{2}\sqrt{3}\sqrt{6}} = \frac{12}{\sqrt{36}} = 2$$

For $K = 12$, the Nyquist plot intersects the negative axis at -2. Obviously, if $K < 6$, then the plot does not encircle the critical point -1, and the system is stable. If, however, K is equal to or larger than 6, the system becomes unstable. Such systems are stable only for a certain range of constant K and are known as *conditionally stable* systems.

PROBLEMS

1. Find the natural frequencies of the circuits shown in Fig. P-7.1. For each circuit, find the natural frequencies from the impedances seen by breaking at two convenient points and from the admittances across any two node pairs.

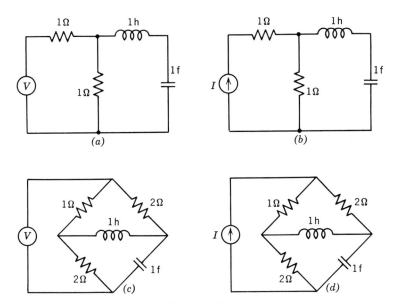

Figure P-7.1

2. The network shown in Fig. P-7.2 is a degenerate case. Find the natural frequencies of this network by breaking at (1) aa'; and (2) at bb'. Comment upon your results.

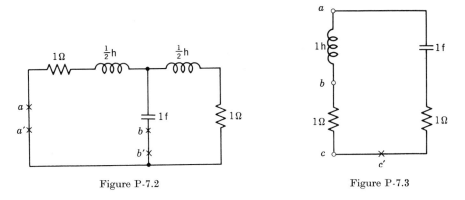

Figure P-7.2   Figure P-7.3

3. Find the natural frequencies of the circuit shown in Fig. P-7.3 from the impedance seen by breaking at terminals cc' and from the admittance seen across

the node pair bc. Now, find the natural frequencies from the admittance seen across the node pair ac. Comment.

4. A network, shown in Fig. P-7.4, has an input impedance $2s + 1$, seen across terminals aa'. A voltage generator in series with resistor R is now connected across these terminals. Determine the value of R, so that the system will have a natural frequency $s = -3$. If the voltage source is replaced by a current source, what is the natural frequency of the circuit?

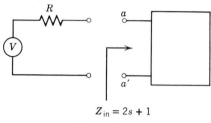

$$Z_{in} = 2s + 1$$

Figure P-7.4

5. Apply the Routh-Hurwitz criterion to determine whether any of the roots of the following polynomials lie in RHP.

(a) $s^5 + s^4 + 2s^3 + s^2 + s + 2$

(b) $s^4 + s^3 + s^2 + 10s + 10$

(c) $8s^4 + 2s^3 + 3s^2 + s + 5$

(d) $10s^4 + 2s^3 + s^2 + 5s + 3$

(e) $s^4 + 5s^3 + 10s^2 + 20s + 24$

(f) $s^6 + 2s^4 + 8s^2 + 2s + 3$

(g) $s^4 + 10s^3 - 8s^2 + 2s + 3$

(h) $s^5 + 2s^4 + 2s^3 + 4s^2 + 11s + 10$

6. Without actually determining all of the roots, find (1) the number of roots in RHP, (2) the number of roots in LHP, and (3) the number of roots on the imaginary axis, for the following polynomials.

(a) $s^5 + 4s^4 + 7s^3 + 8s^2 + 6s + 4$

(b) $s^5 - 9s^3 - 22s^2 - 22s - 8$

(c) $s^5 + 2s^4 + 12s^3 + 32s^2 + 16s + 64$

(d) $s^5 + 3s^4 - 3s^3 - 9s^2 - 4s - 12$

(e) $s^4 - 2s^2 - 3s - 2$

7. Show that if a polynomial

$$a_n s^n + a_{n-1} s^{n-1} + \cdots + a_1 s + a_0 = 0$$

has k roots in RHP, then the inverted polynomial

$$a_0 s^n + a_1 s^{n-1} + \cdots + a_{n-1} s + a_n = 0$$

also has k roots in RHP. [*Hint.* If a polynomial has a root $s_0 = \sigma_0 + j\omega_0$ in RHP, then the reciprocal of this root $1/s_0 = 1/(\sigma_0 + j\omega_0)$ also lies in RHP.]

8. The equivalent circuit of a tunnel diode is shown in Fig. P-7.8. This diode exhibits a negative conductance $-G$ in parallel with a junction capacitance C. A load resistor R is connected across terminals ab. Show that this circuit will become unstable if

$$\frac{1}{G} < R < \frac{LG}{C}$$

If, in addition,

$$R < \left(2\sqrt{\frac{L}{C}} - \frac{LG}{C}\right)$$

then show that the natural frequencies are complex conjugate (in RHP). The transient is an exponentially growing sinusoid. What is the frequency of oscillation? Under what condition will the transient be a monotonically growing exponential?

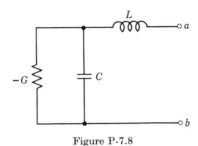

Figure P-7.8

9. For each of the open-loop transfer functions, sketch the Nyquist plot. Determine separately, from each plot, the range of K for which the system is stable. Check your results by applying the Routh-Hurwitz criterion.

$$G(s)H(s) = \text{(a)} \ \frac{K}{(s + 1)(s + 10)}$$

$$\text{(b)} \ \frac{K(s + 1)}{(s + 5)(s + 10)}$$

$$\text{(c)} \ \frac{K}{s(s + 1)(s + 10)}$$

$$\text{(d)} \ \frac{K}{s^2(s + 1)}$$

$$\text{(e)} \ \frac{K(s + 1)}{s^2(s + 10)^2}$$

$$\text{(f)} \ \frac{K(s + 1)}{s(s + 5)^3}$$

$$\text{(g)} \ \frac{K(s + 2)}{(s + 1)(s - 3)}$$

10. Determine whether the Nyquist plot of the open-loop transfer functions shown in Fig. P-7.10 represent stable systems.

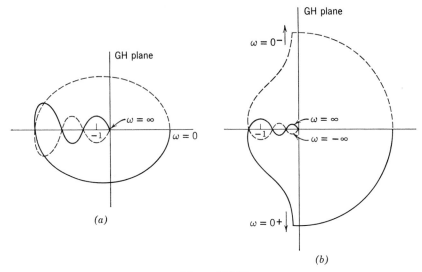

Figure P-7.10

11. (a) A phase-shift oscillator, using a common emitter transistor stage, is shown in Fig. P-7.11a. This is a form of shunt current feedback. If the current gain β of the transistor is large enough, the circuit becomes unstable. The equivalent circuit of the common emitter transistor is shown in Fig. P-7.11b. Find the range of β

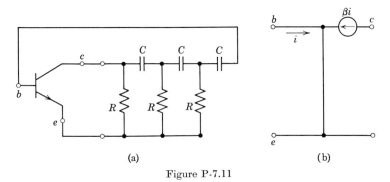

Figure P-7.11

for which the circuit will become unstable and act as an oscillator. What must be the value of β in order to generate sinusoidal oscillations? What is the frequency of oscillation? If β is made larger than this value, what is the nature of the signal generated?

(b) Now interchange all R's with C's and C's with R's in this circuit, and repeat the analysis.

chapter 8

Signal Flow Graphs

A system consists of a number of components. A complex system may consist of a very large number of components and presents a problem as far as graphical representation is concerned. Fortunately, we are mostly concerned with the transmission characteristic (dynamic behavior or the input-output relationship) of a system. Such a behavior can be specified by a transfer function of the system. Therefore, instead of showing the detailed schematic diagram of the system, we may represent it by its transfer function. A system may be divided into subsystems, each of which may be represented by a transfer function. Such a simplified representation is known as *block-diagram* representation. In the previous chapter, the feedback system was represented by a block diagram (Fig. 7.18). Block diagrams may be further simplified by what is known as *signal flow graphs*. Signal flow-graph representation is merely an extension of the block-diagram representation which eliminates the need for drawing blocks and summing elements (or comparators). In this chapter we shall study the details of signal flow graphs.

8.1 SIGNAL FLOW-GRAPH REPRESENTATION

Figure 8.1a shows the block-diagram representation of a system with transfer function $H(s)$. This representation may be further simplified by replacing the block by a path with an arrow indicating the sense in which

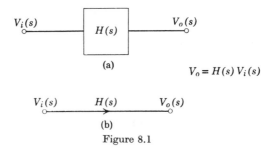

(a)

$$V_o = H(s) V_i(s)$$

(b)

Figure 8.1

the signal is transmitted. Each such path is labeled by the transfer function associated with the path (Fig. 8.1b). The directional arrows indicate the unidirectional flow. This simplified representation is known as the signal flow-graph representation of a system. The transfer function $H(s)$ is called the *transmittance* of the path. Note that a path starts and ends on some node which represents a signal variable in the system. In Fig. 8.1, the path representing $H(s)$ starts at a node representing signal V_i and ends on the node representing signal V_o. The signal that is being transmitted on a path is equal to the signal at the node where the path originated, multiplied by the transmittance of the path. In Fig. 8.1, the signal traveling on the path is V_i times $H(s)$, that is, $H(s)V_i$. At each node there may be a number of incoming branches and a number of outgoing branches. The value of the signal variable at any node is equal to the sum of signals at that node due to all incoming branches. In Fig. 8.2, for example, the node variable e_4 is given by

$$e_4 = t_{14}e_1 + t_{24}e_2 + t_{34}e_3$$

And the node variables e_5 and e_6 are given by

$$e_5 = t_{45}e_4$$
$$e_6 = t_{46}e_4$$

Note that a node acts as a summing point for signals on all of the incoming branches. A subtraction (or comparison) can be effected merely by

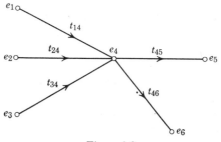

Figure 8.2

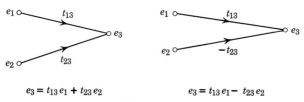

$$e_3 = t_{13}e_1 + t_{23}e_2 \qquad\qquad e_3 = t_{13}e_1 - t_{23}e_2$$

Figure 8.3

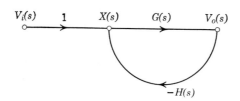

Figure 8.4

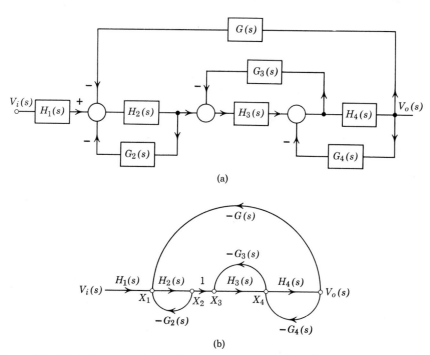

(a)

(b)

Figure 8.5 Block diagram and signal flow-graph representation of a more complex system.

placing a negative sign on the transmittance of the branch whose signal is to be compared or subtracted. This is illustrated in Fig. 8.3.

The feedback system shown in Fig. 7.18 can be represented by a signal flow graph as shown in Fig. 8.4. Figure 8.5 shows a block diagram and the corresponding signal flow-graph representation for a more complex system. The economy due to short-hand representation effected by the signal flow graph is now evident.

8.2 FLOW GRAPHS OF SIMULTANEOUS EQUATIONS

For any system the most important quantity is the over-all transfer function of the system. For example, in the feedback system represented in Fig. 7.18, we are interested in the transfer function $V_o(s)/V_i(s)$. Note that this is also the total transmittance between the input node and the output node. The net transmittance between any two nodes may be easily evaluated by writing the equations at each node. For a simple system shown in Fig. 8.4, for example, we may write equations at nodes X and $V_o(s)$.

$$X(s) = V_i(s) - H(s)V_o(s)$$

and

$$V_o(s) = X(s)G(s)$$

Eliminating $X(s)$ from the above simultaneous equations, we get

$$V_o(s)[1 + G(s)H(s)] = G(s)V_i(s)$$

Hence

$$\frac{V_o(s)}{V_i(s)} = \frac{G(s)}{1 + G(s)H(s)}$$

Therefore, the transmittance between the input and the output node is $G(s)/1 + G(s)H(s)$.

This procedure may be followed to find the desired transmittance for any complex flow graph. To find the transmittance between any two nodes, we write equations corresponding to all nodes. This yields a set of simultaneous algebraic equations from which all of the variables except the input and the output node variables may be eliminated to find the desired transmittance. As an example, consider the signal flow graph in Fig. 8.5. We may write the set of simultaneous equations corresponding to this graph as follows:

$$X_1 = H_1 V_i - G_2 X_2 - G V_o$$
$$X_2 = H_2 X_1$$
$$X_3 = X_2 - G_3 X_4$$
$$X_4 = H_3 X_3 - G_4 V_o$$
$$V_o = H_4 X_4$$

In this graph, for a certain given value of V_i, we have five unknown variables, X_1, X_2, X_3, X_4, and V_o, and five equations. Therefore, each unknown variable can be uniquely determined in terms of V_i. To find the transmittance between the input node (V_i) and the output node (V_o), we need to eliminate the other four variables, X_1, X_2, X_3, and X_4, from the above set of variables. It is evident that a signal flow graph represents a certain set of simultaneous algebraic equations. Conversely, any given set of simultaneous equations can be represented by a signal flow graph. Indeed, it is correct to say that a signal flow graph is simply a graphical way of representing a set of simultaneous algebraic equations. Consider the following set of simultaneous equations.

$$a_{10}X_0 + a_{11}X_1 + a_{12}X_2 + a_{13}X_3 = 0$$
$$a_{20}X_0 + a_{21}X_1 + a_{22}X_2 + a_{23}X_3 = 0$$
$$a_{30}X_0 + a_{31}X_1 + a_{32}X_2 + a_{33}X_3 = 0 \qquad (8.1a)$$

These equations may be rearranged as follows:

$$X_1 = -\frac{a_{10}}{a_{11}} X_0 - \frac{a_{12}}{a_{11}} X_2 - \frac{a_{13}}{a_{11}} X_3$$

$$X_2 = -\frac{a_{20}}{a_{22}} X_0 - \frac{a_{21}}{a_{22}} X_1 - \frac{a_{23}}{a_{22}} X_3$$

$$X_3 = -\frac{a_{30}}{a_{33}} X_0 - \frac{a_{31}}{a_{33}} X_1 - \frac{a_{32}}{a_{33}} X_2 \qquad (8.1b)$$

This set may now be represented graphically as shown in Fig. 8.6. Equation 8.1b is not the only possible way of expressing the set of equations in Eq. 8.1a. It is possible to express this set in a number of ways. It, therefore, follows that a given set of simultaneous equations can be

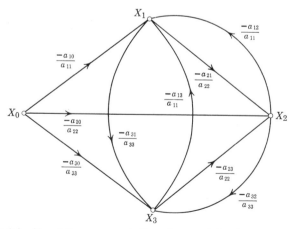

Figure 8.6 Signal flow representation of a set of simultaneous equations.

TABLE 8.I

Some Important Rules for Flow Graph Reduction

	Original graph	Equivalent graph
(1) Cascade transformation	$X_1 \xrightarrow{a} X_2 \xrightarrow{b} X_3$	$X_1 \xrightarrow{ab} X_3$
(2) Parallel transformation	X_1 to X_2 with branches a and b	$X_1 \xrightarrow{a+b} X_2$
(3) Absorption of a node (star–mesh transformation)	X_3, $X_1 \xrightarrow{a} X_5 \xleftarrow{b} X_2$, c up to X_3, d down to X_4	X_3; ac, bc, ad, bd between X_1, X_2, X_3, X_4
(4) Removal of an outgoing branch (special case of 3)	X_3; $X_1 \xrightarrow{a} X_5 \xleftarrow{b} X_2$; c up; d down to X_4	X_3; ac, bc, a, b, d; X_5; X_4
(5) Removal of an incoming branch (special case of 3)	X_3; c up; $X_1 \xrightarrow{a} X_5 \xleftarrow{b} X_2$; d down to X_4	X_3; ac, c, b, ad, d; X_6; X_1, X_2, X_4
(6) Elimination of loop	$X_1 \xrightarrow{c} X_2 \xrightarrow{a} X_3$, b back	$X_1 \xrightarrow{\frac{ac}{1-ab}} X_3$

TABLE 8.1 (Continued)

	Original graph	Equivalent graph
(7) Elimination of cascaded loop		
(8) Elimination of a self-loop		
(9) Elimination of a self-loop		
(10) Branch inversion		

represented by a number of different signal flow graphs. Note that the equation $X = X$ can be expressed by a signal flow graph by a single self-loop (Fig. 8.7). Such self-loops often occur in signal flow graphs. Consider the equation,

$$aX_2 = bX_1 + cX_3$$

This equation may be expressed alternatively,

Figure 8.7 Signal flow graph for identity $X = X$.

$$X_2 = \frac{b}{a+1} X_1 + \frac{1}{a+1} X_2 + \frac{c}{a+1} X_3$$

The signal flow graph of this equation is shown in Fig. 8.8. Signal flow graphs representing linear equations are called linear signal flow graphs.

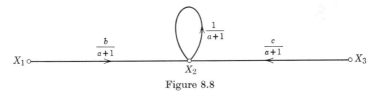

Figure 8.8

8.3 ANALYSIS OF SIGNAL FLOW GRAPHS

Signal flow graphs may be analyzed by three methods.

(1) The direct solution from simultaneous equations associated with the graph.

(2) The graphical solution using step-by-step graph-reduction technique.

(3) The direct solution by inspection of the graph using Mason's rule.

The direct solution from the set of simultaneous equations associated with the graph can be obtained by applying Cramer's rule. We shall now consider the second and the third method of analyzing flow graphs.

Reduction Techniques of Analyzing Flow Graphs

Transmittance between any two nodes may be obtained by solving the simultaneous equations associated with the flow graph. It is also possible to evaluate the desired transmittance by step-by-step reduction of the flow graph. There are a number of useful rules listed in Table 8.1 for such a step-by-step reduction. The reader can easily verify these rules by writing the corresponding equations.

We shall now demonstrate the application of step-by-step reduction in analyzing a signal flow graph. For the sake of illustration, we shall consider the flow graph in Fig. 8.5. This graph and the step-by-step reduction are shown in Fig. 8.9.

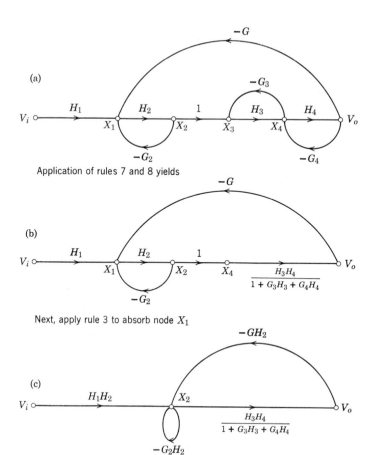

(a)

Application of rules 7 and 8 yields

(b)

Next, apply rule 3 to absorb node X_1

(c)

(d) Eliminate a self-loop at X_2 by rule 9

(e) Eliminate the feedback loop by rule 6

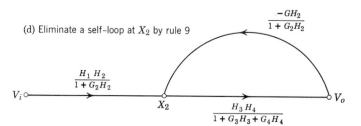

Figure 8.9   Step-by-step reduction of a flow graph.

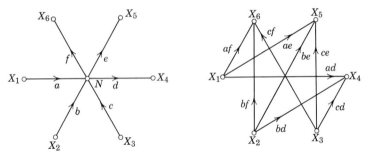

Figure 8.10   Absorption of a node.

The elementary transformations listed in Table 8.1 by no means exhaust the possibilities of additional transformations. One can easily extend these transformations to more complex situations. As an example, the extension of Rule 3 to absorb a node is shown in Fig. 8.10.

The solution of a flow graph by successive reduction techniques is essentially a graphical solution of simultaneous equations.

We shall now consider the third method of analyzing flow graphs.

Solution of a Flow Graph by Inspection

A highly useful rule (Mason's rule) for finding transmittance (or the transfer function) between two nodes is now presented without proof.[1]

We shall define a few terms before explaining the rule.

An *independent node* or a *source node* is a node with at least one branch radiating from it but none directed toward it (examples are node V_i in Figs. 8.4 and 8.5 and node X_0 in Fig. 8.6). All other nodes are *dependent nodes*.

A *path* is a branch or a continuous sequence of branches which can be traversed without meeting any branch directed in the opposite direction (examples are path $X_1 - X_2 - X_3 - X_4$, path $X_1 - X_2 - X_1$, and so on in Fig. 8.5).

An *open path* is a path along which no node is met twice (an example is $V_i - X_1 - X_2 - X_3 - X_4 - V_o$ in Fig. 8.5).

A *loop* is a closed path or a closed loop (examples are loops

---

[1] This rule was originally given by Mason. See S. J. Mason, "Feedback Theory—Further Properties of Signal Flow Graphs," *Proc. IRE*, **44**, 920–926 (1956).

$X_1 - X_2 - X_1$, $X_3 - X_4 - X_3$, $X_4 - V_o - X_4$, and $X_1 - X_2 - X_3 - X_4 - V_o - X_1$ in Fig. 8.5). A self-loop is also considered a loop.

A *path transmittance* is the total transmittance of the path, that is, the product of the branch transmittances on the path.

A *loop transmittance* is the total transmittance of the loop.

The formula for the transmittance T_{xy} between an independent node X and a dependent node Y is

$$T_{xy} = \sum_k T_k \frac{\Delta_k}{\Delta} \tag{8.2}$$

where T_k is the path transmittance of the kth open path between nodes X and Y and

$$\Delta = 1 - \sum_i L_i + \sum_{i,j} L_i' L_j' - \sum_{i,j,k} L_i'' L_j'' L_k'' + \cdots \tag{8.3}$$

In this equation L_i represents the loop transmittance of the ith loop in the graph. Thus ΣL_i represents the sum of all individual loop transmittances in the graph. $L_i' L_j'$ represents the product of the loop transmittances of any two nontouching loops. Thus $\Sigma L_i' L_j'$ is the sum of the products of the loop transmittances of all possible pairs of nontouching loops. Similarly $L_i'' L_j'' L_k''$ represents the product of the loop transmittances of any three nontouching loops, and so on. Δ_k is the value of Δ for that part of the graph which does not touch the kth open path.

We shall illustrate the application of this rule to a flow graph in Fig. 8.5. For this graph, there is only one open path $V_i - X_1 - X_2 - X_3 - X_4 - V_o$. The transmittance along this path is $H_1 H_2 H_3 H_4$. Therefore

$$T_1 = H_1 H_2 H_3 H_4$$

There are a total of four loops: $X_1 - X_2 - X_1$, $X_3 - X_4 - X_3$, $X_4 - V_o - X_4$, and $X_1 - X_2 - X_3 - X_4 - V_o - X_1$. The respective loop transmittances are $-H_2 G_2$, $-H_3 G_3$, $-H_4 G_4$, and $-H_2 H_3 H_4 G$. There are two pairs of nontouching loops:

$$X_1 - X_2 - X_1 \quad \text{and} \quad X_3 - X_4 - X_3$$
$$X_1 - X_2 - X_1 \quad \text{and} \quad X_4 - V_o - X_4$$

There are no combinations of three or more nontouching loops. Therefore

$$\Delta = 1 - (-G_2 H_2 - G_3 H_3 - G_4 H_4 - H_2 H_3 H_4 G)$$
$$+ (G_2 H_2 G_3 H_3 + G_2 H_2 G_4 H_4)$$

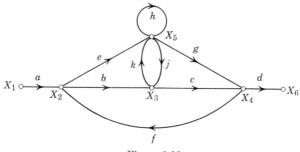

Figure 8.11

Δ_1 is the value of Δ for that part of the graph which does not touch path $V_1 - X_1 - X_2 - X_3 - X_4 - V_o$. Since all feedback loops of the graph touch this path,

$$\Delta_1 = 1 - 0 + 0 - 0 + \cdots = 1$$

and

$$T = \frac{H_1 H_2 H_3 H_4}{1 + G_2 H_2 + G_3 H_3 + G_4 H_4 + H_2 H_3 H_4 G + G_2 H_2 G_3 H_3 + G_2 H_2 G_4 H_4}$$

$$= \frac{H_1 H_2 H_3 H_4}{(1 + G_2 H_2)(1 + G_3 H_3 + G_4 H_4) + (GH_2 H_3 H_4)}$$

This is, of course, the same result as that obtained by graphical reduction of the flow graph in Fig. 8.9.

We shall consider another flow graph as shown in Fig. 8.11. The transmittance between nodes X_1 and X_6 can be found by inspection. There are four open paths between X_1 and X_6.

(1) $X_1 - X_2 - X_3 - X_4 - X_6$ $T_1 = abcd$

(2) $X_1 - X_2 - X_5 - X_4 - X_6$ $T_2 = aegd$

(3) $X_1 - X_2 - X_5 - X_3 - X_4 - X_6$ $T_3 = aejcd$

(4) $X_1 - X_2 - X_3 - X_5 - X_4 - X_6$ $T_4 = abkgd$

There are six loops: $X_2 - X_3 - X_4 - X_2$, $X_2 - X_5 - X_4 - X_2$, $X_2 - X_3 - X_5 - X_4 - X_2$, $X_2 - X_5 - X_3 - X_4 - X_2$, $X_3 - X_5 - X_3$, and $X_5 - X_5$. But there are only two nontouching loops: $X_2 - X_3 - X_4 - X_2$ and $X_5 - X_5$. Therefore

$$\Delta = 1 - (bcf + egf + bkgf + ejcf + kj + h) + bcfh$$

Part of the graph which does not touch open Paths 1 and 2 are shown in Figs. 8.12a and 8.12b. There is no part of the network which does not touch Paths 3 and 4. It is evident that

$$\Delta_1 = 1 - h$$

$$\Delta_2 = \Delta_3 = \Delta_4 = 1$$

and the transmittance T between X_1 and X_6 is given by

$$T = \frac{abcd(1 - h) + aegd + aejcd + abkgd}{1 - (bcf + egf + bkgf + ejcf + kj + h) + bcfh}$$

Note that the transfer function of the simple feedback system shown in Fig. 7.18 can be written by inspection, using Mason's rule. The signal flow graph for this system is shown in Fig. 8.4. There is only one open path with path-transmittance $G(s)$ and only one loop with loop-transmittance $-G(s)H(s)$.

$$T_1 = G(s)$$

$$\Delta = 1 - G(s)H(s)$$

$$\Delta_1 = 1$$

Hence

$$\frac{V_o(s)}{V_i(s)} = \frac{G(s)}{1 + G(s)H(s)}$$

[*Warning.* One should be very cautious in applying the step-by-step reduction method in analyzing signal flow graphs. This method, in general, is prone to many errors. It is therefore advisable to use Mason's rule (analysis by inspection) instead of the step-by-step reduction procedure.]

Signal flow graphs, in general, prove very convenient if the flow graph of the system is already available. In such cases, Mason's rule directly yields the desired solution. If, however, we know only the set of simultaneous linear equations of the system, signal flow-graph analysis loses its advantage. In such a case one has to construct the flow graph from the set of equations and then analyze it by Mason's rule. It is much easier to apply Cramer's rule directly to the original set of equations.

Signal flow graphs prove very convenient in analog-computer simulation. If the branch transmittances in the flow graph are restricted to

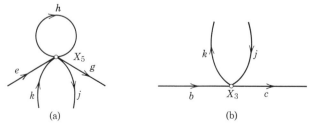

Figure 8.12

$-1/s$, -1 and a ($a < 1$), the signal flow graph can represent the direct setup on the analog computer.[2]

PROBLEMS

1. Draw a signal flow graph of the following sets of simultaneous equations and solve for various dependent variables in terms of independent variable X_0, using (a) graph reduction and (b) Mason's rule.

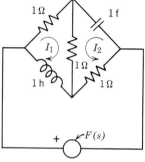

Figure P-8.2

(1) $X = 2X_0 + 3Y + Z$ (2) $X_0 - 3X + 2Y = 0$

$Y = X_0 + 2X + 3Z$ $2X - 5Y + Z = 0$

$Z = 2X_0 + X + Y$ $Y - 4Z = 0$

Solve the equations directly by using Cramer's rule.

2. Draw a signal flow graph (in the frequency domain) for the network shown in Fig. P-8.2. Solve for currents $I_1(s)$ and $I_2(s)$, using (a) graph-reduction techniques and (b) Mason's rule.

3. Write the algebraic equations corresponding to the flow graphs shown in Fig. P-8.3. Solve these

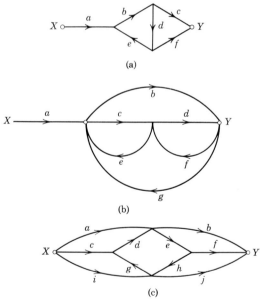

(a)

(b)

(c)

Figure P-8.3 (continued)

[2] For more discussion of this aspect, see L. P. A. Robichaud, M. Boisvert, and J. Robert, *Signal Flow Graphs and Applications*, Chapter 5, Prentice-Hall, Englewood Cliffs, N.J., 1962.

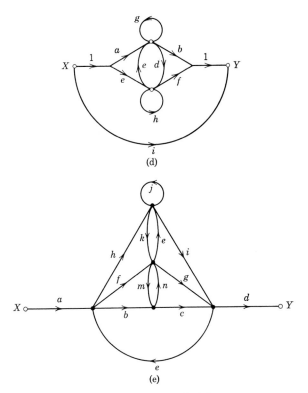

Figure P-8.3 (*concluded*)

equations to find Y/X by using Cramer's rule. Evaluate Y/X from the signal flow graph by using (*a*) reduction techniques and (*b*) Mason's rule.

4. A block diagram of a certain feedback system is shown in Fig. P-8.4. Convert this diagram into a signal flow graph and find the over-all transfer function $V_o(s)/V_i(s)$, using Mason's rule. Now write the set of simultaneous equations for this system and find V_o/V_i from these equations, using Cramer's rule. Comment upon the utility of the two methods.

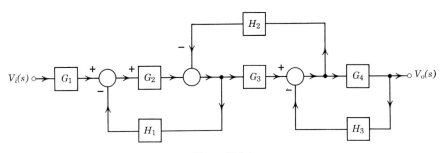

Figure P-8.4

5. A common emitter transistor amplifier and its equivalent circuit is shown in Fig. P-8.5. Write the loop equations for this circuit. Represent these equations by a signal flow graph. Find the voltage gain $V_o(s)/V_1(s)$ from the loop equations by using Cramer's rule and from the flow graph by using Mason's rule. Comment upon the utility of the two methods.

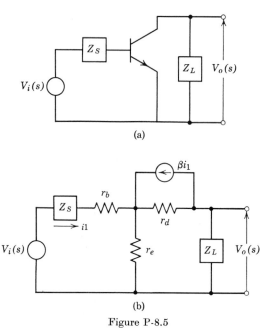

(a)

(b)

Figure P-8.5

chapter 9

Systems with Distributed Parameters

Thus far we have dealt extensively with lumped linear systems which are characterized by ordinary linear differential equations. The basic assumption in the lumped systems is that various physical phenomena are concentrated at a point and the effect of any disturbance initiated at a point in the system is felt instantaneously at every point in the system. These assumptions that the elements of an electrical circuit are concentrated in ideal resistances, inductances, and capacitances or that all of the masses in a mechanical system are concentrated at one point rather than distributed continuously are valid as long as the dimensions of the system elements and the system itself are much smaller compared to the wavelength of the signals to be transmitted. At very high frequencies, the wavelength of the signal is comparable to the system dimensions, and hence the response signal has different phases at different locations in the system. The assumption of instantaneous propagation thus breaks down. Signals, in practice, may not be sinusoidal signals, and hence the phase and frequency of the signal are not meaningful in such cases. However, every signal can be expressed as a discrete or continuous sum of sinusoidal (or exponential) signals, and the above concepts can be readily applied.

In an electrical transmission line, the resistance, the inductance, and the capacitance of the line are distributed uniformly and continuously along the line, and any attempt to lump these parameters is doomed to failure. Moreover, because of such continuous distribution of the system elements, the effect of any disturbance initiated at one point in the system takes a finite time to reach any other point in the system. Therefore, in distributed systems we have to deal with independent variables: time and space. If the system parameters are distributed in three dimensions, then we have four independent variables: three space variables and a time variable. It is evident that the distributed parameter systems will, in general, be characterized by partial-differential equations.

9.1 NATURE OF EQUATIONS ASSOCIATED WITH DISTRIBUTED PARAMETER SYSTEMS

Most of the equations representing linear distributed parameter systems may be classified broadly under a single heading: wave equation. These represent second-order partial-differential equations and have a wide application to the problems of the physical sciences and engineering. They include Laplace's equation, the equation of heat flow, chemical diffusion, skin effect in conductors at high frequencies, density of carriers in semiconductors, and the equation of wave propagation in general. A general wave equation may be represented by the following one.

$$\frac{\partial^2 \varphi}{\partial x^2} + \frac{\partial^2 \varphi}{\partial y^2} + \frac{\partial^2 \varphi}{\partial z^2} = k_1{}^2 \frac{\partial^2 \varphi}{\partial t^2} + k_2 \frac{\partial \varphi}{\partial t} + f(x, y, z, t) \qquad (9.1)$$

The three terms on the left-hand side of Eq. 9.1 are expressed for convenience by $\nabla^2\varphi$. The operator ∇ is called the "del" operator, and $\nabla^2\varphi$ is therefore called (del)$^2\varphi$. Equation 9.1 can now be written as

$$\nabla^2\varphi = k_1{}^2 \frac{\partial^2 \varphi}{\partial t^2} + k_2 \frac{\partial \varphi}{\partial t} + f(x, y, z, t) \qquad (9.2)$$

Some important special cases of Eq. 9.2 are:

I. Laplace's Equation

$$\nabla^2\varphi = 0$$

This is a special case where all of the terms on the right-hand side of Eq. 9.2 are zero. In the Laplace equation, φ may represent the electrostatic potential in a charge-free region, the gravitational potential in free space, the temperature in source-free space, or the velocity potential in the steady flow of an ideal incompressible fluid without vortex motion.

2. Poisson's Equation

$$\nabla^2\varphi = g(x, y, z)$$

In this case, φ and g are functions of space coordinates only. Here φ may represent an electrostatic potential in space where there is a charge distribution $g(x, y, z)$, or it may represent a velocity potential in space where $g(x, y, z)$ is the rate of change of fluid density.

3. Diffusion Equation

$$\nabla^2 \varphi = k_2 \frac{\partial \varphi}{\partial t}$$

This equation is also known as the heat-flow or chemical-diffusion equation. In the heat-flow problem φ may represent the temperature in an isotropic homogeneous medium. In chemical-diffusion problems φ is the concentration of a given substance in a fluid. In semiconductors φ may represent the concentration of excess minority carriers with infinite life time. For carriers with finite life time the governing equation is

$$\nabla^2 \varphi = k_2 \frac{\partial \varphi}{\partial t} + k_3 \varphi$$

For a special case where φ varies with one space variable only, the diffusion equation represents the distribution of voltage and current along a leakage-free noninductive transmission line.

4. Wave Equation in Lossless Systems

In lossless systems without source, the wave equation becomes

$$\nabla^2 \varphi = k_1{}^2 \frac{\partial^2 \varphi}{\partial t^2}$$

This equation governs the electromagnetic wave propagation in a lossless medium. It is also encountered in the vibration of membranes (two-dimensional space variation), the vibration of strings, and in lossless transmission lines (one-dimensional space variation).

Theoretically, all of these problems can be solved by using the Laplace transform method. However, it is not necessarily the best method. There are two reasons for this. First, for more than one independent variable we have to resort to repeated Laplace transforms in various independent variables. As the number of variables increases, these repeated Laplace transforms and the application of proper boundary conditions become prohibitingly complicated. Second, the transfer functions of distributed systems may be irrational, and the transcendental functions and the inverse Laplace transform of such functions can be obtained only by integration in a complex plane. In many cases the degree of complexity in these integrations is of the same nature as that encountered in the solution by classical methods. We therefore expect the Laplace transform method to suit well the problems involving a few independent variables. We shall therefore consider the systems that are distributed only in one space coordinate, for example, the transmission line, the vibrating string, the one-dimensional carrier flow in semiconductors, etc.

9.2 APPLICATIONS TO ONE-DIMENSIONAL DISTRIBUTED SYSTEMS

As seen before, the Laplace transform is viewed as a tool of frequency analysis. In this approach it is necessary to define the concept of a transfer function as applied to distributed parameter systems. The response of the system to a driving function applied at a certain point x_0 will be a function of position x and time t. The response function may be expressed as $r(s, t)$. Let the driving function e^{st} be applied at a certain point x_0 in the system. Since the system is linear and time-invariant, the response at a certain point x_1 will be given by $H_1(s)e^{st}$, where $H_1(s)$ is the transfer function at $x = x_1$. It is evident that the transfer function will vary with x. Therefore, in general, we can express the transfer function by a quantity which is a function of both s and x. Let $H(x, s)$ be the transfer function of the system. Then it follows that if the driving function is e^{st}, then the response at any point x will be given by $H(x, s)e^{st}$. If a driving function $f(t)$ is nonexponential, then it may be expressed as a continuous sum of exponential functions by the Laplace transform, as usual. The response $r(x, t)$, at any point, will evidently be given by the continuous sum of the responses of the system to the individual exponential functions. Thus, if

$$\mathscr{L}[f(t)] = F(s)$$

then

$$r(x, t) = \mathscr{L}^{-1}[H(x, s)F(s)]$$

The inverse transform can be evaluated as usual from the standard tables.

9.3 PROBLEM IN HEAT TRANSFER

For the sake of illustration we shall consider a problem of one-dimensional heat flow in a semi-infinite bar when one end of the bar is held at a constant temperature T_0 starting at an instant $t = 0$.

Here we have a distributed system where the temperature in the bar varies with distance x and time t. The equation for heat flow in such a bar is given by (diffusion equation):

$$\frac{\partial^2 T}{\partial x^2} = \frac{1}{\alpha}\frac{\partial T}{\partial t} \tag{9.3}$$

where T is the temperature of the bar and is a function of both x and t. The term α is the constant of the material and is called the diffusivity. The driving function in this case is a source at $x = 0$ which maintains a constant temperature T_0 and is applied at $t = 0$. The driving function $f(x, t)$ at $x = 0$ may therefore be expressed as

$$f(0, t) = T_0 u(t) \tag{9.4}$$

We shall now find the transfer function $H(x, s)$ from Eq. 9.3.

By definition, if the driving function $T(0, t)$ is e^{st}, then the temperature $T(x, t)$ at any point x is given by

$$T(x, t) = H(x, s)e^{st} \tag{9.5}$$

Substituting Eq. 9.5 in Eq. 9.3,

$$\frac{\partial^2 H}{\partial x^2}e^{st} = \frac{s}{\alpha}He^{st}$$

Since $H(x, s)$ is independent of the variable t, the partial derivative may be replaced by the total derivative. Therefore

$$\frac{d^2 H}{dx^2} = \frac{s}{\alpha}H \tag{9.6}$$

Equation 9.6 is an ordinary second-order differential equation with constant coefficients, and its solution is given by

$$H(x, s) = Ae^{(\sqrt{s/\alpha})x} + Be^{-(\sqrt{s/\alpha})x} \tag{9.7}$$

where A and B are arbitrary constants.

We immediately see that the constant A in Eq. 9.7 must be zero, for otherwise $H(x, s)$ will be infinity at $x = \infty$, which is impossible. Therefore

$$H(x, s) = Be^{-\sqrt{s/\alpha}\,x}$$

The driving function is applied at $x = 0$. Therefore, the driving function

$$f(0, t) = T_0 u(t) \tag{9.8}$$

Hence

$$F(0, s) = T_0/s$$

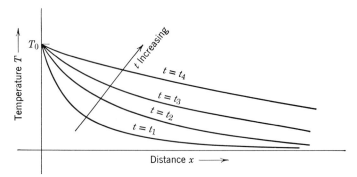

Figure 9.1   Temperature distribution of a semi-infinite bar.

and

$$T(x, t) = \mathscr{L}^{-1}\left[H(x, s)\frac{T_0}{s}\right]$$

$$= \mathscr{L}^{-1}\left[Be^{-\sqrt{s/\alpha}\,x}\frac{T_0}{s}\right] \tag{9.9}$$

The inverse transform of the function in the brackets is found from the table of transforms in Appendix A.

$$T(x, t) = BT_0\, erfc\left(\frac{x}{2\sqrt{\alpha t}}\right) \tag{9.10}$$

But the temperature at $x = 0$ is T_0. Therefore

$$T(0, t) = T_0 = BT_0\, erfc(0)$$

Hence

$$B = \frac{1}{erfc(0)}$$

$$= 1$$

Therefore

$$T(x, t) = T_0\, erfc\left(\frac{x}{2\sqrt{\alpha t}}\right) \tag{9.11}$$

Note that $T(x, t)$ is a function of both x and t and therefore may be represented graphically by a family of curves as a function of x and t as a parameter. This is shown in Fig. 9.1.

9.4   THE TRANSMISSION LINE

An electrical transmission line serves as a good example of a distributed parameter system. It is not possible to represent a transmission line by lumped R-L-C elements unless the line is much shorter than the wavelength of the signal to be transmitted. All of the three parameters are distributed uniformly along the line. We shall consider an incremental element Δx along the line. This element of the line may be represented by lumped parameters, since we shall make Δx smaller than the smallest wavelength of the signal to be transmitted on the line. In the limit we shall let Δx go to zero.

Let

R = the resistance of the line per unit length.

L = the inductance of the line per unit length.

G = the conductance of the line per unit length.

C = the capacitance of the line per unit length.

For an incremental length Δx, all of the above values will be multiplied by Δx. The lumped equivalent circuit for an incremental length is shown in Fig. 9.2. For this model we can write two equations based on Kirchhoff's voltage and current laws.

$$\Delta v = -\left[(R\,\Delta x)i + L\,\Delta x\,\frac{di}{dt}\right]$$

and   (9.12)

$$\Delta i = -\left[(G\,\Delta x)v + C\,\Delta x\,\frac{dv}{dt}\right]$$

First, we shall divide both of the equations by Δx and then let Δx go to zero. Since we now have two independent variables x and t, the derivatives become partial. Therefore, we have

$$-\frac{\partial v}{\partial x} = Ri + L\frac{\partial i}{\partial t} \tag{9.13a}$$

and

$$-\frac{\partial i}{\partial x} = Gv + C\frac{\partial v}{\partial t} \tag{9.13b}$$

Equations 9.13a and 9.13b form a pair of simultaneous partial-differential equations with v and i as dependent variables and x and t as independent variables.

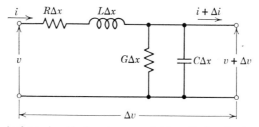

Figure 9.2   Equivalent circuit of an incremental length Δx of a transmission line.

Differentiating Eqs. 9.13a and 9.13b throughout with respect to x and t, respectively,

$$-\frac{\partial^2 v}{\partial x^2} = R\frac{\partial i}{\partial x} + L\frac{\partial^2 i}{\partial t \partial x} \qquad (9.14a)$$

and

$$-\frac{\partial^2 i}{\partial x \partial t} = G\frac{\partial v}{\partial t} + C\frac{\partial^2 v}{\partial t^2} \qquad (9.14b)$$

Since x and t are independent of each other, the order of differentiation may be reversed. Therefore

$$\frac{\partial^2 i}{\partial t \partial x} = \frac{\partial^2 i}{\partial x \partial t}$$

The elimination of variable i by substituting Eqs. 9.14b and 9.13b in Eq. 9.14a yields

$$\frac{\partial^2 v}{\partial x^2} = LC\frac{\partial^2 v}{\partial t^2} + (RC + LG)\frac{\partial v}{\partial t} + RGv \qquad (9.15)$$

In a similar way after eliminating the variable v from Eqs. 9.13a and 9.13b we obtain

$$\frac{\partial^2 i}{\partial x^2} = LC\frac{\partial^2 i}{\partial t^2} + (RC + LG)\frac{\partial i}{\partial t} + RGi \qquad (9.16)$$

Note that Eqs. 9.15 and 9.16 have analogous forms. In fact, these equations are dual of one another with the following analogous quantities:

$$v \leftrightarrow i \qquad R \leftrightarrow G \qquad L \leftrightarrow C$$

This duality is also evident from Eqs. 9.13a and 9.13b. Equations 9.15 and 9.16 are known as *telegraphist's equations* or *telephone equations*. Note that Eqs. 9.15 and 9.16 have the same form as the general one-dimensional wave equation (9.1).

9.5 THE TRANSFER FUNCTION OF A TRANSMISSION LINE

As stated before, a system may have a large number of transfer functions, depending upon the choice of the locations of the response and the driving function. There are, however, two transfer functions which are highly useful in analyzing the transmission-line problems. For convenience we shall assume a transmission line of length l and terminated by an impedance Z_L at $x = l$. The driving function or the generator is applied at $x = 0$ (Fig. 9.3).

We shall define the two transfer functions $H_v(x, s)$ and $H_i(x, s)$ of a transmission line with respect to the driving voltage applied at $x = 0$

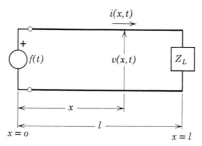

Figure 9.3 A transmission line terminated at $x = l$ and the generator connected at $x = 0$.

and the consequent voltage and current responses at a distance x from the generator. Thus, if a voltage e^{st} is applied at $x = 0$, then the consequent voltage and current at any point x is $H_v(x, s)e^{st}$ and $H_i(x, s)e^{st}$, respectively. The reference directions of the voltage and the current at any point x are shown in Fig. 9.3. Observe that the impedance seen in the positive x direction at any point x is given by

$$Z(x, s) = \frac{v(x, t)}{i(x, t)} = \frac{H_v(x, s)}{H_i(x, s)} \tag{9.17}$$

Evaluation of H_v and H_i

We are given that, if

$$v(0, t) = e^{st} \tag{9.18a}$$

then

$$v(x, t) = H_v e^{st} \tag{9.18b}$$

and

$$i(x, t) = H_i e^{st} \tag{9.18c}$$

Substituting Eq. 9.18b in Eq. 9.15, we get

$$\frac{d^2 H_v}{dx^2} e^{st} = [LCs^2 + (RC + LG)s + RG]H_v e^{st}$$

Therefore

$$\frac{d^2 H_v}{dx^2} = (R + Ls)(G + Cs)H_v$$

$$= \gamma^2 H_v \tag{9.19}$$

where

$$\gamma^2 = (R + Ls)(G + Cs) \tag{9.20}$$

The term γ is called the *propagation constant*. Equation 9.19 is a linear ordinary differential equation for which the solution can be written by inspection:

$$H_v(x, s) = Ae^{-\gamma x} + Be^{\gamma x} \tag{9.21}$$

where A and B are arbitrary constants to be determined by boundary conditions. It follows from Eqs. 9.18a and 9.18b that if a voltage e^{st} is applied at $x = 0$, then the voltage at any point x is given by

$$v(x, t) = [Ae^{-\gamma x} + Be^{\gamma x}]e^{st} \qquad (9.22)$$

The substitution of Eq. 9.22 in Eq. 9.13b yields

$$-\frac{\partial i}{\partial x} = (G + Cs)[Ae^{-\gamma x} + Be^{\gamma x}]e^{st} \qquad (9.23)$$

Integrating both sides of Eq. 9.23 with respect to x, we obtain

$$i(x, t) = (G + Cs)\left[\frac{A}{\gamma} e^{-\gamma x} - \frac{B}{\gamma}e^{\gamma x}\right]e^{st} \qquad (9.24)$$

The constant of integration will, in general, be $K(t)$, some arbitrary function of time. However, for a linear time invariant system, $i(x, t)$ must be of the form $H(x, s)e^{st}$. Hence $K(t)$ must be of the form $K(s)e^{st}$. But in order that Eq. 9.16 be satisfied by $i(x, t)$ in Eq. 9.24, we must have $K(s) = 0$. Hence the constant of integration in Eq. 9.24 is zero.

Equation 9.24 may be expressed as

$$i(x, t) = \frac{1}{Z_0(s)} [Ae^{-\gamma x} - Be^{\gamma x}]e^{st}$$

where

$$Z_0(s) = \frac{\gamma}{G + Cs} = \sqrt{\frac{R + Ls}{G + Cs}} \qquad (9.25)$$

The quantity $Z_0(s)$ has the dimensions of impedance and is called the *characteristic impedance* of the line.

We now have[1]

$$v(x, t) = [Ae^{-\gamma x} + Be^{\gamma x}]e^{st} \qquad (9.26a)$$

$$i(x, t) = \frac{1}{Z_0} [Ae^{-\gamma x} - Be^{\gamma x}]e^{st} \qquad (9.26b)$$

---

[1] Note that
$$\gamma^2 = (R + Ls)(G + Cs)$$
and
$$\gamma = \pm\sqrt{(R + Ls)(G + Cs)}$$

Therefore, there are two possible values of γ. Observe that Eqs. 9.26a and 9.26b are symmetrical with respect to $+\gamma$ and $-\gamma$. Therefore, the choice of a positive or a negative root of γ^2 is immaterial. For convenience, we shall assume henceforth that the root with a positive sign is chosen.

The boundary conditions are

$$v(0, t) = e^{st} \tag{9.27a}$$

and, since the voltages and currents are exponential functions, the ratio of the voltage to the current at $x = l$ must be the impedance at $x = l$, that is, $Z_L(s)$. Hence

$$Z_L = \frac{v(l, t)}{i(l, t)} \tag{9.27b}$$

The substitution of the condition of Eq. 9.27a in Eq. 9.26a yields

$$1 = A + B \tag{9.28a}$$

and the substitution of Eqs. 9.26a and 9.26b in Eq. 9.27b yields

$$Z_L = Z_0 \frac{Ae^{-\gamma l} + Be^{\gamma l}}{Ae^{-\gamma l} - Be^{\gamma l}} \tag{9.28b}$$

Solving Eqs. 9.28a and 9.28b simultaneously, we get

$$A = \frac{1}{1 + \rho(s)e^{-2\gamma l}} \tag{9.29a}$$

and

$$B = \frac{\rho(s)e^{-2\gamma l}}{1 + \rho(s)e^{-2\gamma l}} \tag{9.29b}$$

where

$$\rho(s) = \frac{Z_L(s) - Z_0(s)}{Z_L(s) + Z_0(s)} \tag{9.30}$$

The term $\rho(s)$ is known as the *reflection coefficient*. Equations 9.26a and 9.26b may now be expressed as

$$v(x, t) = \left[\frac{e^{-\gamma(x-l)} + \rho e^{\gamma(x-l)}}{e^{\gamma l} + \rho e^{-\gamma l}} \right] e^{st} \tag{9.31}$$

and

$$i(x, t) = \frac{1}{Z_0} \left[\frac{e^{-\gamma(x-l)} - \rho e^{\gamma(x-l)}}{e^{\gamma l} + \rho e^{-\gamma l}} \right] e^{st} \tag{9.32}$$

Note that the impedance seen at any point x in the positive x direction is given by

$$Z(x, s) = \frac{v(x, t)}{i(x, t)} = Z_0 \left[\frac{e^{-\gamma(x-l)} + \rho e^{\gamma(x-l)}}{e^{-\gamma(x-l)} - \rho e^{\gamma(x-l)}} \right] \tag{9.33}$$

The transfer functions are obtained by comparing Eqs. 9.18b and 9.18c with Eqs. 9.31 and 9.32. It is evident that

$$H_v(x, s) = \left[\frac{e^{-\gamma(x-l)} + \rho e^{\gamma(x-l)}}{e^{\gamma l} + \rho e^{-\gamma l}} \right] \tag{9.34}$$

and

$$H_i(x, s) = \frac{1}{Z_0}\left[\frac{e^{-\gamma(x-l)} - \rho e^{\gamma(x-l)}}{e^{\gamma l} + \rho e^{-\gamma l}}\right] \tag{9.35}$$

We shall now consider a number of special cases.

9.6 THE INFINITE LINE

The case of an infinite line is of great theoretical interest since it clearly demonstrates the nature of propagation of a signal along a transmission line.

To obtain the transfer function of the infinite line, we let $l = \infty$ in Eqs. 9.34 and 9.35. Note that when $l = \infty$, the terms $e^{\gamma(x-l)}$ and $e^{-\gamma l}$ become zero and the transfer functions are reduced to

$$H_v(x, s) = e^{-\gamma x} \tag{9.36}$$

and

$$H_i(x, s) = \frac{e^{-\gamma x}}{Z_0} \tag{9.37}$$

The impedance $Z(x, s)$ at any point x looking in the positive x direction of an infinite line is given by

$$Z(x, s) = \frac{H_v(x, s)}{H_i(x, s)} = Z_0$$

Therefore, the impedance at any point looking in the positive x direction of an infinite line is given by its characteristic impedance Z_0.

We are now in a position to investigate the nature of signal propagation along the infinite line. Equations 9.36 and 9.37 imply that if a voltage e^{st} is applied at $x = 0$, then the voltage and current at any point x is given by $e^{-\gamma x}e^{st}$ and $[e^{-\gamma x}/Z_0]e^{st}$, respectively. If an arbitrary voltage $f(t)$ is applied at $x = 0$, the response may be found by expressing $f(t)$ as a continuous sum of exponentials by means of the Laplace transform. The desired response will be the continuous sum of the responses to individual exponential functions. Thus, if $F(s)$ is the Laplace transform of $f(t)$ then the desired voltage $v(x, t)$ and the current $i(x, t)$ will be given by

$$v(x, t) = \mathcal{L}^{-1}[H_v(x, s)F(s)] = \mathcal{L}^{-1}[e^{-\gamma x}F(s)] \tag{9.38}$$

and

$$i(x, t) = \mathcal{L}^{-1}[H_i(x, s)F(s)] = \mathcal{L}^{-1}\left[\frac{e^{-\gamma x}}{Z_0}F(s)\right] \tag{9.39}$$

We shall now consider various special cases.

I. Lossless Line

For a lossless line, $R = G = 0$. Therefore

$$Z_0 = \sqrt{\frac{Ls}{Cs}} = \sqrt{\frac{L}{C}}$$

and

$$\gamma^2 = LCs^2$$
$$\gamma = s\sqrt{LC}$$

For convenience, we shall denote $1/\sqrt{LC}$ by u. Therefore

$$\gamma = \frac{s}{u}$$

Equations 9.38 and 9.39 now become

$$v(x, t) = \mathcal{L}^{-1}[e^{-s(x/u)}F(s)] \tag{9.40a}$$

and

$$i(x, t) = \mathcal{L}^{-1}\left[\sqrt{\frac{C}{L}}e^{-s(x/u)}F(s)\right] \tag{9.40b}$$

Using the time-shift property of the Laplace transform, the inverse transforms in Eqs. 9.40a and 9.40b may be written as

$$v(x, t) = f\left(t - \frac{x}{u}\right) \tag{9.41a}$$

and

$$i(x, t) = \sqrt{\frac{C}{L}}f\left(t - \frac{x}{u}\right) \tag{9.41b}$$

The function $f(t - x/u)$ represents a function $f(t)$ traveling along the line in the positive x direction with a velocity u. This may be seen as follows. The function $f(t - x/u)$ represents $f(t)$ delayed by x/u seconds. At a point x_1, the voltage function $f(t)$ appears with a delay of x_1/u seconds (Fig. 9.4b) and, at a point x_2 (Fig. 9.4c), the same function appears with a delay of x_2/u seconds and so on. On the other hand, at any instant t_0, the waveform $f(t)$ would have just appeared at $x = ut_0$ (Fig. 9.4d). It is evident that the function $f(t - x/u)$ represents the function $f(t)$ traveling along the line in a positive x direction with a velocity $u = 1/\sqrt{LC}$. Figure 9.4d represents the voltage distribution along the line, that is, the voltage as a function of x. Note that in this figure the function appears laterally inverted. (Why?) The voltage $v(x, t)$ as a function of x and t is shown in Fig. 9.4e.

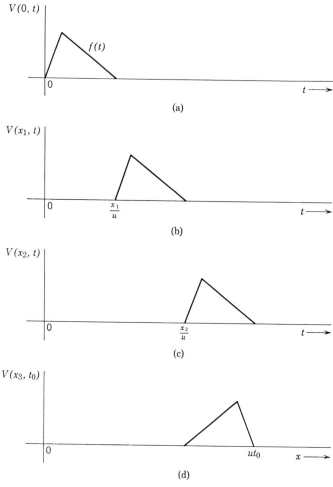

Figure 9.4

Similarly, $f(t + x/u)$ represents the signal $f(t)$ traveling along the line with velocity u in the negative x direction.[2] The expressions $f(t - x/u)$, $f(ut - x)$, $f(x + ut)$, $f(t + x/u)$, and $f(ut + x)$ all represent wave motion.

The wave may be defined as follows. If *a physical phenomenon that occurs at a certain reference position at a given time is reproduced at other places at later times, delayed by the time interval proportional to the distance*

---

[2] For a lossless transmission line, it can be shown that the velocity of propagation $u = 1/\sqrt{LC}$ is equal to the velocity of the propagation of light in the medium, that is, $u = 1/\sqrt{\mu\varepsilon} = 3 \times 10^8$ meters per second in free space. See, for instance, E. C. Jordan, *Electromagnetic Waves and Radiating Systems*, Prentice-Hall, New York, 1950, pp. 213–216; H. Skilling, *Electric Transmission Lines*, Chapter 6, McGraw-Hill, New York, 1951.

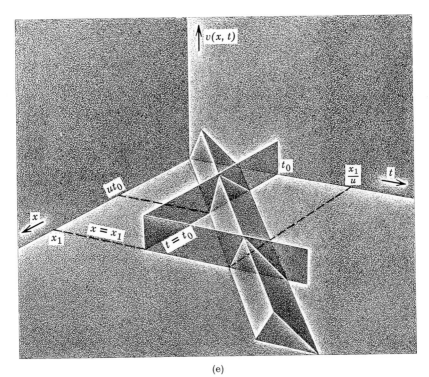

(e)

Figure 9.4 (*concluded*)

from the reference position, then the group of phenomena constitute a wave.[3]
Note that a wave is not necessarily a repetitive phenomenon in time.
Equation 9.41b represents the current distribution. It is evident that the
current waveform is also traveling in positive x direction with a velocity
u. Observe that the impedance at any point x looking in the positive x
direction is given by

$$Z(x, s) = Z_0 = \sqrt{\frac{L}{C}}$$

It therefore follows that the impedance at any point looking in the positive
x direction of an infinite lossless line is a resistive constant $\sqrt{L/C}$.

2. Distortionless Line

A transmission line is called a distortionless line if the parameters
satisfy the condition:

$$LG = RC \tag{9.42}$$

[3] E. C. Jordan, p. 115, cited in reference 2.

Under this condition,

$$\gamma^2 = (R + Ls)(G + Cs)$$

$$= \frac{C}{L}(R + Ls)^2$$

and

$$\gamma = \sqrt{\frac{C}{L}}(R + Ls) \tag{9.43}$$

$$= \frac{s}{u} + R\sqrt{\frac{C}{L}} = \frac{s}{u} + G\sqrt{\frac{L}{C}}$$

and

$$Z_0 = \sqrt{\frac{R + Ls}{G + Cs}}$$

$$= \sqrt{\frac{L}{C}} \tag{9.44}$$

Substituting Eq. 9.43 in Eqs. 9.38 and 9.39, we have

$$v(x, t) = \mathcal{L}^{-1}[e^{-(R\sqrt{C/L}+s/u)x}F(s)] \tag{9.45a}$$

and

$$i(x, t) = \mathcal{L}^{-1}\left[\sqrt{\frac{C}{L}}\,e^{-(R\sqrt{C/L}+s/u)x}F(s)\right] \tag{9.45b}$$

Application of the time-shifting property of Laplace transform to Eqs. 9.45a and 9.45b yields

$$v(x, t) = e^{-R\sqrt{C/L}\,x}f\left(t - \frac{x}{u}\right) \tag{9.46a}$$

$$i(x, t) = \sqrt{\frac{C}{L}}\,e^{-R\sqrt{C/L}\,x}f\left(t - \frac{x}{u}\right) \tag{9.46b}$$

Equations 9.46a and 9.46b represent the voltage and current waveforms traveling along the line in a positive x direction with a velocity u. The signal $f(t)$ retains its waveform all along the line and hence this line is called the distortionless line. Note, however, that the signal is attenuated exponentially as it travels along the line. This is evident by the exponential attenuation factor $e^{-\sqrt{C/L}\,Rx}$. The impedance of the distortionless line at any point x, as seen from Eq. 9.44, is a resistive constant $\sqrt{L/C}$. The voltage waveform, as it travels along the line, is shown in Fig. 9.5.

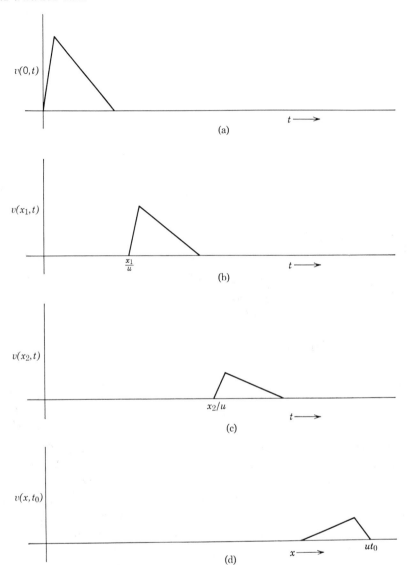

Figure 9.5

3. Line with Small Losses

If the losses in the line are small, so that

$$\frac{R}{Ls} \ll 1 \qquad \text{and} \qquad \frac{G}{Cs} \ll 1, \qquad (9.47)$$

then

$$\gamma = [(R + Ls)(G + Cs)]^{1/2}$$
$$= [LCs^2 + s(RC + LG) + RG]^{1/2}$$

Since the losses are very small, RG is much smaller compared to the other terms. Hence

$$\gamma \simeq [LCs^2 + s(RC + LG)]^{1/2}$$

$$= s\sqrt{LC}\left[1 + \frac{RC + LG}{LCs}\right]^{1/2}$$

The second term in the brackets is much smaller compared to 1 and hence, using binomial expansion, we get

$$\gamma \simeq s\sqrt{LC}\left[1 + \frac{1}{2}\left(\frac{R}{Ls} + \frac{G}{Cs}\right)\right] = \frac{s}{u} + \frac{\sqrt{LC}}{2}\left(\frac{R}{L} + \frac{G}{C}\right) \qquad (9.48)$$

Note that γ for the line with small losses (Eq. 9.48) has the same form as that for the distortionless line. Hence, in the region where the approximations of Eq. 9.47 are valid, the line behaves exactly like a distortionless line. In practice, most of the transmission lines have small losses and thus behave similar to distortionless lines.

9.7 THE FINITE LINE

In practice, the infinite line does not exist. Its study, however, facilitates our understanding of the signal propagation along the line. As we observed in previous sections, the signal propagates along the line with a constant velocity u. If the line is infinite in length, the signal will continue to propagate along it indefinitely. What will happen if the line is terminated abruptly at some point? This is perhaps the most important problem in the study of transmission lines since, in practice, we deal with finite lines terminated by a load impedance. The transfer functions of a finite line terminated by an impedance Z_L at $x = l$ and fed by a generator at $x = 0$ (Fig. 9.3) have been derived previously (Eqs. 9.34 and 9.35). The two transfer functions are given by

$$H_v(x, s) = \frac{e^{-\gamma(x-l)} + \rho e^{\gamma(x-l)}}{e^{\gamma l} + \rho e^{-\gamma l}} \qquad (9.49a)$$

and

$$H_i(x, s) = \frac{1}{Z_0}\left[\frac{e^{-\gamma(x-l)} - \rho e^{\gamma(x-l)}}{e^{\gamma l} + \rho e^{-\gamma l}}\right] \qquad (9.49b)$$

where

$$\rho(s) = \frac{Z_L(s) - Z_0(s)}{Z_L(s) + Z_0(s)}$$

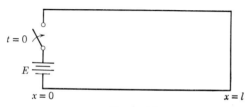

Figure 9.6

To start with, let us assume that the line is short-circuited at $x = l$, that is, $Z_L = 0$ (Fig. 9.6). Then the reflection coefficient becomes

$$\rho(s) = \frac{0 - Z_0}{0 + Z_0} = -1$$

The transfer functions now become

$$H_v(x, s) = \frac{e^{-\gamma(x-l)} - e^{\gamma(x-l)}}{e^{\gamma l} - e^{-\gamma l}} \tag{9.50a}$$

and

$$H_i(x, s) = \frac{1}{Z_0}\left[\frac{e^{-\gamma(x-l)} + e^{\gamma(x-l)}}{e^{\gamma l} - e^{-\gamma l}}\right] \tag{9.50b}$$

Suppose a constant voltage E is applied at the generator end at $t = 0$, then (Fig. 9.6):

$$f(t) = Eu(t)$$

and

$$F(s) = \frac{E}{s}$$

$$v(x, t) = \mathcal{L}^{-1}[H_v(x, s)F(s)]$$

$$= \mathcal{L}^{-1}\left[\frac{E}{s}\frac{e^{-\gamma(x-l)} - e^{\gamma(x-l)}}{e^{\gamma l} - e^{-\gamma l}}\right] \tag{9.51}$$

$$= \mathcal{L}^{-1}\left[\frac{E}{s}\frac{e^{-\gamma(x-l)}}{e^{\gamma l}}\frac{[1 - e^{2\gamma(x-l)}]}{(1 - e^{-2\gamma l})}\right] \tag{9.52}$$

Using the infinite series expansion,

$$\frac{1}{1 - e^{-2\gamma l}} = 1 + e^{-2\gamma l} + e^{-4\gamma l} + e^{-6\gamma l} + \cdots.$$

we get

$$v(x, t) = \mathcal{L}^{-1}\frac{E}{s}[e^{-\gamma x} - e^{-\gamma(2l-x)}][1 + e^{-2\gamma l} + e^{-4\gamma l} + \cdots]$$

$$= \mathcal{L}^{-1}\left[\frac{E}{s}e^{-\gamma x} - \frac{E}{s}e^{-\gamma(2l-x)} + \frac{E}{s}e^{-\gamma(2l+x)} - \frac{E}{s}e^{-\gamma(4l-x)} + \cdots\right] \tag{9.53}$$

For a lossless line,

$$\gamma = \frac{s}{u}$$

and

$$v(x, t) = \mathcal{L}^{-1}\left[\frac{E}{s} e^{(-x/u)s} - \frac{E}{s} e^{-[(2l-x)/u]s} + \frac{E}{s} e^{-[(2l+x)/u]s} - \frac{E}{s} e^{-[(4l-x)/u]s}\right.$$
$$\left. + \cdots\right] \tag{9.54}$$

Using the time-shifting property, the inverse transform of the right-hand side of Equation 9.54 may be written term by term.

$$v(x, t) = E\left[u\left(t - \frac{x}{u}\right) - u\left(t - \frac{2l - x}{u}\right) + u\left(t - \frac{2l + x}{u}\right)\right.$$
$$\left. - u\left(t - \frac{4l - x}{u}\right) + \cdots\right] \tag{9.55}$$

Equation 9.55 is the desired solution. In order to obtain an insight into the nature of the propagation on a finite line, we shall interpret Eq. 9.55 term by term. At time $t = 0$, when the switch is closed in Fig. 9.6, the signal starts propagating in the positive x direction. The signal does not know that the line is terminated at $x = l$ and, hence, the signal propagates as if the line were infinite. At the time $t = l/u$, the signal has reached the termination which is short-circuited and hence must have zero voltage at all times. However, the signal that reaches this point has a constant magnitude E. We therefore have an impossible situation. Nature, however, has ingenious ways of meeting such paradoxes. At this point we look back at Eq. 9.21 and observe that a general expression for the transfer function H_v of a transmission line is given by

$$H_v(x, s) = (Ae^{-\gamma x} + Be^{\gamma x})$$

For a lossless line, $\gamma = s/u$, and we get

$$H_v(x, s) = Ae^{(-x/u)s} + Be^{(x/u)s}$$

If a driving voltage $f(t)$ has a Laplace transform $F(s)$ then the voltage along the line is given by

$$v(x, t) = \mathcal{L}^{-1}[Ae^{(-x/u)s}F(s) + Be^{(x/u)s}F(s)]$$
$$= Af\left(t - \frac{x}{u}\right) + Bf\left(t + \frac{x}{u}\right)$$

We observed that $f(t - x/u)$ represents the function $f(t)$ propagating along positive x direction with a velocity u. Similar arguments lead to the conclusion that $f(t + x/u)$ represents the function $f(t)$ propagating in the negative x direction with a velocity u. Therefore, a general solution of the transmission line equations contains signals propagating in either direction (positive or negative x). In other words, the transmission line equations are satisfied by signals propagating in either direction. This fact is of crucial importance in meeting the paradox in our problem. We have the situation where the voltage propagating from the source has a magnitude E when it reaches the short circuit at $x = l$. The short circuit must, however, have zero voltage all of the time. We have to satisfy the boundary condition that $v(l, t) = 0$ and also the line equations. These conditions are fulfilled by a peculiar phenomenon known as *reflection*. As soon as the voltage wave E reaches the termination at the instant $t = l/u$, the termination gives rise to a voltage wave of $-E$ volts which starts propagating toward the generator at the instant $t = l/u$. The total voltage at the termination is E volts, due to the direct signal from the generator, and $-E$ volts caused by the reflected signal. Hence, the boundary condition at $x = l$ is satisfied at every instant. The reflected wave does not violate the laws of the propagation on the transmission line, since we observed that a signal propagating in a negative x direction also satisfied the equations of a transmission line. This solution, although it looks attractive in the beginning, causes some more headaches. As the reflected wave travels toward the generator with voltage $-E$, it cancels the E volts at every point, due to the direct wave. At the instant $t = 2l/u$, the reflected wave reaches the generator and makes the voltage at $x = 0$ go to zero. But this is impossible, since at $x = 0$ we have a constant voltage E. Hence, to meet this boundary condition, another reflected wave of E volts starts from $x = 0$ at $t = 2l/u$ in a positive x direction. At $t = 3l/u$ this wave reaches the short circuit which, in turn, must give rise to another reflected wave of $-E$ volts at $t = 3l/u$ propagating toward the generator. The cycle keeps on repeating indefinitely. The infinite terms in Eq. 9.55 precisely express this phenomenon of endless reflections. As soon as the switch is closed at $t = 0$, the voltage E propagates in a positive x direction with a velocity u and reaches the point x at $t = x/u$. Hence, the voltage at x is $Eu(t - x/u)$. The first term on the right-hand side of Eq. 9.55 represents this direct propagation from the generator. At $t = l/u$, a reflected wave of $-E$ volts starts at $x = l$ toward the generator and will reach the point x, $(l - x)/u$ seconds later. Hence, the voltage $-E$ appears at the point x at $t = l/u + (l - x)/u = (2l - x)/u$. The second term in Eq. 9.55 represents the first reflected signal. Similarly, the third term expresses the second reflected signal E volts from the generator end, and arrives at the point x at $t = (2l + x)/u$. The fourth term represents the third reflected signal $-E$ volts from the termination,

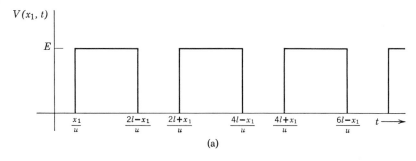

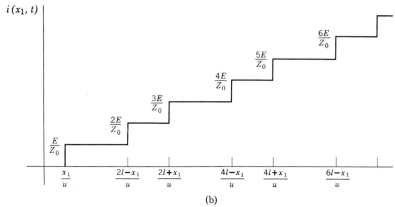

Figure 9.7 (a) The voltage waveform appearing at $x = x_1$. (b) A current waveform appearing at $x = x_1$.

and arrives at the point x at $t = (4l - x)/u$ and so on. The voltage waveform at some point x_1 is shown in Fig. 9.7a. Let us now consider the current waveform at some point x. For a voltage E applied at $x = 0$, we have

$$i(x, t) = \mathscr{L}^{-1}\left[H_i(x, s)\frac{E}{s}\right] \tag{9.56}$$

Substituting the expression for H_i (Eq. 9.50b) in Eq. 9.56, we get

$$i(x, t) = \mathscr{L}^{-1}\left[\frac{E}{sZ_0}\frac{e^{-\gamma(x-l)} + e^{\gamma(x-l)}}{e^{\gamma l} - e^{-\gamma l}}\right]$$

Using manipulations similar to those in Eqs. 9.52 to 9.54, we get

$$i(x, t) = \mathscr{L}^{-1}\left[\frac{E}{sZ_0}\frac{e^{-\gamma(x-l)}}{e^{\gamma l}}\frac{[1 + e^{2\gamma(x-l)}]}{(1 - e^{-2\gamma l})}\right]$$

$$= \mathscr{L}^{-1}\frac{E}{sZ_0}[e^{-\gamma x} + e^{-\gamma(2l-x)}][1 + e^{-2\gamma l} + e^{-4\gamma l} + \cdots]$$

For a lossless line, $\gamma = s/u$. Therefore

$$
i(x,\, t) = \frac{1}{Z_0} \mathscr{L}^{-1} \left[\frac{E}{s} e^{(-x/u)s} + \frac{E}{s} e^{-[(2l-x)/u]s} + \frac{E}{s} e^{-[(2l+x)/u]s} \right.
$$

$$
\left. + \frac{E}{s} e^{-[(4l-x)/u]s} + \cdots \right]
$$

$$
= \frac{E}{Z_0} \left[u\left(t - \frac{x}{u}\right) + u\left(t - \frac{2l-x}{u}\right) + u\left(t - \frac{2l+x}{u}\right) \right.
$$

$$
\left. + u\left(t - \frac{4l-x}{u}\right) + \cdots \right] \tag{9.57}
$$

Notice the difference between the expression for voltage (Eq. 9.55) and that for current (Eq. 9.57) at a point x. Whereas the voltage reflections change sign alternately, all the current reflections are additive. The current waveform at a point x_1 is shown in Fig. 9.7b. It is therefore evident that although the voltage at $x = x_1$ keeps on alternating between zero and E (Fig. 9.7a), the current increases monotonically in steps of E/Z_0 units as shown in Fig. 9.7b. This is also expected by intuition, since the current in a short-circuited line excited by a constant voltage must go to infinity. The current, however, does not reach the infinite value instantaneously, as is usually thought, but increases in finite steps.

The reason for the current waveform increasing monotonically despite the fact that voltage alternates can be easily seen. The direct wave of E volts reaches the termination at $t = l/u$. The current i_d, due to this direct wave, is E/Z_0 and its direction is shown in Fig. 9.8. At this instant $t = l/u$, a reflected wave of $-E$ volts starts at $x = l$ toward the generator. Note that the direction of current due to the reflected voltage wave of $-E$ volts moving toward the generator is the same as that of i_d. Therefore, although the voltages cancel, the currents add, due to the two waves. This same phenomenon is repeated at every reflection occurring at either end of the line. At every reflection the current builds up in equal steps. Hence, although the voltage on the line fluctuates between zero and E volts, the current increases monotonically in steps of E/Z_0.

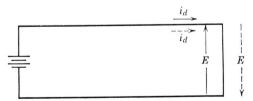

Figure 9.8   The direct and reflected voltage and current at a short circuit.

9.8 THE REFLECTION COEFFICIENT

We just considered a special case of an impedance termination $Z_L = 0$. When a traveling voltage wave meets a short circuit along its way, it gives rise to a reflected wave of the same magnitude but of opposite sign. This need not be the case for a general termination. The reflected wave must be of such a nature as to satisfy the boundary condition at the termination. We shall now look into the nature of a reflected wave at a general termination Z_L (Fig. 9.9). A direct voltage wave $A_d e^{st}$ will be assumed to reach the termination Z_L at $t = 0$. Before reaching the termination, the direct wave cannot anticipate the termination and hence the line appears as an infinite line before $t = 0$. Hence, the direct wave current i_d must be $(A_d/Z_0)e^{st}$. At $t = 0$, the direct wave reaches the termination and is unable to fulfill the boundary condition which requires that the ratio of voltage to current must be Z_L. For the direct wave, this ratio is Z_0, and therefore to meet the boundary condition a reflected voltage wave $A_r e^{st}$ starts at the termination in the negative x direction. The reflected wave also cannot anticipate any termination on the left-hand end, and hence the line appears as an infinite line and the reflected current is $i_r = (A_r/Z_0)e^{st}$ in the negative x direction. The resultant voltage v_t and the resultant current i_t at the termination are given by

$$v_t = A_d e^{st} + A_r e^{st}$$

and

$$i_t = \frac{1}{Z_0} (A_d e^{st} - A_r e^{st})$$

The boundary conditions will be satisfied if

$$Z_L = \frac{v_t}{i_t} = Z_0 \frac{A_d + A_r}{A_d - A_r} \tag{9.58}$$

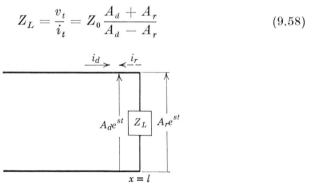

Figure 9.9

The solution of Eq. 9.58 yields

$$\frac{A_r}{A_d} = \frac{Z_L(s) - Z_0(s)}{Z_L(s) + Z_0(s)} = \rho(s) \qquad (9.59)$$

It therefore follows that the boundary condition will be fulfilled if the reflected wave is ρ times the direct wave or forward wave. Thus, ρ is the measure of the amount of reflection and is therefore called the *reflection coefficient*. Note that ρ depends only upon Z_L and Z_0. The ratio of forward and reflected voltages is ρ, but the ratio of forward and reflected currents is $-\rho$. The minus sign arises because the reference direction of current is taken as the positive x direction in the upper conductor, and the forward and reflected currents have an opposite direction. For a special case of short-circuited termination, $Z_L = 0$ and $\rho = -1$. Therefore, the voltage reflection coefficient is -1, and the current reflection coefficient is 1. If the line is open-circuited at $x = l$ (that is, $Z_L = \infty$), then $\rho = 1$. In this case the voltage reflection coefficient is 1, but the current reflection coefficient is -1. This is also evident from the boundary condition, since an open circuit must have zero current at all times, a reflected current must be equal and opposite to the forward current. Note that at the generator end, the impedance of the ideal voltage generator is zero, and hence the reflection coefficient at the generator end should be calculated by substituting $Z_L = 0$ in Eq. 9.59. If the generator were an ideal current source, then Z_L would equal ∞ at the generator.

If $Z_L = Z_0$, then it is evident from Eq. 9.59 that $\rho = 0$. Thus, if a line is terminated by its characteristic impedance, no reflection occurs at the termination, and at the input terminals the line appears as if it were infinitely long. The boundary conditions are met without any need for the reflected wave, since the ratio of the forward voltage and current is Z_0.

The above discussion on the reflection coefficient, although it assumes only exponential signals, does not restrict its conclusions to exponential signals alone. Any arbitrary function can always be expressed as a continuous sum of exponential signals by a Laplace transform. The reflection coefficient is a function of s and should be written as $\rho(s)$. If the forward voltage wave is an arbitrary function $f(t)$ and its Laplace transform is $F(s)$, then the reflected voltage wave v_r will be given by

$$v_r = \mathcal{L}^{-1}[\rho(s)F(s)] \qquad (9.60a)$$

and the reflected current wave i_r will be given by

$$i_r = \mathcal{L}^{-1}\left[\frac{-\rho(s)F(s)}{Z_0(s)}\right] \qquad (9.60b)$$

The relationship between the forward and reflected waves can also be arrived at by considering the transfer function $H_v(x, s)$ in Eq. 9.34. If the driving voltage $f(t)$ has a Laplace transform $F(s)$, then the voltage $v(x, t)$ may be written as

$$v(x, t) = \mathscr{L}^{-1}[F(s)H_v(x, s)]$$

$$= \mathscr{L}^{-1}\left[F(s)\frac{e^{-\gamma(x-l)} + \rho(s)e^{\gamma(x-l)}}{e^{\gamma l} + \rho(s)e^{-\gamma l}}\right]$$

$$= \mathscr{L}^{-1}\left\{F(s)\frac{e^{-\gamma(x-l)}}{e^{\gamma l}}\frac{[1 + \rho(s)e^{2\gamma(x-l)}]}{[1 + \rho(s)e^{-2\gamma l}]}\right\}$$

$$= \mathscr{L}^{-1}\{F(s)[e^{-\gamma x} + \rho(s)e^{-\gamma(2l-x)}][1 - \rho(s)e^{-2\gamma l}$$

$$+ \rho^2(s)e^{-4\gamma l} + \cdots]\}$$

For a lossless line $\gamma = s/u$. Therefore

$$v(x, t) = \mathscr{L}^{-1}[F(s)e^{(-x/u)s} + F(s)\rho(s)e^{-[(2l-x)/u]s}$$

$$- F(s)\rho(s)e^{-[(2l+x)/u]s} + \cdots] \qquad (9.61)$$

It can easily be seen that the second term on the right-hand side of Eq. 9.61 represents the voltage reflected at the termination. This component of voltage v_{r_1} can be expressed as

$$v_{r_1}(x, t) = \mathscr{L}^{-1}[F(s)\rho(s)e^{-[(2l-x)/u]s}] \qquad (9.62)$$

The exponential term merely expresses the delay of $(2l - x)/u$ seconds. Otherwise Eq. 9.62 is identical with Eq. 9.60a. The third term represents the reflected voltage component at the generator end. Since for an ideal voltage source the generator impedance is zero, $Z_L = 0$ and $\rho = -1$, we merely have a sign change in this term.

Example 9.1

A lossless transmission line of length $10u$ units with a characteristic impedance $10\,\Omega$ is terminated by an inductor of 10 henries. A triangular voltage shown in Fig. 9.10a is applied at the generator end of the line. Determine the voltage at $x = 6u$ for the first 20 seconds.

Solution. The signal traveling at a velocity u will take 10 seconds to reach the termination, and the reflected wave that starts at the termination at $t = 10$ will take another 10 seconds to reach the generator. Since we are interested in the solution for the first 20 seconds only, we need to consider only one reflection at the load termination. The desired voltage $v(x, t)$ is given by

$$v(x, t) = \mathscr{L}^{-1}[F(s)H_v(x, s)]$$

We substitute the expression for $H_v(x, s)$ and expand it as usual. This is done in Eq. 9.61. Since we are interested only in the first reflection, we choose only the first two terms on the right-hand side of Eq. 9.61.

$$v(x, t) = \mathscr{L}^{-1}[F(s)e^{(-x/u)s} + F(s)\rho(s)e^{-[(2l-x)/u]s}] \qquad (9.63)$$

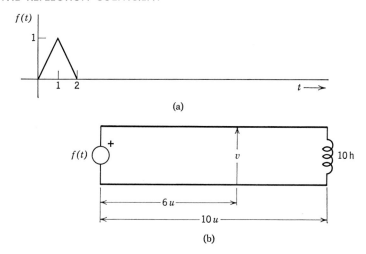

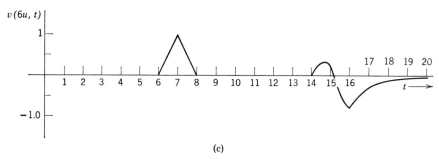

(c)

Figure 9.10   (a) The driving voltage at $x = 0$.   (b) A transmission line terminated by an inductor.   (c) The voltage response at $x = 6$ of the triangular input voltage at $x = 0$.

In our case

$$
\left.\begin{array}{c}
x = 6u \\
l = 10u
\end{array}\right\}
$$

and

$$
\rho(s) = \frac{Z_L - Z_0}{Z_L + Z_0} = \frac{10s - 10}{10s + 10} = \frac{s - 1}{s + 1}
$$

(9.64)

and

$$
\begin{aligned}
F(s) &= \mathcal{L}[f(t)] \\
&= \mathcal{L}[tu(t) - 2(t - 1)u(t - 1) + (t - 2)u(t - 2)] \\
&= \frac{1}{s^2} - \frac{2}{s^2}e^{-s} + \frac{e^{-2s}}{s^2} \\
&= \frac{(1 - 2e^{-s} + e^{-2s})}{s^2}
\end{aligned}
$$

(9.65)

Substituting Eqs. 9.64 and 9.65 in Eq. 9.63, we get

$$v(6u, t) = \mathscr{L}^{-1}\left[\frac{(1 - 2e^{-s} + e^{-2s})}{s^2} e^{-6s} + \frac{(1 - 2e^{-s} + e^{-2s})}{s^2}\frac{(s - 1)}{(s + 1)} e^{-14s}\right]$$

$$= \mathscr{L}^{-1}\left[\frac{(1 - 2e^{-s} + e^{-2s})}{s^2}(e^{-6s} + e^{-14s})\right.$$

$$\left. - 2(1 - 2e^{-s} + e^{-2s})\left(\frac{1}{s + 1} + \frac{1}{s^2} - \frac{1}{s}\right)e^{-14s}\right]$$

$$= f(t - 6) + f(t - 14) - 2[e^{-(t-14)} + (t - 14) - 1]u(t - 14)$$
$$+ 4[e^{-(t-15)} + (t - 15) - 1]u(t - 15) - 2[e^{-(t-16)}$$
$$+ (t - 16) - 1]\,u(t - 16)$$

The voltage $v(6u, t)$ is plotted in Fig. 9.10c.

9.9   TRANSFER FUNCTIONS WITH NONIDEAL SOURCES

The transfer functions H_v and H_i have been derived when the source is an ideal voltage source. In practice, however, a source may have an internal impedance $Z_s(s)$ as shown in Fig. 9.11a. The transfer functions in such a case can be easily determined. We first replace the transmission line by an equivalent impedance Z_{eq}, determined from Eq. 9.33 by letting $x = 0$. Note that reflections occur both at the load and the generator terminations. Hence, we shall define two reflection coefficients:

$$\rho_l(s) = \frac{Z_L - Z_0}{Z_L + Z_0} \quad \text{and} \quad \rho_s(s) = \frac{Z_s - Z_0}{Z_s + Z_0} \tag{9.66}$$

Substituting $x = 0$ and $\rho = \rho_l$ in Eq. 9.33, we get

$$Z_{eq} = Z_0 \frac{e^{\gamma l} + \rho_l e^{-\gamma l}}{e^{\gamma l} - \rho_l e^{-\gamma l}} \tag{9.67}$$

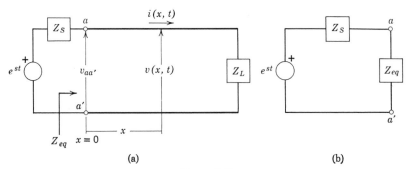

(a)   (b)

Figure 9.11

From Fig. 9.11b, it is evident that the voltage at the input terminals of the transmission line is attenuated by a factor $Z_{eq}/(Z_s + Z_{eq})$, and hence the new transfer functions H_v' and H_i'. will be the same as those in Eqs. 9.34 and 9.35 but attenuated by a factor $Z_{eq}/(Z_s + Z_{eq})$. Thus

$$H_v'(x, s) = \frac{Z_{eq}}{Z_s + Z_{eq}} H_v(x, s)$$

$$H_i'(x, s) = \frac{Z_{eq}}{Z_s + Z_{eq}} H_i(x, s)$$

(9.68)

Substituting Eqs. 9.34, 9.35, 9.66, and 9.67 in Eq. 9.68, and rearranging the terms we get

$$H_v'(x, s) = \frac{Z_0}{Z_0 + Z_s} \left[\frac{e^{-\gamma x} + \rho_l(s)e^{-\gamma(2l-x)}}{1 - \rho_l(s)\rho_s(s)e^{-2\gamma l}} \right]$$

$$H_i'(x, s) = \frac{1}{Z_0 + Z_s} \left[\frac{e^{-\gamma x} - \rho_l(s)e^{-\gamma(2l-x)}}{1 - \rho_l(s)\rho_s(s)e^{-2\gamma l}} \right]$$

(9.69)

Example 9.2

Find the voltage at the load of a lossless transmission line terminated by 50 Ω. The line is driven by a constant voltage source of 100 volts through a source resistance of 300 Ω. The characteristic impedance of the line is 100 Ω and the length is $10u$.

This problem can be readily solved by using Eq. 9.69. We shall, however, consider a qualitative approach.

The wave starts at the generator, not knowing that it is terminated at $l = 10u$. Hence, at the input terminals, the wave sees its characteristic impedance of 100 Ω. Therefore the direct wave, starting at the generator at $t = 0$, has a magnitude of

$$(100) \frac{100}{300 + 100} = 25 \text{ volts}$$

Until $t = 10$, the voltage at the load is zero. At $t = 10$, the direct wave of 25 volts reaches the load and, being unable to fulfill the boundary conditions instantaneously, gives rise to a reflected wave. The reflection coefficient is given by

$$\rho_l = \frac{Z_L - Z_0}{Z_L + Z_0} = -\frac{1}{3}$$

Hence the reflected wave must have a magnitude of

$$25 \times (-\tfrac{1}{3}) = -8.33 \text{ volts}$$

The voltage at the load is therefore $(25 - 8.33) = 16.67$ volts.

At $t = 20$, the reflected wave of -8.3 volts reaches the generator and, being unable to fulfill the boundary conditions, gives rise to another reflected wave now traveling toward the load. The reflection coefficient ρ_s is given by

$$\rho_s = \frac{Z_s - Z_0}{Z_s + Z_0} = \frac{1}{2}$$

Hence the new wave, starting at $t = 20$ at the source, has a magnitude of

$$-8.33 \times \tfrac{1}{2} = -4.17 \text{ volts.}$$

This new wave reaches the load at $t = 30$ and gives rise to a reflected wave of the magnitude of

$$(-4.17) \times (-\tfrac{1}{3}) = 1.39 \text{ volts}$$

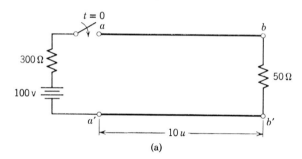

(a)

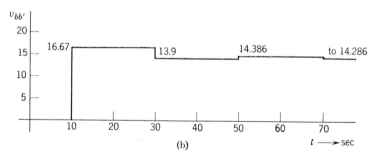

(b)

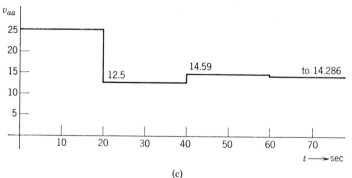

(c)

Figure 9.12

The voltage at the load is now

$$16.67 - 4.17 + 1.39 = 13.9 \text{ volts}$$

This wave reaches the generator at $t = 40$ and a new wave starts at the generator of the magnitude of $1.39 \times \frac{1}{2} = 0.695$ volts. This wave reaches the load at $t = 50$ and gives rise to a reflected wave of $(0.695) \times (-\frac{1}{3}) = -0.232$ volts.
Hence the voltage at the load is now

$$13.9 + 0.695 - 0.232 = 14.363 \text{ volts}$$

The cycle keeps on repeating, the voltage at the load oscillates, and finally converges to a value of

$$100 \times \left(\frac{50}{300 + 50} \right) = 14.286 \text{ volts}$$

The variation of the load voltage as a function of time is shown in Fig. 9.12b. The voltage variation at the source terminals aa' may similarly be calculated. Figure 9.12c shows the voltage at terminals aa'. In a similar manner the voltage at any intermediate point may be computed. To calculate the current waveform a similar procedure may be followed except that the reflection coefficients for the current are negative of those for the voltage waveforms.

9.10 THE SINUSOIDAL STEADY-STATE SOLUTION OF A TRANSMISSION LINE

Transmission lines are extensively used as in communication systems and electronic circuits. In communication systems they may be used for the transmission of signals, or as a part of a radiating system. In electronic circuits, at very high frequencies ($f > 150$ mc) where conventional lumped circuit elements become difficult to construct, a transmission line of a proper length and with a proper termination can serve the purpose of any circuit element such as a resistor, a capacitor, an inductor, or a transformer. All these applications require a familiarity with the sinusoidal steady-state behavior of a transmission line.

For lumped system it was shown that if $H(s)$ is the transfer function of a system, then its sinusoidal steady-state behavior is completely specified by $H(j\omega)$. For a sinusoidal driving function of frequency ω, the steady-state response is also a sinusoidal signal of the same frequency, of a magnitude equal to $|H(j\omega)|$ and shifted in phase with respect to the driving function by $\underline{/H(j\omega)}$. This result also holds true for distributed parameter systems. If $H(x, s)$ is the transfer function, then the sinusoidal steady-state response is completely determined by $H(x, j\omega)$. For a sinusoidal input signal, the response at a point x has a magnitude of $|H(x, j\omega)|$ and is shifted in phase with respect to the input signal by $\underline{/H(x, j\omega)}$. We have already derived the transfer functions H_v and H_i. To study the steady-state response of the system we merely have to replace s by $j\omega$ in these transfer functions and in the other equations that we derived previously.

For $s = j\omega$, the transmission line parameters γ, Z_0, ρ, etc. will become

$$\gamma = [(R + j\omega L)(G + j\omega C)]^{1/2}$$

$$Z_0 = \left[\frac{(R + j\omega L)}{(G + j\omega C)}\right]^{1/2}$$

$$\rho(j\omega) = \frac{Z_L(j\omega) - Z_0}{Z_L(j\omega) + Z_0}$$

In almost all of these applications, the transmission lines have negligible losses and therefore can be taken as lossless lines, that is, $R = G = 0$. For a lossless line,

$$\gamma = j\omega\sqrt{LC} = \frac{j\omega}{u}$$

and

$$Z_0 = \sqrt{\frac{L}{C}} \tag{9.70}$$

Substituting $s = j\omega$ and $\gamma = j\omega/u$ in Eqs. 9.34, 9.35, and 9.33, we get

$$H_v(x, j\omega) = \frac{e^{-j\omega(x-l)/u} + \rho e^{j\omega(x-l)/u}}{e^{j\omega l/u} + \rho e^{-j\omega l/u}} \tag{9.71a}$$

and

$$H_i(x, j\omega) = \frac{1}{Z_0}\left[\frac{e^{-j\omega(x-l)/u} - \rho e^{j\omega(x-l)/u}}{e^{j\omega l/u} + \rho e^{-j\omega l/u}}\right] \tag{9.71b}$$

These are the transfer functions of a line terminated by an impedance Z_L at $x = l$ and fed by the generator at $x = 0$. It is, however, convenient to choose the coordinates such that the load impedance is located at the origin. This is easily accomplished by changing the reference point. Let us define a new variable:

$$y = x - l$$

We now have

$$y = 0 \qquad \text{when} \quad x = l$$

$$y = -l \qquad \text{when} \quad x = 0$$

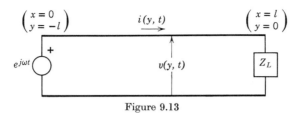

Figure 9.13

Thus the load Z_L is now at $y = 0$ and the generator is at $y = -l$ (Fig. 9.13). Substituting $y = x - l$ in Eqs. 9.71a and 9.71b, we get

$$H_v(y, j\omega) = \frac{e^{-j\omega y/u} + pe^{j\omega y/u}}{e^{j\omega l/u} + pe^{-j\omega l/u}} \tag{9.72a}$$

and

$$H_i(y, j\omega) = \frac{1}{Z_0}\left[\frac{e^{-j\omega y/u} - pe^{j\omega y/u}}{e^{j\omega l/u} + pe^{-j\omega l/u}}\right] \tag{9.72b}$$

For convenience, we shall denote ω/u by β:

$$\beta = \frac{\omega}{u}$$

The term β is also known as the *phase constant* and is equal to the change of phase angle per unit length of the transmission line. This can be easily seen from the equations:

$$\omega = \text{angular velocity} = \frac{d\theta}{dt}$$

and

$$u = \text{velocity of propagation} = \frac{dy}{dt}$$

Therefore

$$\beta = \frac{\omega}{u} = \frac{d\theta}{dy}$$

Thus β represents the rate of change of the phase angle of the signal with distance. Substituting β for ω/u in Eqs. 9.72a and 9.72b, we get

$$H_v(y, j\omega) = \frac{e^{-j\beta y} + pe^{j\beta y}}{e^{j\beta l} + pe^{-j\beta l}} \tag{9.73a}$$

$$H_i(y, j\omega) = \frac{1}{Z_0}\left[\frac{e^{-j\beta y} - pe^{j\beta y}}{e^{j\beta l} + pe^{-j\beta l}}\right] \tag{9.73b}$$

Thus, for a transmission line of length l, and terminated by a load impedance Z_L at $y = 0$, if a voltage $e^{j\omega t}$ is applied at $y = -l$, then the voltage and current at any point y are given by $H_v e^{j\omega t}$ and $H_i e^{j\omega t}$.

$$v(y, t) = \left[\frac{e^{-j\beta y} + pe^{j\beta y}}{e^{j\beta l} + pe^{-j\beta l}}\right]e^{j\omega t} \tag{9.74a}$$

and

$$i(y, t) = \frac{1}{Z_0}\left[\frac{e^{-j\beta y} - \rho e^{j\beta y}}{e^{j\beta l} + \rho e^{-j\beta l}}\right] e^{j\omega t} \tag{9.74b}$$

It also follows that the impedance seen at any point y, looking in a positive y direction, is $Z(y, j\omega)$, given by

$$Z(y, j\omega) = \frac{v(y, t)}{i(y, t)} = Z_0\left[\frac{e^{-j\beta y} + \rho e^{j\beta y}}{e^{-j\beta y} - \rho e^{j\beta y}}\right] \tag{9.74c}$$

Therefore, the input impedance Z_i seen by the generator is $Z(-l, j\omega)$, given by

$$Z_i = Z(-l, j\omega) = Z_0\left[\frac{e^{j\beta l} + \rho e^{-j\beta l}}{e^{j\beta l} - \rho e^{-j\beta l}}\right] \tag{9.74d}$$

For a given frequency the denominators of the bracketed expressions in Eqs. 9.74a and 9.74b are constant. For convenience, we shall denote this constant by k:

$$k = \frac{1}{e^{j\beta l} + \rho e^{-j\beta l}} \tag{9.75}$$

Substituting Eq. 9.75 in Eq. 9.74, we obtain

$$v(y, t) = k(e^{-j\beta y} + \rho e^{j\beta y})e^{j\omega t}$$

and

$$i(y, t) = \frac{k}{Z_0}(e^{-j\beta y} - \rho e^{j\beta y})e^{j\omega t}$$

It is evident that the voltage and current distribution at any point have two components. Substituting $\beta = \omega/u$ in these equations, we obtain

$$v(y, t) = ke^{j\omega(t-y/u)} + k\rho e^{j\omega(t+y/u)}$$

and

$$i(y, t) = \frac{k}{Z_0} e^{j\omega(t-y/u)} - \frac{k}{Z_0} e^{j\omega(t+y/u)}$$

We have already seen that a function $f(t - x/u)$ represents a function $f(t)$ moving in a positive x direction with a velocity u. Hence, $ke^{j\omega(t-y/u)}$ represents a wave motion in a positive y direction (toward the load), that is, the function $ke^{j\omega t}$ moving in a positive y direction. We call this a forward component of the voltage. Similarly, the component $k\rho e^{j\omega(t+y/u)}$ represents a wave motion in a negative y direction (toward the generator), that is, a function $k\rho e^{j\omega t}$ moving toward the generator. This component is obviously the reflected component of the voltage. Note that the ratio of the amplitudes of the reflected and forward component is ρ

$$\frac{\text{Amplitude of the reflected signal}}{\text{Amplitude of the forward signal}} = \rho \tag{9.76}$$

Similarly, for current, there is a forward component $(k/Z_0)e^{j\omega(t-y/u)}$ and a reflected component $(-k/Z_0)\rho e^{j\omega(t+y/u)}$. The reflection coefficient for current is $-\rho$ for the reasons explained in Section 9.8.

9.11 THE DISTRIBUTION OF VOLTAGE AND CURRENT ON THE LINE

It is highly instructive to consider the amplitude distribution of the voltage and current along a transmission line. The amplitude distribution is given by

$$V(y) = k(e^{-j\beta y} + \rho e^{j\beta y}) \tag{9.77a}$$

$$I(y) = \frac{k}{Z_0}(e^{-j\beta y} - \rho e^{j\beta y}) \tag{9.77b}$$

We shall first consider the simple case of $Z_L = 0$. For this case, $\rho = -1$, and the voltage and current distribution now is given by

$$V(y) = k(e^{-j\beta y} - e^{j\beta y}) \tag{9.78a}$$

$$I(y) = \frac{k}{Z_0}(e^{-j\beta y} + e^{j\beta y}) \tag{9.78b}$$

Equations 9.78a and 9.78b may be expressed as

$$V(y) = -2jk \sin \beta y \tag{9.79a}$$

and

$$I(y) = 2\frac{k}{Z_0} \cos \beta y \tag{7.79b}$$

The voltmeter and an ammeter connected at an appropriate point will read only the magnitude and not the phase. The absolute magnitudes of the expression are important and are plotted in Fig. 9.14a. Note that both the voltage and current distribution go through successive maxima and successive minima at a distance of π/β units along the line. Moreover, the voltage maxima occurs where the current goes through minima ($I = 0$) and vice versa. At a given frequency f, the wavelength λ and the velocity of propagation u are related by

$$\lambda = \frac{u}{f} = \frac{2\pi u}{\omega} = \frac{2\pi}{\beta} \tag{9.80}$$

Thus, the successive maxima (and minima) are located at half the wavelength along the line.

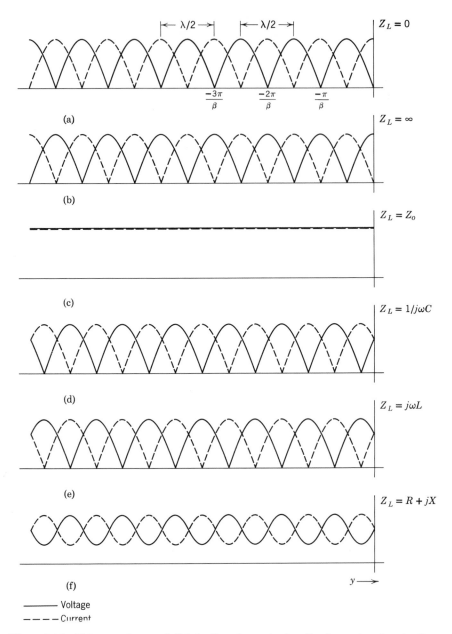

Figure 9.14   Voltage and current distribution along a lossless line for various terminations.

Next we shall consider the case of arbitrary terminations. In general, Z_L is a complex quantity and therefore ρ is also a complex quantity. Let

$$\rho = |\rho|\, e^{j\theta} \tag{9.81}$$

Substituting Eq. 9.81 in Eq. 9.77, we get

$$V(y) = k[e^{-j\beta y} + |\rho|\, e^{j(\beta y+\theta)}] \tag{9.82a}$$

and

$$I(y) = \frac{k}{Z_0}\left[e^{-j\beta y} - |\rho|\, e^{j(\beta y+\theta)}\right] \tag{9.82b}$$

The maximum absolute value of $V(y)$, as seen from Eq. 9.82a, is $k[1 + |\rho|]$ and occurs when

$$-\beta y = \beta y + \theta + 2n\pi \qquad (n = 0, 1, 2 \cdots)$$

or

$$y = \frac{-(2n\pi + \theta)}{2\beta} \tag{9.83a}$$

and, similarly, the minimum absolute value of $V(y)$ is $k[1 - |\rho|]$ and occurs when

$$-\beta y = \beta y + \theta + (2n + 1)\pi$$

or

$$y = \frac{-[(2n + 1)\pi + \theta]}{2\beta} \tag{9.83b}$$

It is evident from Eqs. 9.83a and 9.83b that the successive maxima and minima of the absolute magnitude of the voltage distribution are separated by a distance of π/β or $\lambda/2$ units along the line. Similar considerations apply for the current distribution. From Eq. 9.82b it can be seen that the maximum absolute value of the current is $(k/Z_0)(1 + |\rho|)$ and occurs at

$$y = \frac{-[(2n + 1)\pi + \theta]}{2\beta} \tag{9.84a}$$

and the minimum absolute value of the current is $(k/Z_0)[1 - |\rho|]$ and occurs at

$$y = \frac{-(2n\pi + \theta)}{2\beta} \tag{9.84b}$$

The voltage and current distributions for various load conditions are shown in Fig. 9.14. Notice that when $Z_L = Z_0$ the line is said to be matched, and there is no reflected wave. Hence, the amplitude is constant everywhere along the line. Under these conditions (that is, $Z_L = Z_0$)

all of the incident energy is absorbed by the load. When $Z_L \neq Z_0$, part of the energy in the incident wave is reflected by means of a traveling wave in a negative y direction. The two waves traveling in opposite directions cause the amplitudes of the voltage and current to fluctuate. When $Z_L = R + jX$ in general, the minimum value of the voltage and currents is not zero and hence the distribution does not go through zero value.

The kind of voltage and current distribution patterns encountered in such cases $(Z_L \neq Z_0)$ are known as the *standing waves*. Standing waves are therefore generated by the interference of the two traveling waves propagating in opposite directions. It is interesting to seek the physical reasoning behind the interference patterns. Let us consider a lossless transmission line terminated by a short circuit as shown in Fig. 9.15. We shall assume a sinusoidal wave propagating toward this load. The wave moving in a positive y direction can be expressed by $ke^{j(\omega t - \beta y)}$. Note that the phase angle of this wave is given by $(\omega t - \beta y)$. Therefore, at any given instant, the phase angle drops as we move in a positive y direction. Similarly, as we move toward the generator, the phase angle at any given instant increases with distance at the rate of β radians per unit length. This is quite logical; since the wave is traveling in a positive y direction, the phase angles at larger values of y lag behind those at smaller values of y. On the other hand, a reflected wave (moving in $-y$ direction) can be expressed as $ke^{j(\omega t + \beta y)}$, and the phase angle increases as we move toward the load and drops as we move toward the generator at a rate of β radians per unit length.

Assume that a forward wave of k volts arrives at the load termination $Z_L = 0$. But at a short circuit, the net voltage must be zero. Hence, a reflected wave of $-k$ volts must start at the shorted terminal and propagate toward the generator. We shall observe the interference patterns of the forward and reflected waves with the help of phasor diagrams as shown in Fig. 9.15. At the load termination, the two voltage waves are exactly in opposite phase and hence cancel one another (the net voltage at a short circuit must be zero). Thus, at the load termination, the forward voltage wave V_f will be represented by a phasor at zero angle, and the reflected voltage wave V_r will be represented by another phasor at π radians. Suppose now we move along the line a distance of $\lambda/8$ units. The phase of the forward wave must increase by $\beta\lambda/8$ radians, and that of the reflected wave must decrease by $\beta\lambda/8$ radians. But

$$\beta = \frac{\omega}{u} \qquad \text{and} \qquad u = f\lambda = \omega\lambda/2\pi$$

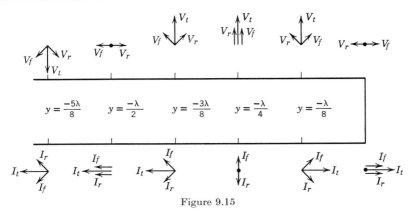

$$y = \frac{-5\lambda}{8} \qquad y = \frac{-\lambda}{2} \qquad y = \frac{-3\lambda}{8} \qquad y = \frac{-\lambda}{4} \qquad y = \frac{-\lambda}{8}$$

Figure 9.15

Hence

$$\beta = 2\pi/\lambda$$

and

$$\frac{\beta\lambda}{8} = \frac{\pi}{4}$$

Thus, at $y = -\lambda/8$,

$$\underline{/V_f} = \left(0 + \frac{\pi}{4}\right) = \frac{\pi}{4} \qquad \text{and} \qquad \underline{/V_r} = \left(\pi - \frac{\pi}{4}\right) = \frac{3\pi}{4}$$

(See Fig. 9.15.) The resultant voltage has a phase angle of $\pi/2$ and a magnitude of $\sqrt{2}k$. At $y = -\lambda/4$, the phase angle of V_f increases by $\pi/2$ and the phase of V_r drops by $\pi/2$. Thus, $\underline{/V_f} = (0 + \pi/2) = \pi/2$ and $\underline{/V_r} = (\pi - \pi/2) = \pi/2$. Here, both waves add in phase and the magnitude is $2k$. At $y = -3\lambda/8$, $\underline{/V_f} = 3\pi/4$ and $\underline{/V_r} = \pi/4$, and the resultant has a phase of $\pi/2$, and the magnitude again drops to $\sqrt{2}k$. At $y = -\lambda/2$, $\underline{/V_f} = \pi$ and $\underline{/V_r} = 0$. The two waves cancel, and the voltage is always zero at this point. This same pattern repeats as we move toward the generator. Thus, the voltage goes to zero at intervals of $\lambda/2$ units and thus gives rise to standing waves as shown in Fig. 9.14a. For the current waves, the same considerations apply. But the forward current wave and the reflected current wave are in phase at the short (see Fig. 9.15). Hence, the current is maximum at $y = 0$. The current phasors are shown at the bottom of the line in Fig. 9.15. It is evident from this diagram that the net current is maximum where the net voltage is minimum and vice versa.

For the general case of an arbitrary load termination, similar considerations hold true. But the magnitude of the reflection coefficient is less than unity, in general, and hence the reflected wave is smaller than the forward wave. There is now only a partial cancellation of the waves at the point of voltage minima, and hence we get the standing wave pattern as shown in Fig. 9.14f for the case $Z_L = R + jX$.

Since the voltage is maximum where the current is minimum, and vice versa, the input impedance at the point of voltage maxima will be maximum and the input impedance at the point of voltage minima will be minimum. From Eq. 9.83a it follows that the maximum input impedance of the line occurs at

$$y = \frac{-(2n\pi + \theta)}{2\beta}$$

and is a pure resistance given by (see Eq. 9.82):

$$[Z_i]_{max} = \frac{[v(y)]_{max}}{[i(y)]_{min}} = Z_0 \frac{1 + |\rho|}{1 - |\rho|} \tag{9.85a}$$

Similarly the minimum input impedance of the line occurs at

$$y = \frac{-[(2n + 1)\pi + \theta]}{2\beta}$$

and is given by a pure resistance:

$$[Z_i]_{min} = \frac{[v(y)]_{min}}{[i(y)]_{max}} = Z_0 \frac{1 - |\rho|}{1 + |\rho|} \tag{9.85b}$$

We define the quantity standing wave ratio S as

$$S = \frac{1 + |\rho|}{1 - |\rho|} = \frac{[v(y)]_{max}}{[v(y)]_{min}} = \frac{[i(y)]_{max}}{[i(y)]_{min}} \tag{9.86}$$

The standing wave ratio is therefore a measure of the relative magnitudes of the maximum and minimum amplitudes of the distribution pattern.

$$[Z_i]_{max} = S Z_0 \tag{9.87a}$$

$$[Z_i]_{min} = \frac{Z_0}{S} \tag{9.87b}$$

From all of this discussion it is evident that if a transmission line is used to transmit signals, it must be terminated so that a minimum amount of energy is reflected at the load termination. Ideally, therefore, for the purpose of the transmission of signals, a line should be terminated by its characteristic impedance. If this is not possible, then it should be terminated so as to make $|\rho|$ minimum.

Transmission Line with Losses

If the losses in the line cannot be neglected, then we have to use general expressions for γ and Z_0 in Eqs. 9.20 and 9.25. For the sinusoidal steady-state response, if $R << \omega L$ and $G << \omega C$:

$$Z_0 \simeq \sqrt{\frac{L}{C}}$$

and

$$\gamma = \sqrt{(R + j\omega L)(G + j\omega C)}$$

$$= j\omega\sqrt{LC}\sqrt{\left(1 + \frac{R}{j\omega L}\right)\left(1 + \frac{G}{j\omega C}\right)}$$

If $R << \omega L$ and $G << \omega C$:

$$\gamma \simeq j\omega\sqrt{LC}\left[1 + \frac{R}{2j\omega L}\right]\left[1 + \frac{G}{2j\omega C}\right]$$

$$\simeq j\omega\sqrt{LC}\left[1 + \frac{R}{2j\omega L} + \frac{G}{2j\omega C}\right]$$

$$= \frac{R}{2\sqrt{L/C}} + \frac{G\sqrt{L/C}}{2} + j\omega\sqrt{LC}$$

$$= \frac{R}{2Z_0} + \frac{GZ_0}{2} + \frac{j\omega}{u}$$

$$= \alpha + j\beta$$

where

$$\alpha = \frac{R}{2Z_0} + \frac{GZ_0}{2}$$

and

$$\beta = \frac{\omega}{u}$$

α is known as the attenuation constant. Therefore, when losses are taken into account, the propagation constant γ has a finite real part. The transfer function for a lossy line can be obtained by replacing $j\beta$ by $(\alpha + j\beta)$ in Eqs. 9.73a and 9.73b.

$$H_v(y, j\omega) = \frac{e^{-(\alpha+j\beta)y} + \rho e^{(\alpha+j\beta)y}}{e^{(\alpha+j\beta)l} + \rho e^{-(\alpha+j\beta)l}}$$

$$H_i(y, j\omega) = \frac{1}{Z_0}\left[\frac{e^{-(\alpha+j\beta)y} - \rho e^{(\alpha+j\beta)y}}{e^{(\alpha+j\beta)l} + \rho e^{-(\alpha+j\beta)l}}\right]$$

The voltage and current distribution along the line can be obtained by replacing $j\beta$ by $(\alpha + j\beta)$ in Eqs. 9.74a and 9.74b. If we let

$$k = \frac{1}{e^{(\alpha+j\beta)l} + \rho e^{-(\alpha+j\beta)l}}$$

then

$$v(y, t) = k(e^{-\alpha y}e^{-j\beta y} + \rho e^{\alpha y}e^{j\beta y})e^{j\omega t} \tag{9.88a}$$

$$i(y, t) = \frac{k}{Z_0}(e^{-\alpha y}e^{-j\beta y} - \rho e^{\alpha y}e^{j\beta y})e^{j\omega t} \tag{9.88b}$$

These equations can be interpreted in a manner similar to that used for a lossless line. The signal $e^{-\alpha y}e^{-j(\beta y - \omega t)}$ represents a wave propagating in a positive y direction and its amplitude is attenuating exponentially (due to losses in the line). Similarly, the signal $e^{\alpha y}e^{j(\beta y + \omega t)}$ represents a wave propagating in $-y$ direction, and its amplitude is also attenuating exponentially as it progresses. Since the reflected wave attenuates as it progresses toward the generator, the amplitude of the reflected wave is smaller near the generator end, whereas the forward wave is stronger at the generator end and attenuates as it moves toward the load. We therefore expect that near the generator end, the forward wave predominates and the reflected wave is very small. Thus, the effect of the interference of two waves is noticeable at the load end, but at the generator end there is essentially a forward wave with a constant amplitude. If the amplitude distribution of voltages and currents for a lossy line is plotted using Eqs. 9.88a and 9.88b, the interference pattern shows that amplitude variations are predominant near the load end and become smaller near the generator end. This is shown in Fig. 9.16.

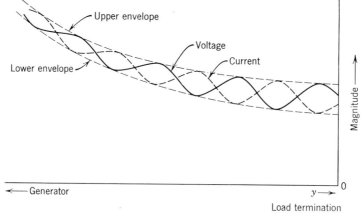

Figure 9.16   Voltage and current distribution for a lossy line.

9.12 THE TRANSMISSION LINE AS A CIRCUIT ELEMENT

The transmission of energy from one point to the other is only one of the applications of transmission lines. As stated before, another important application is the use of the sections of a transmission line as circuit elements at ultra high frequencies. Above 150 mc, it becomes difficult to construct conventional lumped elements, and at the same time the wavelength becomes small enough to warrant the use of transmission line sections as circuit elements. These elements can be used up to 3000 mc when the wavelength becomes too small, and thus the physical size of the required sections also becomes too small. Above 3000 mc the use of waveguides and cavity resonators becomes attractive.

Although it was desirable to keep the reflections at a minimum for the application of energy transmission, it becomes necessary to deliberately mismatch and create reflections for the application of the line as a circuit element. In all of these lines the quantity Z_i, the input impedance seen by the generator, is of great interest. The input impedance Z_i is the ratio of the voltage to the current at the generator. The expression for Z_i is already derived in Eq. 9.74d.

$$Z_i = Z_0 \left[\frac{e^{j\beta l} + \rho e^{-j\beta l}}{e^{j\beta l} - \rho e^{-j\beta l}} \right] \tag{9.89}$$

We shall first consider a short-circuited line, that is, $Z_L = 0$ and $\rho = -1$. Substituting $\rho = -1$ in Eq. 9.89, we get

$$\begin{aligned} Z_i &= Z_0 \left[\frac{e^{j\beta l} - e^{-j\beta l}}{e^{j\beta l} + e^{-j\beta l}} \right] \\ &= Z_0 \frac{2j \sin \beta l}{2 \cos \beta l} \\ &= j Z_0 \tan \beta l \end{aligned} \tag{9.90}$$

The input impedance of a shorted line is thus a pure reactance X of magnitude $Z_0 \tan \beta l$. Note that any desired value of the reactance in the range of $(-\infty, \infty)$ may be obtained by choosing the proper length of the line.

If, instead, the line is open-circuited, then

$$|Z_L| = \infty \quad \text{and} \quad \rho = 1$$

and

$$\begin{aligned} Z_i &= Z_0 \left[\frac{e^{j\beta l} + e^{-j\beta l}}{e^{j\beta l} - e^{-j\beta l}} \right] \\ &= -j Z_0 \cot \beta l \end{aligned} \tag{9.91}$$

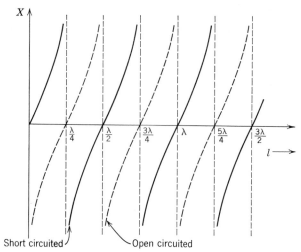

Figure 9.17   The plot of reactance as a function of l for shorted and open sections.

The input impedance of an open-circuited line is also a pure reactance X of magnitude $-Z_0 \cot \beta l$. By choosing the proper value of l, it is possible to obtain any desired value of the reactance in the range ($-\infty$ to ∞). The plot of reactance versus length for shorted and open sections is shown in Fig. 9.17. The reactance X is plotted as function of length l.

Since $\beta = 2\pi/\lambda$,

$$Z_i = \begin{cases} jZ_0 \tan\left(\dfrac{2\pi l}{\lambda}\right) & \text{for the shorted line} \qquad (9.92\text{a}) \\[2em] -jZ_0 \cot\left(\dfrac{2\pi l}{\lambda}\right) & \text{for the open line} \qquad (9.92\text{b}) \end{cases}$$

The length l can be plotted directly in terms of the wavelength as shown in Fig. 9.17.

From this figure it is evident that a shorted section acts as an inductor for $l < \lambda/4$ (positive reactance) and acts as a capacitor for $\lambda/4 < l < \lambda/2$ (negative reactance). For $l = \lambda/4$ the reactance is infinity. Let us consider a shorted section which is a quarter wavelength at a certain frequency ω_0. For $\omega < \omega_0$, $l < \lambda/4$ and the section looks inductive. On the other hand, for $\omega > \omega_0$, $l > \lambda/4$ and the section looks capacitive (Fig. 9.18). At $\omega = \omega_0$, $l = \lambda/4$ and the section has infinite reactance. This is precisely the behavior of a parallel resonant circuit. Therefore, a shorted quarter-wave section acts like a parallel resonant circuit. We can arrive at the same conclusion by considering Eq. 9.92a.

$$X = Z_0 \tan \frac{2\pi l}{\lambda}$$

But

$$\lambda = \frac{2\pi}{\beta} = \frac{2\pi}{\omega/u} = \frac{2\pi u}{\omega}$$

Therefore, for a shorted line,

$$X = Z_0 \tan \frac{\omega}{u} l$$

The reactance as a function of ω is sketched in Fig. 9.18. Notice that a shorted section behaves like a parallel resonant circuit, the frequency of resonance being

$$\omega = \frac{\pi u}{2l}$$

or

$$l = \frac{\pi u}{2\omega} = \frac{\pi}{2\beta} = \frac{\lambda}{4}$$

Similarly, it can be shown that an open section of length $\lambda/2$ acts as a parallel resonant circuit. One can easily prove, on similar lines, that a shorted section of length $\lambda/2$ and an open section of length $\lambda/4$ act as a series resonant circuit.

From Fig. 9.17 it is evident that the reactance of a section of length $(l + n\lambda/2)$ for integral values of n is the same as that of the line of length l. Thus, a shorted section of length $(\lambda/4 + n\lambda/2)$ and an open section of length $(\lambda/2 + n\lambda/2)$ act as parallel resonant circuits. Similarly, a shorted section of length $(\lambda/2 + n\lambda/2)$ and an open section of length $(\lambda/4 + n\lambda/2)$

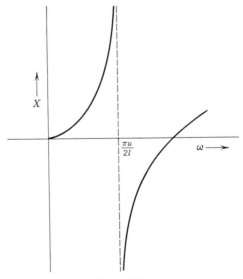

Figure 9.18

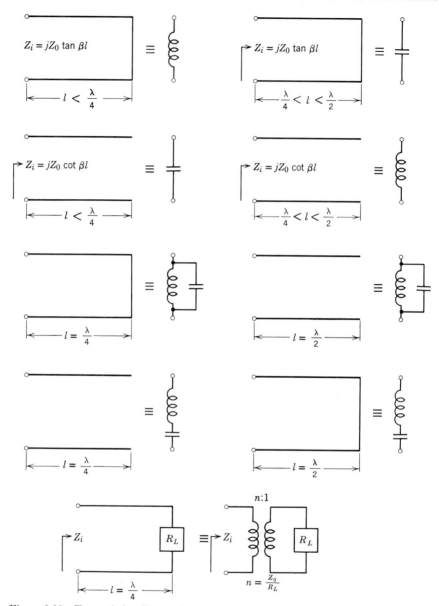

Figure 9.19   Transmission line sections and their equivalent lumped circuit elements.

act as series resonant circuits. Figure 9.19 shows some line sections and their equivalent lumped circuit elements.

Although transmission line sections can be represented by equivalent lumped circuit elements, it should be noted that the equivalence holds true only at a given frequency. The reactance of an inductor varies linearly with frequency, whereas the reactance of a shorted line of length

$l < \lambda/4$ varies according to the equation

$$X = Z_0 \tan \frac{\omega l}{u}$$

Thus, a shorted section of length $l < \lambda/4$ behaves as a frequency-dependent inductor L given by

$$L = \frac{Z_0 \tan \omega l/u}{\omega}$$

All of the above equations are derived for an ideal lossless line. For such a line, the input impedance of a shorted quarter-wave line or an open half-wave line is ideally infinity. In practice, however, all of the transmission lines have some losses, and this causes the input impedance of the above sections to be resistive. The equivalent input resistance for low-loss lines for these sections, however, is very high, making these sections equivalent to a high Q parallel resonant circuit. If R and G represent the series resistance and parallel conductance of the line per unit length, then it can be shown that for a shorted quarter-wave line or an open half-wave line, the input impedance is a pure resistance R_i given by[4]

$$R_i = \frac{8Z_0}{\lambda(GZ_0 + R/Z_0)}$$

An open section of a quarter wavelength can also be used as a transformer. The input impedance Z_i is given by Eq. 9.74d. For

$$l = \frac{\lambda}{4}$$

$$\beta l = \frac{\pi}{2}$$

and Eq. 9.74d becomes

$$\begin{aligned}
Z_i &= Z_0 \left[\frac{e^{j\pi/2} + \rho e^{-j\pi/2}}{e^{j\pi/2} - \rho e^{-j\pi/2}} \right] \\
&= Z_0 \left[\frac{1 + \rho e^{-j\pi}}{1 - \rho e^{-j\pi}} \right] \\
&= Z_0 \left[\frac{1 - \rho}{1 + \rho} \right] \\
&= Z_0 \left[\frac{1 - \dfrac{(Z_L - Z_0)}{(Z_L + Z_0)}}{1 + \dfrac{(Z_L - Z_0)}{(Z_L + Z_0)}} \right] \\
&= \frac{Z_0^2}{Z_L}
\end{aligned}$$

[4] See, for instance, S. Ramo and J. Whinnery, *Fields and Waves in Modern Radio*, Wiley, New York, 1953.

If the load impedance is resistive, that is, $Z_L = R_L$, then

$$Z_i = \frac{Z_0^2}{R_L}$$

For a lossless line, Z_0 is a pure resistance, and therefore Z_i is also resistive. Thus, a transmission line section of quarter wavelength acts as an ideal transformer of turns ratio n given by

$n:1$

R_L

Z_i

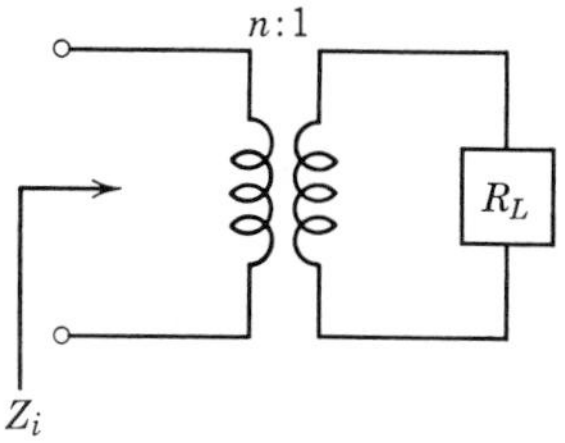

Figure 9.20   The lumped equivalent circuit of a quarter wave transmission line.

$$Z_i = n^2 R_L$$

$$= \frac{Z_0^2}{R_L}$$

Therefore

$$n = \frac{Z_0}{R_L}$$

This is shown in Fig. 9.20.

9.13 TRANSMISSION LINE CHART

Various quantities associated with transmission lines may be computed from the equations developed thus far. There are, however, some graphical short cuts available to compute the input impedance of a section of length l of a lossless line terminated by a load impedance Z_L. The input impedance is given by Eq. 9.74d.

$$Z_i = Z_0 \frac{e^{j\beta l} + \rho e^{-j\beta l}}{e^{j\beta l} - \rho e^{-j\beta l}}$$

This equation may be expressed in a number of alternative ways. If we substitute ρ in terms of Z_L and Z_0 in this equation, we get

$$Z_i = Z_0 \frac{Z_L \cos \beta l + j Z_0 \sin \beta l}{Z_0 \cos \beta l + j Z_L \sin \beta l} \tag{9.93}$$

However, a more useful form is obtained by factoring $e^{j\beta l}$ from the numerator and denominator of Eq. 9.74d.

$$Z_i = Z_0 \frac{1 + \rho e^{-j2\beta l}}{1 - \rho e^{-j2\beta l}} \tag{9.94}$$

Therefore

$$\frac{Z_i}{Z_0} = Z_n = \frac{1 + \rho e^{-j2\beta l}}{1 - \rho e^{-j2\beta l}} \tag{9.95}$$

The term Z_n is defined as the ratio of Z_i to Z_0 and is called the *normalized impedance*. In general, Z_n is a complex quantity and may be expressed as

$$Z_n = R + jX$$

ρ is also a complex quantity and may be expressed as $|\rho|\, e^{j\theta}$. Let us denote $\rho e^{-j2\beta l}$ by another complex variable W:

$$W = u + jv = \rho e^{-j2\beta l}$$

Equation 9.95 may now be expressed as

$$Z_n = R + jX = \frac{1+W}{1-W} = \frac{1+u+jv}{1-u-jv} \tag{9.96}$$

Separating the real and imaginary parts of Eq. 9.96, and equating them to R and X respectively, we get

$$R = \frac{1-(u^2+v^2)}{(1-u)^2+v^2}$$

and

$$X = \frac{2v}{(1-u)^2+v^2}$$

or

$$\left(u - \frac{R}{1+R}\right)^2 + v^2 = \left(\frac{1}{1+R}\right)^2 \tag{9.97a}$$

and

$$(u-1)^2 + \left(v - \frac{1}{X}\right)^2 = \frac{1}{X^2} \tag{9.97b}$$

Equations 9.97a and 9.97b can be used to plot the loci of constant R and X in the W plane (with u and v as coordinates). It is evident that the loci of constant R will be circles with centers on the u axis at $u = R/(1+R)$ and radii equal to $1/(R+1)$. Similarly, the loci of constant X will also be circles with centers at $(1, 1/X)$ and radii equal to $1/X$. The loci for various values of R and X in the W plane are shown in Fig. 9.21.

Note that the outermost circle corresponds to $R = 0$ and is centered at $(0, 0)$ and has a radius of unity. The outer circle may be drawn to a suitable scale, so that the radius of this circle will be unity on this scale. All other distances will be measured with reference to this scale.

Every point in the W plane now corresponds to a certain value of R and X. This means that for every value of W, there is a corresponding value of Z_n. This chart relates the two quantities Z_n and W graphically.

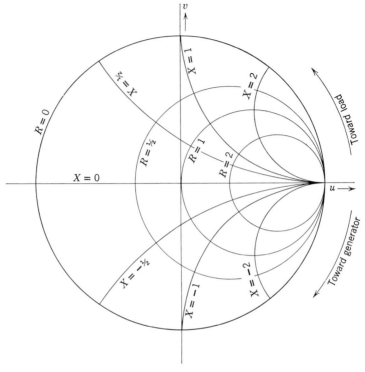

Figure 9.21

Thus, if we want to find the input impedance of a line of length l and terminated by load impedance Z_L, we first compute $W = \rho e^{-j2\beta l}$ for this line. Then we make use of the chart in Fig. 9.21 to find the value of Z_n for this value of W. The input impedance is related to Z_n by the equation:

$$Z_n = \frac{Z_i}{Z_0}$$

Thus, the input impedance may be computed.

If for a certain problem W is known, we can locate this point in the W plane. This point corresponds to certain values of R and X given by the loci in Fig. 9.21. Thus, Z_n can be evaluated by inspection of Fig. 9.21 if the value of W is known. Conversely, if the value of Z_n is known, the corresponding value of W can be found from this chart.

This chart, known as the *Smith chart*, proves to be very versatile and can be used to solve most of the problems encountered in the steady-state transmission line theory. Now we shall illustrate its application to find the input impedance of a line of length l and terminated by impedance Z_L.

The normalized impedance Z_n is defined as

$$Z_n = \frac{Z_i}{Z_0}$$

To find the value of Z_n from the Smith chart we must locate the value of W corresponding to the problem. By definition,

$$W = \rho e^{-j2\beta l} \tag{9.98}$$

In general, ρ is complex and may be expressed as $|\rho|\, e^{j\theta}$. We first locate ρ in the W plane on a circle of radius $|\rho|$ and at an angle θ from the u axis (Fig. 9.22b).

From Eq. 9.98 it is evident that W may be found by advancing ρ through an angle $-2\beta l$ or by rotating this point along the circle of radius $|\rho|$ through angle $2\beta l$ radians in a clockwise direction. Once W is located, the corresponding values of R and X can be read from the loci intersecting at that point, and thus Z_n may be found.

Example 9.3

Find the input impedance at 300 Mc of a transmission line of a characteristic impedance of 50 Ω and of a length of 0.25 meter, terminated with an impedance of $(50 + j50)\,\Omega$ (Fig. 9.22a).

First, we must locate ρ on the W plane. ρ may be calculated in a straightforward manner from its definition and plotted on the W plane. There is, however, an easier way of doing this. We observe that

$$W = \rho e^{-j2\beta l}$$

Therefore, at $l = 0$, $W = \rho$. Therefore, to find ρ, we need only to find W corresponding to $l = 0$. Also, the input impedance of the line terminated by impedance Z_L and length $l = 0$ is the load impedance Z_L itself. Therefore, $Z_n = Z_L/Z_0$ for $l = 0$. In our case, Z_L/Z_0 is $(1 + j1)$. The loci of $R = 1$ and $X = 1$ intersect at point A (Fig. 9.22b). Therefore, this must be the point representing W corresponding to $l = 0$. We then draw a circle with the center at the origin and passing through point A. The desired input impedance can be found by rotating the point A through an angle $2\beta l$ in a clockwise direction.

$$\beta l = \left(\frac{\omega}{u}\right)(0.25)$$

$$= \left(\frac{2\pi \times 300 \times 10^6}{3 \times 10^8}\right)0.25$$

$$= \frac{\pi}{2} \text{ radians}$$

We therefore rotate point A through angle π in a clockwise direction. The

new point is B as shown in Fig. 9.22b. The values of R and X, corresponding
to point B are $\frac{1}{2}$ and $-\frac{1}{2}$, respectively. Therefore

$$Z_n = \frac{Z_i}{Z_0} = \frac{1}{2}(1 - j1)$$

and

$$Z_i = \tfrac{1}{2}(1 - j1)Z_0$$
$$= (25 - j25)\,\Omega$$

It also now becomes evident that the same procedure in reverse can be applied
to find the load termination if the input impedance of the line is given. Observe
that rotation in a clockwise direction amounts to moving toward the generator,

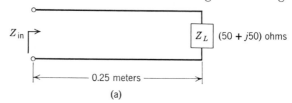

(a)

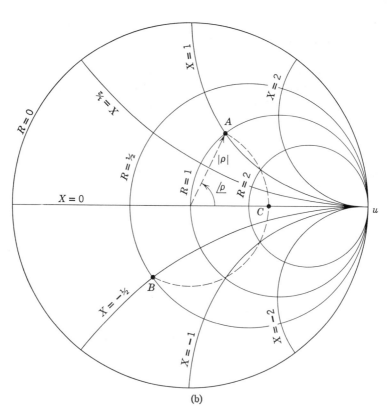

(b)

Figure 9.22

and similarly the rotation in a counterclockwise direction amounts to moving toward the load. Thus, if the impedance at any point on the transmission line is known, then the impedance at any other point on the line can be found by rotating this point through the proper angle in the right direction.

In practice, the lengths of the line are often specified in terms of wavelengths. If we move a distance of wavelength λ along the line, this corresponds to rotation through an angle $2\beta\lambda$ along the Smith chart. But

$$2\beta\lambda = \frac{2\omega\lambda}{u}$$

where

$$u = f\lambda \quad \text{and} \quad \omega = 2\pi f$$

Therefore

$$2\beta\lambda = 4\pi$$

Thus, rotation of 4π corresponds to a distance of one wavelength along the line and the rotation through angle 2π corresponds to a distance of $\lambda/2$. On the Smith chart, it is customary to mark the rotation in terms of angles, as well as wavelengths. This can be seen from the standard Smith chart shown in Fig. 9.24.

The Smith Chart as an Admittance Chart

In the previous part of this section the Smith chart was constructed so as to read various impedances along the line. It is also possible to use this chart directly to read admittances instead of impedances. Let

$$Y_L = \frac{1}{Z_L}, \quad Y_0 = \frac{1}{Z_0}$$

and

$$Y_i = \frac{1}{Z_i}$$

and let

$$\rho_y = \frac{Y_L - Y_0}{Y_L + Y_0} = \frac{\dfrac{1}{Z_L} - \dfrac{1}{Z_0}}{\dfrac{1}{Z_L} + \dfrac{1}{Z_0}}$$

$$= \frac{Z_0 - Z_L}{Z_0 + Z_L} = -\rho$$

From Equation 9.94,

$$Y_i = Y_0 \frac{1 - \rho e^{-j2\beta l}}{1 + \rho e^{-j2\beta l}}$$

$$= Y_0 \frac{1 + \rho_y e^{-j2\beta l}}{1 - \rho_y e^{-j2\beta l}}$$

and

$$\frac{Y_i}{Y_0} = Y_n = \left[\frac{1 + \rho_y e^{-j2\beta l}}{1 - \rho_y e^{-j2\beta l}}\right]$$

This equation has exactly the same form as that of Eq. 9.95, except that the impedances are replaced by admittances and ρ is replaced by $\rho_y(\rho_y = -\rho)$. Therefore, the Smith chart can be used to find normalized admittances directly when ρ is replaced by ρ_y (that is, $-\rho$).

$$Y_n = G + jB = \frac{1 + \rho_y e^{-j2\beta l}}{1 - \rho_y e^{-j2\beta l}}$$

The loci of constant R now become the loci of constant G and the loci for constant X become the loci for constant B.

9.14 STUB MATCHING OF TRANSMISSION LINES

When transmission lines are to be used to transmit signals, it is necessary to minimize the reflections. If the reflections are present, not only the energy transferred to the load is small but the efficiency of the transmission is also low. Each successive reflection means that energy travels back and forth and, while doing so, some energy is dissipated due to losses of the line. Therefore, ideally, a line should be terminated by its characteristic impedance. However, this is not always possible. Under such conditions, the losses due to reflection can be minimized by what is known as *stub matching*.

It was shown previously (Eqs. 9.87a and 9.87b) that the impedance along the line with standing waves varies from its maximum value of a pure resistance of magnitude SZ_0 at a voltage maximum to its minimum value of a pure resistance of magnitude Z_0/S at a voltage minimum. It follows that the input admittance is a conductance of magnitude $1/SZ_0$ at the voltage maximum and a conductance of magnitude S/Z_0 at a voltage minimum. It can be shown that at an intermediate point, the conductive part of the admittance is exactly $1/Z_0$ (see Problem 19). The admittance at this point is complex and also has a reactive part of jB. Let d be the distance of this point from the load termination (Fig. 9.23a). The input admittance seen at d is $(1/Z_0 + jB)$. If we can neutralize the susceptance jB by another susceptance $-jB$ across the line at this point, then the net admittance seen by the line will be $1/Z_0$ and the rest of the line for all of the length l will be properly matched (Fig. 9.23). Since a short-circuited lossless transmission line has an input impedance Z_i, given by

$$Z_i = jZ_0 \tan \beta l_s$$

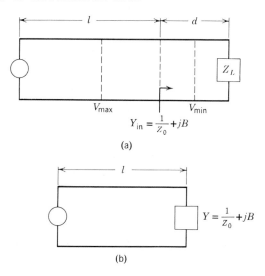

(a)

(b)

(c)

Figure 9.23

and

$$Y_i = \frac{-j}{Z_0} \cot \beta l_s$$

it is possible to obtain this neutralizing admittance by a short-circuited line stub of proper length. The length l_s of this stub is so chosen that

$$\frac{-j}{Z_0} \cot \beta l_s = -jB$$

We may choose an open-circuited stub instead of a short-circuited one. For an open-circuited stub,

$$Y_i = \frac{j}{Z_0} \tan \beta l_0$$

and the length l_0 in this case will be given by

$$\frac{j}{Z_0} \tan \beta l_0 = -jB$$

When the proper stub is connected across this point, the line is perfectly matched from the generator to the point of stubbing. There are, however, standing waves on the stub and the rest of the line between the stub and the load.

Since the points of voltage maxima and voltage minima repeat every half wavelength, the point where the stub can be located also repeats every half wavelength. Thus, we may have chosen the point at a distance $(\lambda/2 + d)$ or at a distance $(n\lambda/2 + d)$ units from the load. However, to minimize the loss, the stub should be located at the point nearest to the load. The calculations for the stubbing point and the length of the stub are greatly facilitated by the Smith chart.

Example 9.4

A lossless line with a characteristic impedance of $50\,\Omega$ is terminated by a load of $(100 + j100)\,\Omega$. Find the position and the length of a short-circuited stub to match the line.

We should use admittance functions here instead of impedance functions.

$$Y_0 = \frac{1}{50}$$

$$Y_L = \frac{1}{100 + j100}$$

$$\frac{Y_L}{Y_0} = \frac{50}{100 + j100} = 0.25 - j0.25$$

Thus, the normalized admittance Y_n at the load is $(0.25 - j0.25)$. We mark the point A on the Smith chart (Fig. 9.24) at the intersection of the locus representing $G = 0.25$ and the locus representing $B = -0.25$ (note that these are the same loci as those representing $R = 0.25$ and $X = -0.25$). Now a circle is drawn with the center at the origin and passing through point A. (The point A is given by $0.62\,e^{-j150°}$; this point represents ρ_y.) We move along this circle toward the generator until we meet the locus representing $G = 1$. This is the point A'. The total distance along the circular path from A to A' is 0.22 wavelengths. Therefore, we must locate the stub at $0.22\,\lambda$ units from the load. The normalized input admittance is read at point A'. At this point the intersecting G and B loci have the values $G = 1$ and $B = 1.6$.

$$(Y_n)_{A'} = (1 + j1.6)$$

We must connect a stub across this point with a normalized input admittance of $-j1.6$.

IMPEDANCE OR ADMITTANCE COORDINATES

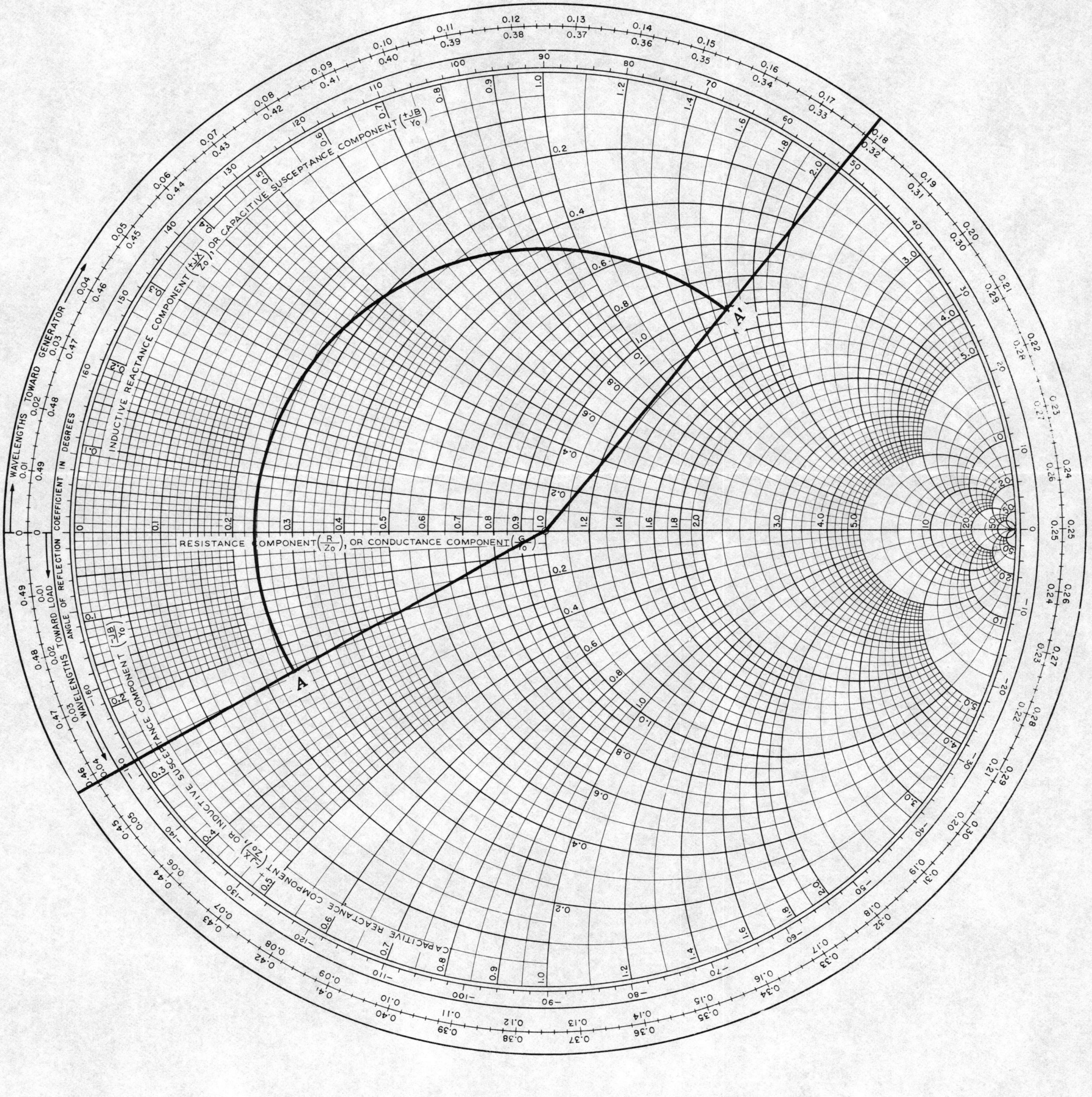

Figure 9.24

For a short-circuited stub,

$$Y_i = \frac{-j}{Z_0} \cot \beta l_s$$

or

$$\frac{Y_i}{Y_0} = Y_n = -j \cot \beta l_s$$

$$Y_n = -j1.6 = -j \cot \beta l_s$$

$$= -j \cot \frac{2\pi l}{\lambda}$$

Hence

$$1.6 = \cot \frac{2\pi l}{\lambda}$$

or

$$\frac{2\pi l}{\lambda} = 0.558 \text{ radians}$$

and

$$l = 0.089 \, \lambda$$

Thus, a shorted stub of length 0.089λ should be connected across the line at a distance of 0.22λ from the load. The procedure on the Smith chart is shown in Fig. 9.24.

PROBLEMS

1. A voltage $v(t)$ is applied to a lossless transmission line in series with an impedance Z_s as shown in Fig. P-9.1. Let

$$Z_s = Z_0 \quad \text{(the characteristic impedance of the line)}$$
$$Z_L = 0$$
$$v(t) = A u(t)$$

and

$$l = 10u \quad (u \text{ is the velocity of propagation)}$$

Find the voltage and current waveforms at $x = 5u$ for all time t. Explain the results obtained. Is it possible to obtain these results merely by inspection? Explain.

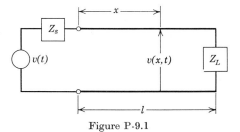

Figure P-9.1

2. Repeat Problem 1 if $Z_0 = 10\ \Omega$ and if:

(a) $Z_L = 3Z_0$, $Z_s = \dfrac{1}{15}\,Z_0$

(b) Z_L is a capacitor 0.1 f and $Z_s = 10\ \Omega$.

(c) Z_L is the series combination of a resistor of 10 Ω and an inductor of 10 henries; and $Z_s = 10\ \Omega$.

(d) Z_L is the same as in b and $Z_s = (10/3)\ \Omega$ (find the solution for $t < 30$ only).

(e) $Z_L = Z_s$ and Z_L is the same as that in b (find the solution for $t < 30$ only).

3. A current source is connected across a lossless transmission line of length l and terminated by impedance Z_L (Fig. P-9.3). Find the transfer function of the transmission line when the response is considered as (a) a voltage $v(x, t)$, and (b) a current $i(x, t)$.

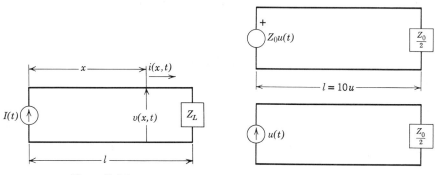

Figure P-9.3   Figure P-9.4

4. Two lossless lines, shown in Fig. P-9.4, are identical in every respect except their driving sources. One line is driven by a voltage source of $Z_0 u(t)$ volts and the other is driven by a current source of $u(t)$ amps. The load terminations on both lines are $Z_0/2$. Find the voltage and current waveforms at $x = 5u$. Explain why you get the same waveforms on both lines for $0 < t < 25$ and different waveforms for $t > 25$.

5. In Problem 4, let both of the lines be terminated by a capacitor of 0.01 farads. Find the voltage and current waveforms at $x = 5u$ for $0 < t < 35$ sec. Assume that $Z_0 = 10\ \Omega$.

6. An impedance Z_x is placed at a distance l_1 in series with a lossless transmission line of length l, as shown in Fig. P-9.6. Find the transfer functions H_v and H_i for $x < l_1$ and $x > l_1$.

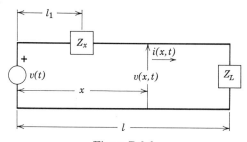

Figure P-9.6

7. In Problem 6, if:

$$Z_L = Z_0$$
$$Z_x = Z_0$$
$$l = 10u \text{ and } l_1 = 5u$$
$$v(t) = 10[u(t) - u(t-1)]$$

Find the voltage and current waveforms at $x = 2u$ and $8u$.

8. Find the transfer functions H_v and H_i for a lossless line shown in Fig. P-9.8 for $0 < x < l_1$ and $l_1 < x < l_2$.

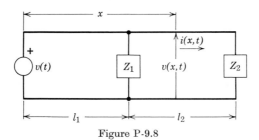

Figure P-9.8

9. In Problem 8, if:

$$l_1 = 5u$$
$$l_2 = 5u$$
$$v(t) = u(t)$$
$$Z_1 = 0.01 \text{ farad capacitor}$$
$$Z_2 = Z_0 = 10 \ \Omega$$

Find the voltage and current waveforms at $x = 2u$ and $x = 8u$ for $0 < t < 12$.

10. A lossless line of length l_1 branches into two transmission lines of length l_2 each and terminated by impedances Z_1 and Z_2, respectively, as shown in Fig. P-9.10. Find the transfer functions H_v and H_i for a general point on the line and a general point lying on either of the branches. Assume that the characteristic impedance is Z_0 for all branches.

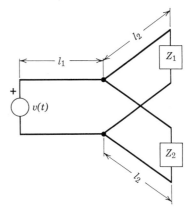

Figure P-9.10

11. In Problem 10, if:

$$Z_1 = Z_2 = Z_0$$
$$l_1 = l_2 = 10u$$
$$v(t) = u(t)$$

Find the voltage and current waveforms at load Z_1.

12. Repeat Problem 11, if:

$$Z_1 = Z_0 = 10 \ \Omega$$
$$Z_2 = 5\text{-}\Omega \ \text{resistor}$$

13. An open-circuited transmission line of length d is driven by a battery of 100 V through a source of 1000 Ω. If the characteristic impedance of the line is 10 Ω, find the voltage and current waveforms at the input terminals of the line.

14. Show that

$$v(t) = f_1\left(t - \frac{x}{u}\right) + f_2\left(t + \frac{x}{u}\right)$$

satisfied the lossless-line equation (Eq. 9.15 with $R = G = 0$) where $f_1(t)$ and $f_2(t)$ are any well-behaved functions.

15. A lossless line has an inductance of 10 microhenries/meter. What is the characteristic impedance of the line?

16. Show that

$$Z_0 = \sqrt{Z_{sc}Z_{oc}}$$

where Z_{sc} and Z_{oc} are the input impedances of the line when $Z_L = 0$ and ∞, respectively.

17. Derive voltage and current equations similar to Eqs. 9.74a and 9.74b, if the driving function is a current source instead of a voltage source.

18. A lossless transmission line with $Z_0 = 50$ is terminated by a 100-Ω resistor in parallel with a 5.3 pf capacitor. Find the reflection coefficient and standing wave ratio. The line is driven by a sinusoidal voltage source at $f = 300$ Mc. What is the shortest distance of the voltage maxima and minima from the load termination? What is the value of the maximum and minimum input impedances along the line. Solve the problem analytically as well as graphically using the Smith chart.

19. Derive the general expression for the distance from a load where a stub may be placed for matching.

20. A 300-Ω line ($Z_0 = 300$) is terminated in a load impedance of $(450 - j414) \ \Omega$. The line is 1.75 meters long and is excited by a signal of frequency 100 Mc. If $u = 3 \times 10^8$ meters/sec, find the input impedance, the reflection coefficient, the standing-wave ratio, and the position of the voltage maximum and the voltage minimum.

21. A 300-Ω lossless line is terminated by an impedance of $(210 + j150) \ \Omega$. If the line is 2.146 meters long, find the input impedance of the line if the signal frequency is 300 Mc. Find the reflection coefficient and standing-wave ratio. Where is the first voltage maxima and minima located from the load? It is decided to use a single short-circuited stub to match the line. Find the shortest distance of the stub from the load and the length of the stub.

22. A short-circuited quarter-wave line is used as a parallel resonant circuit. The quality factor Q of this resonant circuit may be defined as

$$Q = \frac{\omega_0}{\omega_2 - \omega_1}$$

where ω_0 is the signal frequency and ω_1, ω_2 are the frequencies where the magnitude of the input impedance of the section drops to 70.7 percent of its magnitude at ω_0. Assume small losses and the attenuation constant $\alpha \simeq R/2Z_0 + GZ_0/2$. Show that for a short-circuited quarter-wave line

$$Q = \frac{\omega_0 C Z_0}{(GZ_0 + R/Z_0)}$$

23. A lossless 100-Ω line is terminated by an impedance of 50 Ω. It is desired to connect a resistor R at a distance l_2 from the load (Fig. P-9.23) so that the line will be matched from the generators to the terminals aa'. Find the length l_2 and resistance R.

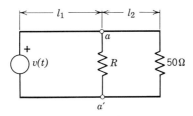

Figure P-9.23

24. A lossless line of length l and terminated by an arbitrary resistance

$$R_L (R_L \neq Z_0)$$

is driven by a sinusoidal source of variable frequency. The input impedance is a function of the frequency as shown in Fig. P-9.24. Show that the length of the line is given by

$$l = \frac{u}{2 \Delta f}$$

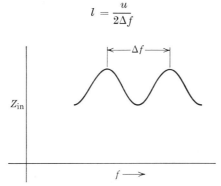

Figure P-9.24

25. Derive the partial-differential equations governing the following transmission lines.

(a) An inductive-conductive line ($R = C = 0$).
(b) A resistive-capacitive line ($L = G = 0$).

26. Determine the voltage $v(x, t)$ along an infinite resistive-capacitive line when the input voltage applied at $x = 0$ is $u(t)$.

27. Derive the partial-differential equations governing the capacitive-conductive and resistive inductive lines shown in Fig. P-9.27; S has the units of inverse capacitance (volts/coulomb) and Γ has the unit of inverse inductance (amp/volt-sec). Find the transfer functions of these lines.

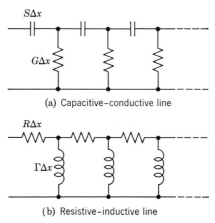

(a) Capacitive–conductive line

(b) Resistive–inductive line

Figure P-9.27

28. Find the natural frequencies of a lossless line of length l and terminated by

(a) $Z_L = 0$ (b) $Z_L = \infty$

chapter 10

The Convolution Integral

It was mentioned in the earlier chapters that convolution is one of the most important concepts in the field of frequency analysis. It is important in the analysis of systems as well as signals. In linear systems the explicit relationship between the driving function and the response can be expressed by the convolution integral. In communication theory, important theorems such as the modulation theorem and the sampling theorem can be viewed as special cases of convolution. The correlation functions (autocorrelation and crosscorrelation) which occur in signal-detection theory and in the study of random signals are also really a form of convolution. In this chapter, we shall study convolution as applied to the analysis of linear systems. The applications of convolution to communication theory and signal detection will be studied in Chapters 11 and 12.

10.1 SYSTEM ANALYSIS BY CONVOLUTION

Consider a system with the transfer function $H(s)$. If $r(t)$ is the response of the system to a driving function $f(t)$ and if $R(s)$ and $F(s)$ are their respective transforms, then

$$R(s) = F(s)H(s) \qquad (10.1)$$

It was shown in Chapter 6 that $h(t)$, the unit impulse response[1] of the system, is the inverse transform of $H(s)$. Thus

$$R(s) = \mathscr{L}[r(t)], \qquad F(s) = \mathscr{L}[f(t)], \qquad \text{and} \quad H(s) = \mathscr{L}[h(t)]$$

Therefore, the application of the time convolution theorem to Eq. 10.1 yields

$$r(t) = f(t) * h(t) \tag{10.2}$$

$$= \int_{-\infty}^{\infty} f(\tau)h(t - \tau)\, d\tau \tag{10.3}$$

This is a significant result since it exhibits the explicit relation between the response and the driving function in the time domain. Note that if $f(t)$ is a noncausal function, we must use the bilateral Laplace transform in the above equations. Equation 10.3 is still valid.

The response of a system to an impulse at $t = 0$ must necessarily be a causal function for any physical system. Hence, $h(t)$ is a causal function.

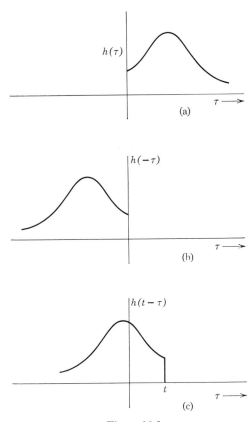

Figure 10.1

---

[1] The unit impulse response of a system is also called *Green's function*.

In addition, if the driving function is also a causal function, then the limits of integration in Eq. 10.3 can be changed. For causal $f(t)$, $f(\tau) = 0$ for $\tau < 0$ and hence the lower limit of integration in Eq. 10.3 can be changed to zero. Similarly, since $h(t)$ is a causal function, $h(t - \tau)$ is zero for $\tau > t$. This can be easily seen from Fig. 10.1. The function $h(-\tau)$ is merely a reflection of $h(\tau)$ about the vertical axis passing through the origin. The function $h(t - \tau)$ is obtained by displacing $h(-\tau)$ by t seconds along the positive τ axis. It is obvious that if $h(\tau)$ is causal, then $h(t - \tau)$ is zero for $\tau > t$. Hence the upper limit of integration may be changed to $\tau = t$ from $\tau = \infty$. Thus, Eq. 10.3 may be written as

$$r(t) = f(t) * h(t)$$

$$= \int_{-\infty}^{\infty} f(\tau)h(t - \tau)\, d\tau, \qquad f(t) \text{ and } h(t) \text{ both general} \qquad (10.4a)$$

$$= \int_{-\infty}^{t} f(\tau)h(t - \tau)\, d\tau, \qquad f(t) \text{ general and } h(t) \text{ causal} \qquad (10.4b)$$

$$= \int_{0}^{\infty} f(\tau)h(t - \tau)\, d\tau, \qquad f(t) \text{ causal, but } h(t) \text{ general} \qquad (10.4c)$$

$$= \int_{0}^{t} f(\tau)h(t - \tau)\, d\tau, \qquad \text{both } h(t) \text{ and } f(t) \text{ causal} \qquad (10.4d)$$

10.2 CONVOLUTION AS A SUPERPOSITION OF THE IMPULSE RESPONSE

In Chapter 2 it was indicated that the analysis of linear systems can be simplified by exploiting the principle of superposition. The analysis is considerably simplified if an arbitrary driving function can be expressed as a sum (discrete or continuous) of the functions whose response can be found with less difficulty. It was also indicated that an arbitrary driving function can be expressed as a continuous sum of exponential functions, impulse functions, step functions, ramp functions, and other functions of higher powers of t. The case of exponential functions (frequency analysis) has been extensively discussed in previous chapters. The remaining possibilities will now be considered. We shall first consider the case of impulse functions. It will be shown that an arbitrary driving function $f(t)$ can be expressed as a continuous sum of impulse functions. The response $r(t)$ is then given by the continuous sum of responses to various impulse components. In fact, we shall see that the convolution integral in Eq. 10.4 precisely expresses the response as a continuous sum of the responses to individual impulse components.

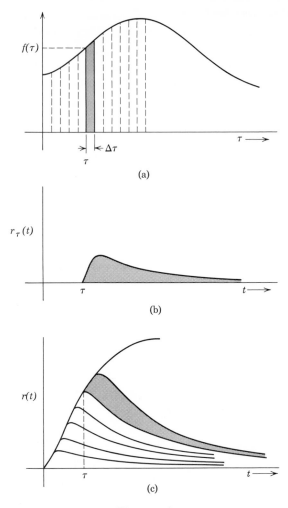

Figure 10.2

A function $f(\tau)$ may be represented as a sum of narrow pulses of width $\Delta\tau$ and height $f(\tau)$, as shown in Fig. 10.2a. We use here the variable τ in order to avoid confusion with variable t which is the general parameter for which the response is desired. In the limit, $\Delta\tau$ is made very small and each narrow pulse becomes an impulse of strength $f(\tau)\,\Delta\tau$. The desired response $r(t)$ will be the sum of the responses of the system to the individual impulse components up to $\tau = t$. The response of the system at any time t to a pulse of strength $f(\tau)\,\Delta\tau$ occurring at τ will be designated by $r_\tau(t)$. Naturally the function $r_\tau(t)$ starts at $t = \tau$ and is zero for $t < \tau$ (Fig. 10.2b). The desired response $r(t)$ is the sum of all such responses to the individual impulse components of $f(\tau)$. This is clearly illustrated in Fig. 10.2c.

The response of the system to a unit impulse occurring at τ is $h(t - \tau)$. Since $r_\tau(t)$ is the response system to an impulse of strength $f(\tau) \, \Delta\tau$, it follows that

$$r_\tau(t) = \lim_{\Delta\tau \to 0} f(\tau)h(t - \tau) \, \Delta\tau \qquad (10.5)$$

The desired response $r(t)$ is the sum of such responses. Since we are interested in the response at a general time t, the response due to the impulses occurring at $\tau > t$ will have no influence. Hence the summation should be carried out over $\tau = 0$ to $\tau = t$. Thus

$$r(t) = \sum_{\tau=0}^{t} r_\tau(t)$$

$$= \lim_{\Delta\tau \to 0} \sum_{\tau=0}^{t} f(\tau)h(t - \tau) \, \Delta\tau \qquad (10.6)$$

In the limit when $\Delta\tau \to 0$, the discrete sum becomes an integral.

$$r(t) = \int_0^t f(\tau)h(t - \tau) \, d\tau \qquad (10.7)$$

This is exactly the same result as that obtained by the direct application of the convolution theorem. If the function $f(t)$ involves impulse functions at the origin, then the lower limit of the integral in Eq. 10.7 should be taken as 0^- instead of 0. Therefore, in general,

$$r(t) = \int_{0^-}^t f(\tau)h(t - \tau) \, d\tau \qquad (10.8)$$

We can also derive this result in a slightly different way. It is obvious from Fig. 10.2a that a function $f(t)$ can be expressed as

$$f(t) = \lim_{\Delta\tau \to 0} \sum_{\tau=0}^{t} f(\tau) \, \Delta\tau \, \delta(t - \tau)$$

In the limit the sum becomes the integral and we have

$$f(t) = \int_0^t f(\tau) \, \delta(t - \tau) \, d\tau$$

The above integral expresses $f(t)$ as a continuous sum of impulse functions. The response of the system will naturally be given by the continuous sum of responses to these impulse components. Since the unit impulse response of the system is $h(t)$, it follows that

$$r(t) = \int_0^t f(\tau)h(t - \tau) \, d\tau$$

which is the same result as that in Eq. 10.7.

The result expressed in Eq. 10.7 is very important indeed. The response of the system has been obtained by the method which involves separating the driving function into a continuous sum of impulse functions. Note that we have assumed the system to be initially de-energized. If the system involves an initial storage of energy, then the initial-condition generators must be included. Each of the initial-condition generators acts as an independent driving function and the response can be found as the sum of the responses to the driving function and the initial-condition generators.

We now have three methods of analysis of linear systems.

(1) The time-domain analysis (the solution of the set of integro-differential equations of the system).

(2) The frequency-domain analysis (the solution of the set of algebraic equations in variable s).

(3) The convolution-integral analysis.

In the case of the convolution integral, all of the analysis is still carried out in terms of the variable t and, therefore, the convolution-integral analysis may be viewed as another method of the time-domain analysis. It is clear from Eq. 10.7 that the response of the system can be found from the knowledge of the driving function $f(t)$ and the unit impulse response $h(t)$. It follows, therefore, that the transmission characteristics of a given system are completely specified by the impulse response $h(t)$. Hence, $h(t)$ is the time-domain counterpart of $H(s)$. The convolution-integral analysis is convenient if the impulse response of the system is known. It is relatively easy to determine a unit impulse response of a system experimentally.

Example 10.1

We shall analyze the network in Example 6.2, using the convolution technique. The transfer function of the network was found to be

$$H(s) = \frac{s}{s^2 + 2s + 5}$$

Therefore

$$h(t) = \mathcal{L}^{-1}[H(s)] = e^{-t}[\cos 2t - \tfrac{1}{2}\sin 2t]u(t)$$

The driving function $f(t)$ is given by

$$f(t) = 100u(t)$$

The response $r(t)$ may be written as a convolution integral of $f(t)$ and $h(t)$.

$$r(t) = \int_0^t f(\tau)h(t - \tau)\,d\tau$$

$$= \int_0^t 100u(\tau)\,e^{-(t-\tau)}[\cos 2(t - \tau) - \tfrac{1}{2}\sin 2(t - \tau)]\,d\tau$$

$$= 100\int_0^t e^{-(t-\tau)}\cos 2(t - \tau)\,d\tau - 50\int_0^t e^{-(t-\tau)}\sin 2(t - \tau)\,d\tau$$

Let $2(t - \tau) = x$; then $d\tau = -dx/2$

$$r(t) = -50 \int_{2t}^{0} e^{-x/2} \cos x \, dx + 25 \int_{2t}^{0} e^{-x/2} \sin x \, dx$$

$$= 50 \, e^{-t} \sin (2t) u(t)$$

This is the same result as that obtained in Example 6.2.

Example 10.2

Find

$$\mathscr{L}^{-1} \frac{1}{(s + a)(s + b)}$$

This problem can be easily solved by expanding the above function by partial fractions. However, we shall use the convolution theorem to derive the result. From Table 5.1, we have

$$e^{-at}u(t) \longrightarrow \frac{1}{s + a} \; ; \qquad e^{-bt}u(t) \longrightarrow \frac{1}{s + b}$$

From the convolution theorem it follows that

$$e^{-at}u(t) * e^{-bt}u(t) \longrightarrow \frac{1}{(s + a)(s + b)}$$

Hence

$$\mathscr{L}^{-1}\left[\frac{1}{(s + a)(s + b)}\right] = \int_{0}^{t} e^{-a\tau} e^{-b(t-\tau)} \, d\tau$$

$$= e^{-bt} \int_{0}^{t} e^{-(a-b)\tau} \, d\tau$$

$$= \frac{1}{a - b} (e^{-bt} - e^{-at}) \, u(t)$$

10.3 SOME CONVOLUTION RELATIONSHIPS

The symbolic representation of convolution suggests that convolution is a special kind of multiplication. Indeed it is possible to write the laws of convolution algebra along lines that are similar to those for ordinary multiplication.

I. Commutative Law

$$f_1(t) * f_2(t) = f_2(t) * f_1(t) \tag{10.9}$$

This relationship can be easily proved as follows:

$$f_1(t) * f_2(t) = \int_{-\infty}^{\infty} f_1(\tau) f_2(t - \tau) \, d\tau$$

Changing the variable τ to $t - x$ we get

$$f_1(t) * f_2(t) = \int_{-\infty}^{\infty} f_2(x) f_1(t - x) \, dx$$
$$= f_2(t) * f_1(t)$$

2. Distributive Law

$$f_1(t) * [f_2(t) + f_3(t)] = f_1(t) * f_2(t) + f_1(t) * f_3(t) \qquad (10.10)$$

The proof is trivial.

3. Associative Law

$$f_1(t) * [f_2(t) * f_3(t)] = [f_1(t) * f_2(t)] * f_3(t) \qquad (10.11)$$

This law follows from the convolution theorem and from the fact that

$$F_1(s)[F_2(s) F_3(s)] = [F_1(s) F_2(s)] F_3(s)$$

10.4 GRAPHICAL INTERPRETATION OF CONVOLUTION

The graphical interpretation of convolution is very useful in system analysis as well as in communication theory. It permits one to grasp visually the results of many abstract relationships. This is particularly true in communication theory. In linear systems, graphical convolution is very helpful in analysis if $f(t)$ and $h(t)$ are known only graphically. For the sake of illustration, let us consider $f_1(t)$ and $f_2(t)$ as rectangular and triangular pulses as shown in Fig. 10.3a. We shall find the convolution $f_1(t) * f_2(t)$ graphically. By definition,

$$f_1(t) * f_2(t) = \int_{-\infty}^{\infty} f_1(\tau) f_2(t - \tau) \, d\tau \qquad (10.12)$$

The independent variable in the convolution integral is τ (Eq. 10.12). The functions $f_1(\tau)$ and $f_2(-\tau)$ are shown in Fig. 10.3b. Note that $f_2(-\tau)$ is obtained by folding $f_2(\tau)$ about the vertical axis passing through the origin. The term $f_2(t - \tau)$ represents the function $f_2(-\tau)$ shifted by t seconds along the positive τ axis. Figure 10.3c shows $f_2(t_1 - \tau)$. The value of the convolution integral at $t = t_1$ is given by the integral in Eq. 10.12 evaluated at $t = t_1$. This is clearly the area under the product curve of $f_1(\tau)$ and $f_2(t_1 - \tau)$. This area is shown shaded in Fig. 10.3d. The value of $f_1(t) * f_2(t)$ at $t = t_1$ is equal to this shaded area and is plotted in Fig. 10.3f. We choose different values of t, shift the function $f_2(-\tau)$ accordingly, and find the area under the new product curve. These areas represent the

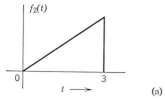
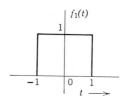

(a)

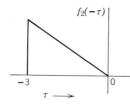
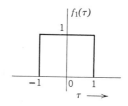

(b)

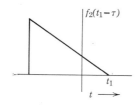
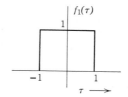

(c)

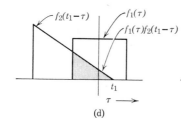

(d)

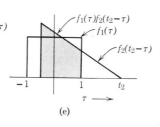

(e)

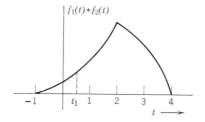

(f)

Figure 10.3

value of the convolution function $f_1(t) * f_2(t)$ at the respective values of t. The plot of the area under the product curve as a function of t represents the desired convolution function $f_1(t) * f_2(t)$.

The graphical mechanism of convolution can be appreciated by visualizing the function $f_2(-\tau)$ as a rigid frame which is being progressed along the τ axis by t_1 seconds. The function represented by this frame is multiplied by $f_1(\tau)$, and the area under the product curve is the value of the convolution function at $t = t_1$. Therefore, to find the value of $f_1(t) * f_2(t)$ at any time, say $t = t_0$, we displace the rigid frame representing $f_2(-\tau)$ by t_0 seconds along the τ axis and multiply this function with $f_1(\tau)$. The area under the product curve is the desired value of $f_1(t) * f_2(t)$ at $t = t_0$. To find the function $f_1(t) * f_2(t)$, we progress the frame successively by different amounts and find the areas of the product curve at various positions. The plot of the area as a function of displacement of the frame represents the required convolution function $f_1(t) * f_2(t)$. To summarize:

(1) Fold the function $f_2(\tau)$ about the vertical axis passing through the origin of the τ axis and obtain the function $f_2(-\tau)$.

(2) Consider the folded function as a rigid frame and progress it along the τ axis by an amount, say t_0. The rigid frame now represents the function $f_2(t_0 - \tau)$.

(3) The product of the function represented by this displaced rigid frame with $f_1(\tau)$ represents the function $f_1(\tau)f_2(t_0 - \tau)$, and the area under this curve is given by

$$\int_{-\infty}^{\infty} f_1(\tau)f_2(t_0 - \tau)\, d\tau = [f_1(t) * f_2(t)]_{t=t_0}$$

(4) Repeat this procedure for different values of t by successively progressing the frame by different amounts and find the values of the convolution function $f_1(t) * f_2(t)$ at those values of t.

Note that to find the convolution function $f_1(t) * f_2(t)$ for the positive values of t, we progress the frame along the positive τ axis; whereas for the negative values of t, the frame is progressed along the negative τ axis.

It was shown in Eq. 10.9 that the convolution of $f_1(t)$ with $f_2(t)$ is equal to the convolution of $f_2(t)$ with $f_1(t)$. That is,

$$f_1(t) * f_2(t) = f_2(t) * f_1(t)$$

Therefore, we may have kept $f_2(\tau)$ fixed and taken the mirror image of $f_1(\tau)$ in the graphical convolution in Fig. 10.3. We get the same results either way. This is clearly illustrated in Fig. 10.4 where Fig. 10.4a represents $f_1(t) * f_2(t)$ and Fig. 10.4b represents $f_2(t) * f_1(t)$.

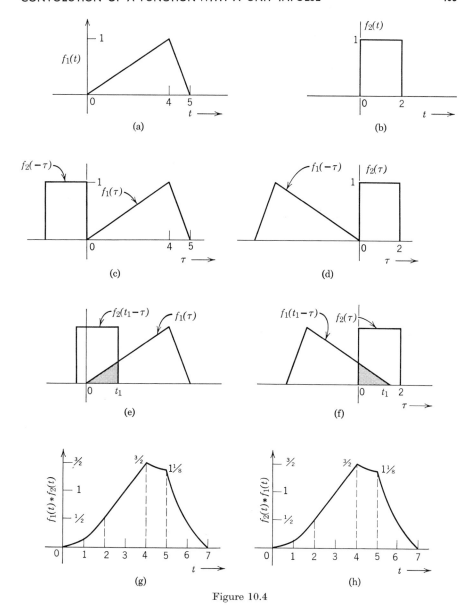

Figure 10.4

10.5 CONVOLUTION OF A FUNCTION WITH A UNIT IMPULSE

The convolution of a function $f(t)$ with a unit impulse function $\delta(t)$ yields the function $f(t)$ itself. This may be shown as follows. Let

$$f(t) \longleftrightarrow F(\omega) \tag{10.13}$$

and since

$$\delta(t) \leftrightarrow 1$$

it follows from the time convolution theorem that

$$f(t) * \delta(t) \leftrightarrow F(\omega) \tag{10.14}$$

It is therefore evident that

$$f(t) * \delta(t) = f(t) \tag{10.15}$$

We therefore conclude that the convolution of a unit impulse function with a function $f(t)$ reproduces the function itself. This is a very significant result and will be used often in Chapter 11.

This result can be derived alternatively by directly evaluating the convolution integral. By definition,

$$f(t) * \delta(t) = \int_{-\infty}^{\infty} f(\tau)\delta(t - \tau)\, d\tau$$

Using commutative property (Eq. 10.9), we get

$$f(t) * \delta(t) = \delta(t) * f(t) = \int_{-\infty}^{\infty} \delta(\tau)f(t - \tau)\, d\tau$$

Note that $\delta(\tau)$ exists only at $\tau = 0$ and has a zero value everywhere else. Hence the integrand is zero for all values of τ except $\tau = 0$. Consequently, the function $f(t - \tau)$ is meaningful only at $\tau = 0$, and hence $f(t - \tau)$ may be replaced by $f(t)$. Thus

$$f(t) * \delta(t) = \int_{-\infty}^{\infty} \delta(\tau)f(t)\, d\tau$$

$$= f(t)\int_{-\infty}^{\infty} \delta(\tau)\, d\tau$$

$$= f(t)$$

Hence

$$f(t) * \delta(t) = f(t)$$

This result is also evident graphically. The reader may verify this result by convolving $f(t)$ with $\delta(t)$ graphically as discussed in Section 10.4. A simple extension of Eq. 10.15 yields

$$f(t) * \delta(t - T) = f(t - T) \tag{10.16}$$

$$f(t - t_1) * \delta(t - t_2) = f(t - t_1 - t_2) \tag{10.17}$$

$$\delta(t - t_1) * \delta(t - t_2) = \delta(t - t_1 - t_2) \tag{10.18}$$

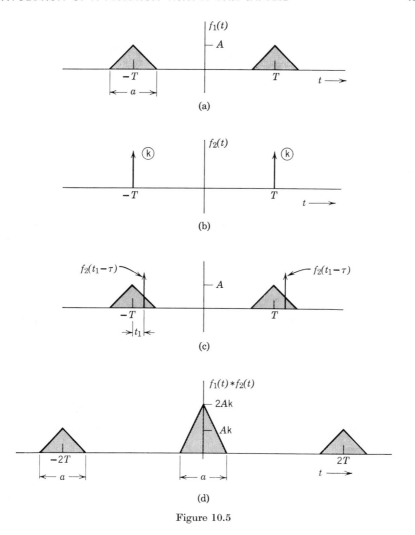

Figure 10.5

Example 10.3

Find graphically the convolution of $f_1(t)$ (Fig. 10.5a) with a pair of impulses of strength k each, as shown in Fig. 10.5b.

Following the procedure of graphical convolution described in Section 10.4, we fold back $f_2(\tau)$ about the ordinate to obtain $f_2(-\tau)$. Since $f_2(\tau)$ is an even function of τ, $f_2(-\tau) = f_2(\tau)$. The convolution of $f_1(\tau)$ with $f_2(\tau)$ thus reduces to convolution of $f_1(\tau)$ with two impulses. From the property of an impulse function to reproduce the function by convolution (Eq. 10.15), it can be easily seen that each impulse produces a triangular pulse of height Ak at the origin $(t = 0)$. Hence the net height of the triangular pulse is $2Ak$ at the origin. As the function $f_2(t - \tau)$ is moved farther in a positive direction, the impulse originally located at $-T$ encounters the triangular pulse at $\tau = T$, and reproduces the triangular pulse of height Ak at $t = 2T$. Similarly the impulse originally located at T reproduces a triangular pulse of height Ak at $t = 2T$. The final result of convolution is shown in Fig. 10.5d.

10.6 IDEAL DIFFERENTIATOR AND INTEGRATOR

Let us find the transfer function of an ideal differentiator and integrator. The response of an ideal differentiator to a causal function $f(t)$ is df/dt. If $F(s)$ is the transform of $f(t)$, then $sF(s)$ is the transform of df/dt [note that since $f(t)$ is a causal function, $f(0^-)$ is zero]. It is therefore evident that the transfer function of an ideal differentiator is given by $H(s) = s$.

Also the Laplace transform of the definite integral $\int_0^t f(t)\, dt$ is $F(s)/s$. Obviously the transfer function of an ideal integrator is $H(s) = 1/s$ (Fig. 10.6). These results can be easily extended to higher orders of differentiating and integrating systems. A system with the transfer function s^n acts as an ideal nth differentiator and a system with the transfer function s^{-n} acts as an ideal nth integrator.

10.7 RESPONSE OF A LINEAR SYSTEM TO THE DERIVATIVE OR INTEGRAL FUNCTION

One of the significant properties of a linear system is that the response of the system to the derivative or integral of any function $f(t)$ is also the derivative or integral respectively of the response to $f(t)$.

Symbolically, this fact may be expressed as follows. If

$$f(t) \rightarrow r(t)$$

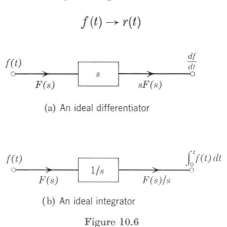

(a) An ideal differentiator

(b) An ideal integrator

Figure 10.6

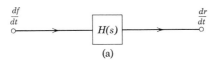

(a)

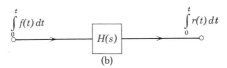

(b)

Figure 10.7

then

$$\frac{df}{dt} \rightarrow \frac{dr}{dt} \tag{10.19}$$

and

$$\int_0^t f(t)\, dt \rightarrow \int_0^t r(t)\, dt \tag{10.20}$$

This may be easily shown in the following way.

If $r(t)$ is the response of a system with the transfer function $H(s)$, to the driving function $f(t)$, and if $R(s)$ and $F(s)$ are the transforms of $r(t)$ and $f(t)$, respectively, then for an initially de-energized system,

$$R(s) = H(s)F(s) \tag{10.21}$$

Multiplying both sides of Eq. 10.21 by s:

$$sR(s) = sH(s)F(s)$$
$$= H(s)sF(s) \tag{10.22}$$

Note that since both $f(t)$ and $r(t)$ are causal functions, $r(0^-)$ and $f(0^-)$ are zero, and $sR(s)$ and $sF(s)$ are the transforms of dr/dt and df/dt, respectively. It therefore follows from Eq. 10.22 that dr/dt is the response of the system to the driving function df/dt (Fig. 10.7).

Also $F(s)/s$ and $R(s)/s$ are the transforms of $\displaystyle\int_0^t f(t)\, dt$ and $\displaystyle\int_0^t r(t)\, dt$ respectively and, by arguments similar to the one above, it follows that

$$\int_0^t f(t)\, dt \rightarrow \int_0^t r(t)\, dt$$

Both of these results (Eqs. 10.19 and 10.20) can be extended to higher order derivatives and integrals.

The result of this discussion may be expressed succinctly in this manner: if

$$f(t) \rightarrow r(t) \tag{10.23}$$

then

$$f^{(n)}(t) \rightarrow r^{(n)}(t)$$

where n is either a positive or negative integer, and

$$f^{(n)}(t) = \frac{d^n f}{dt^n} \qquad \text{for positive } n$$

and

$$f^{(n)}(t) = \int_0^t \int_0^t \cdots \int_0^t \int_0^t f(t) \, dt^n \qquad \text{for negative } n$$

10.8 THE UNIT STEP RESPONSE OF A SYSTEM

A unit step $u(t)$ can be expressed as the integral of a unit impulse function $\delta(t)$.

$$u(t) = \int_0^t \delta(t) \, dt \tag{10.24}$$

The lower limit should be 0^- to be exact, since we are integrating an impulse at the origin. The lower limit will be tacitly assumed to be 0^- although it will be written as 0 for convenience. If the response of the system to a unit impulse function is $h(t)$, then it follows from Eq. 10.20 that the response of the system to a unit step function will be $\int_0^t h(t) \, dt$. That is, if

$$\delta(t) \rightarrow h(t)$$

then

$$u(t) = \int_0^t \delta(t) \, dt \rightarrow \int_0^t h(t) \, dt \tag{10.25}$$

Let us designate the unit step response[2] of a system by $g(t)$. Then it follows that

$$g(t) = \int_0^t h(t) \, dt \tag{10.26}$$

Therefore, the unit step response is the integral of the unit impulse response of the system. And

$$\mathcal{L}[g(t)] = \mathcal{L}\left[\int_0^t h(t) \, dt\right] = \frac{H(s)}{s} \tag{10.27}$$

[2] The unit step response is sometimes called the *indicial response*.

10.9 SYSTEM ANALYSIS BY SUPERPOSITION, USING STEP FUNCTIONS: THE SUPERPOSITION INTEGRAL

The convolution integral in Eq. 10.4 expresses the response of a system in terms of its unit impulse response. By a slight modification in the procedure it is possible to express the response in terms of the unit step response of the system. Consider Eq. 10.1:

$$R(s) = F(s)H(s)$$
$$= sF(s)\frac{H(s)}{s}$$

Since $f(t)$ is a causal function, $sF(s)$ is the transform of $f'(t)$. Also $H(s)/s$ is the transform of $g(t)$, the unit step response of the system (Eq. 10.27). Hence, the application of the convolution theorem to the above equation yields

$$r(t) = f'(t) * g(t) \tag{10.28a}$$

$$= \int_{-\infty}^{\infty} f'(\tau)g(t-\tau)\,d\tau \qquad [f(t) \text{ and } g(t) \text{ both general}] \tag{10.28b}$$

$$= \int_{0}^{\infty} f'(\tau)g(t-\tau)\,d\tau \qquad [f(t) \text{ causal and } g(t) \text{ general}] \tag{10.28c}$$

$$= \int_{0}^{t} f'(\tau)g(t-\tau)\,d\tau \qquad [f(t) \text{ and } g(t) \text{ both causal}] \tag{10.28d}$$

In order to guard against the possibility of an impulse at the origin in the integrand, the lower limit should be taken as 0^-. Thus Eq. 10.28d becomes

$$r(t) = \int_{0^-}^{t} f'(\tau)g(t-\tau)\,d\tau \tag{10.28e}$$

This integral is known as the *superposition integral* or *Duhamel's integral*. Note that the superposition integral is really a convolution integral.

The superposition integral expresses the response of a system in terms of its unit step response. As we shall see the superposition integral actually expresses the response of a system as a continuous sum of the responses to the step components of $f(t)$.

A driving function $f(\tau)$ can be approximated by a staircase function, as shown in Fig. 10.8. The approximated function can now be expressed as a sum of a large number of step functions. An infinitesimal step located at τ has an amplitude given by

$$\Delta f = \frac{df}{d\tau}\Delta\tau$$

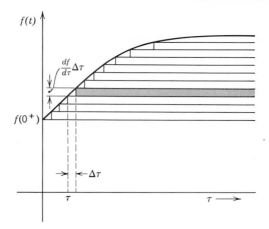

Figure 10.8

The response due to such an infinitesimal step at τ is given by

$$r_\tau(t) = \frac{df}{d\tau} \Delta\tau\, g(t - \tau)$$

The desired response is the sum of the responses due to all the individual step components from $\tau = 0^-$ to $\tau = t$:

$$r(t) = \lim_{\Delta\tau \to 0} \sum_{\tau=0^-}^{t} r_\tau(t) = \lim_{\Delta\tau \to 0} \sum_{0^-}^{t} \frac{df}{d\tau} \Delta\tau\, g(t - \tau)$$

In the limit the discrete sum becomes an integral:

$$r(t) = \int_{0^-}^{t} \frac{df}{d\tau} g(t - \tau)\, d\tau \tag{10.29}$$

We have thus expressed the response of a system as a continuous sum of the responses to various unit step components of the driving function. The integral in Eq. 10.29 is the same as we obtained before in Eq. 10.28. We can also derive this result in a slightly different way. It is obvious from the above discussion that $f(t)$ can be expressed as a continuous sum of step functions.

$$f(t) = \lim_{\Delta\tau=0} \sum_{\tau=0^-}^{t} \frac{df}{d\tau} \Delta\tau\, u(t - \tau)$$

$$= \int_{0^-}^{t} \frac{df}{d\tau} u(t - \tau)\, d\tau \tag{10.30}$$

The response of the system to a unit step function is $g(t)$. Hence the response of the system to $f(t)$ will be given by

$$r(t) = \int_{0^-}^{t} \frac{df}{d\tau} g(t - \tau)\, d\tau \tag{10.31}$$

This is, of course, the same result as obtained previously. The above integral may be separated into two integrals.

$$r(t) = \int_{0^-}^{0^+} f'(\tau)g(t - \tau)\, d\tau + \int_{0^+}^{t} f'(\tau)g(t - \tau)\, d\tau \qquad (10.32)$$

The function $f(\tau)$ is a causal function and hence there is a possibility of a jump discontinuity at $\tau = 0$ (see Fig. 10.8). Since $f(0^-) = 0$, the jump discontinuity is $f(0^+)$. Therefore, $df/d\tau$ at $\tau = 0$ is an impulse of strength $f(0^+)$.

$$\frac{df}{d\tau}(0) = f(0^+)\, \delta(\tau)$$

Also

$$g(t - \tau) = g(t) \text{ at } \tau = 0$$

Equation 10.32 now becomes

$$r(t) = \int_{0^-}^{0^+} f(0^+)g(t)\, \delta(\tau)\, d\tau + \int_{0^+}^{t} f'(\tau)g(t - \tau)\, d\tau$$

$$= f(0^+)g(t) + \int_{0^+}^{t} f'(\tau)g(t - \tau)\, d\tau \qquad (10.33)$$

Equation 10.33 represents the alternative form of the superposition integral. This expression is more commonly used in the literature. Equation 10.29, however, is more concise and should be preferred over Eq. 10.33. The conciseness of Eq. 10.29 is the result of the inclusion of the origin in the integral by taking the lower limit as 0^-.

A Different Form of the Superposition Integral

The commutative property of the convolution permits us to write Eq. 10.28a as

$$r(t) = g(t) * f'(t)$$

$$= \int_{0^-}^{t} g(\tau)f'(t - \tau)\, d\tau \qquad (10.34)$$

Note that $f(t - \tau)$ has a jump discontinuity of $f(0^+)$ at $\tau = t$. Hence $f'(t - \tau)$ is an impulse of strength $f(0^+)$ at $\tau = t$. Consequently, Eq. 10.34 may be expressed as

$$r(t) = \int_{0^-}^{t^-} g(\tau)f'(t - \tau)\, d\tau + \int_{t^-}^{t^+} g(\tau)f'(t - \tau)\, d\tau$$

$$= \int_{0^-}^{t^-} g(\tau)f'(t - \tau)\, d\tau + \int_{t^-}^{t^+} g(t)f(0^+)\, \delta(\tau)\, d\tau$$

$$= f(0^+)g(t) + \int_{0^-}^{t^-} g(\tau)f'(t - \tau)\, d\tau \qquad (10.35)$$

10.10 SYSTEM ANALYSIS BY SUPERPOSITION OF THE FUNCTIONS OF THE HIGHER ORDER OF t: THE GENERALIZED CONVOLUTION INTEGRAL

We have already seen that a function $f(t)$ can be expressed as a continuous sum of impulse and step functions. This procedure can be extended to ramp functions and functions of higher powers of t.

A unit ramp function $tu(t)$ may be expressed as

$$tu(t) = \int_0^t u(t)\, dt$$

$$= \int_0^t \int_0^t \delta(t)\, dt^2 \tag{10.36}$$

If we designate the response of a system to a unit ramp function by $k_1(t)$, then from Eqs. 10.23 and 10.36 it follows that

$$k_1(t) = \int_0^t \int_0^t h(t)\, dt^2$$

Hence

$$\mathscr{L}[k_1(t)] = \frac{H(s)}{s^2} \tag{10.37}$$

We have

$$R(s) = H(s)F(s)$$

$$= s^2 F(s)\, \frac{H(s)}{s^2} \tag{10.38}$$

It is obvious that $s^2 F(s)$ is the transform of $f''(t)$. Hence the application of the convolution theorem to Eq. 10.38 yields

$$r(t) = f''(t) * k_1(t)$$

$$= \int_{0-}^t f''(\tau)k_1(t-\tau)\, d\tau \tag{10.39}$$

Equation 10.39 represents the response of a system in terms of its unit ramp response. By graphical aids similar to those used for the impulse and step functions, it can be shown that Eq. 10.39 expresses the response of the system as a continuous sum of the responses of the ramp component of $f(t)$.

In general, an arbitrary function $f(t)$ can be expressed as a continuous sum of the nth power function $t^n u(t)$. The response can therefore be expressed as a continuous sum of the responses to these nth order components.

$$R(s) = \frac{H(s)}{s^{n+1}}\, s^{n+1}\, F(s)$$

Note that $(1/n!)t^n u(t)$ is the $(n + 1)$th integral of $\delta(t)$. Hence the response of the system to $(1/n!)t^n u(t)$ is the $(n + 1)$th integral of $h(t)$ and will be denoted by $h^{-(n+1)}(t)$. It also follows that

$$\mathscr{L}[h^{-(n+1)}(t)] = \frac{H(s)}{s^{n+1}}$$

and

$$r(t) = f^{(n+1)}(t) * h^{-(n+1)}(t) \tag{10.40}$$

$$= \int_{0^-}^{t} f^{(n+1)}(\tau) h^{-(n+1)}(t - \tau) \, d\tau \tag{10.41}$$

Equation 10.40 may be alternatively expressed as

$$r(t) = h^{-(n+1)}(t) * f^{(n+1)}(t) \tag{10.42}$$

$$= \int_{0^-}^{t} h^{-(n+1)}(\tau) f^{(n+1)}(t - \tau) \, d\tau \tag{10.43}$$

Example 10.4

A voltage $e^{-t}u(t)$ is applied to a series R-C network as shown in Fig. 10.9. We shall find the voltage $v_0(t)$ by using various techniques developed thus far.

The transfer function $H(s)$ is given by

$$H(s) = \frac{1/s}{(1/2) + (1/s)} = \frac{2}{s + 2}$$

Therefore

$$h(t) = \mathscr{L}^{-1}[H(s)] = 2e^{-2t}u(t)$$

The response $r(t)$ in this case is the output voltage $v_o(t)$ and will now be determined by various methods.

I. Frequency Domain Analysis:

$$R(s) = F(s)H(s)$$

$$= \left(\frac{1}{s + 1}\right)\left(\frac{2}{s + 2}\right)$$

$$= \frac{2}{s + 1} - \frac{2}{s + 2}$$

$$r(t) = \mathscr{L}^{-1}[R(s)] = 2(e^{-t} - e^{-2t})u(t)$$

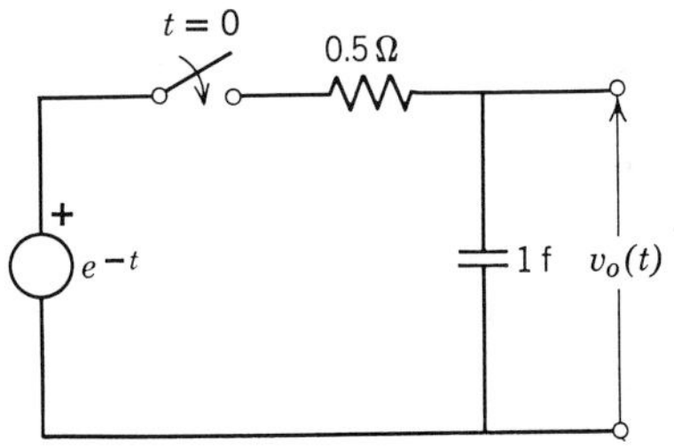

Figure 10.9

2. Convolution Integral I:

$$r(t) = f(t) * h(t) = \int_0^t f(\tau)h(t - \tau)\,d\tau$$
$$= \int_0^t e^{-\tau}2e^{-2(t-\tau)}\,d\tau$$

Note that the integrand above does not possess impulse at the origin and consequently the lower limit may be taken as 0^+. Therefore

$$r(t) = 2e^{-2t}[e^\tau]_0^t$$
$$= 2(e^{-t} - e^{-2t})u(t)$$

3. Convolution Integral II:

$$r(t) = h(t) * (f(t)) = \int_0^t h(\tau)f(t - \tau)\,d\tau$$
$$= \int_0^t 2e^{-2\tau}e^{-(t-\tau)}\,d\tau$$
$$= -2e^{-t}[e^{-\tau}]_0^t$$
$$= 2(e^{-t} - e^{-2t})u(t)$$

4. Superposition Integral I (Eq. 10.33):

$$r(t) = f'(t) * g(t)$$
$$= f(0^+)g(t) + \int_{0^+}^t f'(\tau)g(t - \tau)\,d\tau$$

$$f(0^+) = 1 \qquad \text{and} \qquad g(t) = \int_0^t h(t)\,dt = (1 - e^{-2t})u(t)$$

Hence

$$r(t) = (1 - e^{-2t})u(t) + \int_{0^+}^t \frac{d}{d\tau}\, e^{-\tau}[1 - e^{-2(t-\tau)}]\,d\tau$$
$$= 2(e^{-t} - e^{-2t})u(t)$$

5. Superposition Integral II (Eqs. 10.35):

$$r(t) = g(t) * f'(t)$$
$$= f(0^+)g(t) + \int_{0^+}^{t^-} g(\tau)f'(t - \tau)\,d\tau$$
$$= (1 - e^{-2t})u(t) + \int_0^t (1 - e^{-2\tau})[-e^{-(t-\tau)}]\,d\tau$$
$$= 2(e^{-t} - e^{-2t})u(t)$$

In general (Eq. 10.40):

$$r(t) = f^{(n+1)}(t) * h^{-(n+1)}(t)$$
$$= h^{-(n+1)}(t) * f^{(n+1)}(t)$$

It is evident that $r(t)$ can be expressed by an endless number of integrals by assigning all possible integral values to n in the above equations.

10.11 SPECIFICATION OF A LINEAR SYSTEM

It is obvious from the discussion thus far that the transmission characteristics of a linear system may be completely specified in a variety of
ways. It may be specified by its transfer function, unit impulse response,
unit step response, unit ramp response, or its response to a function of any
power of t in general. Thus a system can be analyzed from the knowledge
of either one of the above-mentioned characteristics. In practice, however,
the transfer function, unit impulse response, and unit step response are
more commonly specified. Experimentally, the unit step response is the
simplest to evaluate. The unit impulse response is obviously the derivative of the unit step response. And the transfer function is the Laplace
transform of the unit impulse response. All of these specifications are
obviously related, and one can be derived from another.

10.12 GENERALIZATION OF THE CONVOLUTION INTEGRAL

Equations 10.40 and 10.42 suggest that a convolution of two functions
can be expressed in a variety of ways. If $f_1(t)$ and $f_2(t)$ are two functions
with transforms $F_1(s)$ and $F_2(s)$, respectively, then it follows that

$$f_1(t) * f_2(t) \rightarrow F_1(s)F_2(s)$$

But

$$F_1(s)F_2(s) = s^n F_1(s) \frac{F_2(s)}{s^n}$$

and also

$$f_1^{(n)}(t) * f_2^{(-n)}(t) \rightarrow s^n F_1(s) \frac{F_2(s)}{s^n} = F_1(s)F_2(s)$$

Hence it follows that

$$f_1(t) * f_2(t) = f_1^{(n)}(t) * f_2^{(-n)}(t) \tag{10.44}$$

10.13 DIFFERENTIATION AND INTEGRATION
OF THE CONVOLUTION FUNCTIONS

A slight modification of Eq. 10.42 yields a property of the convolution
functions which is extremely useful in the numerical computations of the
convolution integral.

We have

$$R(s) = H(s)F(s)$$

From this equation it follows that

$$s^{j+k} R(s) = [s^j H(s)][s^k F(s)] \qquad (10.45)$$

and

$$\begin{aligned} s^{j+k} R(s) &= \mathscr{L}[r^{(j+k)}(t)] \\ s^j H(s) &= \mathscr{L}[h^{(j)}(t)] \\ s^k F(s) &= \mathscr{L}[f^{(k)}(t)] \end{aligned} \qquad (10.46)$$

Application of the convolution theorem to Eq. 10.45 yields

$$r^{(j+k)}(t) = h^{(j)}(t) * f^{(k)}(t) \qquad (10.47a)$$

that is

$$r^{(j+k)}(t) = \int_{0^-}^{t} h^{(j)}(\tau) f^{(k)}(t - \tau) \, d\tau \qquad (10.47b)$$

where j and k may be any positive or negative integers. When $j + k$ is positive, Eq. 10.47 provides the expression for the $(j + k)$th derivative of $r(t)$, and when $j + k$ is negative this equation expresses the $(j + k)$th integral of $r(t)$. If $j + k$ is positive, then it follows from Eq. 10.47 that

$$r(t) = \int_0^t \int_0^t \cdots \int_0^t [h^{(j)}(t) * f^{(k)}(t)] \, dt^{(j+k)} \qquad (10.48)$$

$$= \int_0^t \int_0^t \cdots \int_0^t \int_0^t h^{(j)}(\tau) f^{(k)}(t - \tau) \, d\tau \, dt^{(j+k)} \qquad (10.49)$$

where j and k may be any positive or negative integers.

The practical implications of Eq. 10.48 are very important in evaluating the convolution of the two functions $f(t)$ and $\varphi(t)$. It is often much easier to convolve the derivatives of these functions rather than the functions themselves. In such cases, Eq. 10.47 can be utilized to our advantage. Assume that the jth derivative of $f(t)$ and the kth derivative of $\varphi(t)$ are convenient to convolve. According to Eq. 10.47 this convolution is the $(j + k)$th derivative of the desired function $r(t)$. We therefore integrate $j + k$ times the convolution of $f^{(j)}(t)$ and $\varphi^{(k)}(t)$ to obtain $r(t)$.

We have shown in Eq. 10.15 that the convolution of any function with an impulse function yields the function itself. It is therefore much easier to convolve any function with an impulse function or a sequence of impulse functions. Equation 10.47 can be used advantageously if either of the functions to be convolved will yield a sequence of impulse functions after differentiating a sufficient number of times.

Consider, for example, the two functions $f(t)$ and $\varphi(t)$ shown in Figs. 10.10a and 10.10b, respectively. It can be seen that the second derivative of $f(t)$ and the first derivative of $\varphi(t)$ will yield sequences of impulse functions. Since $\varphi(t)$ has to be differentiated only once to obtain a sequence

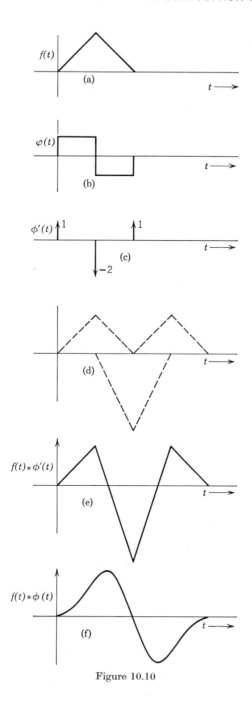

Figure 10.10

of impulses, we shall differentiate $\varphi(t)$ once (Fig. 10.10c) and evaluate the convolution of $f(t)$ with $\varphi'(t)$. This is easily done graphically (Fig. 10.10d). The result of this convolution is shown in Fig. 10.10d. The desired convolution $f(t) * \varphi(t)$ is obtained by integrating $f(t) * \varphi'(t)$ once. The final result of this integration is shown in Fig. 10.10f.

This technique of convolution can be employed in the numerical methods of computing the convolution of two arbitrary functions $f(t)$ and $\varphi(t)$. There are a number of possibilities based on Eq. 10.47 which can be used in the numerical techniques of evaluating the convolution of two functions. In the following section we shall discuss some of these important techniques.

10.14 NUMERICAL TECHNIQUES IN CONVOLUTION

We shall discuss here two techniques: the impulse train approximation and the straight line segment approximation.

I. Impulse Train Approximation

It was shown (Eq. 10.18) that a convolution of the two impulse functions is also an impulse function:

$$\delta(t - t_1) * \delta(t - t_2) = \delta(t - t_1 - t_2)$$

In the numerical evaluation of the response it is therefore desirable to reduce both of the functions to be convolved to an impulse form. This may be easily achieved. A given function $f(t)$ is first approximated by a staircase function, as shown in Fig. 10.11a. The width α of each step may be chosen to conform to the accuracy desired. The smaller the width of each step, the higher the accuracy. It is clear from Fig. 10.11a that the function $f(t)$ can be approximated by narrow adjacent pulses of the width α.

Furthermore, for the purpose of convolution, each narrow pulse occupying the region $n\alpha < t < (n + 1)\alpha$ may be approximated by an impulse of strength equal to the area of the pulse and located at $t = n\alpha$. We have therefore approximated the function $f(t)$ with a sequence of impulses located at $t = 0, \alpha, 2\alpha, 3\alpha, \ldots$, etc. The strength of the $(n + 1)$th impulse in this sequence is $\alpha f(n\alpha)$. We may therefore approximate $f(t)$ with a sequence of impulses as

$$\begin{aligned}
f(t) &\simeq \alpha f(0)\, \delta(t) + \alpha f(\alpha)\, \delta(t - \alpha) + \alpha f(2\alpha)\, \delta(t - 2\alpha) \\
&\quad + \cdots + \alpha f(n\alpha)\, \delta(t - n\alpha) + \cdots \\
&= \alpha[f(0)\, \delta(t) + f(\alpha)\, \delta(t - \alpha) + f(2\alpha)\, \delta(t - 2\alpha) + \cdots \\
&\quad + \cdots + f(n\alpha)\, \delta(t - n\alpha) + \cdots]
\end{aligned} \tag{10.50a}$$

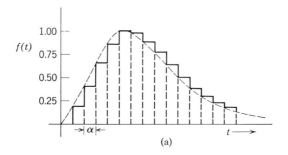

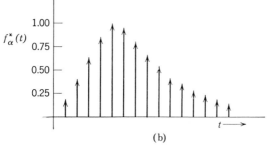

Figure 10.11

For convenience, we shall represent $f(0)$, $f(\alpha)$, $f(2\alpha)$, ..., etc. by f_0, $f_1, f_2, \ldots$, etc. In general, $f(n\alpha)$ will be denoted by f_n. Equation 10.50a may now be expressed as

$$f(t) \simeq \alpha[f_0\, \delta(t) + f_1\, \delta(t - \alpha) + f_2\, \delta(t - 2\alpha) + \cdots + f_n\, \delta(t - n\alpha) + \cdots]$$
(10.50b)

We come to an important result here. Any arbitrary function $f(t)$ can be approximated by a sequence of impulses as expressed in Eq. 10.50b for the purpose of convolution. Equation 10.50b may be rearranged as

$$\frac{1}{\alpha}f(t) \simeq [f_0\, \delta(t) + f_1\, \delta(t - \alpha) + f_2\, \delta(t - 2\alpha) + \cdots + f_n\, \delta(t - n\alpha) + \cdots]$$
(10.51)

The right-hand side of Eq. 10.51 is a sequence of impulses. Note that the strength of the $(n + 1)$th impulse in this sequence is equal to f_n. For convenience, we shall denote this sequence of impulses by a function $f_\alpha^*(t)$. We therefore have

$$\frac{1}{\alpha}f(t) \simeq f_\alpha^*(t)$$

where

$$f_\alpha^*(t) = f_0\, \delta(t) + f_1\, \delta(t - \alpha) + f_2\, \delta(t - 2\alpha) + \cdots + f_n\, \delta(t - n\alpha) + \cdots$$
(10.52)

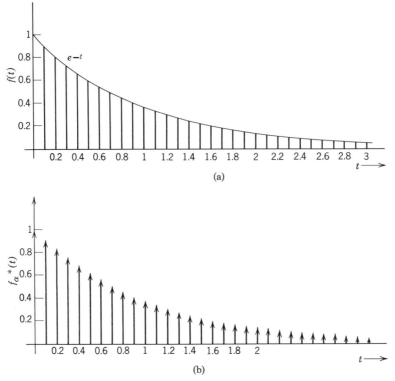

Figure 10.12 (a) The exponential function e^{-t}. (b) Impulse train approximation of $(1/\alpha)e^{-t}$.

Note that $f_\alpha^*(t)$ is a sequence of impulses located at $t = 0$, α, 2α, 3α, ..., etc., and the strength of an impulse located at $t = n\alpha$ is merely f_n or $f(n\alpha)$ which is the ordinate of $f(t)$ at $t = n\alpha$. Therefore, $f_\alpha^*(t)$ can be represented graphically merely by drawing ordinates of $f(t)$ at $t = 0$, α, 2α, 3α, ..., etc. and letting the height of each ordinate represent the strength of the impulse at that point. This is done for three functions as shown in Figs. 10.11 to 10.13. Note that

$$\frac{1}{\alpha} f(t) \simeq f_\alpha^*(t)$$

and

$$f(t) \simeq \alpha f_\alpha^*(t) \tag{10.53}$$

The approximation procedure may be written step by step as follows.

(1) Choose an interval α. The smaller the interval, the higher the accuracy and the more the labor.

(2) Draw ordinates at intervals of α starting at $t = 0$.

(3) Label the height of each ordinate.

(4) Each ordinate now represents an impulse of strength equal to the height of the ordinate. This sequence of impulses represents $f_\alpha{}^*(t)$.

The procedure is illustrated for an exponential function $e^{-t}u(t)$ and for an arbitrary function $v(t)$ in Figs. 10.12 and 10.13, respectively. We shall now develop the graphical procedure of convolving two functions represented by sequences of impulses.

Let $f(t)$ and $\varphi(t)$ be two continuous functions approximated by sequences of impulses separated by intervals of α seconds.

$$f(t) \simeq \alpha f_0\, \delta(t) + \alpha f_1\, \delta(t - \alpha) + \alpha f_2\, \delta(t - 2\alpha)$$
$$+ \cdots + \alpha f_n\, \delta(t - n\alpha) + \cdots \tag{10.54a}$$

and

$$\varphi(t) \simeq \alpha \varphi_0\, \delta(t) + \alpha \varphi_1\, \delta(t - \alpha) + \alpha \varphi_2\, \delta(t - 2\alpha)$$
$$+ \cdots + \alpha \varphi_n\, \delta(t - n\alpha) + \cdots \tag{10.54b}$$

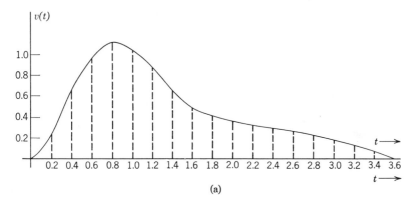

(a)

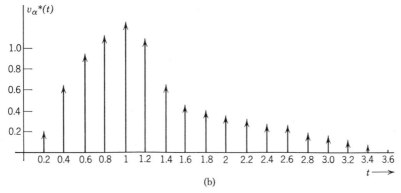

(b)

Figure 10.13   (a) $v(t)$. (b) Approximation of $(1/\alpha)v(t)$ by a train of impulses.

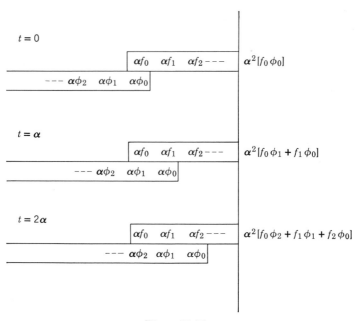

Figure 10.14

In the graphical convolution a mirror image of one of the functions, say $\varphi(t)$, is taken about the vertical axis. This imaged function is shifted in a positive direction by an amount t_0. The area under the product curve of the two impulse trains is the value of $f * \varphi$ at $t = t_0$. The convolution of two impulses is again an impulse of strength equal to the product of the strengths of the individual impulses. It is therefore very simple to convolve the two sequences of the impulse functions. The graphical picture of convolution in such cases is considerably facilitated by imagining that the two sequences are written on the two strips of paper (Fig. 10.14). The sequence for $\varphi(t)$ is written in reverse order as required by its imaging about the vertical axis. The sequence for $f(t)$ is written on a fixed strip, whereas the sequence for $\varphi(t)$ is written in reverse order on a movable strip which can slide past the other strip and can be progressed one position at a time. At $t = 0$ the two impulses αf_0 and $\alpha \varphi_0$ superimpose, and the value of $f(t) * \varphi(t)$ at $t = 0$ is an impulse of strength $\alpha^2 f_0 \varphi_0$. At time $t = \alpha$ the φ strip progresses one position, and the two impulses from each sequence superimpose upon one another. The value of the convolution at $t = \alpha$ is therefore an impulse of strength $\alpha^2(f_0 \varphi_1 + f_1 \varphi_0)$ (see Fig. 10.14). Similarly, at $t = 2\alpha$, the φ strip progresses two positions and the value of the convolution is given by an impulse of strength $\alpha^2(f_0 \varphi_2 + f_1 \varphi_1 + f_2 \varphi_0)$. It can be seen that, in general, the value of convolution at

$t = n\alpha$ is given by[3]

$$f(t) * \varphi(t) \big|_{t=n\alpha} = \alpha^2(f_0\varphi_n + f_1\varphi_{n-1} + f_2\varphi_{n-2} + \cdots f_n\varphi_0)\, \delta(t - n\alpha)$$

$$= \alpha^2\, \delta(t - n\alpha) \sum_{m=0}^{n} f_m\varphi_{n-m} \tag{10.55}$$

We see that $f * \varphi$ is also a train of impulses separated by intervals of α. Therefore, $f * \varphi$ can be expressed as a sequence of impulses and the right-hand side of Eq. 10.55 represents the $(n + 1)$th term in this sequence. We may summarize the result as follows. If $f_0, f_1, f_2, f_3, \ldots, \varphi_0, \varphi_1, \varphi_2, \varphi_3, \ldots$, are the values of $f(t)$ and $\varphi(t)$ respectively at $t = 0, \alpha, 2\alpha, 3\alpha, \ldots$, then convolution of $f(t)$ with $\varphi(t)$ can be approximated by a sequence of impulses at intervals of α seconds, as given by

$$f(t) * \varphi(t) \simeq \alpha^2 f_0\varphi_0\, \delta(t) + \alpha^2(f_0\varphi_1 + \varphi_0 f_1)\, \delta(t - \alpha)$$

$$+ \alpha^2(f_0\varphi_2 + f_1\varphi_1 + f_2\varphi_0)\, \delta(t - 2\alpha) + \cdots$$

$$+ \cdots + \alpha^2\, \delta(t - n\alpha) \sum_{m=0}^{n} f_m\varphi_{n-m} + \cdots \tag{10.56}$$

$$= \alpha^2 \sum_{n} \left[\sum_{m=0}^{n} f_m\varphi_{n-m} \right] \delta(t - n\alpha) \tag{10.57}$$

The convolution of the two continuous functions $f(t)$ and $\varphi(t)$ is also a continuous function. However, we approximated both $f(t)$ and $\varphi(t)$ with sequences of impulse functions, and therefore the convolution is also a sequence of impulses. We must convert this sequence of impulses into a continuous function. To achieve this we reverse the process of approximation. Previously, we approximated a continuous function with a sequence of impulses. Now we would like to approximate a sequence of impulses by a continuous function. Let us denote the convolution of $f(t)$ and $\varphi(t)$ by a function $r(t)$.

$$r(t) = f(t) * \varphi(t) \tag{10.58}$$

The function $r(t)$ may now be approximated by a sequence of impulses at intervals of α seconds.

$$r(t) \simeq \alpha r_0\, \delta(t) + \alpha r_1\, \delta(t - \alpha) + \alpha r_2\, \delta(t - 2\alpha)$$

$$+ \cdots + \alpha r_n\, \delta(t - n\alpha) + \cdots \tag{10.59}$$

[3] This equation holds true when both $f(t)$ and $\varphi(t)$ are causal. For a general case, the summation must be carried over for $m = -\infty$ to ∞.

A comparison of Eqs. 10.56 and Eq. 10.59 yields

$$r_0 = r(0) = \alpha f_0 \varphi_0$$
$$r_1 = r(\alpha) = \alpha(f_0\varphi_1 + f_1\varphi_0)$$
$$r_2 = r_2(2\alpha) = \alpha(f_0\varphi_2 + f_1\varphi_1 + f_2\varphi_0) \qquad (10.60)$$
$$r_n = r(n\alpha) = \alpha \sum_{m=0}^{n} f_m \varphi_{n-m}$$

The values of $r(t)$ at $t = 0, \alpha, 2\alpha, 3\alpha, \ldots$, etc. are thus found from Eq. 10.60. These values are plotted on a graph. A smooth curve through these points represents the desired function $r(t) = f(t) * \varphi(t)$. We shall demonstrate the procedure by an example.

Example 10.5

A voltage $v(t)$ shown graphically in Fig. 10.13a is applied to a series R-C network in Fig. 10.15. We shall find the output voltage $r(t)$ by using the numerical method discussed above to evaluate the convolution.

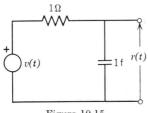

The transfer function of the circuit is $1/(s + 1)$ and the impulse response $h(t)$ is $e^{-t}u(t)$. The voltage $r(t)$ can be found by convolving $h(t)$ with $v(t)$.

$$r(t) = h(t) * v(t) \qquad (10.61)$$

Figure 10.15

Both e^{-t} and $v(t)$ are approximated by a sequence of impulses at intervals of $\alpha = 0.1$ seconds in Figs. 10.12 and 10.13. From these figures one can represent both these functions as sequences of impulse functions. Note that $h_0, h_1, h_2, h_3, \ldots$, are given by 1, 0.904, 0.82, 0.73, 0.67, 0.606, $\ldots$, etc. as shown in Fig. 10.12, and $v_0, v_1, v_2, v_3, \ldots$, are given by 0, 0.07, 0.2, 0.4, 0.65, $\ldots$, etc. as shown in Fig. 10.13. Actually the sequence for e^{-t} will have an infinite number of terms but the higher numbered terms become negligibly small and can be assumed to be zero. From Eq. 10.60 it follows that

$$r_0 = \alpha h_0 v_0 = (0.1)(1)(0) = 0$$
$$r_1 = 0.1[(1)(0.07) + (0.904)(0)] = 0.007$$
$$r_2 = 0.1[(1)(0.2) + (0.904)(0.07) + (0.82)(0)] = 0.0263$$
$$r_4 = 0.1[(1)(0.4) + (0.904)(0.2) + (0.82)(0.07) + (0.73)(0)] = 0.0638$$

In this way the values of $r(t)$ at $t = 0, 0.1, 0.2, 0.3, \ldots$, etc. may be computed. The computation is considerably facilitated by writing the two sequences on two sheets of paper. The sequence for $h(t)$ is written normally on one paper and the sequence for $v(t)$ is written from right to left. The two sequences are superimposed in a manner described previously. The computation can be easily

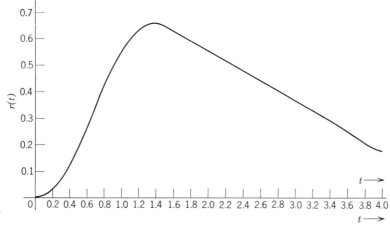

Figure 10.16

programmed on a digital computer. A general program for a computer may be prepared to evaluate the convolution of any two functions by the above procedure. The values of $r(t)$ thus obtained are plotted in Fig. 10.16, and a smooth curve is drawn through these points.

2. Straight-Line Segment Approximation

Numerical evaluation of a convolution can also be performed by an alternative method of approximating either one or both of the functions to be convolved by straight lines. If a function $f(t)$ is approximated by straight line segments, then the second derivative of this approximated function yields a sequence of impulses. According to Eq. 10.47, the convolution of this sequence of impulses with another function $\varphi(t)$ yields the second derivative of the desired convolution of $f(t)$ and $\varphi(t)$. If

$$r(t) = f(t) * \varphi(t) \qquad (10.62)$$

then

$$r^{(2)}(t) = f^{(2)}(t) * \varphi(t) \qquad (10.63)$$

The result of this convolution is integrated twice to obtain the desired convolution of $f(t)$ and $\varphi(t)$. We shall demonstrate the effectiveness of this approach by considering the same example of the R-C network in Fig. 10.15. In this problem,

$$r(t) = h(t) * v(t)$$

where $h(t)$ is e^{-t} and $v(t)$ is shown graphically in Fig. 10.13a.

We shall approximate $v(t)$ by straight line segments and differentiate this approximated function twice to obtain the sequence of impulses.

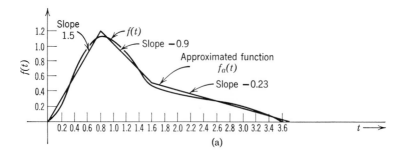

(a)

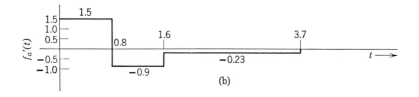

(b)

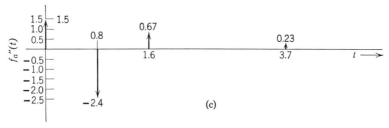

(c)

Figure 10.17 (continued).

This is shown in Figs. 10.17a to 10.17c. The function $f(t)$ is approximated by three straight line segments as shown in Fig. 10.17a. This approximated function, when differentiated twice, yields four impulses as shown in Fig. 10.17c. Next we convolve e^{-t} with this sequence of impulses. The result of the convolution is shown in Fig. 10.17e. The function in Fig. 10.17e is now integrated twice to obtain the desired convolution $h(t) * v(t)$. The final result is shown in Fig. 10.18. This compares fairly well with the result obtained by the previous method of impulse train approximation.

Alternatively one may replace the function e^{-t} by its approximate equivalent sequence of impulses and convolve this sequence of impulses with the sequence obtained for $v^{(2)}(t)$ (Fig. 10.17c).

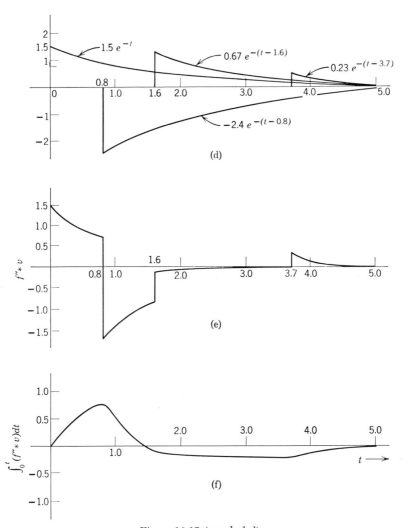

Figure 10.17 (*concluded*).

The accuracy of the straight line segment approach depends upon how closely the approximation has been effected. It is obvious that the accuracy can be improved as much as desired by approximating the function with a large number of straight line segments to fit the curve closely.[4]

---

[4] To improve the accuracy, Guillemin has suggested differentiating the exact function first and then approximating the first derivative by straight line segments. See E. A. Guillemin, "Computational Techniques which Simplify the Correlation between Steady State and Transient Response of Filters and other Networks," *Proc. National Electronics Conference*, 1953, Vol. 9, 1954. Also see J. G. Truxal, *Automatic Feedback Control System Synthesis*, pp. 375–389, McGraw-Hill, New York, 1955.

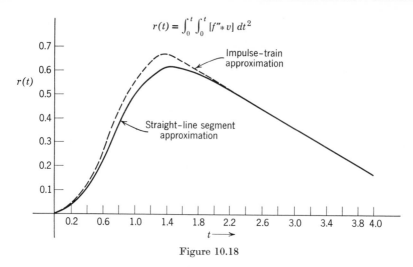

$$r(t) = \int_0^t \int_0^t [f'' * v] \, dt^2$$

Figure 10.18

A function may be approximated by a staircase function instead of straight line segments. In this case, it is necessary to differentiate the approximate function only once to obtain the sequence of impulses.

The numerical techniques for convolution discussed above can be conveniently used to determine the response of a system to a given driving function. If the description of the system is not available analytically, one may find the impulse response of the system experimentally. Actually it is much easier to obtain a unit step response $g(t)$ of a system experimentally than to obtain the unit impulse response. Hence in practice one usually obtains $g(t)$ experimentally. The unit impulse response $h(t)$ is then determined by differentiating $g(t)$. The process of differentiation may be simplified by approximating $g(t)$ by a staircase function which yields a sequence of impulses after differentiation. Hence $h(t)$ is obtained directly as a sequence of impulses and there is no further need to approximate for the purpose of convolution.

PROBLEMS

1. (a) Using the convolution integral, evaluate the response of a system. The unit impulse response $h(t)$ of a system and the driving function $f(t)$ are given below.

$h(t)$	$f(t)$
(1) $u(t)$	$tu(t)$
(2) $e^{-at}u(t)$	$tu(t)$
(3) $(1 - e^{-at})u(t)$	$e^{-at}u(t)$
(4) $u(t)$	$e^{-a|t|}$
(5) $e^{-at}u(t)$	$e^{-a|t|}$
(6) $te^{-at}u(t)$	$te^{-b|t|}$

(b) Verify these results by determining the response from frequency analysis techniques. (*Hint.* Verify that $f(t) * h(t) \rightharpoonup F(s)H(s)$. For pairs 4, 5 and 6, use the bilateral Laplace transform.)

2. (a) An all-pass lattice network has a unit impulse response $[2e^{-t}u(t) - \delta(t)]$. Using convolution techniques, evaluate the response of this network to a driving function $e^{t}u(-t)$. Sketch the driving function and the response. Comment.

(b) Verify the result by using frequency analysis techniques. (*Hint.* Use the bilateral Laplace transform.)

3. Evaluate $f_1 * f_2$ and $f_2 * f_1$ for the functions shown in Fig. P-10.3.

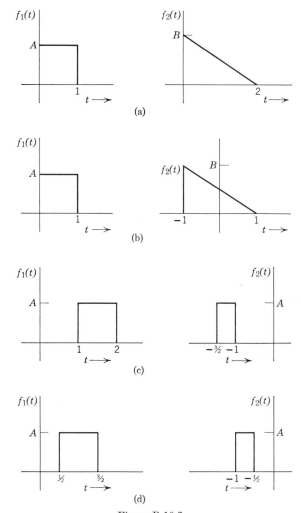

(a)

(b)

(c)

(d)

Figure P-10.3

4. In Problem 3, if $f_1(t)$ represents the unit impulse response of a system, determine by using the frequency domain techniques the response of the system if $f_2(t)$ represents in each case the driving function.

5. In Problem 3, if $f_1(t)$ and $f_2(t)$ represent the unit step response of the system and the driving function, respectively, evaluate by using superposition integral the response of the system.

6. In Problem 3, let $f_1(t)$ represent the unit impulse response of a system. The function $f_1(t)$ may be differentiated to obtain a sequence of impulses. Evaluate, using Eq. 10.49, the response $r(t)$ of the system if $f_2(t)$ represents the driving function. That is,

$$r(t) = \int_0^t \left(\frac{df_1}{dt} * f_2 \right) dt$$

7. A function $f(t)$, shown in Fig. P-10.7a, is convolved with a periodic impulse train shown in Fig. P-10.7b. Find the result by graphical convolution techniques. Verify the results, using frequency domain analysis.

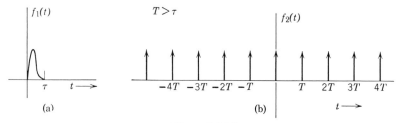

Figure P-10.7

8. Show that a causal function $f(t)$ can be expressed as a continuous sum of unit ramp functions as

$$f(t) = \int_0^t \frac{d^2f}{d\tau^2} (t - \tau) d\tau$$

Hint. Use the convolution theorem.

9. Find $\varphi(t)$ if it is given that

(a) $f(t) = \dfrac{d}{dt}[f(t) * \varphi(t)]$

(b) $f(t) = \displaystyle\int_0^t [f(t) * \varphi(t)] dt$

10. The unit impulse response $h(t)$ of a system is shown in Fig. P-10.10. Find the response of the system to $f(t)$ shown in Figs. P-10.10b to P-10.10d (next page).

11. (a) Determine the impulse response of the transmission line shown in Fig. 9.6, the response being the voltage at $x = l$.

(b) Repeat part (a) if the response is the current at $x = l$.

(c) Using convolution techniques, determine the voltage and current response at $x = l$ when a constant voltage E is applied at $x = 0$ and $t = 0$.

12. (a) Find the unit impulse response of the transmission line shown in Fig. 9.10b (for $t < 26$ seconds only), the response being the voltage at $x = 6u$.

(b) If a voltage $f(t)$, shown in Fig. 9.10a, is applied to the input terminals, determine the response at $x = 6u$, using convolution techniques. Solve for $0 < t < 26$ seconds only.

13. Determine the voltage at terminals bb' of the transmission line shown in Fig. 9.12a, using convolution techniques.

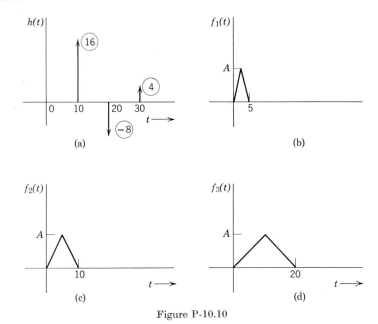

Figure P-10.10

14. Show that the current $i(t)$ in a series R-C circuit ($R = 1$ ohm, $C = 1$ farad) when driven by an eternal exponential voltage e^{-2t} is infinity. Generalize this result; that is, show that the response of a system to an eternal exponential signal e^{st} is infinity if e^{st} decays at a rate faster than the transient response of the system.

chapter 11

Introduction to Communication Systems

In communication engineering one is concerned with the transmission of various signals from one point to the other. We encounter this problem in radio and television broadcasting, long distance communication on telephone lines, satellite communication, remote control systems, telemetering, etc. In this chapter we shall study some of the systems of communication.

The signals are transmitted from one point to the other through a channel which may be in the form of a transmission line (such as a telephone channel) or merely an open space in which the signals bearing the desired information are radiated (such as radio and television broadcasting, satellite communication, etc.). Each of the signals to be transmitted generally has a small finite bandwidth compared to the bandwidth of the channel itself. It is therefore wasteful to transmit one signal at a time on the channel. The channel is being operated very much below its capacity to transmit information. We cannot, however, directly transmit more than one signal at a time because this will cause an interference between the signals, and it will be impossible to recover the individual signals at the receiving end. This means that it is not possible by a direct method to transmit more than one conversation on a telephone line or to broadcast more than one radio or television station at a time. We shall presently see that by using *frequency multiplexing* or *time multiplexing* techniques it is possible to transmit several signals simultaneously on a channel.

11.1 FREQUENCY MULTIPLEXING AND TIME MULTIPLEXING

As mentioned before, the transmission of one signal at a time on a channel is a highly wasteful situation. We can surmount this difficulty, however, if we can shift the frequency spectrum of various signals so that they occupy different frequency ranges without overlapping. We have already seen in Chapter 4 (frequency shifting) that it is possible to shift the frequency spectrum of a signal by modulating it (that is, multiplying the signal by a sinusoidal signal). Therefore, it should be possible to transmit a large number of signals at the same time on one channel by using modulation techniques.

For the case of several signals, the spectrum of each individual signal is translated by a proper amount so that there is no overlap between the spectra of various signals. At the receiving end, the various signals can be separated by using appropriate filters. The individual spectra which are thus separated, however, do not represent the original signal because they have been translated from their original position. Thus, to obtain the original signal, each individual spectrum is retranslated by a proper amount to bring it back to its original form.

Modulation, however, also serves another very useful purpose for systems which transmit signals by radiation in space. It can be shown from the theory of electromagnetic waves that a signal can be radiated effectively only if the radiating antenna is of the order of one-tenth or more of the wavelength corresponding to the frequencies of signals to be radiated. For human speech, the maximum frequency is about 10,000 cps, which corresponds to a minimum wavelength of 30,000 meters. Thus, to radiate electromagnetic waves corresponding to the frequency range of the human voice, one would need an antenna of several miles in length. This is rather impractical. The process of modulation shifts the frequency spectrum to any desired higher frequency range making it easier to radiate by electromagnetic waves. In practice all the radio and television signals are modulated, thus in effect shifting the frequency spectrum of the desired signal to a very high frequency range. Modulation, therefore, not only allows the simultaneous transmission of several signals without interfering with each other, but also makes it possible to transmit (radiate) these signals effectively.

The process of modulation discussed above is not the only way of transmitting several signals simultaneously on a channel. We shall presently show that a bandlimited signal (a signal which has no spectral components beyond a certain frequency f_m cps) is uniquely specified by its values at intervals $1/(2f_m)$ seconds (the uniform sampling theorem). It will be shown that the complete signal can be reconstructed from the knowledge of the signal at these instants alone. We therefore need to transmit only the samples of the signal at these finite number of instants. The channel is thus occupied only at these instants and conveys no signals for the rest of the time. During this idle period we may transmit the samples of other signals. We can thus interweave the samples of several signals on the channel. At the receiving end, these samples can be separated by a proper synchronous detector.

We can therefore transmit several signals simultaneously on a channel, provided that these signals can be separated at the receiving end. Each signal can be specified in the time domain or the frequency domain. Therefore, at the receiving end, we may recover the individual signals either in the time domain or the frequency domain. In the method of frequency translation, all of the signals are mixed in the time domain, but their spectra are so separated that they occupy different frequency bands. At the receiving end, we can recover the various individual signals by using proper filters. Here, we have recovered the spectrum of individual signals, and hence this method actually separates at the receiving end the various signals in the frequency domain. This approach, where different signals share the different frequency intervals, is known as *frequency multiplexing*. In the latter approach, the samples of various signals are interweaved, and the samples of individual signals can be separated at the receiving end by the proper synchronous detector. In this method we actually recover the various signals in the time domain. It will be seen later that the frequency spectra of all these signals occupy the same frequency range and are actually mixed. This approach, where all of the signals share the different time intervals, is known as *time multiplexing*.

Both of these techniques can be studied conveniently, using the convolution theorem derived in Chapter 4. This theorem is perhaps the most powerful tool in frequency analysis and communication theory. The modulation theorem and the sampling theorem are merely special cases of the convolution theorem. In Chapter 10, we studied convolution and its graphical interpretation in great detail. In the present chapter the concept of convolution will be extensively used to study basic communication systems. We shall briefly review the convolution theorem and show that the sampling theorem and the modulation theorem follow as special cases of convolution.

11.2 THE MODULATION AND SAMPLING THEOREMS

It was shown in Chapter 4 that if
$$f_1(t) \leftrightarrow F_1(\omega)$$
$$f_2(t) \leftrightarrow F_2(\omega)$$
then
$$f_1(t) * f_2(t) \leftrightarrow F_1(\omega)F_2(\omega) \qquad \text{(time convolution theorem)}$$
and
$$f_1(t)f_2(t) \leftrightarrow \frac{1}{2\pi}[F_1(\omega) * F_2(\omega)] \qquad \text{(frequency convolution theorem)}$$

Thus the convolution of two functions in the time domain is equivalent to the multiplication of their spectra in the frequency domain. Similarly, the multiplication of two functions in the time domain implies a convolution of their spectra in the frequency domain.

It was shown in Chapter 10 (Eq. 10.15) that the convolution of a unit impulse function with a function $f(t)$ reproduces the function itself, that is,

$$f(t) * \delta(t) = f(t) \qquad\qquad (11.1a)$$

$$f(t) * \delta(t - T) = f(t - T) \qquad\qquad (11.1b)$$

The modulation theorem and the sampling theorem will now be derived, using the concept of convolution.

1. The Modulation from the Convolution Theorem

We shall now show that the modulation theorem is really a special case of the convolution theorem (frequency convolution). A sinusoidal signal $\cos \omega_c t$ is said to be *amplitude-modulated* by a signal $f(t)$ when the signal $\cos \omega_c t$ is multiplied by $f(t)$. The spectral density function of the amplitude-modulated signal $f(t) \cos \omega_c t$ will now be determined. Modulation obviously represents the multiplication of two signals, $f(t)$ and $\cos \omega_c t$, in the time domain, and hence the spectral density function of the modulated signal $f(t) \cos \omega_c t$ is obtained by convolving the spectral density functions of $f(t)$ and $\cos \omega_c t$.

Let $F(\omega)$ represent the Fourier transform (spectral density function) of $f(t)$. The transform of $\cos \omega_c t$ is given by two impulses $\pi[\delta(\omega - \omega_c) + \delta(\omega + \omega_c)]$ (Table 4.1).
$$f(t) \leftrightarrow F(\omega)$$
$$\cos \omega_c t \leftrightarrow \pi[\delta(\omega + \omega_c) + \delta(\omega - \omega_c)] = \Phi(\omega)$$

Therefore, according to the convolution theorem,

$$f(t) \cos \omega_c t \leftrightarrow \frac{1}{2\pi} [F(\omega) * \Phi(\omega)] = \frac{1}{2} F(\omega) * [\delta(\omega + \omega_c) + \delta(\omega - \omega_c)]$$

From Eq. 11.1 it follows that

$$f(t) \cos \omega_c t \leftrightarrow \frac{1}{2} [F(\omega + \omega_c) + F(\omega - \omega_c)] \qquad (11.2a)$$

Similarly, it can be shown that

$$f(t) \sin \omega_c t \leftrightarrow \frac{j}{2} [F(\omega + \omega_c) - F(\omega - \omega_c)] \qquad (11.2b)$$

This is the same result as that obtained in Chapter 4 (Eq. 4.54).

We therefore conclude that the multiplication of a signal $f(t)$ by a sinusoidal signal of the frequency ω_c translates its spectrum by $\pm\omega_c$.

We could have obtained these results (Eq. 11.2) directly by graphical convolution of $F(\omega)$ with the spectrum of $\cos \omega_c t$. $F(\omega)$ in general may

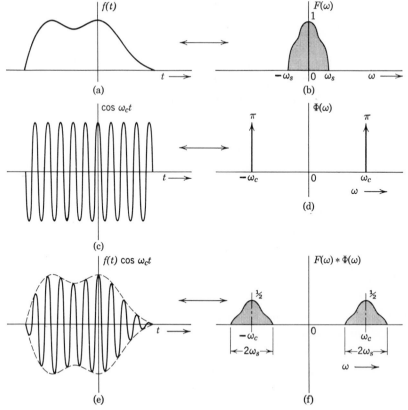

Figure 11.1

be complex, and hence strictly speaking its representation as a real function of ω in Fig. 11.1 may not be adequate. But it suffices to indicate our line of reasoning used in evaluating the convolution by graphical techniques. We fold back $\Phi(\omega)$ about the vertical axis $\omega = 0$. Since $\Phi(\omega)$ is an even function, the folded function is the same as $\Phi(\omega)$. We now progress the two impulses in a positive direction, and find that until $\omega = \omega_c - \omega_s$ the convolution is zero. But beyond this frequency the impulse originally located at $-\omega_c$ will reproduce $F(\omega)$ at $\omega = \omega_c$. Similarly, when we move the pair of impulses in a negative direction, the other impulse will reproduce $F(\omega)$ at $\omega = -\omega_c$. Since the impulses have a strength of π, we get

$$F(\omega) * \Phi(\omega) = \pi[F(\omega + \omega_c) + F(\omega - \omega_c)]$$

Hence

$$f(t) \cos \omega_c t \leftrightarrow \tfrac{1}{2}[F(\omega + \omega_c) + F(\omega - \omega_c)]$$

Similarly, it can be shown that

$$f(t) \sin \omega_c t \leftrightarrow \frac{j}{2}[F(\omega + \omega_c) - F(\omega - \omega_c)]$$

2. The Sampling Theorem from the Convolution Theorem

The sampling theorem has a deep significance in communication theory. It states the following.

A bandlimited signal which has no spectral components above a frequency f_m cycles per second is uniquely determined by its values at uniform intervals less than $1/2f_m$ seconds apart.

This theorem is known as the *uniform sampling theorem* since it pertains to the specification of a given signal by its samples at uniform intervals of $1/2f_m$ seconds.[1] This implies that if the Fourier transform of $f(t)$ is zero beyond a certain frequency $\omega_m = 2\pi f_m$, then the complete information about $f(t)$ is contained in its samples spaced uniformly at a distance less than $1/2f_m$ seconds. This is illustrated in Fig. 11.2. The function $f(t)$ is sampled once every T seconds ($T \leqslant 1/2f_m$) or at a rate greater than or

[1] This theorem is actually a special case of the general sampling theorem which is stated.

If a signal is bandlimited and if the time interval is divided into equal parts forming subintervals such that each subdivision comprises an interval T seconds long where T is less than $1/2f_m$, and if one instantaneous sample is taken from each subinterval in any manner, then a knowledge of the instantaneous magnitude of each sample plus a knowledge of the instants within each subinterval at which the sample is taken contains all of the information of the original signal.

See, for instance, H. S. Black, *Modulation Theory*, Van Nostrand, New York, 1953, p. 41.

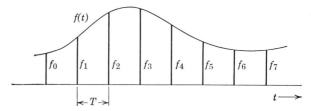

Figure 11.2

equal to $2f_m$ samples per second. The successive samples are labeled as $f_0, f_1, f_2, \ldots$, etc. It follows from the sampling theorem that these samples contain the information about $f(t)$ at every value of t. The sampling rate, however, must be at least twice the highest frequency f_m present in the spectrum of $f(t)$. To say it another way, the signal must be sampled at least twice during each period or cycle of its highest frequency component.

The sampling theorem can be easily proved with the help of the frequency convolution theorem. Consider a band-limited signal $f(t)$ which has no spectral components above f_m cycles per second. This means that $F(\omega)$, the Fourier transform of $f(t)$, is zero for $|\omega| > \omega_m$ ($\omega_m = 2\pi f_m$). Suppose we multiply the function $f(t)$ by a periodic impulse function $\delta_T(t)$ (Fig. 11.3c). The product function is a sequence of impulses located at regular intervals of T seconds and having strengths equal to the values of $f(t)$ at the corresponding instants. The product $f(t)\delta_T(t)$ indeed represents the function $f(t)$ sampled at a uniform interval of T seconds. We shall denote this sampled function by $f_s(t)$ (see Fig. 11.3e).

$$f_s(t) = f(t)\delta_T(t)$$

The frequency spectrum of $f(t)$ is $F(\omega)$. It was shown in Chapter 4 (Eq. 4.45) that the Fourier transform of a uniform train of impulse function $\delta_T(t)$ is also a uniform train of impulse function $\omega_0 \delta_{\omega_0}(\omega)$ (Fig. 11.3d). The impulses are separated by a uniform interval $\omega_0 = 2\pi/T$.

$$\delta_T(t) \longleftrightarrow \omega_0 \delta_{\omega_0}(\omega)$$

The Fourier transform of $f(t)\delta_T(t)$ will, according to the frequency convolution theorem, be given by the convolution of $F(\omega)$ with $\omega_0 \delta_{\omega_0}(\omega)$.

$$f_s(t) \longleftrightarrow \frac{1}{2\pi}[F(\omega) * \omega_0 \delta_{\omega_0}(\omega)]$$

Substituting $\omega_0 = 2\pi/T$, we get

$$f_s(t) \longleftrightarrow \frac{1}{T}[F(\omega) * \delta_{\omega_0}(\omega)] \qquad (11.3)$$

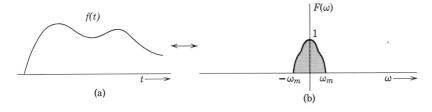

(a)   (b)

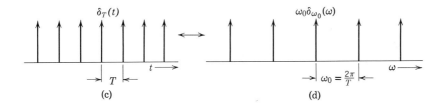

(c)   (d)

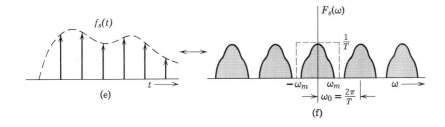

(e)   (f)

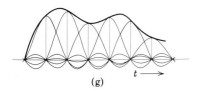

(g)

Figure 11.3

From Eq. 11.3 it is evident that the spectrum of the sampled signal $f_s(t)$ is given by the convolution of $F(\omega)$ with a train of impulses. Functions $F(\omega)$ and $\delta_{\omega_0}(\omega)$ (shown in Figs. 11.3*b* and 11.3*d*, respectively) can be convolved graphically by the procedure described in Section 10.4. In order to perform this operation, we fold back the function $\delta_{\omega_0}(\omega)$ about the vertical axis $\omega = 0$. Since $\delta_{\omega_0}(\omega)$ is an even function of ω, the folded function is the same as the original function $\delta_{\omega_0}(\omega)$. To perform the operation of convolution, we now progress the whole train of impulses

$[\delta_{\omega_0}(\omega)]$ in a positive ω direction. As each impulse passes across $F(\omega)$, it reproduces $F(\omega)$ itself. Since the impulses are spaced at a distance $\omega_0 = 2\pi/T$, the operation of convolution yields $F(\omega)$ repeating itself every ω_0 radian/second as shown in Fig. 11.3f. The spectral density function (the Fourier transform) of $f_s(t)$ is therefore the same as $F(\omega)$ but repeating itself periodically, every ω_0 radian/second. This function will be designated as $F_s(\omega)$. Note that $F(\omega)$ will repeat periodically without overlap as long as $\omega_0 \geqslant 2\omega_m$, or

$$\frac{2\pi}{T} \geqslant 2(2\pi f_m)$$

that is,

$$T \leqslant \frac{1}{2f_m} \tag{11.4}$$

Therefore, as long as we sample $f(t)$ at regular intervals less than $1/2f_m$ seconds apart, $F_s(\omega)$, the spectral density function of $f_s(t)$, will be a periodic replica of $F(\omega)$ and therefore contains all the information of $f(t)$. We can easily recover $F(\omega)$ from $F_s(\omega)$ by allowing the sampled signal to pass through a low-pass filter which will only allow frequency components below f_m and attenuate all the higher frequency components. It is therefore evident that the sampled function $f_s(t)$ contains all of the information of $f(t)$. To recover $f(t)$ from $f_s(t)$, we allow the sampled function $f_s(t)$ to pass through a low-pass filter which permits the transmission of all of the components of frequencies below f_m and attenuates all of the components of frequencies above f_m. The ideal filter characteristic to achieve this is shown dotted in Fig. 11.3f.

Note that if the sampling interval T becomes larger than $1/2f_m$, then the convolution of $F(\omega)$ with $\delta_{\omega_0}(\omega)$ yields $F(\omega)$ periodically. But now there is an overlap between successive cycles, and $F(\omega)$ cannot be recovered from $F_s(\omega)$. Therefore, if the sampling interval T is made too large, the information is partly lost, and the signal $f(t)$ cannot be recovered from the sampled signal $f_s(t)$. This conclusion is quite logical since it is reasonable to expect that the information will be lost if the sampling is too slow. The maximum interval of sampling $T = 1/2f_m$ is also called the *Nyquist interval*.

In the preceding discussion $F(\omega) * \delta_{\omega_0}(\omega)$ was obtained graphically. The same result can also be readily derived by analytical procedure. We have

$$\delta_{\omega_0}(\omega) = \delta(\omega) + \delta(\omega - \omega_0) + \cdots + \delta(\omega - n\omega_0) + \cdots$$
$$+ \delta(\omega + \omega_0) + \cdots + \delta(\omega + n\omega_0) + \cdots$$
$$= \sum_{n=-\infty}^{\infty} \delta(\omega - n\omega_0)$$

From Eq. 11.3, it follows that

$$F_s(\omega) = \frac{1}{T}[F(\omega) * \delta_{\omega_0}(\omega)] = \frac{1}{T}\left[F(\omega) * \sum_{n=-\infty}^{\infty} \delta(\omega - n\omega_0)]\right]$$

$$= \frac{1}{T} \sum_{n=-\infty}^{\infty} F(\omega) * \delta(\omega - n\omega_0)$$

From Eq. 11.1 it follows that

$$F_s(\omega) = \frac{1}{T} \sum_{n=-\infty}^{\infty} F(\omega - n\omega_0) \tag{11.5}$$

The right-hand side of Eq. 11.5 represents function $F(\omega)$ repeating itself every ω_0 radian/sec. This is exactly the same result as obtained by graphical convolution.

Recovering f(t) from Its Samples

As discussed earlier, the original function can be recovered by passing the sampled function through a low-pass filter with a cutoff frequency ω_m. This is obviously an operation in the frequency domain. Because of the duality in the frequency domain and the time domain there is an equivalent operation in the time domain to recover $f(t)$ from its samples. We shall now explore this possibility.

Let us consider a signal $f(t)$ sampled at a minimum required rate $(2f_m$ samples per second). In this case

$$T = \frac{1}{2f_m} \quad \text{and} \quad \omega_0 = \frac{2\pi}{T} = 4\pi f_m = 2\omega_m$$

Hence Eq. 11.5 becomes

$$F_s(\omega) = \frac{1}{T} \sum_{n=-\infty}^{\infty} F(\omega - 2n\omega_m) \tag{11.6a}$$

As observed before, the spectrum $F(\omega)$ can be obtained by filtering $F_s(\omega)$ through a low-pass filter of cutoff frequency ω_m. It is obvious that such an operation of filtering is equivalent to multiplying $F_s(\omega)$ by a gate function $G_{2\omega_m}(\omega)$. Hence, from Eq. 11.6a, we get

$$F_s(\omega)G_{2\omega_m}(\omega) = \frac{1}{T} F(\omega)$$

Therefore

$$F(\omega) = T F_s(\omega)G_{2\omega_m}(\omega) \tag{11.6b}$$

The application of the time convolution theorem to Eq. 11.6b yields

$$f(t) = Tf_s(t) * \frac{\omega_m}{\pi} Sa(\omega_m t)$$

$$= f_s(t) * Sa(\omega_m t) \tag{11.6c}$$

The sampled function $f_s(t)$ is given by

$$f_s(t) = \sum_n f_n \delta(t - nT)$$

Where f_n is the nth sample of $f(t)$. Hence

$$f(t) = \sum_n f_n \delta(t - nT) * Sa(\omega_m t)$$

$$= \sum_n f_n Sa[\omega_m(t - nT)] \tag{11.6d}$$

It is obvious that $f(t)$ can be constructed in the time-domain from its samples according to Eq. 11.6d. Graphically each sample is multiplied by a sampling function and all of the resulting waveforms are added to obtain $f(t)$. This is shown in Fig. 11.3g.

Most of the signals, in practice, closely approximate the band-limited signals. It should be stated here that strictly speaking a band-limited signal does not exist. It can be shown that if a signal exists over a finite interval of time it contains the components of all frequencies.[2] However, for all signals, in practice, the spectral density functions diminish at higher frequencies. Most of the energy is carried by components lying within a certain frequency interval and, for all practical purposes, a signal may be considered to be bandlimited. The error introduced by ignoring high frequency components is negligible.

The sampling theorem is an important concept, for it allows us to replace a continuous bandlimited signal by a discrete sequence of its samples without the loss of any information. The information content of a continuous bandlimited signal is thus equivalent to discrete pieces of information. Since the sampling principle specifies substantially the least number of discrete values necessary to reproduce a continuous signal, the problem of transmitting such a signal is reduced to that of transmitting a finite number of values.

[2] This follows from the Paley-Wiener criterion discussed in Chapter 6 (Section 6.15). If $F(\omega)$ is bandlimited $[F(\omega) = 0$, for $|\omega| > \omega_m]$, then $F(\omega)$ violates the Paley-Wiener condition and hence its inverse transform $f(t)$ exists for all negative values of time. Therefore a bandlimited signal exists over an infinite time interval. Conversely, a signal which exists only over a finite interval of time cannot be bandlimited.

Communication Systems

We are now ready to discuss various communication systems. As mentioned before, it is possible to transmit several signals simultaneously on a channel. There are two commonly used techniques for this purpose: the frequency sharing (frequency multiplexing) and the time sharing (time multiplexing) techniques. It is also possible to use a combination of both of the techniques.

In frequency multiplexing, the spectra of various signals are translated by proper amounts so as to occupy different frequency intervals. In time multiplexing, the various signals are sampled, and the samples of all of the signals are interlaced. We shall now discuss various methods of transmitting and recovering these signals, using these techniques.

11.3 AMPLITUDE MODULATION: SUPPRESSED-CARRIER (AM/SC) SYSTEMS

This technique essentially translates the frequency spectrum of the signal to be transmitted by multiplying it by a sinusoidal signal of the frequency by which the spectrum is desired to be translated. From the frequency convolution theorem, it is evident that the spectrum of $f(t) \cos \omega_c t$ is the same as that of $f(t)$, but shifted by $\pm \omega_c$ radians per second (Fig. 11.4e). That is, if

$$f(t) \leftrightarrow F(\omega)$$

then

$$f(t) \cos \omega_c t \leftrightarrow \tfrac{1}{2}[F(\omega + \omega_c) + F(\omega - \omega_c)]$$

The signal $\cos \omega_c t$ is called the *carrier*. The multiplication of $\cos \omega_c t$ by $f(t)$ is really equivalent to varying the carrier amplitude in proportion to $f(t)$. Hence, this mode of transmission is known as *amplitude modulation* (AM). The carrier signal $\cos \omega_c t$ is said to be *modulated* by the signal $f(t)$. Signal $f(t)$ is thus a *modulating signal*, and the carrier signal $\cos \omega_c t$ is the *modulated signal*.

The amplitude modulation therefore translates the frequency spectrum by $\pm \omega_c$ radians per second. To recover the original signal $f(t)$ from the modulated signal, it is necessary to retranslate the spectrum to its original position. The process of retranslation of the spectrum to its original position is referred to as *demodulation* or *detection*.

The spectrum of the modulated waveform (Fig. 11.4e) can be conveniently retranslated to the original position by multiplying the modulated signal by $\cos \omega_c t$ at the receiving end. Since multiplication in the time

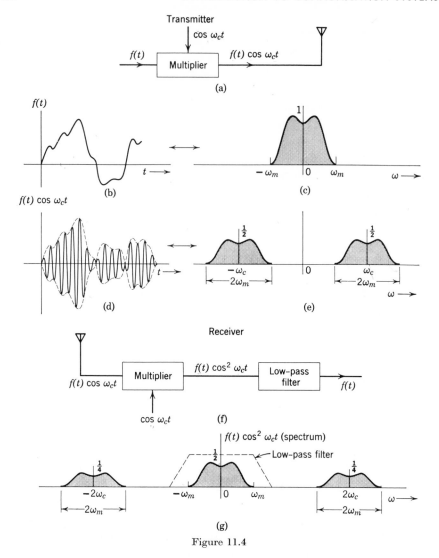

Figure 11.4

domain is equivalent to convolving the spectra in the frequency domain, it is evident that the spectrum of the resultant signal $[f(t) \cos^2 \omega_c t]$ will be obtained by convolving the spectrum of the received signal (Fig. 11.4d) with the spectrum of $\cos \omega_c t$ (two impulses at $\pm \omega_c$). A little reflection shows that this convolution yields the spectrum shown in Fig. 11.4g. This result may also be obtained directly from the identity:

$$f(t) \cos^2 \omega_c t = \tfrac{1}{2} f(t)[1 + \cos 2\omega_c t] = \tfrac{1}{2}[f(t) + f(t) \cos 2\omega_c t] \quad (11.7)$$

Therefore, if

$$f(t) \leftrightarrow F(\omega)$$

then

$$f(t) \cos^2 \omega_c t \leftrightarrow \tfrac{1}{2} F(\omega) + \tfrac{1}{4} F(\omega + 2\omega_c) + \tfrac{1}{4} F(\omega - 2\omega_c) \quad (11.8)$$

It is evident from the spectrum in Fig. 11.4g that the original signal $f(t)$ can be recovered by using a low-pass filter which will allow $F(\omega)$ to pass and will attenuate the remaining components centered around $\pm 2\omega_c$. A possible form of low-pass filter characteristic is shown (dotted) in Fig. 11.4g. The system required at the receiving end to recover the signal $f(t)$ from the received modulated signal $f(t) \cos \omega_c t$ is shown in Fig. 11.4f. It is interesting to observe that multiplication of $f(t)$ by $\cos \omega_c t$ translates its spectrum by $\pm \omega_c$. The new spectrum can be retranslated to its original position by another translation of $\pm \omega_c$ which is accomplished by the multiplication of the modulated signal by $\cos \omega_c t$ at the receiver (in the process, we get an additional spectrum at $\pm 2\omega_c$ which is filtered out). The process at the receiving end is therefore exactly the same as that required at the transmitting end. Hence this method of recovering the original signal is called *synchronous detection* or *coherent detection*.

It is obvious from this discussion that in this system it is necessary to generate the carrier signal $\cos \omega_c t$ at the receiving end exactly at the same frequency as that of the carrier at the transmitting end. Any error in the carrier frequencies at the transmitter and the receiver gives rise to serious distortion. This can be easily shown. Suppose the carrier frequency at the transmitting end is ω_c and that at the receiving end is $(\omega_c + \Delta\omega)$. Then the modulated signal received at the receiver is $f(t) \cos \omega_c t$. The signal is now multiplied by $\cos (\omega_c + \Delta\omega)t$ to demodulate at the receiving end. The resultant signal is $f(t) \cos \omega_c t \cos (\omega_c + \Delta\omega)t$ and can be expressed as

$$f(t) \cos \omega_c t \cos (\omega_c + \Delta\omega)t = \tfrac{1}{2} f(t) [\cos \Delta\omega t + \cos (2\omega_c + \Delta\omega)t]$$

The term $\cos (2\omega_c + \Delta\omega)$ represents a spectrum centered at frequency $(2\omega_c + \Delta\omega)$ and is filtered out by a low-pass filter. The output of this filter is therefore given by $\tfrac{1}{2} f(t) \cos \Delta\omega t$. Thus, instead of recovering the original signal $f(t)$, we obtain the signal $f(t) \cos \Delta\omega t$. Hence, it is of utmost importance to have identical carrier frequencies at the transmitting and the receiving terminals. To achieve this objective, a very expensive and elaborate circuitry is required at the receiver. This is not practical for commercial communication systems such as radio and television. In such cases, a large amount of the carrier is also transmitted along with the modulated signal. This, however, represents a wastage in the power of the carrier since the carrier by itself does not carry any information. Therefore, when the power requirements are critical, the carrier is not transmitted along with the modulated signal $f(t) \cos \omega_c t$, but is generated at the receiver for the purpose of demodulation. The price, of course, is paid in terms of expensive and elaborate circuitry at the receiver. Such systems of communication are known as *suppressed-carrier* (SC), amplitude-modulated (AM) systems and are abbreviated by AM/SC. In such systems a very small amount of the carrier (pilot carrier) is transmitted along with the modulated signal. At the receiver, the pilot carrier is separated by an appropriate filter and is amplified. This weak carrier signal is then used to lock the local oscillator which generates a strong carrier signal of the same frequency as that of the carrier at the transmitter.

The systems where a large amount of carrier power is transmitted along with the modulated signal $f(t) \cos \omega_c t$ need very simple circuitry at the receiver for the purpose of demodulation, but the price is paid in terms of large amounts of power wasted in carrier transmission. Such systems are simply known as *amplitude-modulated* (AM) systems. Commercial AM radio and television are examples of this system. This type of system is discussed in detail in a later section.

Techniques of Frequency Translation

It is obvious from the modulation theorem that a spectrum of any signal can be translated by $\pm \omega_c$ radians per second in the frequency domain by multiplying the signal with a sinusoidal signal of frequency ω_c. This, however, is not the only way to achieve this. We can easily show that a spectrum can be translated by an amount of $\pm \omega_c$ by multiplying the signal by any periodic signal of frequency ω_c, regardless of its waveform. This is obvious intuitively since any periodic waveform of frequency ω_c contains sinusoidal components of frequencies $0, \omega_c, 2\omega_c, 3\omega_c, \ldots$, etc. Hence, the multiplication of a signal $f(t)$ by an arbitrary periodic waveform of frequency ω_c will translate the spectrum of $f(t)$ by $0, \pm \omega_c, \pm 2\omega_c, \pm 3\omega_c$, etc. We are, however, interested only in that part of the spectrum centered around $\pm \omega_c$. This desired spectrum can be separated by using a bandpass filter which will allow to pass the components of frequencies centered around $\pm \omega_c$ and will attenuate all of the other frequencies.

As an example, consider a signal $f(t)$ (Fig. 11.5a) whose spectrum $F(\omega)$ is shown in Fig. 11.5b. Multiplication of this signal by a sinusoidal signal $\cos \omega_c t$ (Fig. 11.5e) shifts the spectrum by $\pm \omega_c$ (Fig. 11.5f). Now, instead of a sinusoidal signal, we shall multiply $f(t)$ by a square wave (Fig. 11.5g) of frequency ω_c. The spectrum of a periodic square wave $p(t)$ is shown in Fig. 11.5h. This spectrum $P(\omega)$ is a sequence of impulses located at $\omega = 0, \pm \omega_c, \pm 3\omega_c, \pm 5\omega_c, \ldots$, etc. (see Fig. 4.21). It is evident that

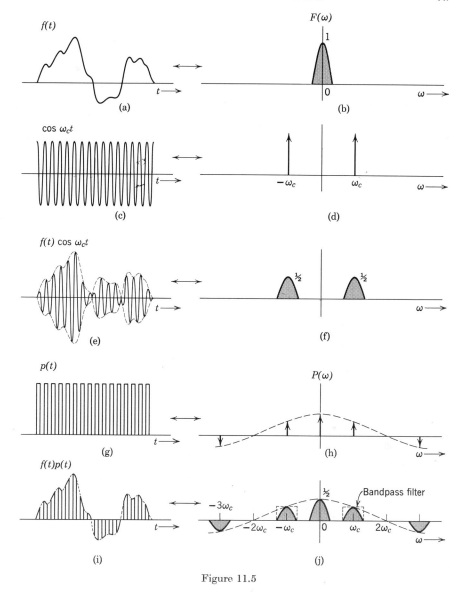

Figure 11.5

the spectrum of $f(t)p(t)$ is given by $(1/2\pi)F(\omega) * P(\omega)$. The result of this convolution performed graphically is shown in Fig. 11.5j.

It can be easily seen from this figure that the multiplication of $f(t)$ by $p(t)$ shifts the spectrum of $f(t)$ by $\omega = 0$, $\pm\omega_c$, $\pm 3\omega_c$, $\pm 5\omega_c$, ..., etc. This result is true for any periodic function of frequency ω_c, regardless of its waveform. In the special case of a square wave, the even harmonics $\pm 2\omega_c$, $\pm 4\omega_c$, ..., etc. are zero. But for a general periodic signal this need not be the case. We therefore conclude that multiplication of a signal $f(t)$ by any periodic signal of frequency ω_c, regardless of the waveform, shifts its spectrum by $\omega = 0, \pm\omega_c, \pm2\omega_c, \pm3\omega_c, \dots$, etc. This result can be readily obtained analytically. Let $\varphi(t)$ be a periodic signal of frequency f_c cps ($\omega_c = 2\pi f_c$). The Fourier transform of a general periodic signal was determined in Chapter 4 (Eq. 4.40). In general, we have

$$\varphi(t) \leftrightarrow 2\pi \sum_{n=-\infty}^{\infty} \Phi_n \, \delta(\omega - n\omega_c) \tag{11.9}$$

when Φ_n represents the coefficient of the nth harmonic in the exponential Fourier series for $\varphi(t)$. It follows from the convolution theorem that

$$f(t)\varphi(t) \leftrightarrow \frac{1}{2\pi} F(\omega) * 2\pi \sum_{n=-\infty}^{\infty} \Phi_n \, \delta(\omega - n\omega_c)$$

$$\leftrightarrow \sum_{n=-\infty}^{\infty} \Phi_n F(\omega) * \delta(\omega - n\omega_c)$$

$$\leftrightarrow \sum_{n=-\infty}^{\infty} \Phi_n F(\omega - n\omega_c) \tag{11.10}$$

It is evident from Eq. 11.10 that the spectrum of $f(t)\varphi(t)$ contains the spectrum $F(\omega)$ itself and $F(\omega)$ translated by $\pm\omega_c, \pm2\omega_c, \dots$, etc. Note that the amplitudes of the successive cycles of $F(\omega)$ are multiplied by constants $\Phi_0, \Phi_1, \Phi_2, \dots$, etc. When $\varphi(t)$ is a square wave, Φ_n can be found from Eq. 3.131a by substituting $T = 2\delta$ and $A = 1$.

$$\Phi_n = \frac{1}{2} \sum_{n=-\infty}^{\infty} Sa\left(\frac{n\pi}{2}\right)$$

Note that

$$Sa\left(\frac{n\pi}{2}\right) = \frac{\sin(n\pi/2)}{(n\pi/2)} = \begin{cases} (-1)^{(n-1)/2}\left[\dfrac{2}{n\pi}\right], & n \text{ odd} \\ 1 & , n = 0 \\ 0 & , n \text{ even} \end{cases}$$

Hence, from Eq. 11.9, we get

$$p(t) \leftrightarrow \pi\,\delta(\omega) + 2 \sum_{\substack{n=-\infty \\ (n\,\text{odd})}}^{\infty} \frac{(-1)^{(n-1)/2}}{n}\,\delta(\omega - n\omega_c) \tag{11.11}$$

and

$$f(t)p(t) \leftrightarrow \frac{1}{2} F(\omega) + \frac{1}{\pi} \sum_{\substack{n=-\infty \\ (n\,\text{odd})}}^{\infty} \frac{(-1)^{(n-1)/2}}{n} F(\omega - n\omega_c) \tag{11.12}$$

Figure 11.5j precisely represents the spectrum represented by Eq. 11.12.

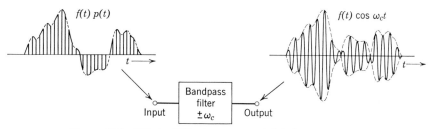

Figure 11.6   Effect of filtering on a modulated square wave.

In amplitude modulation, however, we are interested in the frequency spectrum centered around $\pm\omega_c$ only. This can be obtained by using a bandpass filter which allows to pass the frequency components centered at $\pm\omega_c$ and attenuates the other frequency components. A simple R-L-C resonant circuit tuned at $\omega = \omega_c$ will pass a band of frequencies centered at $\pm\omega_c$, and will filter out the remaining frequency components. It is therefore evident that if we pass the signal $f(t)p(t)$ (Fig. 11.5i) through such a bandpass filter centered at $\pm\omega_c$, the resultant output will be given by $f(t)\cos\omega_c t$ as shown in Fig. 11.6.

The process of frequency translation is also called *frequency conversion* or *frequency mixing*. The systems which perform this function are called *frequency converters* or *frequency mixers*. A modulator or a demodulator both perform the operation of frequency translation, and hence they are also referred to as frequency converters or frequency mixers.

In our discussion of the techniques of frequency translation we shall often be referring to low-pass filters, high-pass filters, and bandpass filters. It is possible to design filters with magnitude characteristics (or phase characteristics) as close to the ideal characteristic as possible by using larger numbers of elements.[3] But in a large number of cases, the undesired frequency components to be filtered out are separated so widely from the desired frequency components that very simple forms of filters may be used.

Modulating Systems (Frequency Converters or Frequency Mixers)

We shall now consider some simple circuits to produce modulation. The process of modulation translates the frequency spectrum. Hence the response of a modulator contains frequencies that are different from those present in the input signal. It is therefore impossible to produce modulation by using linear time-invariant systems because the response of such systems cannot contain frequencies other than those present in the

[3] For information on filter design, see J. D. Ryder, *Networks, Lines and Fields*, Chapter 4, Prentice-Hall, Englewood Cliffs, N.J., 1960.

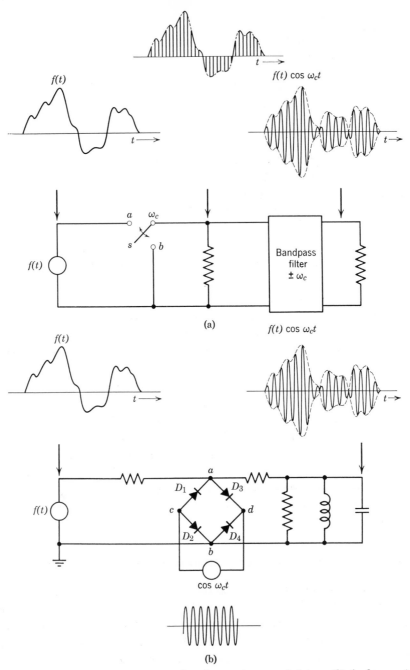

Figure 11.7 (a) Schematic diagram of a chopper-type modulator. (b) A chopper-type balanced modulator (ring modulator), using diodes as switches.

input signal. Modulation can, however, be effected by using time-variant linear systems (such as switching or chopping circuits) or circuits that use nonlinear elements. The nonlinearity provides the actual mechanism for modulation, but often a system producing modulation can be represented as a linear time-variant system.

The schematic diagram of a chopper type of modulator is shown in Fig. 11.7a. The switch s alternates between terminals a and b with frequency ω_c. For one half of the period the switch connects the terminal c to the signal $f(t)$, and for the remaining half period, terminal c is grounded. The output waveform at terminal c is therefore chopped at a frequency ω_c. The chopping operation may be viewed as a multiplication of $f(t)$ by a square wave $p(t)$. As discussed previously, such a chopped waveform contains the spectrum of $f(t)$ translated by $\omega = 0$, $\pm\omega_c$, $\pm3\omega_c, \ldots$, etc., and the desired modulated signal $f(t) \cos \omega_c t$ may be recovered by passing this chopped signal through a bandpass filter centered at $\pm\omega_c$ (Fig. 11.6).

A practical arrangement to achieve such a circuit is shown in Fig. 11.7b. The diodes in this circuit act as the necessary switch here. When the signal $\cos \omega_c t$ is of such polarity as to make the terminal c positive with respect to the terminal d, all of the diodes conduct, assuming that the signal $\cos \omega_c t$ is much larger than the signal $f(t)$. Under these conditions the voltage across the diode D_1 is the same as that across D_2, and hence the terminal a is at the same potential as that of terminal b. Thus, the output terminal a is connected to the ground. When the polarity of the signal $\cos \omega_c t$ makes the terminal d positive with respect to the terminal c, all of the diodes are reverse-biased and act as an open circuit. In this condition, the terminal a is connected to the signal $f(t)$ through a resistance R. It is obvious that the diodes switch the terminal a to the signal $f(t)$ and ground alternately at a frequency ω_c. At the output terminal, a parallel resonant circuit tuned to frequency ω_c acts as a bandpass filter. The output voltage is the desired modulated signal which is proportional to $f(t) \cos \omega_c t$. Note that the modulator circuit discussed here is a linear circuit since a multiplication of $f(t)$ by a constant will increase the output by the same constant. This circuit, however, is time-variant since its parameters change periodically. The modulator shown in Fig. 11.7b is known as a ring modulator.

A linear modulator, in general, may be described as a system whose gain (or the transfer function) can be varied with time by applying a time-varying signal at a certain point. The gain G may be varied proportional to the signal $f(t)$. Thus

$$G = Kf(t)$$

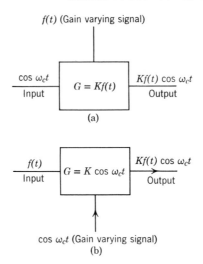

Figure 11.8   Linear modulating systems.

The carrier $\cos \omega_c t$ is applied at the input terminal (Fig. 11.8a). It is evident that the output will be a modulated signal $Kf(t) \cos \omega_c t$. Alternatively, a carrier may be used to vary the gain parameter (Fig. 11.8b), and $f(t)$ may be applied at the input terminals. The example of the ring modulator falls under the latter category. The ring modulator acts as a system whose gain varies between unity and zero at the carrier frequency. The variation of gain with time in this case is not sinusoidal, but rectangular. This, of course, gives rise to unwanted translations at higher harmonics of ω_c which are filtered out.

In practice, the gain parameters of active devices like vacuum tubes (μ) and of transistors (β) depend upon the values of bias voltages and currents. Thus, the gain of these devices can be made to vary with time by varying the bias signals, using appropriate signals. Details of such modulating (and demodulating) systems using vacuum tubes and transistors may be found in texts on electronic circuits.[4]

As stated before, the modulation can also be achieved by using nonlinear devices. A typical nonlinear device characteristic is shown in Fig. 11.9a. A semiconductor diode is a good example of such a device.

A nonlinear characteristic such as this may be approximated by a power series.

$$i = ae + be^2$$

[4] C. L. Alley and K. W. Atwood, *Electronic Engineering*, Chapter 14, Wiley, New York, 1962; W. H. Evans, *Introduction to Electronics*, Chapter 10, Prentice-Hall, Englewood Cliffs, N.J., 1962.

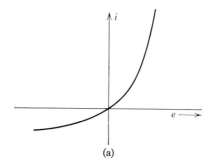

(a)

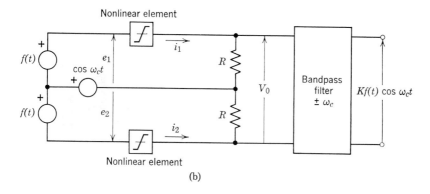

(b)

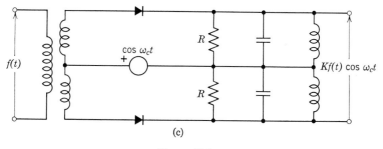

(c)

Figure 11.9

Transistors and vacuum tubes also exhibit similar relationships between the input and the output under large signal conditions. A possible arrangement for the use of nonlinear elements for modulation is shown in Fig. 11.9b.

To analyze this circuit, we shall consider the nonlinear element in series with the resistance R as a composite nonlinear element whose terminal voltage e and the current i are related by a power series:

$$i = ae + be^2$$

The voltages e_1 and e_2 (Fig. 11.9b) are given by

$$e_1 = \cos \omega_c t + f(t)$$

and

$$e_2 = \cos \omega_c t - f(t)$$

It is obvious that the currents i_1 and i_2 are given by

$$\begin{aligned} i_1 &= ae_1 + be_1^2 \\ &= a[\cos \omega_c t + f(t)] + b[\cos \omega_c t + f(t)]^2 \end{aligned} \qquad (11.13a)$$

and

$$i_2 = a[\cos \omega_c t - f(t)] + b[\cos \omega_c t - f(t)]^2 \qquad (11.13b)$$

The output voltage v_o is given by

$$v_o = i_1 R - i_2 R \qquad (11.14)$$

Substitution of Eq. 11.13 in Eq. 11.14 yields

$$v_o(t) = 2R[2bf(t) \cos \omega_c t + af(t)]$$

The signal $af(t)$ in this equation can be filtered out by using a bandpass filter tuned to ω_c at the output terminals. Semiconductor diodes can be conveniently used for the nonlinear elements in this circuit. A practical form of such a modulator is shown in Fig. 11.9c. All of the modulators discussed above generate a suppressed-carrier amplitude-modulated signal and are known as *balanced modulators*.

Demodulation (Detection) of Suppressed-Carrier Modulated Signals

At the receiver end, to recover the original signal $f(t)$, we need to demodulate the received signal $f(t) \cos \omega_c t$. As seen before, the process of demodulation is also equivalent to translation of the spectrum and can be achieved by multiplying the modulated signal $f(t) \cos \omega_c t$ by the signal $\cos \omega_c t$ (synchronous detection). Therefore, the same circuits as those used for the process of modulation can be employed for the purpose of demodulation. There is, however, one difference in the modulating and demodulating circuits. The output spectrum of the modulator was centered around frequencies $\pm \omega_c$, and hence it was necessary to use a bandpass filter tuned to ω_c at the output of the modulator circuit. In the case of the demodulator, however, the output spectrum is $F(\omega)$, and is centered at $\omega = 0$. Hence we need to use a low-pass filter at the output terminals of the demodulator in order to filter out the undesired high-frequency components which are centered at $\pm \omega_c$, $\pm 2\omega_c$, $\pm 3\omega_c$, ..., etc. The demodulator using switching (chopper-type) and using nonlinear

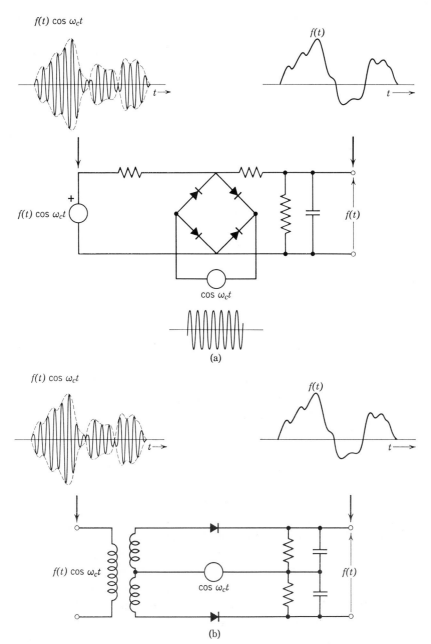

Figure 11.10   (a) A ring demodulator.   (b) A demodulator that uses nonlinear elements.

elements is shown in Figs. 11.10a and 11.10b. Note that the low-pass filter is provided at the output terminals of each circuit by an R-C circuit.

The demodulation may be accomplished by multiplying the modulated signal ($f(t)$ cos $\omega_c t$) by any periodic signal of frequency ω_c. If $\varphi(t)$ is a periodic signal of frequency ω_c, then its Fourier transform $\Phi(\omega)$ may be written as (Eq. 11.9):

$$\varphi(t) \leftrightarrow 2\pi \sum_{n=-\infty}^{\infty} \Phi_n \delta(\omega - n\omega_c)$$

It is obvious that if the modulated signal $f(t)$ cos $\omega_c t$ is multiplied by $\varphi(t)$, the resultant spectrum will be given by

$$f(t) \text{ cos } \omega_c t \ \varphi(t) \leftrightarrow \pi[F(\omega - \omega_c) + F(\omega + \omega_c)] * \sum_{n=-\infty}^{\infty} \Phi_n \delta(\omega - n\omega_c)$$

$$\leftrightarrow \pi \sum_{n=-\infty}^{\infty} \Phi_n\{F[\omega - (n + 1)\omega_c] + F[\omega - (n - 1)\omega_c]\}$$

It is evident that this spectrum contains a term $F(\omega)$ which can be filtered out by using a low-pass filter.

A Chopper Amplifier

The principle of frequency translation also finds a useful application in d-c and low-frequency amplifiers. Due to practical considerations of the sizes required for the coupling capacitors, it is very difficult to build amplifiers to amplify very low frequencies. Since the capacitor acts as an open circuit at lower frequencies, the sizes of the coupling capacitors required for a multistage amplifier for satisfactory gain are extremely large. Hence to amplify d-c signals and signals of very low frequencies, direct coupling is used. The direct coupling, however, introduces a serious problem of drift in the quiescent operating point of the amplifier. The drift introduced by the environmental changes varies the output signal, and this variation cannot be distinguished from that introduced by the input signal itself. This problem is overcome by using a chopper amplifier which essentially shifts the spectrum of the input signal from a lower frequency range to a suitable higher range of frequencies where it can be easily amplified. The amplified signal is now demodulated to get back the amplified form of the original low-frequency signal.

Any of the circuits discussed above may be used. It is customary, however, to use a mechanical chopper for modulation and demodulation. The mechanical chopper has a switch which vibrates between two terminals and makes and breaks the contacts with these terminals

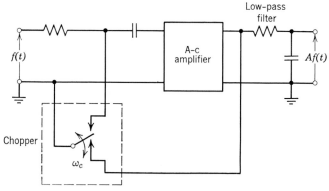

Figure 11.11   A chopper amplifier.

periodically. Since the processes of modulation and demodulation both need the carrier of the same frequency, it is necessary to use the same chopper for modulation and demodulation as shown in Fig. 11.11.

The capacitor at the input terminal filters out the component of the spectrum centered around $\omega = 0$ (d-c) and allows the rest of the components. The spectrum of the input signal is thus the same as that of the input signal $f(t)$ but shifted by $\omega = \pm\omega_c, \pm 3\omega_c, \pm 5\omega_c, \ldots$, etc. This signal is amplified and again multiplied by a square wave by the chopper at the output. This process retranslates the spectrum back to $\omega = 0$. There are also additional undesired components of the spectrum centered around $\omega = \pm\omega_c, \pm 2\omega_c, \ldots$, etc, which are filtered out at the output terminals by a low-pass filter (see Problem 18 at the end of the chapter).

11.4 SINGLE SIDEBAND TRANSMISSION

In the process of amplitude modulation, the original spectrum $F(\omega)$ is translated by $\pm\omega_c$ as shown in Fig. 11.12b. The unmodulated signal occupied the bandwidth of ω_m (Fig. 11.12a), whereas the same signal after modulation occupies a bandwidth of $2\omega_m$. It is therefore evident that the price of the frequency translation discussed thus far is paid in terms of doubling the bandwidth. However, this need not be the case. A glance at Fig. 11.12b shows that in transmitting the complete spectrum shown in this figure, we are transmitting redundant information. The spectrum $F(\omega)$ has been shifted at ω_c and $-\omega_c$. These two spectra are identical. Each of them contains the complete information of $F(\omega)$. So why transmit both spectra? Why not transmit only one of the two? This, however, is impossible because we have shown in Chapter 4 that for any physical signal, the spectrum is an even function of ω. A spectrum which

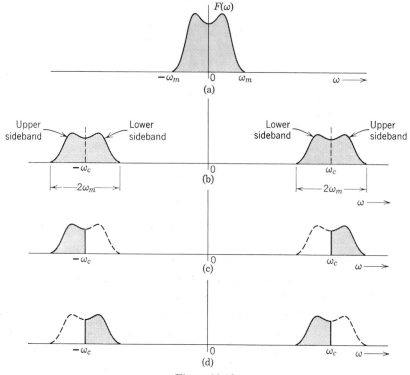

Figure 11.12

is not symmetrical about the vertical axis passing through the origin does not represent a real signal, and hence cannot be transmitted. But there is a way out of this. We observe that the spectrum centered around ω_c is composed of two parts: one portion lies above ω_c and is known as the upper sideband, and the other portion lies below ω_c and is known as the lower sideband. Similarly, the spectrum centered around $-\omega_c$ has upper and lower sidebands (Fig. 11.12b). We now observe from Fig. 11.12b, that the two upper sidebands (or the two lower sidebands) of the spectrum contain the complete information in $F(\omega)$. Hence, instead of transmitting the complete spectrum in Fig. 11.12b, it is sufficient to transmit only either the upper or the lower sidebands of the spectrum (shown in Figs. 11.12c and 11.12d). Note that the two upper sidebands or the two lower sidebands are an even function of ω and hence represent a real signal. The original signal $f(t)$ can be recovered from these upper or lower sidebands by appropriate frequency translation. To transmit the sidebands we now need only one half as much bandwidth (ω_m). This mode of transmission is referred to as *single sideband transmission* (SSB), in contrast to the *double sideband transmission* (DSB) discussed previously.

Generation of Single Sideband Signals[5]

To generate an SSB signal, all that is required is to filter out one of the sidebands from the modulated signals obtained from the balanced modulators discussed previously. The suppressed-carrier amplitude-modulated signal obtained from the balanced modulator is passed through an appropriate band-pass filter which will allow the desired sidebands to pass and filter out the remaining sidebands. The filter required to perform this function must have very nearly an ideal filter characteristic at frequency ω_c. In other words, the filter must have a sharp cutoff characteristic at ω_c in order to reject all of the frequencies on one side of ω_c and accept all of the frequencies on the other side of ω_c. From a practical standpoint, it is easier to design a filter with a sharp cutoff characteristic at lower frequencies. Hence the spectrum $F(\omega)$ is first translated to a lower frequency $\pm\omega_c$, where one of the sidebands is filtered out. After this filtering, the spectrum is then translated to a desired higher frequency $\pm\omega_c$ from $\pm\omega_{c_1}$. Actually, the translation may be achieved successively in more than one step. The spectrum $F(\omega)$ is translated to a first lower frequency $\pm\omega_{c_1}$ where one of the sidebands is attenuated. The single sideband spectrum at $\pm\omega_{c_1}$ still contains some residual undesired sidebands due to imperfect filtering. Hence this spectrum is translated to the intermediate frequency ω_{c_2}, where again it is subjected to the filtering process to remove the residual of the unwanted sidebands. This spectrum is finally translated to the desired higher frequency ω_c.

Phase-Shift Method

It is also possible to generate SSB signals by an indirect method of *spectral phase shifting*. For simplicity, let us assume that the signal $f(t)$ is $\cos \omega_s t$. Therefore, $F(\omega)$ is represented by two impulses at $\pm\omega_s$ (Fig. 11.13a). The modulated signal with carrier $\cos \omega_c t$ is given by $\cos \omega_s t \cos \omega_c t$ and has the spectrum of $F(\omega)$ shifted by $\pm\omega_c$ (Fig. 11.13b). The SSB spectrum (lower sideband) is given by two impulses at $\pm(\omega_c - \omega_s)$ as shown in Fig. 11.13c. It is evident that the signal corresponding to this SSB spectrum (Fig. 11.13c) is given by $\cos (\omega_c - \omega_s)t$. Therefore, generation of an SSB signal for a special case of $f(t) = \cos \omega_s t$ is equivalent to generation of signal $\cos (\omega_c - \omega_s)t$. From the trigonometric identity we have

$$\cos (\omega_c - \omega_s)t = \cos \omega_s t \cos \omega_c t + \sin \omega_s t \sin \omega_c t$$

[5] For more information on SSB techniques the reader is referred to a special issue of IRE on SSB transmission. Single Sideband Issue, *Proc. IRE*, Vol. 44, No. 12, December 1956.

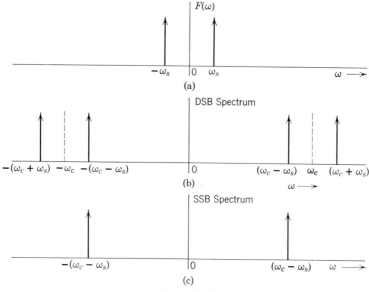

Figure 11.13

Thus, the desired SSB signal can be produced by adding $\cos \omega_s t \cos \omega_c t$ and $\sin \omega_s t \sin \omega_c t$. The signal $\cos \omega_s t \cos \omega_c t$ can be easily produced from any balanced modulator discussed previously. The signal $\sin \omega_s t \sin \omega_c t$ can be expressed as $\cos (\omega_s t - \pi/2) \cos (\omega_c t - \pi/2)$. Hence, this signal can be produced by a balanced modulator, provided that the signal $\cos \omega_s t$ and the carrier $\cos \omega_c t$ both are shifted in phase by $-\pi/2$ (Fig. 11.14). Although we have derived this result for a special case of $f(t) = \cos \omega_s t$, it holds true for any general waveform. This is because every waveform can be expressed as a continuous sum of sinusoidal (or exponential) signals. Hence, the SSB signal corresponding to $f(t)$ is given by

$$ f(t) \cos \omega_c t + f_p(t) \sin \omega_c t $$

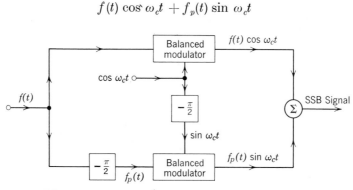

Figure 11.14   Phase-shift method of generating SSB.

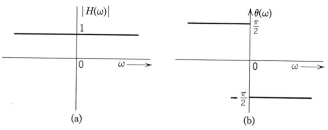

Figure 11.15

where $f_p(t)$ is the signal obtained by shifting the phase of each frequency component of $f(t)$ by $-\pi/2$. The schematic diagram of such an arrangement is shown in Fig. 11.14.

A rigorous proof for the above result for any general function $f(t)$ will now be given. A phase-shift system to shift the phase of the frequency components by $-\pi/2$ has a unit magnitude function. Thus, the magnitudes of the frequency components remain unchanged, but the phase of all of the positive frequency components is shifted by $-\pi/2$. Since the phase spectrum is an odd function of ω, the phases of all of the negative frequency components are shifted by $+\pi/2$. The magnitude and phase spectrum of a phase-shift system is shown in Fig. 11.15.

$$|H(\omega)| = 1$$

$$\theta(\omega) = \underline{/H(\omega)} = \frac{\pi}{2} - \pi u(\omega)$$

Therefore, the transfer function $H(\omega)$ of this phase-shift system is given by

$$H(\omega) = |H(\omega)|\, e^{j\theta(\omega)}$$

$$= e^{j[\pi/2 - \pi u(\omega)]}$$

and if

$$f(t) \leftrightarrow F(\omega)$$

then

$$f_p(t) \leftrightarrow F(\omega)e^{j[\pi/2 - \pi u(\omega)]}$$

$$= jF(\omega)e^{-j\pi u(\omega)} \tag{11.15}$$

and, from the modulation theorem, we have

$$f(t)\cos \omega_c t \leftrightarrow \tfrac{1}{2}[F(\omega + \omega_c) + F(\omega - \omega_c)] \tag{11.16a}$$

and, from Eqs. 11.15 and 11.2b, it follows that

$$f_p(t)\sin \omega_c t \leftrightarrow -\tfrac{1}{2}[F(\omega + \omega_c)e^{-j\pi u(\omega+\omega_c)} - F(\omega - \omega_c)e^{-j\pi u(\omega-\omega_c)}] \tag{11.16b}$$

and

$$[f(t) \cos \omega_c t + f_p(t) \sin \omega_c t] \leftrightarrow \tfrac{1}{2} F(\omega - \omega_c)[1 + e^{-j\pi u(\omega - \omega_c)}]$$
$$+ \tfrac{1}{2} F(\omega + \omega_c)[1 - e^{-j\pi u(\omega + \omega_c)}] \quad (11.17)$$

Note that

$$u(\omega - \omega_c) = \begin{cases} 0, & \omega < \omega_c \\ 1, & \omega > \omega_c \end{cases}$$

and

$$u(\omega + \omega_c) = \begin{cases} 0, & \omega < -\omega_c \\ 1, & \omega > -\omega_c \end{cases}$$

Hence

$$1 + e^{-j\pi u(\omega - \omega_c)} = \begin{cases} 2, & \omega < \omega_c \\ 0, & \omega > \omega_c \end{cases}$$

But this is, by definition, $2u(\omega_c - \omega)$. Hence

$$1 + e^{-j\pi u(\omega - \omega_c)} = 2u(\omega_c - \omega) \quad (11.18a)$$

and, similarly,

$$1 - e^{-j\pi u(\omega + \omega_c)} = 2u(\omega + \omega_c) \quad (11.18b)$$

Hence, from Eqs. 11.17 and 11.18, it follows that

$$[f(t) \cos \omega_c t + f_p(t) \sin \omega_c t] \leftrightarrow [F(\omega - \omega_c)u(\omega_c - \omega) + F(\omega + \omega_c)$$
$$\times u(\omega + \omega_c)] \quad (11.19)$$

The spectrum on the right-hand side of Eq. 11.19 precisely expresses the lower sidebands of $[F(\omega - \omega_c) + F(\omega + \omega_c)]$. The term $F(\omega - \omega_c)$ $\times u(\omega_c - \omega)$ represents the function $F(\omega - \omega_c)$ truncated in the region $\omega > \omega_c$ (suppression of the upper sideband), and $F(\omega + \omega_c)u(\omega + \omega_c)$ represents $F(\omega + \omega_c)$ truncated in the region $\omega < -\omega_c$ (suppression of the upper sideband). Thus, the signal in Eq. 11.17 represents the SSB signal with the upper sideband suppressed. If instead of adding we subtract the signals $f(t) \cos \omega_c t$ and $f_p(t) \sin \omega_c t$, the SSB signal with the suppressed lower sideband will result.

Demodulation of SSB Signals

To recover $f(t)$ from the SSB signal, we have to retranslate the spectrum (Figs. 11.12c or 11.12d) back to its original position ($\omega = 0$). This can be easily achieved by synchronous detection. Multiplication of the SSB signal by $\cos \omega_c t$ (synchronous detection) is equivalent to convolution of the spectrum of the SSB signal with the spectrum of $\cos \omega_c t$ (two impulses at $\pm \omega_c$). This is shown in Fig. 11.16 for the case of upper sidebands. The convolution yields $F(\omega)$ and an additional SSB signal translated at $\pm 2\omega_c$ which can be filtered out. Thus, the demodulation of SSB signals

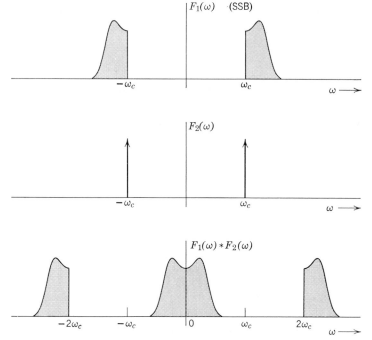

Figure 11.16   Demodulation of SSB signal.

can be accomplished by synchronous detection, and is identical to that used for AM DSB/SC signals. Either of the circuits in Fig. 11.10 may be used for this purpose of demodulation of SSB signals.

As mentioned before, wherever synchronous detection is involved, a small amount of the pilot carrier is transmitted along with the modulated signals. This is the case for both suppressed-carrier DSB and SSB systems. At the receiver end, the pilot carrier is separated by an appropriate filter and is amplified and used further to lock the frequency of the local oscillator. The signal of the local oscillator now has the same frequency as that of the carrier at the transmitter and can be used for synchronous detection.

The stringent requirement of providing a carrier of exactly the right frequency at the receiver and the complex circuitry required to achieve this has been the block in the path of a widespread use of suppressed-carrier systems (DSB and SSB). The degree of precision frequency control required[6] in the 2 to 30 mc frequency range is one part in 10^7. For such commercial communication systems as radio and television a much simpler system, particularly at the receiver, are desired. For such

[6] M. Schwartz: *Information Transmission, Modulation and Noise*, p. 111, McGraw-Hill, New York, 1959.

applications, therefore, a very large carrier power is transmitted. The modulation and demodulation of signals under these conditions is relatively simple and will now be discussed.

II.5 AMPLITUDE MODULATION (AM) WITH LARGE CARRIER POWER

We have seen that the suppressed-carrier systems need very complex circuitry at the receiver for the purpose of generating a carrier of exactly the right frequency required for synchronous detection. But such systems are very efficient from the point of view of power requirements at the transmitter. In point-to-point communications where there is one transmitter for each receiver, substantial complexity in the receiver system can be justified, provided that it results in a large enough saving in expensive high-power transmitting equipment. On the other hand, for a broadcast system with a multitude of receivers for each transmitter it is more economical to have one expensive high-power transmitter and simpler, less expensive receivers. For such applications a large carrier signal is transmitted along with the suppressed-carrier modulated signal $f(t) \cos \omega_c t$, thus obviating the need to generate the carrier signal at the receiving end. Therefore, the transmitted signal is now $e_m(t)$ given by

$$e_m(t) = f(t) \cos \omega_c t + A \cos \omega_c t \qquad (11.20a)$$

It is obvious that the spectrum $e_m(t)$ is the same as that of $f(t) \cos \omega_c t$ except that there are two additional impulses at $\pm \omega_c$ (Fig. 11.17). Therefore

$$e_m(t) \leftrightarrow \tfrac{1}{2}[F(\omega + \omega_0) + F(\omega - \omega_0)] + \pi A[\delta(\omega + \omega_c) + \delta(\omega - \omega_c)] \qquad (11.20b)$$

The modulated signal $e_m(t)$ is shown in Fig. 11.17. This signal (Eq. 11.20a) can be written as

$$e_m(t) = [A + f(t)] \cos \omega_c t \qquad (11.21)$$

It is evident that the modulated signal $e_m(t)$ may be viewed as a carrier signal $\cos \omega_c t$, whose amplitude is given by $[A + f(t)]$. The envelope of the modulated signal is the waveform $f(t)$ shifted by a constant A. Therefore, the recovery of signal $f(t)$ in this case simply reduces to envelope detection. Note that the quantity A should be kept sufficiently large in order to preserve the envelope waveform exactly as $f(t)$. If A is not large enough (Fig. 11.17e), then the envelope waveform is not the same as that of $f(t)$. Under these conditions, $f(t)$ cannot be recovered by

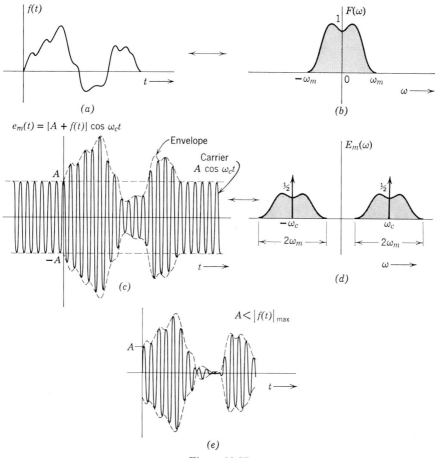

Figure 11.17

a simple process of envelope detection, but has to be detected by a method of synchronous detection (multiplying by cos $\omega_c t$). Therefore, A should be made large enough so that $[A + f(t)]$ is always positive. This is possible if

$$A > |f(t)|_{\max} \qquad (11.22)$$

The techniques of envelope detection will be described later in this section.

The modulated signals, which contain large amounts of the carrier signal so as to satisfy the condition of Eq. 11.22, are simply called amplitude-modulated signals (AM) in contrast to suppressed-carrier amplitude-modulated signals (AM/SC). Thus, the signal $[A + f(t)] \cos \omega_c t$ (Fig. 11.17e) is referred to as an AM signal, whereas the signal $f(t) \cos \omega_c t$ (Fig. 11.4d) is known as an AM/SC signal. We shall presently see that AM signals are much easier to generate and demodulate than AM/SC signals. Some of the methods used for generation and demodulation of AM signals will now be discussed.

Generation of AM Signals

As in the case of AM/SC signals, the AM signals can be generated by a chopper-type (switching) modulator and modulators that use nonlinear devices. In the chopper-type modulator (Fig. 11.18a), the modulating signal $f(t)$ with the carrier signal in series is connected across a chopper which vibrates at a frequency ω_c. The chopper action is equivalent to multiplication of the input signal by a square wave $p(t)$ of frequency ω_c. The spectrum of the resulting signal $v(t)$ can be obtained by convolving the spectra of $[f(t) + k \cos \omega_c t]$ with that of $p(t)$ as shown in Fig. 11.19. The convolution yields the desired spectrum centered at $\pm \omega_c$ and additional unwanted frequency components at $\omega = 0$, $\pm 3\omega_c$, $\pm 5\omega_c$, etc., which can be filtered out by a bandpass filter tuned to ω_c. It is left as an exercise for the reader to derive the result analytically.

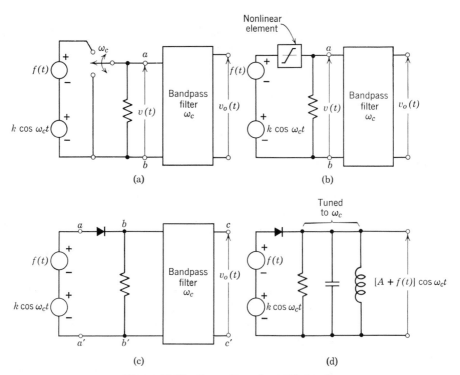

Figure 11.18   Generation of an AM signal.

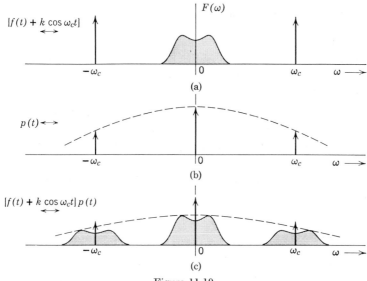

Figure 11.19

A chopper may be constructed by using a diode, as shown in Fig. 11.18c. If we assume the diode to be ideal (zero forward resistance and infinite reverse resistance), and if the carrier amplitude is much greater than the peak value of $f(t)$, then the diode merely acts as a switch, which shorts out when the carrier signal is positive and opens when the carrier signal is negative. Therefore, a diode chops the input signal at frequency ω_c. The spectrum of the resultant signal $v(t)$ is shown in Fig. 11.19c. When this signal is passed through a bandpass filter tuned to ω_c, the desired signal is obtained. Note that the diode here cuts out the negative part of the composite signal $[f(t) + k \cos \omega_c t]$. This is essentially a half-wave rectification of the input signal. Hence, this type of modulator is also known as the rectifier type of modulator.

In a modulator system using the nonlinear device, the modulating mechanism is provided by the nonlinear device (Fig. 11.18b). If we assume that the composite element formed by the nonlinear device and the resistor R in Fig. 11.18b have a power series relationship between the voltage and current,

$$i = ae + be^2 \tag{11.23}$$

then it can be easily shown that the signal $v(t)$ consists of terms representing the modulated signal and unwanted terms which can be filtered out by a bandpass filter tuned to ω_c. A semiconductor diode more closely resembles the nonlinear element satisfying Eq. 11.23 than the ideal diode.

Demodulation of AM Signals

AM signals can be detected by using the synchronous detection techniques that were discussed for AM/SC signals. However, it is possible to demodulate AM signals by much simpler techniques. The detectors for AM signals may be classified as rectifier detectors and envelope detectors. The two types of detectors superficially appear to be equivalent, but both of them operate on entirely different principles. The rectifier detector actually operates on the principle of synchronous detection, whereas the envelope detector is a nonlinear circuit whose output tends to follow the envelope of the input signal. We shall consider both types separately.

Rectifier Detector

This circuit (Fig. 11.20) is essentially the same as a rectifier-type modulator except that the carrier signal is not required. The detector circuit merely rectifies the modulated signal. The rectified signal is the same as the original signal except that the negative cycles are cut off. This is really equivalent to multiplying the signal by unity for positive values and by zero for negative values. Hence it is evident that the rectification is really equivalent to multiplication of the modulated signal by a square wave $p(t)$ of frequency ω_c. The spectrum of the rectified signal is therefore obtained by convolving the spectrum of the modulated

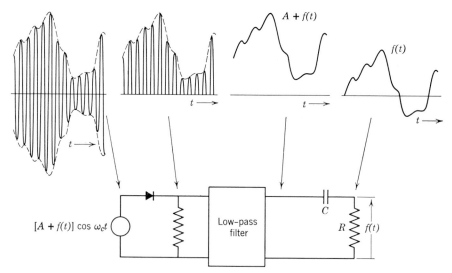

Figure 11.20 A rectifier detector.

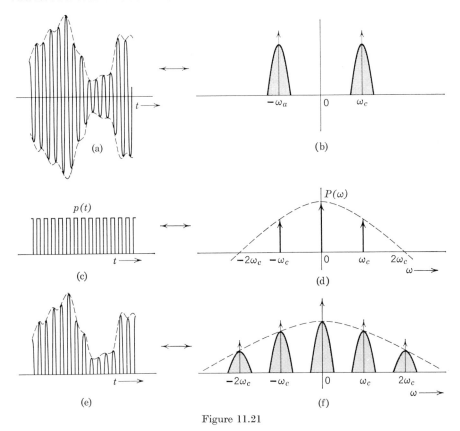

Figure 11.21

signal with that of $p(t)$. The result of the graphical convolution is shown in Fig. 11.21f. It is obvious from this figure that the signal $f(t)$ can be recovered by passing the rectified signal through a low-pass filter. The output of a low-pass filter still contains a d-c term (impulse at the origin). This can be eliminated by placing a capacitor C in the output circuit (Fig. 11.20). The convolution can be readily determined analytically by convolving the spectra of $e_m(t)$ (Eq. 11.20b) and $p(t)$ (Eq. 11.11). It is left as an exercise for the reader to show that this yields the spectrum shown in Fig. 11.21f.

Note that the rectifier type of detection is essentially a synchronous detection since the operation of rectification is equivalent to multiplication of the modulated signal by a periodic signal (square wave) of frequency ω_c. But it is important to realize that the multiplication is performed without any carrier signal. This is the result of a high carrier content in the modulated signal itself. If there were no carrier present (as in the case of a suppressed carrier), then the rectifier operation is not equivalent to multiplication of the input signal by $p(t)$. In general, for any AM signal $[A + f(t)] \cos \omega_c t$, if the condition

$$[A + f(t)] > 0, \qquad \text{for all } t$$

or

$$A > |f(t)|_{\max}$$

is not satisfied, then the rectifier type of detector cannot be used. It is left as an exercise for the reader to show that if the above condition is not satisfied, then the rectification of the modulated signal is not equivalent to multiplication by a periodic square wave $p(t)$, and hence the above method of demodulation cannot be used (see Problem 15 at the end of the chapter). In all such cases where this condition is not satisfied, the signal $f(t)$ may be recovered by synchronous detection requiring an external carrier signal for multiplication at the receiver.

The above discussion also suggests another possibility of detection of suppressed-carrier signals (in general, signals not satisfying the condition of Eq. 11.22). We may add a sufficient amount of carrier to such signals as to make

$$[A + f(t)] > 0, \qquad \text{for all } t$$

and then rectify and filter this signal to recover $f(t)$. Thus, instead of using the carrier to multiply the signal $f(t) \cos \omega_c t$, we add a sufficient amount of carrier to the modulated signal to make it possible to detect it by rectifier-detection techniques.

Envelope Detector

In an envelope detector the output of the detector follows the envelope of the modulated signal. The envelope detector is essentially a rectifier circuit with a capacitor across the output terminals as shown in Fig. 11.22.

On the positive cycle of the input signal, the capacitor C charges up to the peak voltage of the input signal. As the input signal falls below this peak value, the diode is cut off because the capacitor voltage (which is

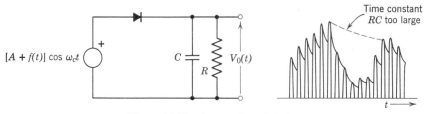

Figure 11.22   An envelope detector.

very nearly the peak voltage) is greater than the input signal voltage, thus causing the diode to open. The capacitor discharges through the resistor R but at a slow rate. During the next positive cycle, at the peak of the input signal, the input signal becomes greater than the capacitor voltage at the peak value, and the diode conducts. The capacitor again charges to the peak value of this new cycle. The capacitor discharges slowly during the cutoff period. Thus, during the cutoff period the capacitor voltage changes very little. During each positive cycle, the capacitor charges up to the peak voltage of the input signal and holds onto this voltage until the next positive cycle. The time constant RC of the output circuit is adjusted so that the exponential decay of the capacitor voltage during the discharge period will approximately follow the envelope (see Problem 16). The voltage across the capacitor now has an undesired ripple of frequency ω_c, which may be filtered out by another low-pass filter.

Superficially, it may appear that the envelope detector is really a rectifier detector for which a low-pass filter is provided by the R-C circuit. This is not true. It can be shown that for the same modulated input signal, the output of the envelope detector is π times as large as that obtained by a rectifier detector (see Problem 14). For the rectifier detector, the low-pass filter (Fig. 11.20) must have a resistive input impedance. Otherwise, the analysis (shown in Fig. 11.21) is not valid. In this analysis it was specifically assumed that the diode had a resistive load. If the load is complex, the analysis is rather complicated. The system is no longer a linear-time variant system, but acts as a nonlinear system. The envelope detector is such a case.

From the above discussion it is evident that the envelope detector is not only more efficient than the rectifier detector, but is also simpler to construct. Hence the envelope detector is almost universally used for the purpose of detecting AM signals. All of the commercial AM receivers use this method for detection.

Power Content of Sidebands and Carrier in AM

In AM signals, the carrier itself does not carry any information, and hence the power transmitted in the carrier signal represents a waste. It is interesting to find the relative contents of power in the carrier and in the sidebands which carry the information. It is difficult to make a generalization with regard to a signal of an arbitrary waveform $f(t)$. We shall consider $f(t)$ here to be a sinusoidal signal:

$$f(t) = K \cos \omega_s t \tag{11.24}$$

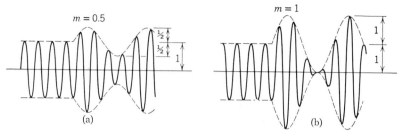

Figure 11.23

The amplitude-modulated signal corresponding to $f(t)$ in Eq. 11.24 is given by

$$e_m(t) = [A + K \cos \omega_s t] \cos \omega_c t$$

For an AM signal, the condition of Eq. 11.22 must be satisfied:

$$[A + f(t)] > 0, \qquad \text{for all } t$$

This implies,

$$A > K$$

Let $K/A = m$. The condition of Eq. 11.22 will be satisfied if $m < 1$. The term m is called the *modulation index*. Thus

$$e_m(t) = A(1 + m \cos \omega_s t) \cos \omega_c t \qquad (11.25)$$

The AM signals for $f(t) = K \cos \omega_s t$ and $m = 0.5$ and 1 are shown in Figs. 11.23a and 11.23b, respectively. The maximum value of $m = 1$ (100 % modulation). We have seen that AM signals with $m > 1$ are not detectable by ordinary techniques such as rectifier detection or envelope detection. Such signals can be detected by synchronous detection. Therefore, in ordinary AM systems the values of $m > 1$ are not allowed.

It is easy to see from Eq. 11.25 the relative power content in the carrier and the sidebands.

$$e_m(t) = A \cos \omega_c t + mA \cos \omega_s t \cos \omega_c t$$

$$= \underbrace{A \cos \omega_c t}_{\text{carrier}} + \underbrace{\frac{mA}{2} [\cos (\omega_c - \omega_s)t + \cos (\omega_c + \omega_s)t]}_{\text{sidebands}} \qquad (11.26)$$

The carrier and sideband terms are shown in Eq. 11.26. It is obvious that the power in the carrier (P_c) and the power carried by the sidebands (P_s) are given by

$$P_c = \frac{A^2}{2}$$

$$P_s = \left(\frac{mA}{2}\right)^2$$

The total power (P_t) transmitted is given by

$$P_t = P_c + P_s = (1 + m^2/2)\frac{A^2}{2}$$

The percentage of power carried by sidebands $= \dfrac{P_s}{P_t} \times 100$

$$= \frac{m^2}{2 + m^2} \times 100\%$$

This is maximum when $m = 1$ (100 % modulation) and

$$\left[\frac{P_s}{P_t}\right]_{max} = \frac{1}{3}$$

Hence for highest modulation index $(m = 1)$ the efficiency of transmission is 33%. Under these conditions 67% of the power is carried by the carrier and, as such, represents waste. For values of m less than unity, the efficiency is less than 33%. Note that for AM/SC there is no carrier and the efficiency is 100%.

11.6 FREQUENCY MULTIPLEXING

It is now quite easy to appreciate the use of modulation to transmit several signals simultaneously. Suppose we want to transmit on a channel simultaneously n signals, each of which is bandlimited. For simplicity we shall assume that each of these signals is bandlimited to ω_m radians/second. We can now modulate each of these n signals with carriers $\omega_1, \omega_2, \ldots, \omega_n$, so that each of the carriers is separated from the adjacent carrier by at least $2\omega_m$ radians per second. Each of the modulated signals has a bandwidth of $2\omega_m$ and is centered at frequencies $\omega_1, \omega_2, \ldots, \omega_m$. (There is a similar spectrum for negative frequencies.) This is shown in Figs. 11.24a and 11.24b. Figure 11.24a shows the spectra of individual signals and Fig. 11.24b shows the combined spectra of all of the modulated signals at the transmitter. At the receiver, various spectra are separated by using proper bandpass filters (Fig. 11.24c). After filtering, the signals are demodulated to obtain the original signals. Radio and television broadcasting and receiving provide a familiar example of frequency multiplexing. Each transmitter transmits a modulated signal with a carrier which is separated from the carriers of other transmitting stations by at least $2\omega_m$. In radio broadcasting this is about 10 kc. The broadcast receiver can pick up any desired signal by proper tuning which allows the desired band to pass and attenuates other frequencies. This signal is now demodulated to obtain the desired signal. However, in almost all

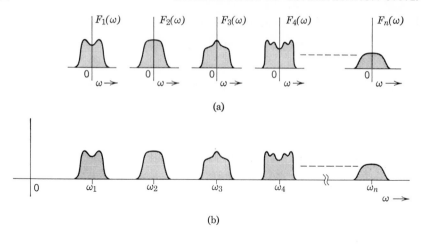

(a)

(b)

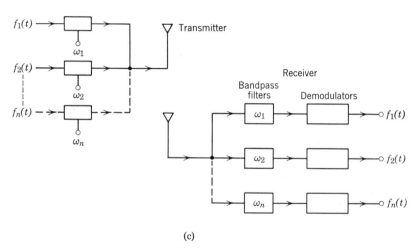

(c)

Figure 11.24

commercial AM receivers, the demodulation is not effected directly. The
modulated signal received is first translated to a fixed lower frequency
known as an intermediate frequency of 455 kc. The translation of the
signal to an intermediate frequency is accomplished by modulating the
incoming signal by a locally generated signal which differs with the incoming carrier by 455 kc. The signal, which is now translated to a fixed
intermediate frequency of 455 kc, is amplified and demodulated to obtain
the desired signal. The advantage of conversion to an intermediate
frequency is that to receive different stations it is necessary to tune only
the first stage (and the local oscillator). All of the amplification is
achieved at a constant intermediate frequency and needs no tuning. The
process of frequency translation is also known as heterodyning. In order

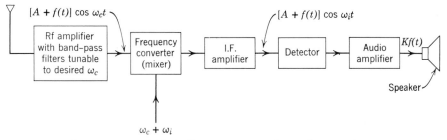

Figure 11.25 A block diagram of a superheterodyne receiver.

to translate the spectrum to a fixed intermediate frequency, the local oscillator must have a frequency above or below the incoming carrier frequency by the intermediate frequency (455 kc). Generally, the local oscillator signal frequency is chosen higher than the incoming carrier by the intermediate frequency. For this choice, such receivers are called superheterodyne receivers. The block diagram of such a receiver is shown in Fig. 11.25.

11.7 PULSE-AMPLITUDE MODULATION

The sampling theorem discussed in Section 11.2 provides the theoretical basis for pulse-modulation techniques. It was shown that a bandlimited signal, which has no spectral components above the frequency f_m cycles per second, is completely specified by its values at intervals $1/2f_m$ seconds apart. Thus, instead of transmitting the complete signal continuously, we need to transmit the signal only at a finite number of instants ($2f_m$ per second). This can be done by sampling the given signal $f(t)$ at uniform intervals $1/2f_m$ seconds apart. It was shown in Section 11.2 that $f(t)$ can be recovered from the sampled function by allowing it to pass through a low-pass filter with a cutoff frequency of f_m.

The function $f(t)$ may be sampled by a train of unit impulses applied to a multiplier circuit (Fig. 11.26a). The impulses are spaced $1/2f_m$ seconds (or less) apart. It is evident that the output signal will be a train of impulses of strengths equal to the values of $f(t)$ at corresponding instants. This is the required sampled signal $f_s(t)$. The sampled function $f_s(t)$ is a product of $f(t)$ and $\delta_T(t)$. Hence the spectrum $F_s(\omega)$ of the sampled function is obtained by convolving $F(\omega)$ with the spectrum of $\delta_T(t)$, which is also a train of impulses of uniform strength $2\omega_m$ and spaced $2\omega_m$ apart (Fig. 11.3d). It is evident from Fig. 11.3f that the sampling process results in a repetition of the spectrum in the frequency domain. If the sampling interval is less than $1/2f_m$ seconds, then there is no

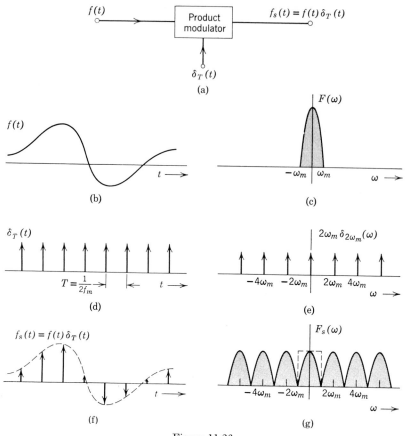

Figure 11.26

overlap between the successive cycles of the periodic spectrum, and $F(\omega)$ can be recovered from $F_s(\omega)$ by a low-pass filter with cutoff at ω_m rps.

The spectrum $F_s(\omega)$ of the sampled signal $f_s(t)$ is given by (Eq. 11.5):

$$F_s(\omega) = \frac{1}{T} \sum_{n=-\infty}^{\infty} F(\omega - n\omega_0) \qquad (11.27)$$

where T is the sampling interval and $\omega_0 = 2\pi/T$. The sampling interval T must be less than or equal to $1/2f_m$. The largest allowable sampling interval $T = 1/2f_m$ seconds is called the Nyquist interval. For the Nyquist interval,

$$T = \frac{1}{2f_m} = \frac{\pi}{\omega_m}$$

and   (11.28)

$$\omega_0 = \frac{2\pi}{T} = 2\omega_m$$

Substituting Eq. 11.28 in Eq. 11.27, we get

$$F_s(\omega) = \frac{\omega_m}{\pi} \sum_{n=-\infty}^{\infty} F(\omega - 2n\omega_m) \qquad (11.29)$$

Various waveforms and their spectra for the case of the Nyquist sampling rate are shown in Fig. 11.26.

The process discussed above samples the function $f(t)$ at certain instants by impulses (instantaneous sampling). It is evident from Fig. 11.26g that the spectrum of such an ideal sampled signal occupies the entire bandwidth ($-\infty$ to ∞); that is, it contains components of all frequencies. In practice, however, such an ideal sampling (instantaneous sampling) cannot be achieved, since it is impossible to generate true impulses. Usually the sampling is performed by very narrow pulses of finite width. Hence, the sampling by such pulses is not instantaneous, but is over a finite time interval. We shall now investigate the effect of such sampling.

Assume that the sampling is performed by periodic rectangular pulses of width τ seconds and repeating every T seconds. We shall denote this pulse train by $p_\tau(t)$ for convenience (Fig. 11.27c). The sampling interval T will be taken as the Nyquist interval $1/2f_m$ seconds. $P_\tau(\omega)$, the spectrum of the pulse train (Eq. 4.41, Fig. 4.21) is shown in Fig. 11.27d. The sampled signal $f_s(t)$ is a product of $f(t)$ and $p_\tau(t)$. Hence, $F_s(\omega)$, the spectrum of

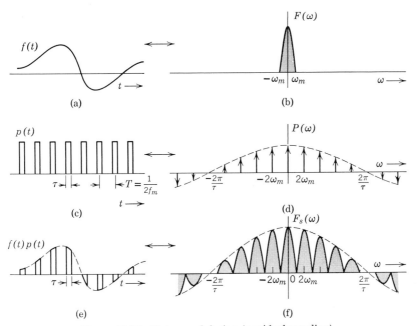

Figure 11.27 Pulse modulation (nonideal sampling).

$f_s(t)$, is obtained by convolving $F(\omega)$ with $P_\tau(\omega)$. The convolution can be readily performed graphically. The result of such a graphical convolution is shown in Fig. 11.27f. The nonideal sampling of $f(t)$ yields the spectrum similar to that of ideal sampling, but with decaying amplitude. We can derive the same result analytically. In this case, we have

$$f_s(t) = f(t)p_\tau(t)$$

Hence

$$F_s(\omega) = \frac{1}{2\pi}F(\omega) * P_\tau(\omega) \tag{11.30}$$

$P_\tau(\omega)$ can be obtained from Eq. 4.41, by setting

$$T = \frac{1}{2f_m} = \frac{\pi}{\omega_m}$$

and

$$\omega_0 = \frac{2\pi}{T} = 2\omega_m$$

$$P_\tau(\omega) = 2A\tau\omega_m \sum_{n=-\infty}^{\infty} Sa(n\tau\omega_m)\,\delta(\omega - 2n\omega_m) \tag{11.31}$$

Substituting Eq. 11.31 in Eq. 11.30, we get

$$\begin{aligned}
F_s(\omega) &= \frac{A\tau\omega_m}{\pi} F(\omega) * \sum_{n=-\infty}^{\infty} Sa(n\tau\omega_m)\,\delta(\omega - 2n\omega_m) \\
&= \frac{A\tau}{T} \sum_{n=-\infty}^{\infty} Sa(n\tau\omega_m)\,F(\omega) * \delta(\omega - 2n\omega_m) \\
&= \frac{A\tau}{T} \sum_{n=-\infty}^{\infty} Sa(n\tau\omega_m)\,F(\omega - 2n\omega_m) \tag{11.32}
\end{aligned}$$

It is obvious that the right-hand side of Eq. 11.32 represents the spectrum $F(\omega)$ repeating itself every $2\omega_m$ rps, but with amplitudes varying as $Sa(n\tau\omega_m)$. This equation therefore represents the spectrum in Fig. 11.27f.

The nonideal sampling of $f(t)$, therefore, results in a repetition of the spectrum of $f(t)$ but with decaying amplitudes. The original signal $f(t)$ can be recovered from the sampled signal $f_s(t)$ by using a low-pass filter with cutoff at ω_m. The demodulation process for pulse modulation (nonideal sampling) is exactly the same as that used for impulse modulation (ideal sampling). Note that the signal can be recovered without any distortion even with nonideal sampling. The bandwidth required for the transmission of an ideal sampled signal (impulse modulation) is infinite, whereas that required for pulse modulation will be finite since the spectrum $F_s(\omega)$ (Fig. 11.27f) decays with frequency, and it has negligible energy content at higher frequencies. As the pulses are made wider, the spectrum decays faster, and hence a smaller bandwidth is required for the transmission. It therefore appears that the pulse modulation (nonideal sampling) is superior to the impulse modulation (ideal sampling) since it requires the smaller bandwidth for transmission. However, what is gained in the frequency domain is lost in the time domain. The pulse modulation needs a larger time interval for transmitting the sampled signal than the impulse modulation. Since the pulses have a finite width, it is possible to transmit only a finite number of signals simultaneously on a time-sharing basis (time multiplexing) for the pulse modulation scheme, whereas ideally it will be possible to transmit any number of signals by using impulse modulation. The pulse modulation described above is known as pulse-amplitude modulation (PAM), since the sampled signal essentially represents the periodic pulse train whose amplitude is modulated by $f(t)$.

Transmission of PAM Signals

The PAM signal may be directly transmitted along a pair of wires. But it cannot be transmitted directly by electromagnetic waves in free space since the PAM spectrum is concentrated at lower frequencies which require impracticably large antennas. Hence the spectrum is translated to a higher frequency by the amplitude-modulation techniques that we discussed previously. At the receiver, the signal is demodulated to retranslate the spectrum to its original position. The output of this demodulator is the pulse train $f_s(t)$ from which $f(t)$ is recovered by filtering it through a low-pass filter. Such systems are designated as PAM/AM systems. The spectrum of PAM signals may also be translated by techniques of frequency modulation (FM) or phase modulation (PM), which

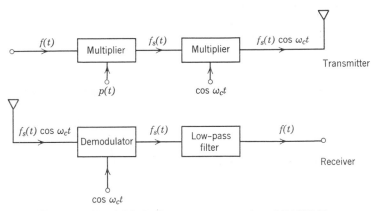

Figure 11.28 A block diagram representation of PAM/AM.

will be discussed later. Such systems are designated by PAM/FM or PAM/PM, respectively. A block diagram representation of a PAM/AM system is shown in Fig. 11.28.

11.8 OTHER FORMS OF PULSE MODULATION

To transmit a signal $f(t)$, it is necessary to transmit the information about its values at intervals $1/2f_m$ seconds apart. The significant point here is that it is not necessary to transmit the bandlimited signal continuously, but complete information about such signals can be transmitted as discrete values. Such a discrete form of information can be transmitted in a number of ways. The pulse-amplitude modulation (PAM), discussed above, is just one example. In PAM signals this information is carried by the amplitudes of the pulses. We may as well have kept the amplitudes

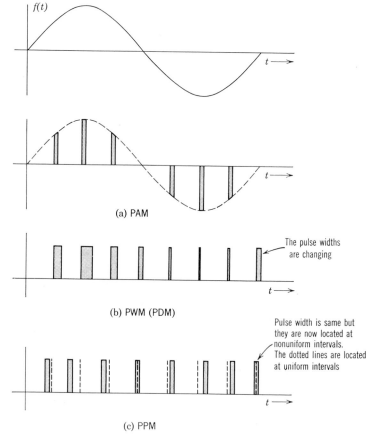

Figure 11.29   Representation of PAM, PWM, and PPM signals.

Digit	Binary equivalent	Pulse–code waveform
0	0000	
1	0001	
2	0010	
3	0011	
4	0100	
5	0101	
6	0110	
7	0111	
8	1000	
9	1001	
10	1010	
11	1011	
12	1100	
13	1101	
14	1110	
15	1111	

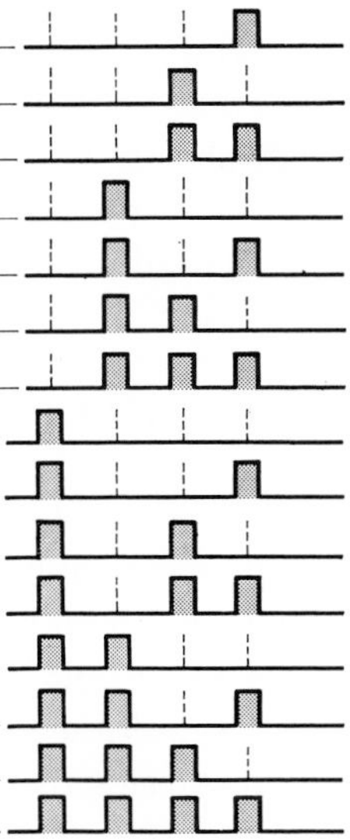

Figure 11.30   A possible form of pulse code.

of all of these pulses constant but varied the width of these pulses in proportion to the values of $f(t)$ at the corresponding instants. Such systems are designated as *pulse-width modulation* (PWM) or *pulse-duration modulation* (PDM) systems. Alternatively, the information may be transmitted by keeping both the amplitude and the width of the pulses constant but changing the positions of the pulses in proportion to the sampled values of $f(t)$ at the corresponding instants. Such systems are known as *pulse-position modulation* (PPM) systems. The PAM, PWM, and PPM signals for a signal $f(t)$ are shown in Fig. 11.29.

Another very important mode of transmission of quantized information is *pulse-code modulation* (PCM). In this system each sample value of $f(t)$ is transmitted as a code formed by a pattern of pulses. A familiar example of PCM is the Morse code which transmits discrete pieces of information (alphanumeric symbols) by a group of pulses arranged in different patterns. The dot is represented by a pulse and the absence of a pulse may represent a dash. Each digit may be represented by a certain pattern of pulses. One such pattern is shown in Fig. 11.30. The representation can be extended to any value positive or negative. The signal $f(t)$ to be transmitted is sampled, and each sample is approximated to the nearest digit. Then the pattern of code representing that value is now transmitted. Thus, instead of one pulse per sample, we need to transmit a group of pulses per sample. Therefore, PCM requires more time interval for the transmission of the same information than other modulation systems. This disadvantage in PCM, however, is offset by its property of being immune to certain types of interferences. To receive a PCM signal, all that is required to know is whether the pulse is present or absent, regardless of the amplitude and shape of the pulse. Thus, any external interference which may tend to introduce distortion in the height or width of the pulses has no influence whatsoever on PCM signals.

11.9 TIME MULTIPLEXING

The sampling theorem makes it possible to transmit the complete information in a continuous bandlimited signal by transmitting mere samples of $f(t)$ at regular intervals. The transmission of these samples engages the channel only part of the time, and it is possible to transmit several signals simultaneously on the time sharing basis. This is done by sampling all of the signals to be transmitted and interlacing these samples as shown in Fig. 11.31. In this figure the samples of two signals are shown interlaced. At the receiver the samples of each signal are separated by appropriate techniques. We shall describe briefly the outline of a time-multiplexed transmitter and receiver system.

Figure 11.32 shows a block diagram representation of a transmitter and a receiver of a time-multiplexed system. At the transmitter, the commutator is switched from channel to channel in a sequence by the timing circuit, which also generates the sampling pulses. Thus, the commutator connects different channels in a sequence to the sampling circuit, which samples all of the signals in a sequence by pulses generated by the timing circuit. The commutator switching and the sampling pulses are in synchronism. The output of the sampling circuit is thus a signal which consists of samples of all of the signals interlaced. At the receiver, another timing circuit which is in synchronism with that at the transmitter is

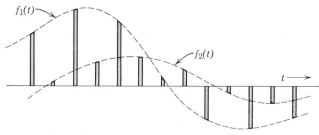

Figure 11.31   Time multiplexing of two signals.

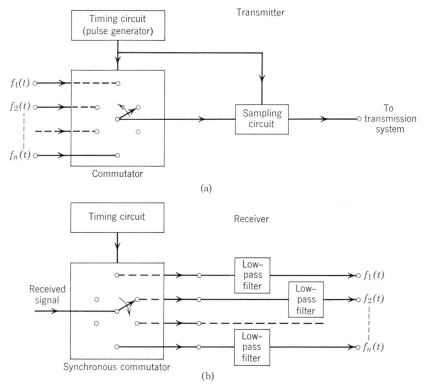

Figure 11.32   Time multiplexing of n channels.

used to switch the commutator to different channels.[7] The samples of various signals are now properly separated. The desired signal is recovered from each channel by a low-pass filter.

The Sampling Rate

If the samples of a bandlimited signal are to carry complete information of the signal, then the rate of sampling must never be less than $2f_m$ samples per second. The minimum sampling rate ($2f_m$ samples per second) is the *Nyquist rate*. It is obvious that the Nyquist rate results in a repetition of the signal spectrum without overlap and without any free interval between the successive cycles as shown in Fig. 11.33a. To recover the signal $f(t)$ from such a sampled signal, it is therefore necessary to use an ideal low-pass filter which will allow all of the frequencies $\omega < \omega_m$ to pass unattenuated, and attenuate all of the frequencies above ω_m. A

---

[7] For details of such switching arrangement, see M. Schwartz, *Information Transmission, Modulation, and Noise*, Chapter 4, McGraw-Hill, New York, 1959.

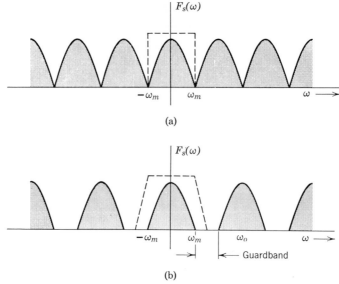

Figure 11.33   The spectrum of a sampled signal.

practical low-pass filter with very sharp cutoff characteristics could be
built, but needs a large number of elements. The stringent requirements
on the filter can be relieved by sampling the signal at a rate higher than
the Nyquist rate. It can be easily seen that, under these conditions, the
sampling results in repetition of the signal spectrum with a free band
(*guardband*) between successive cycles as shown in Fig. 11.33*b*. It is
obvious from this figure that the original signal can be recovered from the
sampled signal by a low-pass filter which need not have a sharp cutoff
characteristic.

A similar situation occurs in frequency multiplexing. The spectra of
various signals are separated by a guardband for the same reasons as
mentioned above. In time multiplexing the samples of various signals
are interlaced. An interlacing that is too close calls for stringent requirements on the receiving system which separates the samples of different
signals. Hence the samples of successive signals are also separated by a
small time interval called the *guard time interval*.

11.10 BANDWIDTH REQUIRED FOR TRANSMISSION OF PAM SIGNALS

In order to be able to compare the PAM system with other systems, it
is important to know the bandwidth required for the transmission of
PAM signals. The spectrum of a PAM signal is shown in Fig. 11.27*f*.

It is evident from this figure that to transmit a PAM signal completely we need an infinite bandwidth. We shall show, however, that all the information contained in the samples can be completely transmitted by a finite bandwidth.

If it is desired to time multiplex n continuous signals bandlimited to f_m cps each, then we need to transmit $2f_m$ samples per second per signal. Hence, time multiplexing of these n signals calls for transmission of $2nf_m$ pulses per second. We shall now show that the information in these $2nf_m$ pulses can be transmitted over a bandwidth of nf_m cps.

At first glance, it appears that we need an infinite bandwidth for transmission of PAM signals because we are transmitting rectangular pulses which have spectra occupying all of the frequency range. It must be remembered, however, that we are really not interested in the shape of the pulses. We need to know only the heights of the pulses. Hence, any distortion in the pulse shape is immaterial as long as the height of the pulse is retained.

The output of the time multiplexer consists of $2nf_m$ pulses per second which are contributed by each of the n signals at a rate of $2f_m$ samples per second. The question is: What is the bandwidth required to transmit $2nf_m$ pieces of information (samples) per second? From the sampling theorem it follows that a continuous signal bandlimited to W cps can be transmitted by $2W$ pieces of information (samples) per second. Conversely we can state that $2nf_m$ samples per second define a continuous signal bandlimited to nf_m cps. We can consider these $2nf_m$ samples to be samples of some continuous signal $\varphi(t)$ bandlimited to nf_m cps. Indeed we can construct such a signal $\varphi(t)$ from the knowledge of these samples according to Eq. 11.6d. Hence, instead of transmitting the discrete $2nf_m$ samples per second, we may transmit the corresponding continuous signal $\varphi(t)$ defined by these samples. Since this signal is bandlimited to nf_m cps, the bandwidth required is nf_m cps.

How can we obtain $\varphi(t)$ from the $2nf_m$ samples per second? The discrete pulses are merely samples of $\varphi(t)$ and hence from the previous discussion it follows that $\varphi(t)$ can be obtained by passing these discrete samples through a low-pass filter with a cutoff frequency nf_m cps.

The signal represented by discrete $2nf_m$ pulses per second is $\varphi_s(t)$ and its spectrum is $\Phi_s(\omega)$. Note that $\Phi_s(\omega)$ is formed by periodic repetition of $\Phi(\omega)$. Signals $\varphi(t)$ and $\varphi_s(t)$ and their spectra are shown in Fig. 11.34. For an alternative proof of this result, see Black.[8] This result is very significant and will be used again in Chapter 14 to derive the maximum amount of information that can be transmitted per second by a given

[8] H. S. Black, pp. 258–260, cited in reference 1.

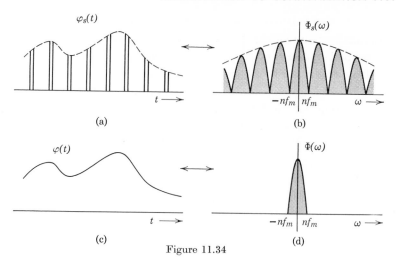

Figure 11.34

channel (channel capacity). However, it must be remembered that if it is desired to reproduce the pulse shape as well as its height, then the required bandwidth is larger than nf_m cps.

It is interesting to note that the bandwidth required for the direct transmission of an n time-multiplexed PAM signal is nf_m. This is exactly equivalent to the bandwidth required for transmitting these n signals using AM/SSB frequency multiplexing. However, it was pointed out that the direct transmission of PAM signals by radiation is impractical, since the energy in such a signal is concentrated at lower frequencies necessitating an unreasonable size of radiating systems. In such cases the whole spectrum of PAM signals is shifted to a higher frequency by amplitude modulation. The resultant signal is called a PAM/AM signal. The process of amplitude modulation gives rise to upper and lower sidebands and hence the required bandwidth is doubled. Thus the bandwidth required for transmission of a PAM/AM signal of time-multiplexed n continuous signals bandlimited to f_m is $2nf_m$ cps. It should be noted that the bandwidth required for the transmission of these n signals by AM/DSB frequency multiplexing is also $2nf_m$ cps. Hence, we conclude that transmission of a signal by PAM needs the same bandwidth as that required for AM/SSB. Similarly, the transmission of a signal by PAM/AM requires the same bandwidth as that for AM/DSB.

11.11 COMPARISON OF FREQUENCY-MULTIPLEXED AND TIME-MULTIPLEXED SYSTEMS

We have discussed two methods of simultaneous transmission of several bandlimited signals on a channel. In frequency-multiplexed systems, all

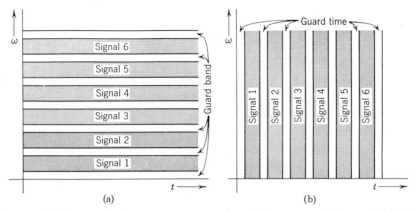

Figure 11.35   Communication space representation of frequency and time multiplexing.

of the signals to be transmitted are amplitude modulated by different frequencies. The modulated signals are all transmitted simultaneously. All of the amplitude modulated signals are continuous signals and are mixed in the time domain. It is not possible to distinguish these signals in the time domain. The spectra of the various modulated signals, however, occupy different bands in the frequency domain and can be separated by appropriate filters. Thus, the signals are all mixed in the time domain but maintain their identity in the frequency domain. In the case of time multiplexing, on the other hand, the samples of each signal remain distinct and can be recognized and separated in the time domain. However, the frequency spectra of the various sampled signals occupy the same frequency region and are all mixed beyond recognition. Thus, the spectrum identity is maintained in frequency-multiplexed signals, whereas the waveshape identity is maintained in time-multiplexed signals. Since a signal is completely specified either by its time-domain or frequency-domain specification, the multiplexed signals can be separated at the receiver by using appropriate techniques in the respective domains.

The distinction between the two systems can be conveniently represented graphically on a communication space which is used to transmit information. The time frequency communication space is shown in Fig. 11.35 for frequency-multiplexed and time-multiplexed systems. For a frequency-multiplexed system, each signal is present on the channel all of the time and all are mixed. But each of them occupies a finite and distinct frequency interval (not occupied by any other signal). This is shown in Fig. 11.35a. On the other hand, in a time-multiplexed system, each signal occupies a distinct time interval (not occupied by any other signal). But the spectra of all of the signals have components in the same frequency interval. This is shown in Fig. 11.35b.

Quantitatively, we have already shown that the bandwidth requirements for the transmission of a given number of signals either by time multiplexing or by frequency multiplexing is the same (PAM and AM/SSB require nf_m cps; PAM/AM and AM/DSB require $2nf_m$ cps). It is therefore evident that for a given channel the number of bandlimited signals that can be simultaneously transmitted by frequency multiplexing or by time multiplexing is the same.

From the practical point of view, the time-multiplexed system proves superior to a frequency-multiplexed system. The first advantage is the simplified circuitry used in time-multiplexed systems compared to that used in frequency-multiplexed systems. In the latter, one needs to generate different carriers for each channel. Moreover each channel occupies a different frequency band, and hence needs a different bandpass filter design. On the other hand, time-multiplexed systems require identical circuits for each channel consisting of relatively simple synchronous switches or gating circuits. The only filters in the detection process are the lowpass filters which are identical for each channel. This circuitry is much simpler compared to the modulators, demodulators, carrier generators, and bandpass filters required in the frequency-multiplexed systems. The second advantage of the time-multiplexed system is the relative immunity from interference within channels (interchannel crosstalk), which arises in frequency-multiplexed systems because of nonlinearities in the amplifiers in the path of transmission. The nonlinearities in various amplifiers produce harmonic distortion and hence will introduce interference within channels (interchannel crosstalk). Hence the nonlinearity requirements in a frequency-multiplexed system are much more stringent than those for a single channel. On the other hand, for time-multiplexed systems, the signals from different channels are not applied to the system simultaneously but are allotted different time intervals. Hence the nonlinearity requirements in a time-multiplexed system are the same as that for a single channel. For these reasons the time-multiplexed systems are being used more and more commonly in such applications as long-distance telephone communication.

11.12 ANGLE MODULATION

In AM signals the amplitude of the carrier is modulated by the signal $f(t)$, and hence the information content of $f(t)$ is carried by the amplitude variations of the carrier. Since a sinusoidal signal is described by three variables—amplitude, frequency, and phase—there exists a possibility of carrying the same information either by varying the frequency or the phase of the carrier. However, by definition, a sinusoidal signal represents an infinite wave train of constant amplitude, frequency, and phase, and hence the variation of either of these three variables of a sinusoidal signal appears to be contradictory to the definition of a sinusoidal signal. For this reason, we have to extend the concept of a sinusoidal signal to a generalized function whose amplitude, frequency, and phase may vary with time. We have already acquainted ourselves with the concept of variable amplitude in connection with AM signals. The variations in frequency and phase will now be considered.

To appreciate the concept of frequency variation it is necessary to define the instantaneous frequency. Figure 11.36a represents a sinusoidal signal $\varphi(t)$ which has a constant frequency ω_0 for $t < T$. At $t = T$, the frequency suddenly changes to $2\omega_0$ and remains constant at this value until $t = 2T$ where it changes to ω_0 again. The changes in the frequency here are abrupt, as shown in Fig. 11.36b, and present no difficulty to an understanding of the concept of variable frequency. The function $\varphi(t)$ is

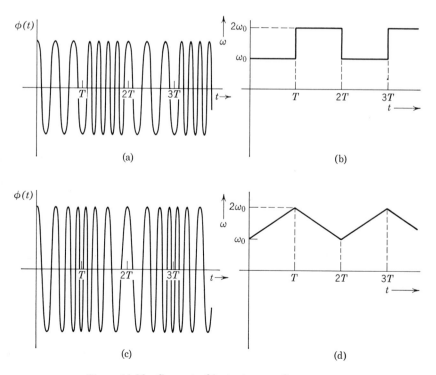

Figure 11.36   Concept of instantaneous frequency.

a sinusoidal signal which has a frequency ω_0 in intervals $2nT < t <$ $(2n + 1)T$ and a frequency $2\omega_0$ in the intervals $(2n + 1)T < t <$ $(2n + 2)T$ (n integral). Next we ask: What will happen if, instead of abrupt variations, we allow a gradual variation in frequency as shown in Fig. 11.36d? Here the frequency of the signal is changing continuously at a uniform rate from ω_0 to $2\omega_0$ within a time interval T. Hence, the frequency of the signal is different at every point. Now, strictly speaking, the signal $f(t)$ in Fig. 11.36c cannot be expressed by an ordinary sinusoidal expression. How can there be a continuous change in frequency in a sinusoidal signal? For this reason we have to define a generalized sinusoidal signal

$$f(t) = A \cos \theta(t) \qquad (11.33)$$

Here θ is the angle of the sinusoidal signal and is a function of t. For an ordinary fixed frequency sinusoidal signal,

$$f(t) = A \cos(\omega_c t + \theta_0)$$

Hence

$$\theta(t) = \omega_c t + \theta_0$$

and

$$\omega_c = \frac{d\theta}{dt} \qquad (11.34)$$

The radian frequency ω_c here is a constant, given by the derivative of the angle $\theta(t)$. In general, this derivative may not be constant. We now define $d\theta/dt$ as the instantaneous frequency ω_i which may vary with time. We, thus, have a relationship between the angle $\theta(t)$ and instantaneous frequency ω_i :

$$\omega_i = \frac{d\theta}{dt}$$

$$\theta = \int \omega_i \, dt \qquad (11.35)$$

It is now easy to appreciate the possibility of transmission of information in $f(t)$ by varying the angle θ of a carrier. Such techniques of modulation, where the angle of the carrier is varied in some manner with a modulating signal $f(t)$, are known as *angle modulation*. There are two methods commonly used in angle modulation: *phase modulation* (PM) and *frequency modulation* (FM). If the angle $\theta(t)$ is varied linearly with $f(t)$, then

$$\theta(t) = \omega_c t + \theta_0 + k_p f(t) \qquad (11.36)$$

Where k_p is a constant, the resulting form is called *phase modulation*. Thus, a signal $A \cos[\omega_c t + \theta_0 + k_p f(t)]$ represents a phase-modulated carrier. Note that the instantaneous frequency ω_i for a phase-modulated carrier is given by

$$\omega_i = \frac{d\theta}{dt} = \omega_c + k_p \frac{df}{dt} \tag{11.37}$$

Hence, in phase modulation, the instantaneous frequency varies linearly with the derivative of the modulating signal. If, however, we vary the instantaneous frequency directly with the modulating signal, we have a frequency modulation. Thus, for a frequency-modulated carrier, the instantaneous frequency ω_i is given by

$$\omega_i = \omega_c + k_f f(t) \tag{11.38}$$

and

$$\theta(t) = \int \omega_i \, dt$$
$$= \omega_c t + k_f \int f(t) \, dt + \theta_0 \tag{11.39}$$

and the signal $A \cos [\omega_c t + \theta_0 + k_f \int f(t) \, dt]$ represents a frequency-modulated carrier.

It is easy to see from the above discussion that although PM and FM are different forms of angle modulation, they are not essentially different. In PM, the angle is varied linearly with the modulating signal, whereas in FM the angle varies linearly with the integral of the modulating signal. Indeed if we integrate the modulating signal $f(t)$ first and then allow it to phase-modulate the carrier, we obtain a frequency-modulated wave. Similarly, if we differentiate $f(t)$ first and use it to frequency-modulate a carrier, the result is a phase-modulated wave. Actually one of the methods of generating FM signals (the Armstrong indirect FM system) does integrate $f(t)$ and uses it to phase-modulate the carrier. In fact, PM and FM are inseparable since any variation in the phase of a carrier results in a variation in the frequency and vice versa. It is, therefore, not necessary to discuss both forms of angle modulation. We shall deal here in some detail with frequency modulation alone, but our discussion is equally valid for phase modulation. Note that for angle modulation the amplitude is always constant. Figures 11.36a and 11.36c are examples of FM carriers.

For a frequency-modulated carrier $f_c(t)$, the angle θ is given by (Eq. 11.39):

$$\theta(t) = \omega_c t + k_f \int f(t) \, dt + \theta_0$$

The term θ_0 is an arbitrary constant and may be taken as zero. Therefore

$$f_c(t) = A \cos [\omega_c t + k_f \int f(t) \, dt] \tag{11.40}$$

Let

$$\int f(t)\, dt = g(t) \tag{11.41}$$

If the function $f(t)$ starts at some time, say at $t = 0$, then the limits of integration of $f(t)$ may be taken as 0 to t:

$$\int_0^t f(t)\, dt = g(t)$$

Then

$$f_c(t) = A \cos\left[\omega_c t + k_f g(t)\right] \tag{11.42}$$

$$= A \cos \omega_c t \cos\left[k_f g(t)\right] - A \sin \omega_c t \sin\left[k_f g(t)\right] \tag{11.43}$$

It is evident from Eq. 11.42 that angle θ of an FM carrier is given by

$$\theta(t) = \omega_c t + k_f g(t)$$

and the instantaneous frequency ω_i is given by

$$\omega_i = \frac{d\theta}{dt} = \omega_c + k_f \frac{dg}{dt}$$

$$= \omega_c + k_f f(t) \tag{11.44}$$

The instantaneous frequency of the carrier is thus a function of time. The carrier frequency deviates from ω_c as shown by Eq. 11.44. The maximum deviation of the carrier frequency is given by $k_f |f(t)|_{\text{max}}$. Thus the constant k_f controls the maximum deviation of the carrier frequency.

Equation 11.43 gives the general equation for an FM carrier. An evaluation of the frequency spectrum of $f_c(t)$, as expressed in this equation, is very difficult. If k_f is very small so that $k_f g(t) << \pi/2$, then Equation 11.42 is greatly simplified and it is quite easy to find its spectrum. But for larger values of k_f the analysis for a general signal $f(t)$ becomes too involved. Under these conditions we derive the results for a specific case of a sinusoidal modulating signal. We shall, therefore, consider two cases. $k_f g(t) << \pi/2$ (narrowband FM) and $k_f g(t) > \pi/2$ (wideband FM).

11.13 NARROWBAND FM

We have seen above that the constant k_f controls the maximum deviation of the carrier frequency. If the maximum deviation of the carrier frequency is made small enough (that is, if k is made sufficently small so that $k_f g(t)$ is much less than $\pi/2$ for all values of t), then

$$\cos\left[k_f g(t)\right] \simeq 1$$
$$\sin\left[k_f g(t)\right] \simeq k_f g(t) \tag{11.45}$$

Substituting Eq. 11.45 in Eq. 11.43, we get

$$f_c(t) = A \cos \omega_c t - A k_f g(t) \sin \omega_c t \qquad (11.46)$$

$$\underbrace{\qquad}_{\text{carrier}} \quad \underbrace{\qquad}_{\text{sideband}}$$

It is interesting to observe that the AM carrier is expressed as (Eq. 11.20a):

$$A \cos \omega_c t + f(t) \cos \omega_c t \qquad (11.47)$$

whereas the narrow band FM carrier is given by

$$A \cos \omega_c t - A k_f g(t) \sin \omega_c t \qquad (11.48)$$

Similarly the narrowband PM carrier is given by

$$A \cos \omega_c t - A k_p f(t) \sin \omega_c t \qquad (11.49)$$

Each signal has a carrier term and the sidebands which are centered at $\pm \omega_c$. If

$$f(t) \longleftrightarrow F(\omega)$$

and

$$g(t) \longleftrightarrow G(\omega)$$

then since

$$g(t) = \int_0^t f(t) \, dt$$

It follows from time integration property (Eq. 4.56) that

$$g(t) \longleftrightarrow \frac{1}{j\omega} F(\omega) \qquad (11.50)$$

Hence

$$G(\omega) = \frac{1}{j\omega} F(\omega) \qquad (11.51)$$

Thus, if $F(\omega)$ is bandlimited to ω_m, then $G(\omega)$ is also bandlimited to ω_m. The frequency spectrum of $f_c(t)$ of the FM carrier in Eq. 11.46 can be found by using Eq. 11.2b. Thus, if

$$f_c(t) \longleftrightarrow F_c(\omega)$$

then

$$F_c(\omega) = \pi A [\delta(\omega - \omega_c) + \delta(\omega + \omega_c)] + \frac{j A k_f}{2} [G(\omega - \omega_c) - G(\omega + \omega_c)]$$

$$(11.52)$$

Comparison of the spectrum of FM (Eq. 11.52) with that of AM (Eq. 11.20b) brings out clearly the similarities and differences between the two types of modulation. In either case, there is a carrier term and sideband component centered at $\pm \omega_c$. The sideband spectrum for FM, however, has a phase shift of $\pi/2$ with respect to the carrier, whereas that of AM is

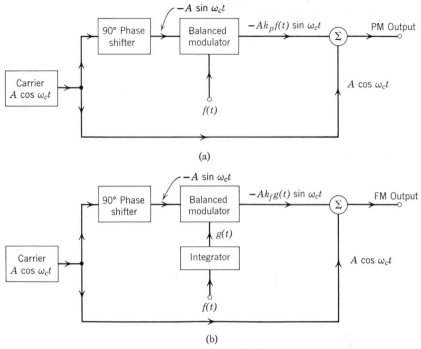

Figure 11.37   Generation of narrowband PM and FM signals, using balanced modulators.

in phase with the carrier. The spectrum $G(\omega) = (1/j\omega)F(\omega)$ and hence if $F(\omega)$ is bandlimited to ω_m, $G(\omega)$ is also bandlimited to ω_m. Thus, a narrowband FM (and a narrowband PM) signal occupies the same bandwidth $(2\omega_m)$ as that occupied by an AM signal It must be remembered, however, that despite apparent similarities, the AM and FM signals have very different waveforms. In an AM signal, the frequency is constant and the amplitude varies with time, whereas in an FM signal the amplitude is constant and the frequency varies with time.

Equations 11.48 and 11.49 suggest a possible method of generating narrowband FM and PM signals by using balanced modulators. The block diagram representation of such systems is shown in Fig. 11.37.

11.14 WIDEBAND FM

If the deviations in the carrier frequency are made large enough, that is, if the constant k_f is chosen large enough so that the condition $k_f g(t) << \pi/2$ is not satisfied, the analysis of FM signals becomes very involved for a general modulating signal $f(t)$. To simplify our discussion, we shall consider $f(t)$ to be a sinusoidal signal $\cos \omega_s t$. Although this may appear to be a severe restriction, the approach nevertheless provides useful information regarding the general nature of FM signals. The modulating signal is given by

$$f(t) = a \cos \omega_s t$$

We may assume that the signal $f(t)$ is switched on at $t = 0$ and hence

$$g(t) = \int_0^t f(t)\, dt = a \int_0^t \cos \omega_s t\, dt$$

$$= \frac{a}{\omega_s} \sin \omega_s t \qquad (11.53)$$

Since the instantaneous frequency ω_i is given by (Eq. 11.44):

$$\omega_i = \omega_c + k_f f(t) = \omega_c + ak_f \cos \omega_s t \qquad (11.54)$$

It is evident from Eq. 11.54 that the maximum deviation in carrier frequency is ak_f radians per second. Substituting Eq. 11.53 in Eq. 11.42, we get the FM carrier $f_c(t)$:

$$f_c(t) = A \cos \left(\omega_c t + \frac{ak_f}{\omega_s} \sin \omega_s t \right) \qquad (11.55)$$

The quantity ak_f/ω_s is the ratio of the maximum deviation of the carrier frequency to the signal frequency, and is called the *modulation index* m_f. Thus

$$f_c(t) = A \cos (\omega_c t + m_f \sin \omega_s t) \qquad (11.56)$$

$$= A \cos \omega_c t \cos (m_f \sin \omega_s t) - A \sin \omega_c t \sin (m_f \sin \omega_s t) \qquad (11.57)$$

Observe that the function $\cos (m_f \sin \omega_s t)$ is a periodic function with period $T = 2\pi/\omega_s$, since

$$\cos (m_f \sin \omega_s t) = \cos [m_f \sin \omega_s (t + 2\pi/\omega_s)]$$

Similarly the function $\sin (m_f \sin \omega_s t)$ is also a periodic function of period $T = 2\pi/\omega_s$. Hence, $f_c(t)$ can be expressed by a Fourier series and has components of frequency $\pm \omega_s$, $\pm 2\omega_s$, $\ldots$, etc. We shall expand $\cos (m_f \sin \omega_s t)$ and $\sin (m_f \sin \omega_s t)$ by the Fourier series.

Note that these functions are given by the real and the imaginary parts, respectively, of the function $e^{jm_f \sin \omega_s t}$. Hence it is convenient to expand this exponential function by the Fourier series. We have

$$e^{jm_f \sin \omega_s t} = \sum_{n=-\infty}^{\infty} C_n e^{jn\omega_s t} \qquad (11.58)$$

where

$$C_n = \frac{1}{T} \int_{-T/2}^{T/2} e^{jm_f \sin \omega_s t} e^{-jn\omega_s t}\, dt$$

where

$$T = 2\pi/\omega_s.$$

Thus

$$C_n = \frac{\omega_s}{2\pi} \int_{-\pi/\omega_s}^{\pi/\omega_s} e^{j(m_f \sin \omega_s t - n\omega_s t)} \, dt \qquad (11.59)$$

Changing the variable, $x = \omega_s t$:

$$C_n = \frac{1}{2\pi} \int_{-\pi}^{\pi} e^{j(m_f \sin x - nx)} \, dx \qquad (11.60)$$

Unfortunately, the above integral cannot be evaluated in closed form. The integrand can be expanded in the Taylor series and then integrated term by term.

$$e^{j(m_f \sin x - nx)} = 1 + j(m_f \sin x - nx) - \frac{(m_f \sin x - nx)^2}{2!} + \cdots$$

$$(11.61)$$

The term-by-term integration yields an infinite series. This integral occurs in many physical problems and is given a special name: the *Bessel function*. It is tabulated in most of the standard tables.[9] The integral

$$\frac{1}{2\pi} \int_{-\pi}^{\pi} e^{j(m_f \sin x - nx)} \, dx$$

is known as the Bessel function of the *first kind* and is denoted by the symbol $J_n(m_f)$.

These functions are plotted in Fig. 11.38 for some integral values of n. Thus

$$C_n = J_n(m_f) \qquad (11.62)$$

and

$$e^{jm_f \sin \omega_s t} = \sum_{n=-\infty}^{\infty} J_n(m_f) e^{jn\omega_s t} \qquad (11.63)$$

$$= \sum_{n=-\infty}^{\infty} J_n(m_f)[\cos n\omega_s t + j \sin n\omega_s t] \qquad (11.64)$$

Furthermore, it can be shown from the integral definition of Bessel functions that

$$J_n(m_f) = J_{-n}(m_f) \qquad n \text{ even}$$
$$= -J_{-n}(m_f) \qquad n \text{ odd} \qquad (11.65)$$

[9] See, for instance, E. Jahnke and F. Emde, *Tables of Functions*, Dover Publications, New York, 1945. It can be shown that

$$J_n(y) = \sum_{r=0}^{\infty} \frac{(-1)^r}{r! \, \Gamma(n + r + 1)} \left[\frac{y}{2}\right]^{n+2r}$$

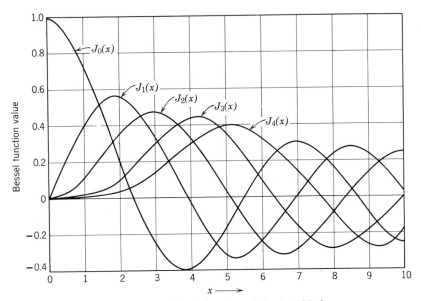

Figure 11.38   Bessel function of the first kind.

Using Eq. 11.65, Eq. 11.64 can now be expressed as

$$e^{jm_f \sin \omega_s t} = J_0(m_f) + 2[J_2(m_f) \cos 2\omega_s t + J_4(m_f) \cos 4\omega_s t + \cdots]$$
$$+ 2j[J_1(m_f) \sin \omega_s t + J_3(m_f) \sin 3\omega_s t + \cdots] \qquad (11.66)$$

But

$$e^{jm_f \sin \omega_s t} = \cos (m_f \sin \omega_s t) + j \sin (m_f \sin \omega_s t) \qquad (11.67)$$

Equating the real and imaginary terms of Eqs. 11.66 and 11.67, we get

$$\cos (m_f \sin \omega_s t) = J_0(m_f) + 2[J_2(m_f) \cos 2\omega_s t + J_4(m_f) \cos 4\omega_s t + \cdots]$$
$$(11.68a)$$

$$\sin (m_f \sin \omega_s t) = 2[J_1(m_f) \sin \omega_s t + J_3(m_f) \sin 3\omega_s t + \cdots] \qquad (11.68b)$$

The spectral distribution of the FM carrier can now be readily obtained by substituting Eq. 11.68 in Eq. 11.57.

$$f_c(t) = A \cos \omega_c t \{J_0(m_f) + 2[J_2(m_f) \cos 2\omega_s t + J_4(m_f) \cos 4\omega_s t + \cdots]\}$$
$$- 2A \sin \omega_c t \{J_1(m_f) \sin \omega_s t + J_3(m_f) \sin 3\omega_s t + \cdots]\} \qquad (11.69)$$
$$= A\{J_0(m_f) \cos \omega_c t + J_1(m_f)[\cos (\omega_c + \omega_s)t - \cos (\omega_c - \omega_s)t]$$
$$+ J_2(m_f)[\cos (\omega_c + 2\omega_s)t + \cos (\omega_c - 2\omega_s)t]$$
$$+ J_3(m_f)[\cos (\omega_c + 3\omega_s)t - \cos (\omega_c - 3\omega_s)t]$$
$$+ \cdots + \cdots\} \qquad (11.70)$$

It is evident from Eq. 11.70 that the modulating signal $f(t)$ of frequency ω_s gives rise to the sideband frequencies $(\omega_c \pm \omega_s)$, $(\omega_c \pm 2\omega_s)$, $(\omega_c \pm 3\omega_s)$, . . . , etc., as shown in Fig. 11.39. It, therefore, appears that

Figure 11.39   FM carrier spectrum.

an FM carrier contains components of infinite frequencies and has an infinite bandwidth. In practice, however, the amplitudes of the spectral components of higher frequencies become negligible and hence almost all of the energy of the FM carrier is contained in the spectral components lying within a finite bandwidth. This can be easily seen from Fig. 11.38. For $m_f << \pi/2$ only $J_0(m_f)$ and $J_1(m_f)$ have any significant magnitude. All of the higher functions $J_2(m_f)$, $J_3(m_f)$, $\ldots$, etc. are negligible. For this case, only the carrier and the first-order sidebands are of significance. This is, of course, the narrowband FM discussed in the previous section. For $m_f = 2$, the functions $J_5(2)$, $J_6(2)$, $\ldots$, etc. have negligible amplitudes. Hence, the significant spectral components of an FM carrier for $m_f = 2$ are ω_c, $\omega_c \pm \omega_s$, $\omega_c \pm 2\omega_s$, $\omega_c \pm 3\omega_s$, and $\omega_c \pm 4\omega_s$. The bandwidth of the significant sidebands in this case is $8\omega_s$. As m_f is increased, more and more, higher-order sidebands become significant. If we consider the significant sidebands to be those which have an amplitude of at least one percent of that of the unmodulated carrier, then for all significant sidebands $J_n(m_f) > 0.01$. The number of significant sidebands for different values of m_f can be found from the plot of the Bessel functions. It can be seen from these plots that $J_n(m_f)$ diminishes rapidly for $n > m_f$. As a rule of thumb, $J_n(m_f)$ is negligible for $n > m_f$. This is particularly true for values of $m_f >> 1$. Thus, for a wideband FM where the number of significant sidebands may be considered to be the integer closest to m_f, $(m_f = n)$. The total bandwidth B of the FM carrier is evidently given by

$$B \simeq 2n\omega_s \simeq 2m_f\omega_s$$

But

$$m_f = \frac{ak_f}{\omega_s}$$

Hence

$$B \simeq 2m_f\omega_s = 2ak_f \qquad (11.71)$$

But, as seen from Eq. 11.54, ak_f is the maximum deviation of the carrier frequency. Hence, the bandwidth required for the transmission of an FM signal is approximately twice the maximum frequency deviation of the carrier. We shall denote the maximum deviation of the carrier by $\Delta\omega$. The exact relationship between the ratio of B and $\Delta\omega$, the frequency

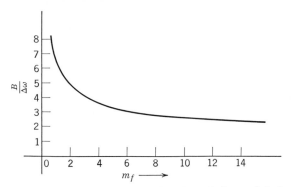

Figure 11.40 Bandwidth of FM signal as a function of the modulation index. (From *Information Transmission, Modulation, and Noise* by M. Schwartz, McGraw-Hill, New York, 1960.)

deviation of the carrier as a function of m_f, is shown in Fig. 11.40. It is evident from this figure that for $m_f >> 1$, the bandwidth B is approximately twice the frequency deviation of the carrier. For this reason, the Federal Communications Commission (FCC) has fixed the maximum value of Δf (frequency deviation) at 75 kc for commercial FM broadcasting stations. The approximate bandwidth required for FM radio is therefore approximately 150 kc.

It is evident from Fig. 11.40 that for wideband FM ($m_f >> \pi/2$), the bandwidth required for transmission is approximately $2\,\Delta\omega$ rps or $2\,\Delta f$ cps. Since

$$\Delta\omega = ak_f = m_f\omega_s$$

the increasing of m_f also increases $\Delta\omega$, proportionately, for a constant value of ω_s. Hence, the bandwidth required for transmission increases with m_f. This is illustrated in Fig. 11.41a. Here ω_s is held constant ($f_s = 5$ kc). The spectra of an FM carrier for $m_f = 1, 2, 5,$ and 10 are shown. The frequency deviation (Δf) is 5, 10, 25, and 50 kc, respectively Note that the bandwidth is approximately $2\,\Delta f$ for the higher values of m_f.

Figure 11.41b shows the case where the frequency deviation $\Delta\omega$ is held constant, and $m_f = \Delta\omega/\omega_s$ is varied by varying ω_s. Here, $\Delta f = 75$ kc and m_f is varied from 10 to 5 by varying f_s from 7.5 to 15 kc. In either case, the bandwidth is approximately

$$2\,\Delta f = 150 \text{ kc.}$$

11.15 SOME REMARKS ON PHASE MODULATION

We have observed that in angle modulated carriers the bandwidth of the resultant signal is approximately twice that of the maximum deviation

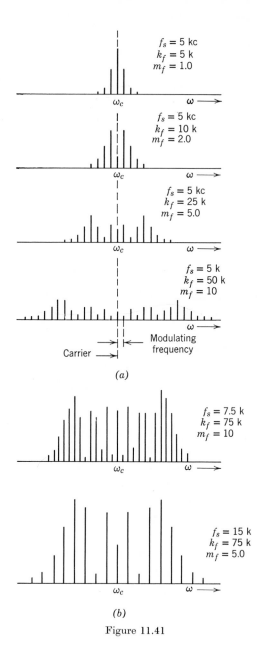

$$(a)$$

$$(b)$$

Figure 11.41

of the carrier frequency. Thus, if the deviation in carrier frequency is maintained constant, the spectrum of the modulated signal has a constant bandwidth.

For FM signals, the instantaneous frequency ω_i is given by Eq. 11.38.

$$\omega_i = \omega_c + ak_f \cos \omega_s t$$

The deviation of the carrier frequency is $\Delta\omega = ak_f$ and is independent of the frequency ω_s of the modulating signal. Hence, for FM signals, the bandwidth is approximately $2\,\Delta\omega = 2ak_f$, regardless of the frequency of the modulating signal. For phase modulation, on the other hand,

$$\theta(t) = \omega_c t + ak_p \cos \omega_s t$$

and

$$\omega_i = \frac{d\theta}{dt} = \omega_c - ak_p \omega_s \sin \omega_s t \qquad (11.72)$$

It is evident from Eq. 11.72 that the maximum deviation of the carrier frequency in PM is not a constant but is given by $ak_p\omega_s$ and varies linearly with ω_s, the frequency of the modulating signal. Hence, the bandwidth required for transmission of a PM carrier is not constant but depends strongly upon the waveform of the modulating signal. The higher values of ω_s need higher bandwidths of transmission. If such higher bandwidths are allotted for PM channels, then the bandwidth is not utilized efficiently for modulating the signal components of lower frequencies. For this reason, the PM system is inferior to the FM system. In practice, however, it is easier to generate a PM signal than an FM signal. It was shown earlier that if we integrate the modulating signal first and then allow it to phase-modulate a carrier, we obtain an FM carrier. Hence, in many systems the FM signals are generated by using PM generators which use the integrated signal $[\int f(t)\,dt]$ for phase modulation.

Thus far, the discussion of wideband angle modulation has been restricted to the special case of a single sinusoidal modulating signal. It is rather difficult to handle a general modulating signal because the process of angle modulation, unlike AM modulation, is inherently a nonlinear process. In amplitude modulation each frequency component of the modulating signal generates its sideband frequency and there is no interaction between the various frequency components. However, in angle modulation, each frequency component of the modulating signal gives rise to a large number of sideband components and, in addition, it can be shown that when more than one modulating frequency is present, sidebands are caused by all of the sum and difference frequencies. The reader is referred to Black for a few more cases of modulating signals.[10]

[10] H. S. Black, pp. 195–202, cited in reference 1. See also S. Goldman, *Frequency Analysis, Modulation, and Noise*, pp. 154–156, McGraw-Hill, New York, 1948.

11.16 POWER CONTENTS OF THE CARRIER AND THE SIDEBANDS IN ANGLE-MODULATED CARRIERS

It was shown that the total power carried by an AM carrier was a function of the modulation index m. For an angle-modulated carrier the amplitude of the carrier is always constant regardless of the modulation index m_f or m_p. Hence, it is reasonable to expect that the power carried by angle-modulated carrier is constant regardless of the extent of modulation. This indeed is the case. The interested reader is referred to Black for a complete proof.[11] The power of an FM carrier is the same as that of the unmodulated carrier, namely, $A^2/2$. The modulated signal, however, has a carrier component and sideband components as expressed in Eq. 11.70. In this equation, $AJ_0(m_f)$ represents the amplitude of the carrier component and $AJ_n(m_f)$ represents the amplitude of the nth-order sideband. It is possible to make $J_0(m_f)$ as small as possible by a proper choice of m_f. In fact, $J_0(m_f) = 0$ for $m_f = 2.405, 5.52$ and so on (see Fig. 11.38). Hence, the power carried by the carrier component can be made as small as desired. In such a situation, most of the power is carried by the sideband components. Hence, by a proper choice of m_f, the efficiency of transmission can be made as close to 100% as desired. Note that as m_f increases the number of sidebands increases and $J_0(m_f)$ decreases, thus increasing the efficiency of transmission.

11.17 NOISE-REDUCTION CHARACTERISTICS OF ANGLE MODULATION

It is obvious from the above discussion that for a given modulating signal the bandwidth required for the transmission of an angle-modulated wave is much larger than that required for the AM wave. For example, if f_s is 10 kc, then the bandwidth of the AM wave is 20 kc, whereas the bandwidth of the corresponding FM wave may be about 150 kc for $\Delta f = 75$ kc. For narrowband FM, the bandwidth is about 20 kc. Under no condition is the bandwidth required for FM less than 20 kc. This is definitely a great disadvantage of the FM system. For this reason, frequency modulation was considered wasteful and of little practical utility in the early days of its discovery[12] (about 1930). This was subsequently proved false by Major Edwin H. Armstrong, a brilliant engineer,

---

[11] H. S. Black, p. 190, cited in reference 1.
[12] J. Carson, "Notes on the Theory of Modulation," *Proc. I.R.E.*, **16**, 966–975 (July 1928).

whose contributions to the field of radio systems are comparable with those of Hertz and Marconi.[13]

It turns out that FM provides better discrimination against noise and interfering signals. It can be shown that under certain conditions the signal-to-noise ratio improves 6 db for each two-to-one increase in bandwidth occupancy.[14] It is not difficult to obtain the reduction in noise interference by about 30:1 (about 1000:1 in power) using wideband FM. The property of noise reduction in FM also follows directly from the theory of communication. We shall show in Chapter 14 that, in general, increasing the bandwidth increases the signal-to-noise ratio of a given signal. On the other hand, if we are willing to tolerate lower signal-to-noise ratio in a signal, then the signal can be transmitted over a lower bandwidth system.

The better discrimination against noise signals in FM systems can also be explained physically. The random noise has variations in the amplitude but has no orderly variation of frequency. Hence, a system which detects shifts in frequency but is nonresponsive to amplitude changes should have better discrimination properties against noise signals. It should be remembered that the property of discriminating noise in angle modulation becomes significant only when the bandwidth required for the transmission is larger, that is, when k_f is large. This means that m_f, the modulation index, should be large. In narrowband FM, the bandwidth required is the same as that of AM and the improvement in signal-to-noise ratio is not significant.

11.18 GENERATION OF FM SIGNALS

FM signals may be generated directly by frequency-modulating the carrier (direct FM) or by integrating the modulating signal first and then allowing it to phase-modulate the carrier (indirect FM).

Indirect FM

Because of the ease of generating the PM carrier, it is often used to generate FM signals indirectly. The block diagram of indirect FM is shown in Fig. 11.42. In practice, the maximum phase deviation of the PM generator is kept small so that the output of the phase modulator

---

[13] E. H. Armstrong, "A Method of Reducing Disturbances in Radio Signalling by a System of Frequency Modulation," *Proc. I.R.E.*, **24** (May 1936).

[14] H. S. Black, p. 181, cited in reference 1.

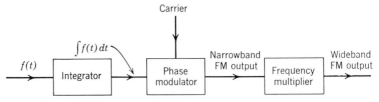

Figure 11.42   A block diagram representation of indirect FM.

yields narrowband FM. The desired value of m_f is achieved by using a frequency multiplier. The narrowband FM at the input of the frequency multiplier is given by

$$f_{c_1}(t) = A \cos (\omega_c t + m_f \sin \omega_s t)$$

The frequency multiplier is a nonlinear device which multiplies the frequency of the input signal by n. The output of the frequency multiplier is thus given by

$$f_{c_2}(t) = A \cos n(\omega_c t + m_f \sin \omega_s t)$$
$$= A \cos (n\omega_c t + nm_f \sin \omega_s t)$$

A simple square law device whose input and output signals are related by

$$e_0(t) = [e_i(t)]^2$$

acts as a frequency multiplier. If

$$e_i(t) = A \cos (\omega_c t + m_f \sin \omega_s t)$$
$$e_0(t) = A^2 \cos^2 (\omega_c t + m_f \sin \omega_s t)$$
$$= \frac{A^2}{2} [1 + \cos (2\omega_c t + 2m_f \sin \omega_s t)]$$

Obviously the frequency of the output signal is twice that of the input signal.

It is evident that the frequency multiplier increases the carrier frequency as well as the modulation index by a factor of n.

One possibility of obtaining phase modulation by using a balanced modulator has already been discussed (Fig. 11.37a). This system, known as the Armstrong indirect FM system, is widely used in practice.

Phase modulation can also be achieved by using the circuit shown in Fig. 11.43. The R-C network introduces a phase shift in the output wave with respect to the input. If $\omega CR << \pi/2$, then the phase shift is approximately given by ωCR radians. If now the resistance R is varied linearly with the modulating signal $f(t)$, the phase shift will be proportional to $f(t)$.

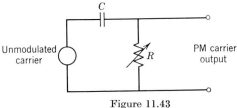

Figure 11.43

In pentodes the output impedance of a tube is a function of a control grid voltage. Thus the variable R may be obtained from the output terminals of a pentode with signal $f(t)$ connected to the control grid terminals. In such systems (Fig. 11.43), the voltage division across R and C causes a slight amplitude modulation in the output. This undesirable effect can be made negligible by making $R \gg 1/\omega_c C$.

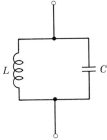

Figure 11.44

Direct FM

In this method the carrier frequency is directly varied linearly with the modulating signal. This is generally achieved by varying one of the frequency-determining elements of the tuned circuit of the oscillator. An oscillator has a tuned circuit as shown in Fig. 11.44. The frequency of oscillation is given by

$$\omega_i = \frac{1}{\sqrt{LC}}$$

It is therefore possible to vary the frequency of the oscillator directly by varying either L or C. Suppose

$$C = C_0 + af(t) = C_0\left[1 + \frac{a}{C_0}f(t)\right].$$

then

$$\omega_i = \frac{1}{\sqrt{LC_0[1 + (a/C_0)f(t)]}}$$

$$\simeq \frac{1}{\sqrt{LC_0}}[1 - (a/2C_0)f(t)] \qquad \text{if} \quad \frac{a}{C_0}f(t) \ll 1$$

$$= \omega_c[1 - (a/2C_0)f(t)] \qquad \text{where} \quad \omega_c = \frac{1}{\sqrt{LC_0}}$$

$$= \omega_c + k_f f(t) \qquad \text{where} \quad k_f = \frac{-a\omega_c}{2C_0}$$

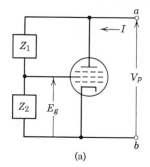 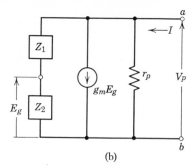

(a)   (b)

Figure 11.45

The same result will be obtained if, instead of varying the capacitor C, the inductor L is varied.

The variable reactance (inductive or capacitive) can be obtained from a subcircuit whose terminal impedance is a reactance which is proportional to the modulating signal. For example, a capacitance of a reverse-biased diode is a function of the voltage across its terminals. The so-called reactance tube circuits yield the variable reactance (inductive or capacitive) across its terminals which is a function of $f(t)$. The schematic diagram of such a circuit is shown in Fig. 11.45a. The equivalent circuit of this arrangement is shown in Fig. 11.45b. Since r_p is quite high, it may be neglected. Thus

$$I = g_m E_g + \frac{V_p}{Z_1 + Z_2} \tag{11.73}$$

and

$$E_g = \frac{Z_2}{Z_1 + Z_2} V_p \tag{11.74}$$

Substituting Eq. 11.74 in Eq. 11.73,

$$I = \left[\frac{g_m Z_2 + 1}{Z_1 + Z_2}\right] V_p$$

Hence the admittance Y_{ab}, seen across terminals ab, is

$$Y_{ab} = \frac{I}{V_p} = \frac{1 + g_m Z_2}{Z_1 + Z_2}$$

Usually, $|g_m Z_2| >> 1$, and if we let $Z_1 >> Z_2$, then

$$Y_{ab} \simeq \frac{g_m Z_2}{Z_1}$$

The transconductance g_m of the tube is a function of grid voltage. If we apply a signal proportional to $f(t)$ at the grid,

$$g_m = g_{m_0} + bf(t)$$

and

$$Y_{ab} = \frac{[g_{m0} + bf(t)]Z_2}{Z_1}$$

It is evident from this equation that if we let $Z_1 = 1/j\omega C_1$ and $Z_2 = R$, then Y_{ab} represents the admittance of a time varying capacitance:

$$C = C_0 + \beta f(t)$$

In all of these cases, the carrier frequency and the modulation index are kept quite small. The desired value of the carrier can be obtained by proper frequency multiplication and frequency translation. The frequency multiplication also increases the modulation index m_f.

Frequency modulation may also be obtained from voltage controlled devices such as a klystron and multivibrators. In these devices, the frequency of oscillation can be controlled by application of the voltage at appropriate points. In a reflex klystron, the oscillation frequency is a function of the repeller voltage.[15] Hence, the frequency can be modulated by applying $f(t)$ to a repeller. In multivibrators the oscillation frequency can be controlled by controlling the voltage at the control terminal (the control grid in vacuum tubes or the base terminals in a transistor).

11.19 DEMODULATION OF FM SIGNALS

To recover the modulating signal $f(t)$ from the FM carrier, we must provide a circuit whose output varies linearly with the frequency of the input signal. FM detectors are therefore frequency-sensitive devices, and are also called *frequency discriminators*. In general, the frequency discriminator consists of a circuit whose gain varies linearly with frequency. Thus, the FM signal is converted into an AM signal by this frequency-sensitive subcircuit. The resultant AM signal is consequently demodulated by an envelope detector using a diode and an R-C circuit. Figure 11.46 shows the simple type of frequency discriminators. In Fig. 11.46a, the first R-L circuit converts the FM signal into an AM signal which is then detected by a diode and the second R-C circuit (envelope detector). In Fig. 11.46c, the FM signal is converted into an AM signal by a tuned circuit which is slightly off-tuned at ω_c as shown in Fig. 11.46d. The

[15] H. A. Atwater *Introduction to Microwave Theory*, McGraw-Hill, New York, 1962.

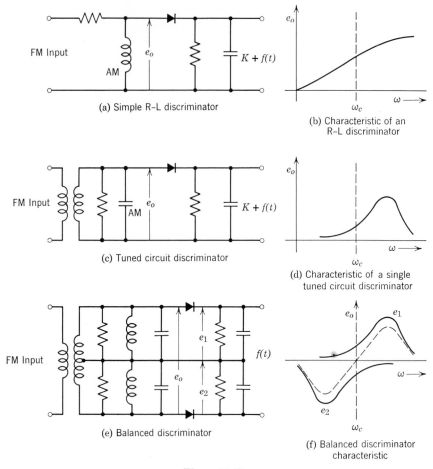

(a) Simple R-L discriminator

(b) Characteristic of an R-L discriminator

(c) Tuned circuit discriminator

(d) Characteristic of a single tuned circuit discriminator

(e) Balanced discriminator

(f) Balanced discriminator characteristic

Figure 11.46

voltage across the tuned circuit roughly varies linearly with the frequency as seen from Fig. 11.46d. The resulting AM signal is then detected by an envelope detector (Fig. 11.46c). The R-L discriminator in Fig. 11.46a has a poor sensitivity. The single tuned circuit discriminator in Fig. 11.46c has a better sensitivity but has a rather nonlinear characteristic with respect to frequency. The balanced discriminator shown in Fig. 11.46e has a high sensitivity, as well as a better linearity. The upper and the lower tuned circuits are tuned above and below the carrier frequency, respectively. The voltages e_1 and e_2 are shown as a function of frequency in Fig. 11.46f. The resultant output $e_o(t)$ as a function of frequency is shown dotted. The balanced discriminator provides excellent linearity compared to the single tuned circuit type of discriminator, because the distortion caused by even harmonics is balanced out in such arrangement. Second, any distortion caused by the residual amplitude modulation present in the input FM carrier is also balanced out.

PROBLEMS

1. Given two periodic functions:

$$f_1(t) = \sum_{n=1}^{10} \cos n\omega_0 t \qquad \omega_0 = 1000 \text{ radians per second}$$

$$f_2(t) = \sum_{n=1}^{5} \cos n\omega_0 t$$

Find and sketch the Fourier transforms $F_1(\omega)$ and $F_2(\omega)$ of the two functions. Find and sketch the Fourier transform of the function $f_1(t)f_2(t)$.

2. The input and the output signals of a square law device are related by

$$e_o(t) = [e_{in}(t)]^2$$

If

$$e_{in}(t) = \sum_{n=101}^{110} \cos n\omega_0 t \qquad \omega_0 = 1000 \text{ radians per second}$$

find and sketch the frequency spectrum of the output signal $e_o(t)$, using the convolution theorem.

3. If a signal

$$e_{in}(t) = Sa(kt)$$

is applied at the input of the square law device in Problem 2, find and sketch the frequency spectrum of the output signal.

4. If $f(t)$ is a continuous signal bandlimited to ω_m rps, then show that

$$\frac{k}{\pi}[f(t) * Sa(kt)] = f(t)$$

for all $k > \omega_m$. Hence show that

$$\frac{\omega_m}{\pi}[Sa(\omega_m t) * Sa(\omega_m t)] = Sa(\omega_m t)$$

(*Hint.* Use the time convolution theorem.)

5. Determine the minimum sampling rate and the Nyquist interval for the following signals.

(a) $Sa(100t)$
(b) $[Sa(100t)]^2$

6. The signals given below are not bandlimited. However, they can be approximated as bandlimited signals. Assume a suitable criterion for such an approximation and find the minimum sampling rate and the Nyquist interval in each case.

(a) $e^{-5|t|}$
(b) $e^{-t} \cos 100t \, u(t)$
(c) $te^{-5t}u(t)$
(d) $G_{10}(t)$

7. A half wave rectified cosine wave may be viewed as a cosine wave multiplied by a square wave $p(t)$ whose Fourier transform is given in Eq. 11.11. Find the Fourier transform of a half wave rectified sinusoidal signal by convolving the spectra of a cosine wave and $p(t)$. Perform the convolution graphically and analytically.

8. Sketch the spectrum of $Sa(200\pi t)$. This signal is sampled by $\delta_T(t)$ for values of $T = 1/400$, $1/200$, and $1/100$ second, respectively. Sketch the spectrum of $\delta_T(t)$ and, by graphical convolution, find the spectrum of the sampled function in each of the three cases. Sketch the sampled function in each case.

9. A balanced modulator circuit can also be used as a synchronous detector. Assuming a piecewise linear model for the diode (Fig. P-11.9a), find the output voltage $e_o(t)$ in the circuit shown in Fig. P-11.9b if

$$\varphi_1(t) = f(t) \cos \omega_c t$$
$$\varphi_2(t) = A \cos \omega_c t$$

Assume $A \gg |f(t)|$, for all t. How can $f(t)$ be recovered from $e_o(t)$? This circuit is also used as a phase discriminator which measures the phase of one sinusoidal waveform with respect to the other. Show that if

$$\varphi_1(t) = \cos (\omega t + \theta)$$
$$\varphi_2(t) = A \cos \omega t$$

then the output voltage $e_o(t)$ contains a d-c term proportional to $\cos \theta$.

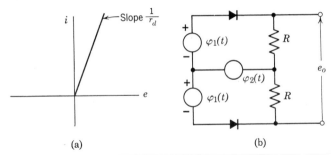

(a)   (b)

Figure P-11.9

10. It is possible to transmit two different signals simultaneously on the same carrier. The two signals are modulated by carriers of the same frequency but in phase quadrature as shown in Fig. P-11.10. Show that the signals can be recovered

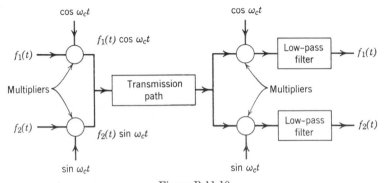

Figure P-11.10

by synchronously detecting the received signal by carriers of the same frequency but in phase quadrature.

11. Detection of an AM/SSB signal is effected by multiplying it by a sinusoidal signal of the carrier frequency (synchronous detection). Derive the spectrum of the output of such a detector analytically.

12. The upper sidebands of an AM signal $f(t) \cos \omega_c t$ are suppressed to obtain an SSB signal. Show that, in the time domain, such SSB signal can be expressed as

$$f_{\text{SSB}}(t) = \tfrac{1}{2}[f(t) \cos \omega_c t + f_h(t) \sin \omega_c t]$$

where

$$f_h(t) = \frac{1}{\pi} \int_{-\infty}^{\infty} \frac{f(\tau)}{t - \tau} \, d\tau$$

[*Hint*:

$$f_h(t) = \frac{1}{\pi}\left[f(t) * \frac{1}{t} \right], \qquad \frac{1}{t} \longleftrightarrow -j\pi \, sgn(\omega)$$

Hence

$$f_h(t) \longleftrightarrow -jF(\omega) \, sgn(\omega)$$

Note that $f_h(t)$ is the Hilbert transform of $f(t)$. (See Problem 4.19.)]

13. An amplitude modulated signal with a large carrier (ordinary AM) is given by

$$[A + f(t)] \cos \omega_c t.$$

This signal is demodulated by a chopper which multiplies the signal by a square wave $p(t)$ of frequency ω_c. Find the spectrum of the output of the chopper. (*Hint*. Use Eq. 11.11.)

14. For an AM wave where $[A + f(t)] > 0$, show that the output of an envelope detector is π times the output obtained by rectifier detector. Assume the forward resistance of the diode to be zero. The efficiency of a rectifier detector may be improved by a factor of 2 by using a full wave rectifier. Show the appropriate circuit of a full wave rectifier detector.

15. (a) Explain, qualitatively, what will happen if an envelope detector (or a rectifier detector) is used to demodulate an AM/SC signal. Explain why this type of demodulation in AM/SC signals is not equivalent to multiplication of the input signal by a square wave $p(t)$.

(b) Figure P-11.15 shows a signal $f(t)$ which is amplitude-modulated (AM/SC). The modulated signal is now fed to an envelope detector. Find the output of the detector.

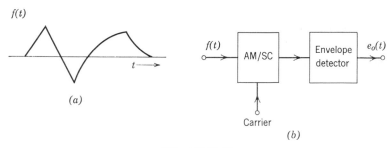

Figure P-11.15

16. The capacitor C of an envelope detector should be large enough to filter out the ripple at the carrier frequency present in the demodulated signal. However, if C is made too large, the time constant RC of the R-C circuit becomes too large and may be unable to follow the envelope of the modulated signal. Discuss carefully the effect of too low and too high values of the time constant. (a) Determine the largest value of the time constant which will enable the detector to follow the envelope of a modulated signal shown in Fig. P-11.16. Assume the period of the modulating signal to be 10^{-3} seconds and the period of the carrier to be much smaller than 10^{-3} seconds. (*Hint.* Approximate the exponential decay of the R-C circuit by the first two terms of the Taylor series and equate the rate of discharge of the R-C circuit to the rate of decay of the envelope.) (b) If the modulating signal were a sinusoidal signal of frequency ω_s, how would you determine the largest value of the time constant which can follow the envelope?

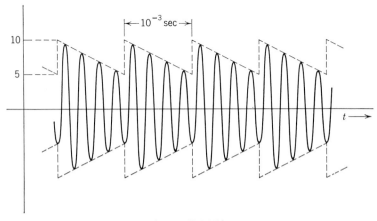

Figure P-11.16

17. Synchronous detection of an AM/SC signal may be carried out by multiplying the received modulated signal by a pulse train $p(t)$ of frequency ω_c as shown in Fig. 11.10. The result of this multiplication is a signal $f(t) \cos \omega_c t p(t)$. Derive the analytical expression for the spectral density function of this signal and show that the signal $f(t)$ can be recovered from the output by using a low-pass filter. (*Hint.* Use Eq. 11.11.)

18. A signal $e_1(t)$, shown in Fig. P-11.18, may be assumed to be bandlimited to a frequency ω_m. This signal is fed to a chopper (a square wave chopper), vibrating at a frequency $\omega_c (\omega_c > 2\omega_m)$, which opens and closes for alternate half cycles. The output of the chopper is fed to an ideal high-pass filter which attenuates all of the frequency components below ω_m (Fig. P-11.18).

(a) Sketch the spectra of $e_2(t)$ and $e_3(t)$.
(b) Sketch the signals $e_2(t)$ and $e_3(t)$.
(c) Indicate how the waveform $e_1(t)$ may be recovered from $e_3(t)$ by using another chopper.

In a chopper amplifier, arrangement similar to that shown in Fig. P-11.18c is employed. The signal $e_3(t)$ is amplified and is fed to another chopper. Figure 11.11 shows such an arrangement. Note that the high-pass filter is provided by the blocking capacitor in the input circuit.

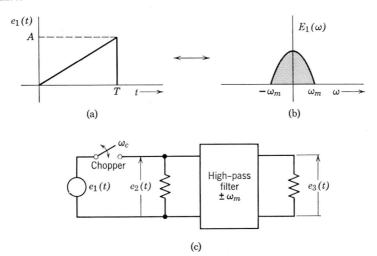

(a)

(b)

(c)

Figure P-11.18

19. Sketch the waveforms at aa', bb', and cc' of a chopper-type modulator shown in Fig. 11.18c. What conditions must be satisfied by the amplitude k of the sinusoidal signal and the modulating signal $f(t)$, so that the output at terminals cc' is an AM signal. Explain. Assume that the input impedance of the bandpass filter is infinity.

20. Generalize the uniform sampling theorem for signals bandlimited to f_m cps but not centered at $\omega = 0$. The positive spectrum of such signals lies between frequencies f_l and f_h where $f_h - f_l = f_m$. Show that the minimum uniform sampling rate for such signals must be $2f_h/n$ samples per second where f_h is the highest frequency of the spectrum and n is the largest integer less than f_h/f_m.

21. The sampling theorem has a dual theorem which applies to time limited signals. If a signal $f(t)$ exists only over a finite time interval, that is, if

$$f(t) = 0, \qquad |t| > T$$

show that the Fourier transform $F(\omega)$ of $f(t)$ is uniquely specified by the values of $F(\omega)$ at a sequence of equidistant points π/T radians apart. Also show that

$$F(\omega) = \sum_{n=-\infty}^{\infty} F\left(\frac{\pi n}{T}\right) Sa(\omega T - n\pi)$$

22. If $f(t)$ is a continuous signal bandlimited to f_m cps and $f_s(t)$ is the sampled signal (sampled uniformly at a $1/2f_m$ seconds interval), then $f(t)$ can be recovered from $f_s(t)$ by allowing it to pass through a low-pass filter. In practice, a holding circuit shown in Fig. P-11.22 is commonly used to recover $f(t)$ from $f_s(t)$. The output

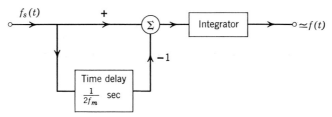

Figure P-11.22

of this circuit approximately resembles $f(t)$. (a) Sketch the waveforms at various points of this circuit for a typical sampled function. (b) What is the transfer function of this circuit? Sketch its frequency response. How closely does it resemble an ideal low-pass filter? [*Hint.* Determine $h(t)$, the unit impulse response of the system.]

23. A 100-mc carrier is frequency-modulated by a sinusoidal signal of 10 kc so that the maximum frequency deviation is 1 mc. Determine the approximate band-width of the FM carrier. Now, find the bandwidth of the FM carrier if the modulating signal amplitude is doubled. Determine the bandwidth of the FM carrier if the frequency of the modulating signal is also doubled.

24. A 100-mc carrier is phase-modulated by a sinusoidal signal of 10 kc with a modulator having $k_p = 100$. Determine the approximate bandwidth of the PM carrier if the modulating signal has unit amplitude. What is the approximate bandwidth if the modulating signal amplitude is doubled? What is the bandwidth if the modulating signal frequency is also doubled?

25. A carrier of the frequency of 100 mc is frequency-modulated by a square wave shown in Fig. P-11.25. If $k_f = 10^6$, find and sketch the spectrum of the modulated carrier. (*Hint.* The FM carrier can be expressed as a sinusoid of one frequency over a part of the cycles and a sinusoid of the other frequency over the remaining cycles. This is equivalent to the sum of two sinusoids, each multiplied by a periodic gate function.)

$f(t)$

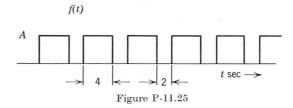

Figure P-11.25

26. A carrier of 100 mc is phase-modulated by a signal $f(t)$ shown in Fig. P-11.26. The modulating system constant k_p is 10^6. (a) Sketch the modulated carrier. (b) Find and sketch the spectrum of the modulated carrier if

(1) $A = 2 \times 10^{-6}$ $T = 2 \times 10^{-6}$
(2) $A = 10^{-6}$ $T = 2 \times 10^{-6}$
(3) $A = 2 \times 10^{-6}$ $T = 10^{-6}$
(4) $A = 10^{-6}$ $T = 10^{-6}$

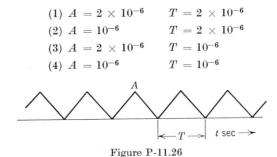

Figure P-11.26

(*Hint.* Find the instantaneous frequency ω_i as a function of time and proceed as in Problem 25.)

chapter 12

Signal Comparison:
Correlation

In Chapters 10 and 11 we studied the application of convolution to linear-system analysis and communication systems. In this chapter the use of convolution for the purpose of signal comparison will be considered.

12.1 SIGNAL COMPARISON

The signals may be compared on the basis of similarity of waveforms. Quantitatively, a comparison may be based upon the amount of the component of one waveform contained in the other waveform. If $f_1(t)$ and $f_2(t)$ are two waveforms, then, as shown in Chapter 3 (Eq. 3.10), the waveform $f_1(t)$ contains an amount $C_{12}f_2(t)$ of that particular waveform $f_2(t)$ in the interval (t_1, t_2) where

$$C_{12} = \frac{\displaystyle\int_{t_1}^{t_2} f_1(t) f_2(t)\, dt}{\displaystyle\int_{t_1}^{t_2} f_2{}^2(t)\, dt} \qquad (12.1)$$

The magnitude of the integral in the numerator of Eq. 12.1 might be taken as an indication of the similarity of the two signals. If this integral vanishes, that is,

$$\int_{t_1}^{t_2} f_1(t) f_2(t)\, dt = 0$$

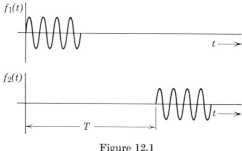

Figure 12.1

then the two signals have no similarity over the interval (t_1, t_2). Such signals are said to be orthogonal over the specified interval. The integral

$$\int_{t_1}^{t_2} f_1(t) f_2(t) \, dt$$

forms the basis of comparison of the two signals $f_1(t)$ and $f_2(t)$ over the interval (t_1, t_2). In general, we are interested in comparing the two signals over the entire interval $(-\infty, \infty)$. In this case the test integral becomes

$$\int_{-\infty}^{\infty} f_1(t) f_2(t) \, dt \tag{12.2}$$

However, there is a difficulty with this test integral. This can be illustrated by an example of a radar pulse. Figure 12.1 shows a transmitted pulse and a received pulse which is delayed with respect to the transmitted pulse by T seconds. Obviously, the two waveforms are identical except that one is delayed with respect to the other. Yet, the test integral in Eq. 12.2 yields zero value because the product $f_1(t)f_2(t)$ is identically zero everywhere. This indicates that the two waveforms have no measure of similarity. This is obviously a wrong conclusion. Hence, in order to search for a similarity between the two waveforms, we must shift one waveform with respect to the other by various amounts and see whether a similarity exists for some amount of shift of one function with respect to the other. The test integral is modified accordingly to

$$\varphi_{12}(\tau) = \int_{-\infty}^{\infty} f_1(t) f_2(t - \tau) \, dt \tag{12.3}$$

where τ is a "*searching*" or a *scanning parameter*. It is obvious that the integral 12.3 is a function of τ. This integral is known as the *crosscorrelation function* between signals $f_1(t)$ and $f_2(t)$, and is denoted by $\varphi_{12}(\tau)$. Note that it is immaterial whether we shift the function $f_1(t)$ by an amount of

τ in the negative direction or shift $f_2(t)$ by the same amount in a positive direction. Thus

$$\varphi_{12}(\tau) = \int_{-\infty}^{\infty} f_1(t + \tau) f_2(t) \, dt \tag{12.4}$$

Equation 12.4 can also be obtained from Eq. 12.3 by changing the variable t to $(t + \tau)$.

Graphically, the crosscorrelation function can be obtained by shifting the function $f_2(t)$ by τ seconds and multiplying it with $f_1(t)$. The area under the product curve gives the value of $\varphi_{12}(\tau)$. The function $f_2(t)$ may be shifted by different amounts. The area under the product curve for various values of τ (shift parameter) generates $\varphi_{12}(\tau)$. Notice the similarity between the operation of correlation and convolution. The graphical operation of correlation is similar to convolution in every respect except that the function $f_2(t)$ is not folded back about the vertical axis. It is, therefore, evident that the correlation of $f_1(t)$ and $f_2(t)$ is equivalent to the convolution of $f_1(t)$ and $f_2(-t)$. Later we shall derive this relationship analytically.

The crosscorrelation function[1] thus provides the measure of similarity between signals $f_1(t)$ and $f_2(t)$ as a function of the searching parameter τ (the shift of one signal with respect to the other). It is now evident that if the two waveforms are similar but shifted with respect to one another, then the crosscorrelation function will be finite over some range of τ indicating the measure of similarity. If the crosscorrelation function vanishes everywhere, the two signals are said to be uncorrelated.

In a similar way

$$\varphi_{21}(\tau) = \int_{-\infty}^{\infty} f_2(t) f_1(t - \tau) \, dt \tag{12.5}$$

$$= \int_{-\infty}^{\infty} f_2(t + \tau) f_1(t) \, dt \tag{12.6}$$

It is easy to see from the definitions of $\varphi_{12}(\tau)$ and $\varphi_{21}(\tau)$ that

$$\varphi_{12}(\tau) = \varphi_{21}(-\tau) \tag{12.7}$$

This means that graphically $\varphi_{12}(\tau)$ is the same as $\varphi_{21}(\tau)$ when it is folded back about the vertical axis at $\tau = 0$.

---

[1] If $f_1(t)$ and $f_2(t)$ are complex functions of the real variable t, then the crosscorrelation function $\varphi_{12}(\tau)$ is defined as

$$\varphi_{12}(\tau) = \int_{-\infty}^{\infty} f_1(t) f_2^*(t - \tau) \, dt$$

$$= \int_{-\infty}^{\infty} f_1(t + \tau) f_2^*(t) \, dt$$

The concept of comparison of the two signals may be applied to the comparison of a signal with itself when shifted by an amount of τ. We define the *autocorrelation* function $\varphi_{11}(\tau)$ as

$$\varphi_{11}(\tau) = \int_{-\infty}^{\infty} f_1(t)f_1(t - \tau)\, dt \qquad (12.8)$$

$$= \int_{-\infty}^{\infty} f_1(t + \tau)f_1(t)\, dt \qquad (12.9)$$

Autocorrelation is thus a measure of similarity of a given function with itself when shifted by an amount of τ. It is obvious from Eqs. 12.8 and 12.9 that

$$\varphi_{11}(\tau) = \varphi_{11}(-\tau) \qquad (12.10)$$

Evidently the autocorrelation function is an even function of τ.

12.2 CORRELATION AND CONVOLUTION

There is a striking resemblance between the operation of correlation and convolution. Indeed, the two integrals are closely related. To obtain the crosscorrelation of $f_1(t)$ and $f_2(t)$ according to Eq. 12.3, we multiply $f_1(t)$ with function $f_2(t)$ displaced by τ seconds. The area under the product curve is the crosscorrelation between $f_1(t)$ and $f_2(t)$ at τ. On the other hand, the convolution of $f_1(t)$ and $f_2(t)$ at $t = \tau$ is obtained by folding $f_2(t)$ backward about the vertical axis at the origin and taking the area under the product curve of $f_1(t)$ and the folded function $f_2(-t)$ displaced by τ. It, therefore, follows that the crosscorrelation of $f_1(t)$ and $f_2(t)$ is the same as the convolution of $f_1(t)$ and $f_2(-t)$. We arrive at the same conclusion analytically. If we denote the convolution of $f_1(t)$ and $f_2(-t)$ by $\rho_{12}(t)$, we have[2]

$$\rho_{12}(t) = f_1(t) * f_2(-t)$$
$$= \int_{-\infty}^{\infty} f_1(\tau)f_2(\tau - t)\, d\tau \qquad (12.11)$$

The dummy variable τ in the above integral may be replaced by another variable x.

$$\rho_{12}(t) = \int_{-\infty}^{\infty} f_1(x)f_2(x - t)\, dx$$

---

[2] Note that

$$f_1(t) * f_2(-t) \neq \int_{-\infty}^{\infty} f_1(t)f_2(-t - \tau)\, d\tau$$

as may be superficially obtained from the definition of convolution. The correct expression is the one given in Eq. 12.11. The reader may convince himself by using the graphical definition of convolution.

Changing the variable from t to τ, we get

$$\rho_{12}(\tau) = \int_{-\infty}^{\infty} f_1(x) f_2(x - \tau)\, dx$$

$$= \varphi_{12}(\tau)$$

Hence

$$\varphi_{12}(\tau) = f_1(t) * f_2(-t)\,|_{t=\tau} = \rho_{12}(\tau) \qquad (12.12)$$

Similarly

$$\varphi_{21}(\tau) = f_1(-t) * f_2(t)\,|_{t=\tau} = \rho_{21}(\tau) \qquad (12.13)$$

and

$$\varphi_{11}(\tau) = f_1(t) * f_1(-t)\,|_{t=\tau} = \rho_{11}(\tau) \qquad (12.14)$$

The relation between correlation and convolution is now evident. All of the techniques used to evaluate the convolution of two functions can be directly applied in order to find the correlation of two functions. In particular, the numerical techniques described in Chapter 10 can be conveniently used to evaluate the correlation. Similarly, all of the results derived for convolution (integration and differentiation) also apply to correlation.

An interesting situation arises when one of the functions is an even function of t. Thus, if $f_2(t)$ is an even function of t,

$$f_2(t) = f_2(-t)$$

It is evident that, in this case, the crosscorrelation and convolution are equivalent.

12.3 SOME PROPERTIES OF CORRELATION FUNCTIONS

Since the convolution of two functions in the time domain is equivalent to the multiplication of their respective spectra in the frequency domain, the operation of the correlation of $f_1(t)$ and $f_2(t)$ must be equal to the multiplication of the spectra of $f_1(t)$ and $f_2(-t)$. At this point we observe that if

$$f(t) \leftrightarrow F(\omega)$$

then

$$f(-t) \leftrightarrow F(-\omega)$$

This follows from the fact that

$$F(\omega) = \int_{-\infty}^{\infty} f(t) e^{-j\omega t}\, dt$$

Hence

$$F(-\omega) = \int_{-\infty}^{\infty} f(t) e^{j\omega t}\, dt$$

The change of the variable $x = -t$ yields

$$F(-\omega) = \int_{-\infty}^{\infty} f(-x)e^{-j\omega x}\, dx$$

Hence

$$f(-t) \leftrightarrow F(-\omega)$$

Thus, if

$$f_1(t) \leftrightarrow F_1(\omega)$$
$$f_2(t) \leftrightarrow F_2(\omega)$$

then it follows that

$$f_1(-t) \leftrightarrow F_1(-\omega)$$

and

$$f_2(-t) \leftrightarrow F_2(-\omega)$$

and

$$\varphi_{12}(\tau) = f_1(t) * f_2(-t) \leftrightarrow F_1(\omega)F_2(-\omega) \tag{12.15}$$

$$\varphi_{21}(\tau) = f_1(-t) * f_2(t) \leftrightarrow F_1(-\omega)F_2(\omega) \tag{12.16}$$

$$\varphi_{11}(\tau) = f_1(t) * f_1(-t) \leftrightarrow F_1(\omega)F_1(-\omega) \tag{12.17}$$

$$= |F_1(\omega)|^2 = \pi S_1(\omega) \tag{12.18}$$

where $S_1(\omega)$ is the energy density spectrum of $f_1(t)$. Equations 12.15 to 12.18 may also be expressed as

$$F_1(\omega)F_2(-\omega) = \int_{-\infty}^{\infty} \varphi_{12}(\tau)e^{-j\omega\tau}\, d\tau \tag{12.19}$$

$$F_1(-\omega)F_2(\omega) = \int_{-\infty}^{\infty} \varphi_{21}(\tau)e^{-j\omega\tau}\, d\tau \tag{12.20}$$

$$|F_1(\omega)|^2 = F_1(\omega)F_1(-\omega) = \int_{-\infty}^{\infty} \varphi_{11}(\tau)e^{-j\omega\tau}\, d\tau \tag{12.21}$$

It follows that the Fourier transform of $\varphi_{11}(\tau)$ yields π times the energy density function of $f_1(t)$ (Eq. 4.71). This result is also known as the *Autocorrelation theorem*.

The Autocorrelation theorem may also be derived directly as

$$\int_{-\infty}^{\infty} \varphi_{11}(\tau)e^{-j\omega\tau}\, d\tau = \int_{-\infty}^{\infty}\int_{-\infty}^{\infty} f_1(t)f_1(t-\tau)e^{-j\omega\tau}\, dt\, d\tau$$

$$= \int_{-\infty}^{\infty} f_1(t)e^{-j\omega t}\, dt \int_{-\infty}^{\infty} f_1(t-\tau)e^{j\omega(t-\tau)}\, d\tau$$

$$= F_1(\omega)\int_{-\infty}^{\infty} f_1(x)e^{j\omega x}\, dx$$

$$= F_1(\omega)F_1(-\omega)$$

$$= |F_1(\omega)|^2$$

Note that the Fourier transform of the autocorrelation function is $|F_1(\omega)|^2$ and, hence, it retains the information regarding only the magnitude of $F_1(\omega)$. The phase information of $F_1(\omega)$ is lost. Hence, a class of functions which have the Fourier transform with the same magnitude function but different phase functions have the same autocorrelation function. We therefore conclude that for a given function $f(t)$, there is a unique autocorrelation function but the reverse is not true. A given autocorrelation function may correspond to an infinite variety of waveforms. This fact is of the utmost significance in the analysis of signals with random variations. For a random signal whose statistical properties do not change with time (stationary random signal), the signal waveform may vary randomly, yet its autocorrelation function (and hence the energy density spectrum) is nonrandom.

The autocorrelation function also exhibits an interesting property:

$$\varphi_{11}(0) = \int_{-\infty}^{\infty} f_1{}^2(t)\, dt \tag{12.22}$$

This follows directly from the equation defining the autocorrelation function (Eqs. 12.8 and 12.9). Thus the value of the autocorrelation function at the origin is equal to the energy of the signal.

Every signal correlates perfectly with itself. As the signal is shifted with respect to itself, the amount of correlation will be reduced. Hence, it is logical to expect that the autocorrelation function will be maximum at $\tau = 0$ (no shift). Now we shall show that this indeed is the case. To show this property, consider the integral:

$$\int_{-\infty}^{\infty} [f_1(t) \pm f_1(t + \tau)]^2\, dt \tag{12.23}$$

This integral is obviously a positive, nonzero quantity for $\tau \neq 0$. (The case of periodic signals where the above integral may become zero for some values of τ will be considered later.)

$$\int_{-\infty}^{\infty} [f_1(t) \pm f_1(t + \tau)]^2\, dt > 0, \qquad \tau \neq 0 \tag{12.24}$$

It follows from this equation that

$$\int_{-\infty}^{\infty} f_1{}^2(t)\, dt + \int_{-\infty}^{\infty} f_1{}^2(t + \tau)\, dt \pm 2 \int_{-\infty}^{\infty} f_1(t) f_1(t + \tau)\, dt > 0 \tag{12.25}$$

The first two integrals in Eq. 12.25 have the same value and it is given by $\varphi_{11}(0)$. It is therefore evident that

$$2\varphi_{11}(0) \pm 2\varphi_{11}(\tau) > 0$$

or

$$\varphi_{11}(0) > \pm\, \varphi_{11}(\tau) \qquad \tau \neq 0 \tag{12.26}$$

Therefore

$$\varphi_{11}(0) > |\varphi_{11}(\tau)| \quad \text{for} \quad \tau \neq 0 \qquad (12.27)$$

Hence, the maximum value of the autocorrelation function occurs at the origin. The autocorrelation function becomes smaller at larger values of τ. This is quite logical because as the function is shifted more and more with respect to itself the correlation is expected to decrease. For random and other nonperiodic signals, with zero average value,

$$\lim_{\tau \to \infty} \varphi_{11}(\tau) = 0 \qquad (12.28)$$

In practice, however, the autocorrelation function becomes quite small for some large finite values of τ. This property of the autocorrelation function plays a crucial role in the correlation method of the detection of a periodic signal in the presence of noise.

Example 12.1

Find the autocorrelation function of a gate function shown in Fig. 12.2 and, hence, determine the energy density spectrum of the function. The gate function in Fig. 12.2a is $AG_T(t)$. To obtain $\varphi_{11}(\tau)$, we shift the gate function by τ seconds (Fig. 12.2b) and multiply the shifted function $AG_T(t - \tau)$ with the original function $AG_T(t)$. It is evident from Fig. 12.2b that the area under the product curve is given by $A^2[T - |\tau|]$. The plot of this function is shown

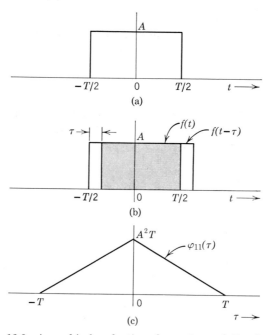

Figure 12.2   A graphical evaluation of an autocorrelation function.

in Fig. 12.2c for various values of τ and, thus, represents $\varphi_{11}(\tau)$. As expected, the correlation is maximum for $\tau = 0$, and decreases for larger values of τ. Note that since the gate function is an even function, the autocorrelation is the same as the convolution in this case.

The energy density spectrum of the gate function in Fig. 12.2a is given by $(1/\pi)$ times the Fourier transform of $\varphi_{11}(\tau)$

$$\Phi_{11}(\omega) = \int_{-\infty}^{\infty} \varphi_{11}(\tau) e^{-j\omega\tau}\, d\tau$$

$$= \int_{-T}^{T} A^2(T - |\tau|) e^{-j\omega\tau}\, d\tau$$

The integral may be evaluated directly or found from the tables of the Fourier transform. The Fourier transform of a triangular pulse is given in Table 4.1B (pair 14),

$$\Phi_{11}(\omega) = A^2 T^2 \left[Sa\left(\frac{\omega T}{2}\right) \right]^2$$

The energy density function $S(\omega) = (1/\pi)\Phi_{11}(\omega)$ and hence

$$S(\omega) = \frac{1}{\pi} A^2 T^2 \left[Sa\left(\frac{\omega T}{2}\right) \right]^2$$

This result may also be evaluated directly from the Fourier transform $F(\omega)$ of the gate function from Table 4.1B. The Fourier transform of a gate function in Fig. 12.2a is given by

$$F(\omega) = A T Sa\left(\frac{\omega T}{2}\right)$$

and

$$S(\omega) = \frac{1}{\pi} |F(\omega)|^2$$

$$= \frac{A^2 T^2}{\pi} \left[Sa\left(\frac{\omega T}{2}\right) \right]^2$$

which is the same result as obtained from the autocorrelation method.

Note that autocorrelation is maximum at $\tau = 0$ and is zero for $|\tau| > T$. It is also evident that $\varphi_{11}(0) = A^2 T$ represents the energy of the rectangular pulse and $\varphi_{11}(\tau)$ is an even function of τ. Important properties of the correlation function are summarized below:

(1) $$\varphi_{11}(0) = \int_{-\infty}^{\infty} f_1{}^2(t)\, dt \qquad\qquad (12.29)$$

(2) $$\varphi_{11}(0) > |\varphi_{11}(\tau)|, \qquad \tau \neq 0 \qquad\qquad (12.30)$$

(3) $$\varphi_{11}(\tau) = \varphi_{11}(-\tau) \qquad\qquad (12.31)$$

(4) $$\varphi_{11}(\tau) \leftrightarrow |F_1(\omega)|^2 = \pi S_1(\omega) \qquad\qquad (12.32)$$

(5) $$\varphi_{12}(\tau) \leftrightarrow F_1(\omega) F_2(-\omega) \qquad\qquad (12.33)$$

(6) $$\varphi_{12}(\tau) = \varphi_{21}(-\tau) \qquad\qquad (12.34)$$

It can also be shown that

(7) $$\varphi_{11}(0) + \varphi_{22}(0) > 2 \, |\varphi_{12}(\tau)| \qquad (12.35)$$

It is obvious from Eq. 12.29 that for a finite energy signal, $\varphi_{11}(0)$ is finite and, from Eq. 12.30, it follows that $\varphi_{11}(\tau)$ is also finite for all values of τ. Similarly, if $f_1(t)$ and $f_2(t)$ are both finite energy signals then, from Eq. 12.35, it is evident that $\varphi_{12}(\tau)$ is finite for all values of τ.

12.4 CORRELATION FUNCTIONS FOR NONFINITE ENERGY SIGNALS

If the signals under consideration have an infinite energy content, that is,

$$\int_{-\infty}^{\infty} f^2(t) \, dt = \infty$$

then it is obvious that the correlation functions as defined in previous sections do not exist. This is the case for random noise signals existing over the entire interval $(-\infty, \infty)$ or for periodic signals. In such cases, a more meaningful quantity is average correlation, defined as

$$\bar{\varphi}_{11}(\tau) = \lim_{T \to \infty} \frac{1}{T} \int_{-T/2}^{T/2} f_1(t) f_1(t - \tau) \, dt \qquad (12.36)$$

$$\bar{\varphi}_{12}(\tau) = \lim_{T \to \infty} \frac{1}{T} \int_{-T/2}^{T/2} f_1(t) f_2(t - \tau) \, dt \qquad (12.37)$$

Periodic Signals

For periodic signals, Eqs. 12.36 and 12.37 can be further simplified. Let $f_1(t)$ and $f_2(t)$ both be periodic functions of period T_1. It follows from the property of a periodic function:

$$f_1(t - \tau) = f_1(t - \tau + T_1) \qquad (12.38)$$

and

$$f_2(t - \tau) = f_2(t - \tau + T_1) \qquad (12.39)$$

and, since $f_1(t)$ is also a periodic function, that is,

$$f_1(t) = f_1(t + T_1)$$

it follows that the integrands in Eqs. 12.36 and 12.37 are periodic functions in variable t with a period T_1. The integral of such a function over each cycle (over any interval T_1) is the same, and hence it is immaterial whether the correlation functions are averaged over a very large interval $(T \to \infty)$ or over one period (T_1). Hence, for periodic functions,

$$\bar{\varphi}_{11}(\tau) = \frac{1}{T_1} \int_{-T_1/2}^{T_1/2} f_1(t) f_1(t - \tau) \, dt \qquad (12.40a)$$

$$\bar{\varphi}_{12}(\tau) = \frac{1}{T_1} \int_{-T_1/2}^{T_1/2} f_1(t) f_2(t - \tau) \, dt \qquad (12.40b)$$

Since the integrands in Eqs. 12.40a and 12.40b are periodic functions of period T_1, it is evident that the average correlation functions will also be periodic functions with the same period. In practice, the term average is often omitted for convenience. Hereafter, it will be understood that the term correlation functions, as applied to periodic signals or infinite energy signals, will always mean average correlation functions.

To reiterate: the autocorrelation and crosscorrelation functions for periodic signals of period T_1 are also periodic with the same period. As we shall see, this is a very significant property which enables us to detect periodic signals in the presence of noise by using correlation techniques. Note that the crosscorrelation function of two periodic signals of different periods with irrational ratio is zero (see Problem 6 and 7 at the end of Chapter 3).

We have seen (Eq. 12.32) that the Fourier transform of an auto-correlation function of a finite energy signal $f(t)$ is π times the energy density function $S(\omega)$ of $f(t)$.

$$\varphi_{ff}(\tau) \longleftrightarrow \pi S(\omega)$$

A similar relationship exists between the average autocorrelation function $\bar{\varphi}_{ff}(\tau)$ and the average power density function $P(\omega)$.

Let

$$f_T(t) = \begin{cases} f(t) & \text{for} \quad t < |T/2| \\ 0 & \text{otherwise} \end{cases}$$

$$f_T(t) \longleftrightarrow F_T(\omega)$$

and

$$|F_T(\omega)|^2 = \pi S_T(\omega)$$

It follows from the definition of an average autocorrelation function that

$$\bar{\varphi}_{ff}(\tau) \longleftrightarrow \lim_{T \to \infty} \frac{1}{T} |F_T(\omega)|^2$$

$$= \lim_{T \to \infty} \pi \frac{S_T(\omega)}{T}$$

As the interval $T \to \infty$, the energy density $S_T(\omega) \to \infty$, and hence the quantity $S_T(\omega)/T$ may approach a limit as $T \to \infty$. We shall denote this limit by $P(\omega)$, the average power density function of $f(t)$.

$$P(\omega) = \lim_{T \to \infty} \frac{1}{T} S_T(\omega)$$

Thus

$$\bar{\varphi}_{ff}(\tau) \leftrightarrow \pi P(\omega)$$

Note that, by definition,

$$\int_0^\infty S_T(\omega)\, d\omega = \int_{-T/2}^{T/2} f_T{}^2(t)\, dt$$

Hence

$$\int_0^\infty P(\omega)\, d\omega = \lim_{T \to \infty} \frac{1}{T} \int_{-T/2}^{T/2} f^2(t)\, dt \qquad (12.41)$$

The right-hand side of Eq. 12.41 represents the mean square value of $f(t)$. Hence the area under the power density function is equal to the mean square value of $f(t)$, and the power density function $P(\omega)$ is given by

$$\bar{\varphi}_{ff}(\tau) \leftrightarrow \pi P(\omega) \qquad (12.42)$$

If we apply a signal with power density spectrum $P_i(\omega)$ at the input terminals of a linear system with a transfer function $H(j\omega)$, then $P_o(\omega)$, the power density spectrum of the output signal, will be given by

$$P_o(\omega) = P_i(\omega)\, |H(j\omega)|^2$$

This follows from the definition of the power density spectrum and the discussion in Section 6.13.

12.5 DETECTION OF PERIODIC SIGNALS IN THE PRESENCE OF NOISE BY CORRELATION

We shall now consider the case of periodic signals that are contaminated with noise. Detection of a periodic signal masked by random noise is of great importance. It finds applications in the detection of radar and sonar signals, the detection of a periodic component in brain waves, and the detection of a cyclical component in ocean wave analysis. Similarly, in many areas of geophysics including meteorology, one of the major problems is the detection of periodic signal components masked by random noise. Correlation techniques provide a powerful tool in the solution of these problems. We shall consider the application of both auto-correlation and crosscorrelation in the detection of a periodic signal masked by noise.

The noise signal encountered in practice is a signal with random amplitude variations. It can be shown that such a signal is uncorrelated with any periodic signal. If $s(t)$ is a periodic signal and $n(t)$ represents the noise signal, then

$$\lim_{T \to \infty} \frac{1}{T} \int_{-T/2}^{T/2} s(t)n(t - \tau) \, dt = 0 \qquad \text{for all } \tau$$

If we denote $\bar{\varphi}_{sn}(\tau)$ as the crosscorrelation function of $s(t)$ and $n(t)$, then[3]

$$\bar{\varphi}_{sn}(\tau) = 0$$

Detection by Autocorrelation

Let $s(t)$ be a periodic signal mixed with a noise signal $n(t)$. Then the received signal $f(t)$ is $[s(t) + n(t)]$. Let $\bar{\varphi}_{ff}(\tau)$, $\bar{\varphi}_{ss}(\tau)$, and $\bar{\varphi}_{nn}(\tau)$ denote the autocorrelation functions of $f(t)$, $s(t)$, and $n(t)$, respectively. Then

$$\bar{\varphi}_{ff}(\tau) = \lim_{T \to \infty} \frac{1}{T} \int_{-T/2}^{T/2} f(t)f(t - \tau) \, dt \qquad (12.43)$$

$$= \lim_{T \to \infty} \frac{1}{T} \int_{-T/2}^{T/2} [s(t) + n(t)][s(t - \tau) + n(t - \tau)] \, dt$$

$$= \bar{\varphi}_{ss}(\tau) + \bar{\varphi}_{nn}(\tau) + \bar{\varphi}_{sn}(\tau) + \bar{\varphi}_{ns}(\tau) \qquad (12.44)$$

since the periodic signal $s(t)$ and noise signal $n(t)$ are uncorrelated,

$$\bar{\varphi}_{sn}(\tau) = \bar{\varphi}_{ns}(\tau) = 0$$

Therefore

$$\bar{\varphi}_{ff}(\tau) = \bar{\varphi}_{ss}(\tau) + \bar{\varphi}_{nn}(\tau) \qquad (12.45)$$

Thus, $\bar{\varphi}_{ff}(\tau)$ has two components: $\bar{\varphi}_{ss}(\tau)$ and $\bar{\varphi}_{nn}(\tau)$. We have already shown that the autocorrelation function of a periodic signal is also a periodic function of the same frequency and the autocorrelation function of a nonperiodic function tends to zero for large values of τ. Since $s(t)$ is a periodic signal and $n(t)$ is a nonperiodic signal, it follows that $\bar{\varphi}_{ss}(\tau)$ is a periodic function whereas $\bar{\varphi}_{nn}(\tau)$ becomes arbitrarily small for large values of τ. Therefore, for sufficiently large values of τ, $\bar{\varphi}_{ff}(\tau)$ is essentially equal to $\bar{\varphi}_{ss}(\tau)$. Therefore, $\bar{\varphi}_{ff}(\tau)$ will exhibit a periodic nature at sufficiently large values of τ.

[3] In general, two signals $f_1(t)$ and $f_2(t)$ are said to be uncorrelated if

$$\lim_{T \to \infty} \frac{1}{T} \int_{-T/2}^{T/2} f_1(t)f_2(t - \tau) = \bar{f}_1 \bar{f}_2 \qquad \text{for all values of } \tau$$

where $\bar{f}_1$ and $\bar{f}_2$ represent the average values (d-c component) of $f_1(t)$ and $f_2(t)$ in the interval $(-T/2, T/2)$. Hence, if either $f_1(t)$ or $f_2(t)$ has a zero average, the crosscorrelation function of the two uncorrelated signals is zero. In the example under consideration the noise signal has a zero average value.

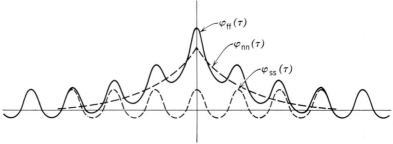

Figure 12.3   An autocorrelation function of a periodic signal masked by noise.

The solution to the problem is now obvious. If $\bar{\varphi}_{ff}(\tau)$ exhibits a periodic nature at sufficiently large values of τ, it follows that $f(t)$ contains a periodic signal of the frequency displayed by $\bar{\varphi}_{ff}(\tau)$. Furthermore, if $\bar{\varphi}_{ff}(\tau)$ does exhibit such a periodic nature it is possible to separate $\bar{\varphi}_{ss}(\tau)$ (periodic component) and $\bar{\varphi}_{nn}(\tau)$ (nonperiodic component). This is shown in Fig. 12.3.

In practice, it is impossible to compute the autocorrelation function of $f(t)$ over an infinite interval. Actually, the integral in Eq. 12.43 is evaluated over a large but finite interval T. This process of integration over only a finite interval causes a certain amount of error. The cross-correlation functions $\bar{\varphi}_{sn}(\tau)$ and $\bar{\varphi}_{ns}(\tau)$ are zero only if the crosscorrelation functions are evaluated over $(-\infty, \infty)$. Thus, for finite value of T, the crosscorrelation functions may not be zero, and hence the expression in Eq. 12.45 is in error by the amount of these terms. In general, as T is made larger, the crosscorrelation terms become smaller. For the purpose of the detection of $s(t)$, it is necessary to make the error terms arising due to the crosscorrelation functions much smaller compared to $\bar{\varphi}_{ss}(\tau)$. If the signal $s(t)$ is very weak, then $\bar{\varphi}_{ss}(\tau)$ has a small amplitude and, under such conditions, it is necessary to make T very large in order to reduce the error terms well below $\bar{\varphi}_{ss}(\tau)$.

The autocorrelation function of a given signal $f(t)$ may be calculated by the numerical techniques used for convolution (see Chapter 10). Using these numerical techniques it is possible to evaluate the function on digital computers. Automatic electronic correlators have also been designed to carry out these operations automatically.[4]

Detection by Crosscorrelation

The detection of a periodic signal can also be carried out by cross-correlating the received signal with another periodic signal of the same

[4] For a description of such a correlator, see Y. W. Lee, *Statistical Theory of Communication*, pp. 264–267, Wiley, New York, 1960.

frequency as that of the signal to be detected. It can be shown that the crosscorrelation technique is much more effective than the autocorrelation technique in the extraction of a periodic signal masked by noise.[5] The disadvantage, however, is that it is necessary to know beforehand the frequency of the signal to be detected. In many cases (for example, radar, sonar, etc.) the frequency is known beforehand. If the frequency is not known beforehand, it may be determined by the autocorrelation technique described above.

We shall now crosscorrelate the received signal

$$f(t) = s(t) + n(t)$$

with a locally generated signal $c(t)$ of the same frequency as that of $s(t)$:

$$\bar{\phi}_{fc}(t) = \lim_{T \to \infty} \frac{1}{T} \int_{-T/2}^{T/2} [s(t) + n(t)]c(t - \tau)\, dt \qquad (12.46)$$

$$= \bar{\phi}_{sc}(\tau) + \bar{\phi}_{nc}(\tau) \qquad (12.47)$$

The term $c(t)$ is a periodic function and is uncorrelated with the random noise signal $n(t)$. Hence $\bar{\phi}_{nc}(\tau)$ is zero. Therefore

$$\bar{\phi}_{fc}(\tau) = \bar{\phi}_{sc}(\tau) \qquad (12.48)$$

Since $s(t)$ and $c(t)$ are signals of the same frequency, it follows that $\bar{\phi}_{sc}(\tau)$ is also a periodic function of the same frequency. It is evident that if the crosscorrelation of the contaminated signal $f(t)$ with $c(t)$ yields a periodic signal, $f(t)$ must contain a periodic component of the same frequency as that of $c(t)$.

It should be noted that in autocorrelation techniques of detection, the autocorrelation of $f(t)$ contains two terms, $\bar{\phi}_{ss}(\tau)$ and $\bar{\phi}_{nn}(\tau)$ and, to arrive at the proper conclusion, one has to observe whether $\bar{\phi}_{ff}(\tau)$ is periodic at very large values of τ where $\bar{\phi}_{nn}(\tau)$ becomes negligible. On the other hand, in the crosscorrelation method the crosscorrelation between $f(t)$ and $c(t)$ gives $\bar{\phi}_{sc}(\tau)$ directly without any additional noise terms. Hence it is possible to conclude whether a periodic component is present or absent in $f(t)$ at any values of τ.

12.6 DETERMINATION OF THE WAVEFORM OF A PERIODIC SIGNAL MASKED BY NOISE

The two methods of detection discussed above provide information on whether or not the received signal contains the periodic signal. These methods, in general, do not provide information on the actual waveform

---

[5] Y. W. Lee, p. 290, cited in reference 4.

of the periodic signal component in the received signal. We shall now show that it is possible to obtain the actual waveform of the periodic signal if the received signal is $f(t)$ crosscorrelated with a periodic impulse function of the same frequency as that of the desired signal component. This is, of course, the special case of detection by crosscorrelation techniques where $c(t)$ is taken as a periodic impulse function $\delta_{T_0}(t)$ and T_0 is the period of the desired signal $s(t)$.

As before, let the received signal $f(t)$ be given by $[s(t) + n(t)]$, where $s(t)$ is a periodic signal of period T_0. A periodic impulse function of period T_0 is represented by $\delta_{T_0}(t)$. This is a train of unit impulses separated by T_0 seconds. Thus, the local periodic signal $c(t)$ in this case is $\delta_{T_0}(t)$. The crosscorrelation function between $f(t)$ and $\delta_{T_0}(t)$ is therefore given by Eq. 12.48.

$$\bar{\varphi}_{fc}(\tau) = \lim_{T \to \infty} \frac{1}{T} \int_{-T/2}^{T/2} [s(t) + n(t)]\, \delta_{T_0}(t - \tau)\, dt$$

$$= \lim_{T \to \infty} \frac{1}{T} \int_{-T/2}^{T/2} s(t)\, \delta_{T_0}(t - \tau)\, dt \qquad (12.49)$$

Since $n(t)$ and $\delta_{T_0}(t)$ are uncorrelated, the crosscorrelation term arising due to these signals is zero.

Also, since both $s(t)$ and $\delta_{T_0}(t)$ are periodic signals of period T_0, the integrand in Eq. 12.49 is a periodic function of period T_0 and its integral over any interval of T_0 duration is the same. Hence, it is immaterial whether the averaging is done over the interval $T(T \to \infty)$ or over one period T_0. Hence

$$\bar{\varphi}_{fc}(\tau) = \frac{1}{T_0} \int_{-T_0/2}^{T_0/2} s(t)\, \delta_{T_0}(t - \tau)\, dt \qquad (12.50)$$

Note that $\delta_{T_0}(t - \tau)$ is a periodic impulse function as shown in Fig. 12.4. In the interval $(-T_0/2,\ T_0/2)$, $\delta_{T_0}(t)$ is given by a single impulse $\delta(t)$. Similarly, $\delta_{T_0}(t - \tau)$ is given by a single impulse $\delta(t - \tau)$ for $|\tau| < T_0/2$. Hence δ_{T_0} may be replaced by $\delta(t - \tau)$ in the integrand of Eq. 12.50 for $-T_0/2 < \tau < T_0/2$. Hence

$$\bar{\varphi}_{fc}(\tau) = \frac{1}{T_0} \int_{-T_0/2}^{T_0/2} s(t)\, \delta(t - \tau)\, d\tau \qquad (12.51)$$

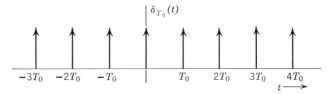

Figure 12.4

From the sampling property of the impulse function, it follows that

$$\bar{\varphi}_{fc}(\tau) = \frac{1}{T_0} s(\tau) \qquad (-T_0 < \tau < T_0) \qquad (12.52)$$

But since both $\bar{\varphi}_{fc}(\tau)$ and $s(\tau)$ are periodic functions of period T_0, it follows that the representation of $\bar{\varphi}_{fc}(\tau)$ in Eq. 12.52 is true for all values of τ.

$$\bar{\varphi}_{fc}(\tau) = \frac{1}{T_0} s(\tau) \qquad (12.53)$$

It is now evident from Eq. 12.52 that the crosscorrelation of $f(t)$ with the periodic impulse function $\delta_{T_0}(t)$ of the same frequency as that of $s(t)$ yields the actual waveform of the desired periodic component $s(t)$.

12.7 EXTRACTION OF A SIGNAL FROM NOISE BY FILTERING

A signal masked by noise can be detected either by correlation techniques or by filtering. Actually, the two techniques are equivalent. The correlation technique is a means of extraction of a given signal in the time domain, whereas filtering achieves exactly the same results in the frequency domain. As we shall see, correlation in the time domain corresponds to filtering action in the frequency domain.

Relationship Between Correlation and Filtering

Consider the crosscorrelation function $\varphi_{12}(\tau)$ of signals $f_1(t)$ and $f_2(t)$. If

$$f_1(t) \leftrightarrow F_1(\omega)$$
$$f_2(t) \leftrightarrow F_2(\omega)$$

then, from Eq. 12.33,

$$\bar{\varphi}_{12}(\tau) \leftrightarrow F_1(\omega)F_2(-\omega)$$

It is obvious that the operation of crosscorrelation of $f_1(t)$ and $f_2(t)$ in the time domain is equivalent to multiplication of the spectra $F_1(\omega)$ and $F_2(-\omega)$ in the frequency domain. The function $\bar{\varphi}_{12}(\tau)$ may be obtained in the time domain by evaluating the integral by a crosscorrelator (Fig. 12.5a). Alternately, if the signal $f_1(t)$ is applied to a system with the transfer function $F_2(-\omega)$, the output will be $\bar{\varphi}_{12}(\tau)$ (Fig. 12.5b). It is thus seen that the crosscorrelation between signals $f_1(t)$ and $f_2(t)$ may be effected by applying the signal $f_1(t)$ to the input terminals of a linear system with the transfer function $F_2(-\omega)$. This operation essentially represents filtering.

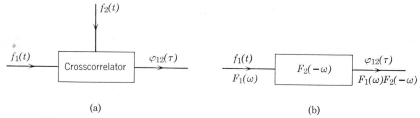

(a)   (b)

Figure 12.5   Crosscorrelation in the time and the frequency domains.

The impulse response $h(t)$ of a system with a transfer function $F_2(-\omega)$ is given by

$$h(t) = \mathscr{F}^{-1}[F_2(-\omega)]$$

But

$$f_2(t) \leftrightarrow F_2(\omega)$$

and

$$f_2(-t) \leftrightarrow F_2(-\omega)$$

Hence

$$h(t) = f_2(-t)$$

To reiterate: *the crosscorrelation function of signals $f_1(t)$ and $f_2(t)$ is the response of a system with transfer function $F_2(-\omega)$ (or the impulse response $f_2(-t)$) when the driving function is $f_1(t)$.*

This result can now be applied to the problem of the detection of a periodic signal from a random noise signal. As before, if we denote $s(t)$ and $n(t)$ as the desired periodic signal component and the random noise component, respectively; then the received signal $f(t)$ is

$$f(t) = s(t) + n(t)$$

The periodic component $s(t)$ present in $f(t)$ can be detected by cross-correlating $f(t)$ with another periodic signal $c(t)$ of the same period as that of $s(t)$. To perform this crosscorrelation we need a system which has a unit impulse response $c(-t)$, or which has a transfer function $C(-\omega)$ where

$$c(t) \leftrightarrow C(\omega)$$
$$c(-t) \leftrightarrow C(-\omega)$$

Since $c(t)$ is a periodic signal of period T_0, $C(\omega)$, the Fourier transform of $c(t)$ will consist of impulses located at $\omega = 0,\ \pm\omega_0,\ \pm2\omega_0,\ \dots,\ \pm n\omega_0$, etc., where $\omega_0 = 2\pi/T_0$. Obviously, $C(-\omega)$ also consists of impulses located at these frequencies. These impulses have magnitudes equal to 2π times the corresponding coefficients of the exponential Fourier series for $c(-t)$ (Eq. 4.40). Thus, if $c(t)$ is expanded by the Fourier series,

$$c(t) = \sum_{n=-\infty}^{\infty} C_n e^{jn\omega_0 t} \qquad \omega_0 = 2\pi/T_0$$

Then the Fourier transform $C(\omega)$ of $c(t)$ is given by (Eq. 4.40):

$$C(\omega) = 2\pi \sum_n C_n \, \delta(\omega - n\omega_0)$$

Since

$$C(-\omega) = C^*(\omega)$$

$$C(-\omega) = 2\pi \sum_n C_n^* \, \delta(\omega - n\omega_0)$$

Thus, $C(-\omega)$ consists of impulses located at $\omega = 0$, $\pm\omega_0$, $\pm 2\omega_0, \ldots$, etc. It is obvious that the transfer function $C(-\omega)$ represents a system which attenuates all of the frequencies except $\omega = 0$, $\pm\omega_0$, $\pm 2\omega_0$, $\pm \cdots$, $\pm n\omega_0$, $\pm \cdots$, $\pm \cdots$. These frequency components also go through relative attenuation given by the corresponding coefficient C_r^* for the rth harmonic. The output signal therefore consists of a signal with frequency components $\omega = 0$, $\pm\omega_0$, $\pm 2\omega_0, \ldots$, etc. It is evident that the operation of crosscorrelation is equivalent to filtering in the frequency domain which allows to pass through only the frequency components of the fundamental frequency of $s(t)$ and its harmonics. In essence, we are merely filtering out all of the noise signal and extracting the desired periodic signal $s(t)$ by a filter which allows only the frequency components present in $s(t)$ to pass through. The various harmonics of $s(t)$, however, go through a different relative attenuation (proportional to C_r^* for the rth harmonic) and hence the output of this filter has the same fundamental frequency (ω_0) as that of $s(t)$ but, in general, its waveform is different from $s(t)$.

If the nature of the filter were such that the relative attenuation of all of the frequency components were uniform, then the output would be an exact replica of $s(t)$. This is precisely what happens when we cross-correlate $f(t)$ with a periodic impulse function $\delta_{T_0}(t)$. The Fourier transform of a periodic impulse function $\delta_{T_0}(t)$ is also a periodic impulse function (uniform impulse train). It is obvious that the crosscorrelation of $f(t)$ with a uniform periodic impulse function is equivalent to passing $f(t)$ through a filter which allows all of the frequency components $\omega = 0$, $\pm\omega_0$, $\pm 2\omega_0, \ldots$, etc. with uniform attenuation. Hence, the output is an exact replica of $s(t)$. Thus, crosscorrelation with a uniform impulse train gives the output of the waveform $s(t)$.

In practice it is impossible to design filters which will allow only discrete frequency components and attenuate completely all of the other frequencies.[6] Actually, one may approach this condition closely by

---

[6] This follows from the Paley-Wiener criterion discussed in Chapter 6.

designing filters with an extremely narrow bandwidth. We can show that this imperfect narrowband filtering is equivalent to performing cross-correlation over a very large but finite interval T. The perfect filtering is equivalent to crosscorrelating over an infinite time interval T. It is evident that it is impossible to avoid this imperfection either by the time-domain approach (crosscorrelation over an infinite interval) or by the frequency-domain approach (discrete frequency filtering).

As an example, consider $c(t)$ to be a sinusoidal signal $\cos \omega_0 t$ and let the crosscorrelation be performed over a finite interval $-T$ to 0 (Fig. 12.6a). The operation of crosscorrelation is equivalent to filtering $f(t)$ through a system which has an impulse response $c(-t)$ [or has a transfer function $C(-\omega)$]. Note that $c(-t)$ can be expressed as a gate function multiplied by $\cos \omega_0 t$ and shifted by $-T/2$ (Fig. 12.6b). It therefore follows from the modulation theorem that $C(-\omega)$, the Fourier transform of $c(-t)$, is a sampling function shifted by $\pm\omega_0$. Figure 12.6c shows the magnitude function of $C(-\omega)$ (the phase function is omitted for convenience). Thus,

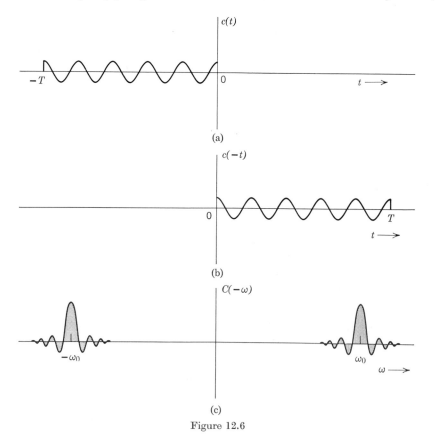

(a)

(b)

(c)

Figure 12.6

the crosscorrelation of $f(t)$ with $c(t)$ over a finite interval $(-T, 0)$ is equivalent to filtering $f(t)$ by a narrowband filter (Fig. 12.6c) which allows frequencies in the vicinity of $\pm \omega_0$ and attenuates the remaining frequencies. If T is made larger, the corresponding filter characteristic becomes narrower. In the limit as $T \to \infty$, $C(-\omega)$ is represented by two impulses at $\pm \omega_0$.

PROBLEMS

1. Prove that

$$\varphi_{11}(0) + \varphi_{22}(0) > 2\,|\varphi_{12}(\tau)| \qquad \text{for} \quad -\infty < \tau < \infty$$

2. Determine and sketch the average autocorrelation functions of the signals shown in Fig. P-12.2. Show that

$$\overline{\varphi}_{55}(\tau) = \overline{\varphi}_{33}(\tau) + \overline{\varphi}_{44}(\tau) + \overline{\varphi}_{34}(\tau) + \overline{\varphi}_{43}(\tau)$$

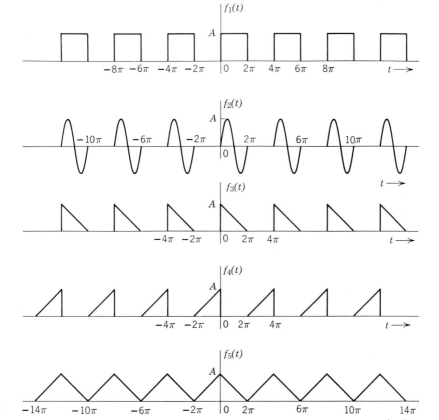

Figure P-12.2

3. Find the following average crosscorrelation functions, referring to the signals in Fig. P-12.2.

$$\overline{\varphi}_{13}(\tau),\ \overline{\varphi}_{14}(\tau),\ \overline{\varphi}_{15}(\tau),\ \overline{\varphi}_{34}(\tau)$$

4. Show that

$$\int_{-\infty}^{\infty} \varphi_{12}(\tau)\,d\tau = \left[\int_{-\infty}^{\infty} f_1(t)\,dt\right]\left[\int_{-\infty}^{\infty} f_2(t)\,dt\right]$$

5. Show that the crosscorrelation of any function $f(t)$ with a unit impulse function $\delta(t)$ yields the function $f(t)$ itself. In general, show that the crosscorrelation of $f(t)$ with $\delta(t - t_0)$ is equal to $f(\tau + t_0)$.

6. If $\varphi_{12}{}^{(n)}(\tau)$ represents the nth derivative of $\varphi_{12}(\tau)$, then show that

$$\varphi_{12}{}^{(j+k)}(\tau) = (-1)^k \int_{-\infty}^{\infty} f_1{}^{(j)}(t) f_2{}^{(k)}(t - \tau)\,dt$$

7. How would you use the results of Problems 5 and 6 to determine the cross-correlation functions of $\varphi_{12}(\tau)$ of the pair of functions shown in Fig. P-12.7? (*Hint*. Differentiate one or both of the functions a sufficient number of times to obtain the sequence of impulses.)

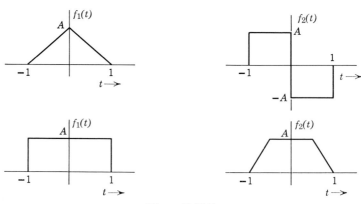

Figure P-12.7

8. Extend the result of Problem 6 to the autocorrelation function. Using this result and that of Problem 5, find the autocorrelation function for each of the signals shown in Fig. P-12.7.

9. It is desired to design a crosscorrelator to crosscorrelate a given function $f(t)$ with $e^{at}u(-t)$ in the form shown in Fig. P-12.9. The signal $f(t)$ is applied at the input terminals of the network and the output should represent the crosscorrelation between $f(t)$ and $e^{at}u(-t)$.

(a) What must be the impulse response of this network?
(b) What is the transfer function of the network?
(c) How will you realize this network, using passive R-C components? Assume that $a = 1$.

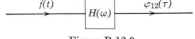

Figure P-12.9

10. Show that if $f_1(t)$ and $f_2(t)$ are complex functions of t, then

$$\varphi_{12}(\tau) \longleftrightarrow F_1(\omega)F_2{}^*(\omega)$$
$$\varphi_{21}(\tau) \longleftrightarrow F_1{}^*(\omega)F_2(\omega)$$

Hence, show that

$$\int_{-\infty}^{\infty} f_1(t)f_2{}^*(t)\,dt = \frac{1}{2\pi}\int_{-\infty}^{\infty} F_1(\omega)F_2{}^*(\omega)\,d\omega$$

$$\int_{-\infty}^{\infty} f_1(t)f_2{}^*(-t)\,dt = \frac{1}{2\pi}\int_{-\infty}^{\infty} F_1(\omega)F_2{}^*(-\omega)\,d\omega$$

What happens to these expressions for the case where $f_1(t)$ and $f_2(t)$ are real functions of t?

11. Show that the power density spectrum of a sinusoidal waveform $\cos \omega_0 t$ (or $\sin \omega_0 t$) is given by

$$P(\omega) = \tfrac{1}{2}\,\delta(\omega - \omega_0)$$

Hint. Consider the limiting case of a sinusoidal signal existing in the interval $|t| < \tau/2$ and zero outside this interval. In the limit, let $\tau \to \infty$ and use the result of Problem 15 at the end of Chapter 4.

12. Show that the power density spectrum of a periodic waveform $f(t)$ is given by

$$P(\omega) = |F_0|^2\,\delta(\omega) + 2\sum_{n=1}^{\infty} |F_n|^2\,\delta(\omega - n\omega_0)$$

where F_n represents the nth coefficient of the exponential Fourier series for $f(t)$. This is really equivalent of Parseval's theorem (Eq. 3.125).

13. If $f_2(t)$ is the response of a linear system to a driving function $f_1(t)$, show that

(a) $$\varphi_{21}(\tau) = \varphi_{11}(\tau) * h(t)$$

(b) $$\varphi_{22}(\tau) = \int_{-\infty}^{\infty} h(\sigma)\,d\sigma \int_{-\infty}^{\infty} h(\alpha)\,d\alpha\,\varphi_{11}(\sigma - \alpha)$$

(c) $$\varphi_{22}(\tau) = \int_{-\infty}^{\infty} \varphi_{hh}(t)\varphi_{11}(\tau - t)\,dt$$

where $h(t)$ is the unit impulse response of the system and $\varphi_{hh}(t)$ is the autocorrelation function of $h(t)$. Also show that

$$\Phi_{22}(\omega) = |H(j\omega)|^2\Phi_{11}(\omega)$$

14. Determine the rms value of a signal $f(t)$ if the average power density function $P(\omega)$ of $f(t)$ is given to be:

$$P(\omega) = \text{(a) } Ae^{-|\omega|}$$
$$\text{(b) } G_W(\omega)$$
$$\text{(c) } |\omega|\,e^{-|\omega|}$$

15. A signal $f(t)$, whose average power density function $P(\omega) = A$, is applied to the input terminals of a circuit whose transfer function is given by

$$H(j\omega) = \text{(a) } G_W(\omega)$$

$$\text{(b) } \frac{\omega_c}{\omega_c + j\omega}$$

Determine the average power density function and the rms value of the output signal in each case. Repeat the problem if

$$|H(j\omega)|^2 = \text{(a)} \ \frac{\omega_c{}^4}{\omega_c{}^4 + \omega^4}$$

$$\text{(b)} \ \frac{\omega_c{}^6}{\omega_c{}^6 + \omega^6}$$

The transfer functions above represent the Butterworth filter of second and third order.

16. Given that

$$f(t) = \sin t + \sin \sqrt{2}t$$

Is this a finite energy signal? Is it a periodic signal? Determine $\varphi_{11}(\tau)$ for this signal. Does $\lim_{\tau \to \infty} \varphi_{11}(\tau) = 0$?

chapter 13

Noise

Signals in the process of transmission always pick up some undesired signals. Indeed, any type of processing performed on a signal tends to introduce these undesired disturbances which we shall call *noise*. The noise is thus an undesirable signal which is not connected with the desired signal in any way. Here, however, we shall restrict ourselves to noise signals which are random, that is, unpredictable in nature. The power-supply hum in a radio receiver, the oscillations in a feedback system, etc., are noise signals according to our definition of noise, but they are not random. They can be predicted and can be eliminated by proper design.

There are various sources of noise. We may broadly classify these sources as (a) man-made noise, (b) the erratic natural disturbances which occur irregularly, and (c) fluctuation noise which arises inside physical systems. The man-made noise arises because of the pick up of un-desired signals from other sources, such as faulty contacts, electrical appliances, ignition radiation, fluorescent lighting, etc. Such noise can always be eliminated by removing the source of the noise. The latter two types of noise sources are non-man made types. The erratic natural noise may arise due to lightning, electrical storms in the atmosphere, or atmospheric disturbances in general. The fluctuation noise is also non-man made, and arises inside physical systems due to spontaneous fluctuations. This type of noise is entirely random and is the one that we are concerned with in this chapter. Basically, there are two important types of fluctuation noise: shot noise and thermal noise. Here we shall study certain properties of this type of noise without going into a detailed description of the statistical properties of these signals. Such a study requires a background in the theory of probability, and is beyond the scope of this book.

13.1 SHOT NOISE

Shot noise is present in both vacuum tubes and semiconductor devices. In vacuum tubes, shot noise arises due to random emission of electrons from the cathode. In semiconductor de-

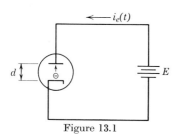

Figure 13.1

vices this effect arises because of the random diffusion of minority carriers and because of the random generation and recombination of hole-electron pairs. The nature of the shot noise will be illustrated by considering the electron emission from the hot cathode of a parallel plane diode shown in Fig. 13.1. At a given temperature, the average number of electrons emitted per second is constant. The process of electron emission, however, is random. This means that if we divide the time axis into a large number of small intervals Δt seconds each, the number of electrons emitted during each of these intervals is not constant but is random. However, on the average, the rate of emission of electrons is constant, provided that it is averaged over a sufficiently long interval of time. Thus, the current formed by emitted electrons is not constant but fluctuates about a mean value. If we observe this current on an oscilloscope with a slow sweep, it will appear essentially constant. However, if the current is observed with a fast sweep, where the time scale is expanded greatly, the uneven nature of the current becomes apparent. This is shown in Fig. 13.2. The diode current thus fluctuates about a certain mean value. We may consider the total current $i(t)$ as composed of a constant current I_0 and a noise current $i_n(t)$ which has a zero mean value.

$$i(t) = I_0 + i_n(t) \tag{13.1}$$

The nature of the fluctuations in $i(t)$ can be better understood by considering the process of the induction of current in the plate of the diode, due to the emission of an electron. Assume that a single electron is emitted from the cathode (Fig. 13.1). This electron acquires velocity as it moves toward the plate and induces a current $i_e(t)$. If the plate and

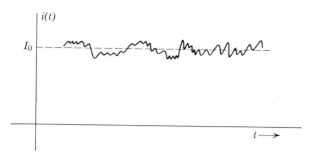

Figure 13.2

the cathode of a diode are separated by d units, then the emitted electron experiences a force of magnitude qE/d in the direction of the plate where q is the charge of an electron and E is the applied voltage. The electron will acquire an acceleration of qE/md units where m is the mass of an electron.

The initial velocity of the emitted electron is usually much smaller compared to the final velocity acquired by the electron at the time it strikes the plate. Hence, the initial velocity may be assumed to be zero. The velocity $v(t)$ at any time t will then be given by

$$v(t) = \frac{qE}{md} t \tag{13.2}$$

The kinetic energy (KE) acquired by an electron at any instant t is $\frac{1}{2} mv^2$ or

$$\text{KE} = \frac{q^2E^2}{2md^2} t^2 \tag{13.3}$$

The power supplied by the battery, however, is $Ei_e(t)$ where $i_e(t)$ is the current induced by the electron.

$$\text{power} = Ei_e(t)$$

The rate of change of KE of the electron must be equal to the power supplied by the battery. Hence

$$Ei_e(t) = \frac{q^2E^2}{md^2} t$$

and

$$i_e(t) = \frac{q^2E}{md^2} t \tag{13.4}$$

The time required for the electron to reach the plate is known as the transit time τ_a and can be readily found from Eq. 13.2.

$$d = \frac{1}{2} \frac{qE}{md} \tau_a{}^2$$

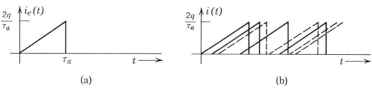

Figure 13.3

and

$$\tau_a = \sqrt{\frac{2m}{qE}}\, d \qquad (13.5)$$

Substituting Eq. 13.5 in Eq. 13.4, we get

$$i_e(t) = \begin{cases} \dfrac{2q}{\tau_a^{\,2}}\, t, & (0 < t < \tau_a) \\[2mm] 0, & (t > \tau_a) \end{cases} \qquad (13.6)$$

Obviously, the induced current goes to zero as soon as the electron reaches the plate at $t = \tau_a$. The current pulse induced by a single electron is shown in Fig. 13.3a. Each emitted electron induces such a pulse. Thus the total plate current is composed of a large number of such triangular pulses distributed randomly as shown in Fig. 13.3b. The sum of all such pulses constitutes the diode current $i(t)$ shown in Fig. 13.2. Note that the area under each pulse is q units. Hence the average value of the plate current is given by

$$I_0 = \bar{n}q \qquad (13.7)$$

where $\bar{n}$ is the average number of electrons emitted per second.

We shall now turn our attention to the description of the current $i(t)$. This current consists of two components: a constant current component I_0 and the time varying component $i_n(t)$. The latter component $i_n(t)$, being random, cannot be specified as a function of time. However $i_n(t)$ represents a stationary random signal and can be specified by its power density spectrum. Since there are $\bar{n}$ pulses per second, it is reasonable to expect that the power density spectrum of $i_n(t)$ will be $\bar{n}$ times the energy density spectrum of $i_e(t)$. This indeed is the case.[1]

Thus, if

$$i_e(t) \longleftrightarrow I_e(\omega) \qquad (13.8)$$

Then $P(\omega)$, the power density spectrum of $i_n(t)$, is given by

$$P(\omega) = \frac{\bar{n}}{\pi}\, |I_e(\omega)|^2 \qquad (13.9)$$

[1] See, for instance, W. B. Davenport, Jr., and W. L. Root, *An Introduction to the Theory of Random Signals and Noise*, Chapter 7, McGraw-Hill, New York, 1958.

$I_e(\omega)$ is the Fourier transform of $i_e(t)$, and can be found by the straight-forward method or may be conveniently found as follows:

$$i_e(t) = \frac{2q}{\tau_a^2} [tu(t) - \tau_a u(t - \tau_a) - (t - \tau_a) u(t - \tau_a)] \qquad (13.10)$$

Taking the Laplace transforms of both sides of Eq. 13.10 and substituting $j\omega$ for s, we get

$$i_e(t) \leftrightarrow I_e(\omega) = \frac{2q}{-\omega^2 \tau_a^2} [1 - e^{-j\omega\tau_a} - j\omega\tau_a e^{-j\omega\tau_a}] \qquad (13.11)$$

Substituting Eq. 13.11 in Eq. 13.9, we get

$$P(\omega) = \frac{\bar{n}}{\pi} |I_e(\omega)|^2$$

$$= \frac{4I_0 q}{\pi(\omega\tau_a)^4} [(\omega\tau_a)^2 + 2(1 - \cos \omega\tau_a - \omega\tau_a \sin \omega\tau_a)] \qquad (13.12)$$

The average power density function $P(\omega)$ can be plotted as a function of ω. As seen from Eq. 13.12, it is more convenient to plot $P(\omega)$ as a function of $\omega\tau_a$ (Fig. 13.4). Note that the power density spectrum is nearly flat for $\omega\tau_a < 0.5$.

The order of magnitude of τ_a can be calculated from Eq. 13.5. The ratio (q/m) for an electron is 1.76×10^{11} coulombs/kg. Hence from Eq. 13.5, we get

$$\tau_a = 3.36 \times 10^{-6} \frac{d}{\sqrt{E}} \text{ second}$$

For a diode with plate-cathode spacing $d = 1$ mm (10^{-3} meters) and with $E = 10$ volts:

$$\tau_a \simeq 10^{-9} \text{ seconds}$$

The power density spectrum of the noise current component in this case will be essentially flat up to:

$$\omega \simeq 0.5 \times 10^9 = 500 \times 10^6 \text{ rps}$$

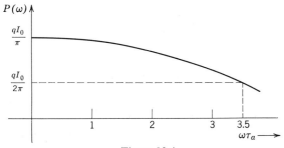

Figure 13.4

This corresponds roughly to about 80 mc. In general, the power density spectrum due to shot noise may be considered constant (qI_0/π) for frequencies below 50 Mc, and

$$P(\omega) = \frac{qI_0}{\pi} \tag{13.13}$$

It is more convenient to consider the power density spectrum as a function of variable f ($f = \omega/2\pi$) instead of ω. The change of the variable from ω to f can be accomplished as follows. The average power of $i_n(t)$ is given by

$$\text{power} = \int_0^\infty P(\omega)\, d\omega$$

Changing the variable from ω to f,

$$\omega = 2\pi f \quad \text{and} \quad d\omega = 2\pi\, df$$

Hence, the power of $i_n(t)$ is given by

$$\text{power} = \int_0^\infty P(\omega)\, d\omega = \int_0^\infty 2\pi P(2\pi f)\, df$$

$$= \int_0^\infty \mathscr{P}(f)\, df$$

where

$$\mathscr{P}(f) = 2\pi P(2\pi f) \tag{13.14}$$

$\mathscr{P}(f)$ represents the average power density function as a function of variable f instead of ω. Hereafter, the word average will be understood, and hence $P(\omega)$ or $\mathscr{P}(f)$ will be simply referred to as the power density function or the power density spectrum.

For shot noise,

$$P(\omega) = \frac{qI_0}{\pi}$$

Hence

$$\mathscr{P}(f) = 2\pi \frac{qI_0}{\pi} = 2qI_0$$

Thus, we have

$$P(\omega) = \frac{qI_0}{\pi} \tag{13.15a}$$

or

$$\mathscr{P}(f) = 2qI_0 \tag{13.15b}$$

The equations derived thus far hold for a diode for which the emission of electrons is limited by the temperature of the cathode. The electric field is assumed to be high enough to attract every electron emitted to the plate. The increase of the electric field therefore cannot increase the

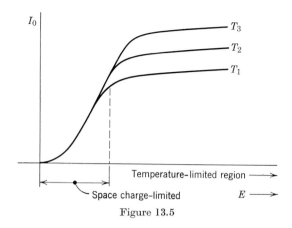

Figure 13.5

average current I_0 (Fig. 13.5). The average current can only be increased by increasing the temperature of the cathode and thereby increasing the rate of electron emission. The volt-ampere characteristic of a typical diode is shown in Fig. 13.5 for three different values of cathode temperature. At lower voltages, not all of the emitted electrons are swept to the plate, and some electrons remain inside the plate-cathode space forming what is known as the *space charge*. The diode operation in this region is known as the *space charge limited* operation. In this region the diode current I_0 can be increased by increasing the plate voltage (Fig. 13.5). In the space-charge limited region, the noise current tends to be smoothed out due to the presence of the space charge, and Eq. 13.15 becomes

$$P(\omega) = \frac{1}{\pi} q I_0 \alpha \tag{13.16a}$$

and

$$\mathscr{P}(f) = 2 q I_0 \alpha \tag{13.16b}$$

where α is a space-charge smoothing factor given by[2]

$$\alpha = 3\left(1 - \frac{\pi}{4}\right) \frac{2kT_c g_d}{q I_0}$$

$$= \frac{1.288 \, kT_c g_d}{q I_0} \tag{13.17}$$

where k is the Boltzmann's constant ($k = 1.38 \times 10^{-23}$ joules/°K), T_c is the cathode temperature (in degrees Kelvin), and g_d is the dynamic conductance of the diode:

$$g_d = \frac{\partial I_0}{\partial E}$$

The value of α varies from 0.01 to 1.

[2] W. B. Davenport and W. L. Root, cited in reference 1.

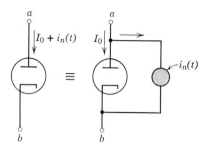

Figure 13.6

In the space-charge region, the diode current I_0 and the voltage E are related by Child's law.

$$I_0 = CE^{3/2}$$

Hence

$$g_d = \frac{3}{2}\frac{I_0}{E} \tag{13.18}$$

The substitution of Eq. 13.17 in Eq. 13.16b yields

$$\mathscr{P}(f) = 4kg_d(0.644T_c) \tag{13.19}$$

Thus

$$\mathscr{P}(f) = 2qI_0 \qquad \text{(for the temperature limited operation)} \tag{13.20a}$$

and

$$\mathscr{P}(f) = 2qI_0\alpha \qquad \text{(for the space-charge limited operation)} \tag{13.20b}$$

$$= 4kg_d(0.644T_c)$$

The next question is how to represent the equivalent circuit of a diode in a manner that will explicitly show the noise current source. The noise current $i_n(t)$, being random, cannot be specified as a function of time. However, the power density spectrum $\mathscr{P}(f)$ of this source is known. Hereafter, we shall always specify the noise sources by their power density spectra. The equivalent circuit for a diode is shown in Fig. 13.6. The noisy diode can be represented as an ideal noiseless diode in parallel with a noise current source $i_n(t)$ which is specified by its power density spectrum in Eq. 13.20.

Shot Noise in a Semiconductor Diode

In semiconductor diodes the random diffusion of minority carriers and the random generation and recombination of hole-electron pairs give rise to noise similar to shot noise in vacuum diodes. To a first approximation at lower frequencies, the power density spectrum of this noise current $i_n(t)$ is given by[3]

$$\mathscr{P}(f) = 2qI_0 \qquad (13.21)$$

where I_0 is the diode current.

Shot Noise in Triodes and Multielectrode Tubes

The mechanism of shot noise in triodes, pentodes, and other multi-electrode vacuum tubes is basically similar to that of the space-charge limited diode. The expression for the power density spectrum of the noise current is similar to that derived for the space charge limited diode (Eq. 13.20b).

It can be shown that for a triode:[4]

$$\mathscr{P}(f) = 4kg_m\left(\frac{0.644T_c}{\sigma}\right) \qquad (13.22)$$

where g_m is the transconductance of the triode given by

$$g_m = \frac{\partial I_p}{\partial E_g}$$

I_p and E_g, being the plate current and grid voltage, respectively, and σ is the constant of a triode which varies between 0.5 to 1. If we designate the quantity in parentheses in Eq. 13.22 by β, we get

$$\mathscr{P}(f) = 4kg_m\beta \qquad (13.23)$$

The equivalent circuit of a noiseless triode is shown in Fig. 13.7b. The shot noise can be taken into account by placing a current source $i_n(t)$ across the plate cathode terminals as shown in Fig. 13.7c. The power density spectrum of $i_n(t)$ is specified by Eq. 13.23.

In Fig. 13.7c, the noise source has been placed in the output circuit. Since the current source in the output circuit is related to the voltage at the grid of a noiseless triode (Fig. 13.7b), it is possible to take the shot noise into account by placing an equivalent noise voltage source at the grid of a noiseless triode. Let the equivalent noise voltage source at the grid be represented by $v_n(t)$ as shown in Fig. 13.7d. This gives rise to a current source at the output $g_m v_n(t)$. Hence

$$v_n(t) = \frac{1}{g_m} i_n(t) \qquad (13.24)$$

[3] A Van der Ziel, "Theory of Shot Noise in Junction Diodes and Junction Transistors," *Proc. IRE*, Vol. 43, No. 11, pp. 1639–1646, November 1955.

[4] W. B. Davenport and W. L. Root, cited in reference 1.

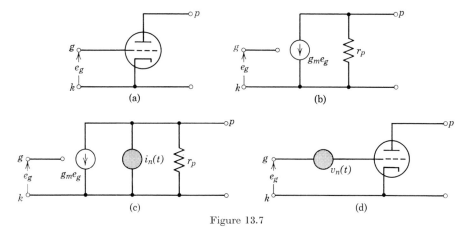

Figure 13.7

If we denote the power density spectrum of $v_n(t)$ by $\mathscr{P}_v(f)$, then from Eq. 13.24 it follows that $\mathscr{P}_v(f)$ and $\mathscr{P}(f)$, the power density spectra of $i_n(t)$, are related by

$$\mathscr{P}_v(f) = \frac{1}{g_m^2}\mathscr{P}(f)$$

$$= \frac{1}{g_m^2}\,4kg_m\beta = 4k\beta/g_m \qquad (13.25)$$

Therefore, the power density spectrum of the equivalent noise voltage source $v_n(t)$ in the grid circuit is given by Eq. 13.25. For convenience, we define new quantity β/Tg_m as R_{eq} where T is the ambient temperature (in degrees Kelvin). By definition,

$$R_{eq} = \frac{\beta}{Tg_m} = \frac{0.644\,T_c}{\sigma Tg_m} \qquad (13.26)$$

T_c, the cathode temperature, is in the range of 1000°K; σ is typically 0.88, and T, the ambient temperature, is about 293°K at normal room temperature. Hence

$$R_{eq} \simeq \frac{2.5}{g_m} \qquad (13.27)$$

The equivalent voltage source in the grid circuit can now be expressed in terms of R_{eq}. From Eqs. 13.25 and 13.26, we get

$$\mathscr{P}_v(f) = 4kTR_{eq} \qquad (13.28)$$

where R_{eq} is given by Eq. 13.27.

The reason for introducing R_{eq} is that it allows us to express shot noise in a form similar to thermal noise in a conductor to be discussed in the next section.

For pentodes and other multielectrode tubes, equivalent circuits similar to those derived for a triode hold true. In multielectrode tubes, there is an additional noise component which arises due to the partition of cathode current between various electrodes. The partitioning, being a random process, introduces an additional noise component. Both the shot noise and the partition noise can be taken into account by a single equivalent voltage source in the grid with a power density spectrum $4kTR_{eqp}$. For pentodes, the R_{eqp} is given by[5]

$$R_{eqp} = \left(1 + \frac{7.7 I_s}{g_{mp}}\right) R_{eqt}$$

where g_{mp} is the transconductance of pentode, I_s is the screen current, and $R_{eqt} = 2.5/g_{mt}$, g_{mt} being the transconductance of the pentode operated as a triode.

In vacuum tubes (and also transistors) there is an additional source of noise called *flicker noise*, which has a power density spectrum proportional to $1/f$. It is obvious that such a noise will be predominant at lower frequencies (generally below a few kilocycles). This noise arises due to slowly varying conditions at the cathode surface, and can be reduced by a proper processing of the cathode surface in vacuum tubes and the surfaces around the junctions in transistors.

13.2 THERMAL NOISE

This type of noise arises due to the random motion of free electrons in a conducting medium such as a resistor. Each free electron inside of a resistor is in motion due to its thermal energy. The path of electron motion is random and zigzag due to a collision with the lattice structure. The net effect of the motion of all electrons obviously constitutes an electric current flowing through the resistor. The direction of current flow is random and has a zero mean value. The autocorrelation function of the thermal noise current is given by[6]

$$\bar{\varphi}_{nn}(\tau) = kTG\alpha e^{-\alpha|\tau|} \tag{13.29}$$

where k is the Boltzmann constant, T is the ambient temperature (in degrees Kelvin), G is the conductance of the resistor (in mhos), and α is the average number of collisions per second of an electron.

[5] "Reference Data for Radio Engineers," 4th edition, International Telephone and Telegraph Corporation, New York, 1956.

[6] J. J. Freeman, *Principles of Noise*, Chapter 4, Wiley, New York, 1958.

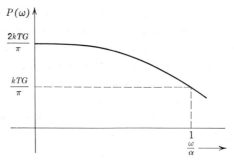

Figure 13.8

The power density spectrum is $1/\pi$ times the Fourier transform of $\tilde{\varphi}_{nn}(\tau)$. The Fourier transform of $\tilde{\varphi}_{nn}(\tau)$ in Eq. 13.29 can be found from pair 15 (Table 4.1B). Thus

$$P(\omega) = \frac{1}{\pi}\mathscr{F}[\tilde{\varphi}_{nn}(\tau)] = \frac{1}{\pi}\frac{2kTG\alpha^2}{\alpha^2 + \omega^2} \tag{13.30}$$

$$= \frac{1}{\pi}\frac{2kTG}{1 + \omega^2/\alpha^2} \tag{13.31}$$

The power density spectrum is plotted in Fig. 13.8 as a function of ω/α. The spectrum may be assumed to be flat for $\omega/\alpha < 0.1$. The order of magnitude of α, the number of collisions per second, is much greater than 10^{12}. Hence the spectrum is essentially flat up to very high frequencies. Usually the spectrum may be considered flat up to frequencies in the range of 10^{13} cps. Hence, for all practical purposes, the power density spectrum due to thermal noise in a resistor may be taken as

$$P(\omega) = \frac{2kTG}{\pi} \tag{13.32a}$$

and

$$\mathscr{P}(f) = 2\pi P(2\pi f)$$
$$= 4kTG \tag{13.32b}$$

The contribution in any circuit due to thermal noise therefore is limited only by the bandwidth of the circuit. Hence, for all practical purposes, the thermal noise is considered to have a constant power density spectrum; that is, it contains all frequencies in equal amount. For this reason, this noise is also called *white noise* (white implying the presence of all colors or frequencies). Thermal noise is also referred to as *Johnson noise* after J. B. Johnson who investigated the noise in conductors.[7] Johnson found

---

[7] J. B. Johnson, "Thermal Agitation of Electricity in Conductors," *Phys. Rev.*, **32**, 97–109 (July 1928).

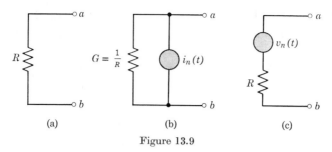

Figure 13.9

that the noise power measured in a conductor was proportional to the absolute temperature and the bandwidth of the measuring instrument. H. Nyquist of the Bell laboratories derived Eq. 13.32 based on thermodynamic reasoning.[8]

From the above discussion it is evident that a resistor R can be represented by a noiseless conductance G ($G = 1/R$) in parallel with a source of noise current $i_n(t)$ whose power density spectrum is given by $4kTG$, as shown in Fig. 13.9b. The Thévenin equivalent of this arrangement (Fig. 13.9b) is shown in Fig. 13.9c. Thus, a resistor R can be represented by a noiseless resistor R in series with a source of noise voltage $v_n(t) = Ri_n(t)$. It is evident that the power density spectrum $\mathscr{P}_v(f)$ of the voltage source will be related to $\mathscr{P}(f)$, the power density spectrum of $i_n(t)$ by R^2 as

$$\mathscr{P}_v(f) = R^2 \mathscr{P}(f)$$
$$= (R^2)(4kTG)$$
$$= 4kTR \tag{13.33}$$

13.3 NOISE CALCULATIONS: SINGLE NOISE SOURCE

We are now in a position to calculate the magnitudes of noise signals in electrical systems in general. We shall deal with a single noise source first.

Consider a circuit containing only noiseless elements (Fig. 13.10). A random noise voltage source $v_{n_i}(t)$ is connected at the input terminals of

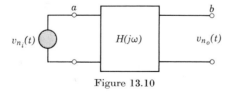

Figure 13.10

[8] H. Nyquist, "Thermal Agitation of Electric Charge in Conductors," *Phys. Rev.*, **32,** 110–113 (July 1928).

this circuit. We shall now determine the magnitude of the noise signal $v_{n_o}(t)$ present at the output terminal due to $v_{n_i}(t)$. Let the transfer function relating the output voltage (at terminals bb') to the input voltage (at terminals aa') be $H(j\omega)$. Let $\mathscr{P}_i(f)$ and $\mathscr{P}_o(f)$ be the power density spectrum of signals $v_{n_i}(t)$ and $v_{n_o}(t)$, respectively. Then from the discussion in Section 12.4, it follows that

$$\begin{aligned}\mathscr{P}_o(f) &= \mathscr{P}_i(f)\,|H(j\omega)|^2\\ &= \mathscr{P}_i(f)\,|H(j2\pi f)|^2\end{aligned} \tag{13.34}$$

The rms value of $v_{n_o}(t)$ can be readily computed from the power density spectrum $\mathscr{P}_o(f)$ by observing the fact that (Eq. 12.41)

$$\int_0^\infty \mathscr{P}_o(f)\,df = \lim_{T\to\infty}\frac{1}{T}\int_{-T/2}^{T/2} v_{n_o}{}^2(t)\,dt \tag{13.35}$$

The integral on the right-hand side of Eq. 13.35 represents the mean square value of $v_{n_o}(t)$. Hence $\sqrt{\overline{v_{n_o}{}^2}}$, the rms value of $v_{n_o}(t)$, is given by

$$\sqrt{\overline{v_{n_o}{}^2}} = \left[\int_0^\infty \mathscr{P}_o(f)\,df\right]^{\!\!1/2} \tag{13.36a}$$

$$= \left[\int_0^\infty \mathscr{P}_i(f)\,|H(j2\pi f)|^2\,df\right]^{\!\!1/2} \tag{13.36b}$$

Note that since the input signal is random it cannot be specified as a function of time. The output signal is also random and hence cannot be specified in the time domain. Whatever noise sources are involved, one approach in the time domain is to determine their correlation functions. In the frequency domain the power density spectrum can be determined from the autocorrelation function.

Example 13.1

As an example consider the R-C network shown in Fig. 13.11. We shall calculate the rms value of the noise voltage across the capacitor terminals aa'. The resistor R is replaced by a noiseless resistance R and a source of noise voltage $v_{n_i}(t)$ whose power density spectrum is given by $4kTR$. The transfer function $H(j\omega)$, which relates the output voltage $v_{n_o}(t)$ to $v_{n_i}(t)$, is obviously:

$$\begin{aligned}H(j\omega) &= \frac{1}{j\omega RC + 1}\\ &= \frac{1}{j2\pi f RC + 1}\end{aligned}$$

The power density spectrum at the output terminals is $\mathscr{P}_o(f)$ given by

$$\begin{aligned}\mathscr{P}_o(f) &= \mathscr{P}_i(f)\,|H(j2\pi f)|^2\\ &= \frac{4kTR}{1 + 4\pi^2 R^2 C^2 f^2}\end{aligned}$$

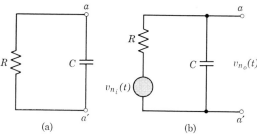

Figure 13.11

From Eq. 13.36, the rms value of the noise voltage is given by

$$\sqrt{\overline{v_{n_o}^2}} = \left[\int_0^\infty \frac{4kTR\,df}{1+4\pi^2 R^2 C^2 f^2} \right]^{1/2}$$

$$= \left[\frac{4kTR}{2\pi RC} \tan^{-1}\left(2\pi f RC\right) \Big|_0^\infty \right]^{1/2} = \sqrt{\frac{kT}{C}}$$

Note that the rms value of the noise voltage across the capacitor C is $\sqrt{kT/C}$ volts and is independent of the value of R. Qualitatively, this phenomenon may be explained by the fact that as R increases the input noise voltage increases but the bandwidth of the circuit ($\omega = 1/RC$) decreases. Hence, noise is accepted only over a smaller frequency range. This tends to keep the rms value of the voltage across C constant, regardless of the value of R.

13.4 MULTIPLE SOURCES: SUPERPOSITION OF POWER SPECTRA

In Fig. 13.10, we have considered the case of a single noise source. With respect to multiple noise sources, we can use the principle of superposition to determine the over-all response due to all sources. This approach is feasible provided that we know the waveforms of each source. For random noise sources we only have the information about the rms values of each waveform in the time domain. The question is: Can we obtain the rms values of the overall response by adding the rms values of the response due to each source. We shall now show that such a procedure is not generally permissible. The principle of superposition, however, can be applied to power density spectra of random independent signals.[9] To show this, consider a signal $v(t)$ formed by the addition of two independent random signals $v_1(t)$ and $v_2(t)$.

$$v(t) = v_1(t) + v_2(t) \tag{13.37}$$

[9] Independent sources are uncorrelated sources.

Let $\mathscr{P}(f)$, $\mathscr{P}_1(f)$, and $\mathscr{P}_2(f)$ be the power density spectra of $v(t)$, $v_1(t)$, and $v_2(t)$, respectively. We shall now determine the relationship between three power density spectra. By definition:

$$\int_0^\infty \mathscr{P}_1(f)\,df = \lim_{T\to\infty} \frac{1}{T} \int_{-T/2}^{T/2} v_1{}^2(t)\,dt \tag{13.38}$$

$$\int_0^\infty \mathscr{P}_2(f)\,df = \lim_{T\to\infty} \frac{1}{T} \int_{-T/2}^{T/2} v_2{}^2(t)\,dt \tag{13.39}$$

$$\int_0^\infty \mathscr{P}(f)\,df = \lim_{T\to\infty} \frac{1}{T} \int_{-T/2}^{T/2} v^2(t)\,dt$$

$$= \lim_{T\to\infty} \frac{1}{T} \int_{-T/2}^{T/2} [v_1(t) + v_2(t)]^2\,dt$$

$$= \lim_{T\to\infty} \frac{1}{T}\left[\int_{-T/2}^{T/2} v_1{}^2(t)\,dt + \int_{-T/2}^{T/2} v_2{}^2(t)\,dt + 2\int_{-T/2}^{T/2} v_1(t)v_2(t)\,dt \right] \tag{13.40}$$

Substituting Eqs. 13.38 and 13.39 in Eq. 13.40, we get

$$\int_0^\infty \mathscr{P}(f)\,df = \int_0^\infty [\mathscr{P}_1(f) + \mathscr{P}_2(f)]\,df + \lim_{T\to\infty} \frac{2}{T} \int_{-T/2}^{T/2} v_1(t)v_2(t)\,dt \tag{13.41}$$

The signals $v_1(t)$ and $v_2(t)$ are assumed to be independent and hence are uncorrelated if one, at least, has a zero mean. The second integral on the right-hand side of Eq. 13.41, therefore, vanishes, and we get

$$\int_0^\infty \mathscr{P}(f)\,df = \int_0^\infty [\mathscr{P}_1(f) + \mathscr{P}_2(f)]\,df$$

This result may be interpreted to mean that the power density spectrum of the sum of two uncorrelated signals with a zero mean is equal to the sum of their individual power density spectra. That is,

$$\mathscr{P}(f) = \mathscr{P}_1(f) + \mathscr{P}_2(f) \tag{13.42}$$

This is a significant result, and it must be stressed that it is valid only for uncorrelated signals. If the signals are correlated, then the second integral on the right-hand side of Eq. 13.41 is nonzero, and Eq. 13.42 does not hold. This result can be extended to any number of uncorrelated signals.

We can now easily see that if the rms values of $v_1(t)$ and $v_2(t)$ are $\sqrt{\overline{v_1{}^2}}$ and $\sqrt{\overline{v_2{}^2}}$, respectively, given by

$$\sqrt{\overline{v_1{}^2}} = \left[\int_0^\infty \mathscr{P}_1(f)\,df\right]^{1/2}$$

$$\sqrt{\overline{v_2{}^2}} = \left[\int_0^\infty \mathscr{P}_2(f)\,df\right]^{1/2} \tag{13.43}$$

Then the rms value of $v(t) = v_1(t) + v_2(t)$, will be given by

$$\sqrt{\overline{v^2}} = \left[\int_0^\infty \mathscr{P}(f)\, df \right]^{\frac{1}{2}} \tag{13.44}$$

The substitution of Eqs. 13.43 and 13.42 in Eq. 13.44 yields

$$\overline{v^2} = \overline{v_1{}^2} + \overline{v_2{}^2} \tag{13.45}$$

To recapitulate: if $v_1(t)$ and $v_2(t)$ are uncorrelated signals, with at least one with a zero mean value, and if

$$v(t) = v_1(t) + v_2(t)$$

Then

$$\sqrt{\overline{v^2}} \neq \sqrt{\overline{v_1{}^2}} + \sqrt{\overline{v_2{}^2}}$$

But

$$\overline{v^2} = \overline{v_1{}^2} + \overline{v_2{}^2}$$

Thus, the mean square value of the sum of two uncorrelated signals is equal to the sum of the mean square values of the individual signals. In the frequency domain this result implies that the principle of superposition applies to the power density spectra.

In a circuit where there are independent multiple noise sources we compute the power density spectra of the response due to each source. The sum of all of these spectra yields the power density spectrum of the resultant response. The rms value of the response now can be readily determined from the power density spectrum.

Example 13.2

Find the rms value of the noise voltage across the output terminals aa' in a diode circuit shown in Fig. 13.12. Assume the diode to be in the temperature limited region.

There are two independent sources of noise: the shot noise in the diode, and the thermal noise in the resistor $100\ \Omega$. The voltage across the resistor is 0.1 volt. Hence, the d-c current through the diode is 1 ma, and the equivalent shot noise current $i_{sh}(t)$ has a power density spectrum $\mathscr{P}_{sh}(f)$ given by

$$\mathscr{P}_{sh}(f) = 2qI_0$$
$$= 2 \times 1.6 \times 10^{-19} \times 10^{-3}$$
$$= 3.2 \times 10^{-22}$$

The thermal noise current $i_{th}(t)$ has a power density spectrum $\mathscr{P}_{th}(f)$ given by

$$\mathscr{P}_{th}(f) = 4kTG$$
$$= 4 \times 1.38 \times 10^{-23} \times 293 \times 10^{-2}$$
$$= 1.60 \times 10^{-22}$$

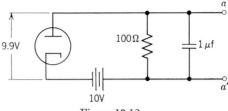

Figure 13.12

assuming that $T = 293°\text{K}$ at room temperature. The dynamic resistance of a diode in the temperature limited region is very high ($\partial v/\partial i \rightarrow \infty$). Hence, for noise calculation, the noiseless diode may be considered as an open circuit and, consequently, is omitted in Fig. 13.13.

The power density spectrum of the output voltage $v_o(t)$ is the sum of the power density spectra due to $i_{sh}(t)$ and $i_{th}(t)$.

The transfer function $H(j\omega)$ relating the output voltage $v_o(t)$ to the current sources in Fig. 13.13 is given by

$$H(j\omega) = \frac{R}{1 + j\omega RC} = \frac{100}{1 + 10^{-4}j\omega}$$

$$= \frac{10^6}{10^4 + j\omega}$$

$$H(j2\pi f) = \frac{10^6}{10^4 + j2\pi f}$$

$$|H(j2\pi f)|^2 = \frac{10^{12}}{10^8 + 4\pi^2 f^2}$$

The power density spectrum at the output due to $i_{sh}(t)$ is $\mathscr{P}_{sh}(f)\,|H(j2\pi f)|^2$ and that due to $i_{th}(t)$ is $\mathscr{P}_{th}(f)\,|H(j2\pi f)|^2$. Hence the total power density spectrum at the output is $\mathscr{P}_o(f)$ given by

$$\mathscr{P}_o(f) = [\mathscr{P}_{sh}(f) + \mathscr{P}_{th}(f)]\,|H(j2\pi f)|^2$$

$$= \frac{4.8 \times 10^{-22} \times 10^{12}}{10^8 + 4\pi^2 f^2}$$

$$= \frac{4.8 \times 10^{-10}}{10^8 \times 4\pi^2 f^2}$$

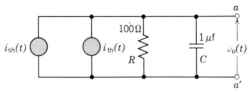

Figure 13.13

The rms voltage $\sqrt{\overline{v_0^2}}$ at the output is given by

$$\overline{v_0^2} = \int_0^\infty \frac{4.8 \times 10^{-10}}{10^8 + 4\pi^2 f^2}\, df$$

$$= \left(\frac{4.8 \times 10^{-10}}{4\pi^2}\right)\left(\frac{2\pi}{10^4}\right)\tan^{-1}\left(\frac{2\pi f}{10^4}\right)\Big|_0^\infty$$

$$= 1.2 \times 10^{-14}$$

Therefore

$$\sqrt{\overline{v_0^2}} = 0.11\ \mu v.$$

13.5 NOISE CALCULATIONS IN PASSIVE CIRCUITS

The expression for the thermal noise power density spectrum for a constant resistor (Eq. 13.33) can be extended to any passive bilateral circuit (containing R-L-C elements only). Consider a resistor R in parallel with a reactance X (Fig. 13.14a). The reactance X is a function of frequency and hence will be expressed as $X(f)$. We shall determine the power density spectrum $\mathscr{P}_o(f)$ of the output voltage across terminals ab. The resistor R is replaced by a noiseless resistor R and a thermal noise current source $i_{\mathrm{th}}(t)$ with a power density spectrum:

$$\mathscr{P}_{\mathrm{th}}(f) = 4kTG = 4kT/R \qquad (13.46)$$

The transfer function relating the output voltage $v_{ab}(t)$ to the current source across terminals ab is given by $H(j\omega)$:

$$H(j\omega) = \frac{jRX(f)}{R + jX(f)} \qquad (13.47)$$

and

$$|H(j2\pi f)|^2 = \frac{R^2 X^2(f)}{R^2 + X^2(f)}$$

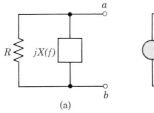
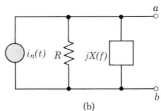

Figure 13.14

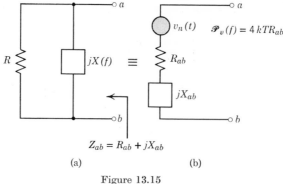

$$Z_{ab} = R_{ab} + jX_{ab}$$

(a)   (b)

Figure 13.15

The power density spectrum of the output voltage is $\mathscr{P}_o(f)$ given by

$$\mathscr{P}_o(f) = \frac{4kT}{R}\frac{R^2 X^2(f)}{R^2 + X^2(f)}$$

$$= 4kT\left[\frac{R X^2(f)}{R^2 + X^2(f)}\right] \tag{13.48}$$

At this point we make an interesting observation. The impedance Z_{ab} across terminals ab (Fig. 13.15) is given by (Eq. 13.47):

$$Z_{ab} = \frac{jRX(f)}{R + jX(f)}$$

$$= \frac{R X^2(f)}{R^2 + X^2(f)} + j\frac{R^2 X(f)}{R^2 + X^2(f)}$$

$$= R_{ab}(f) + jX_{ab}(f) \tag{13.49}$$

The bracketed term in Eq. 13.48 is evidently $R_{ab}(f)$. Hence

$$\mathscr{P}_o(f) = 4kTR_{ab}(f)$$

This result is obviously an extension of the result in Eq. 13.33 and may be applied to any general passive circuit in the thermal equilibrium.[10] This is shown in Fig. 13.16. If Z_{ab}, the impedance seen across terminals ab of a passive R-L-C circuit, is given by

$$Z_{ab}(f) = R_{ab}(f) + jX_{ab}(f) \tag{13.50a}$$

Then $\mathscr{P}_{ab}(f)$, the power density spectrum of the thermal noise voltage

[10] H. Nyquist, cited in reference 8. See also W. B. Davenport, Jr., and W. L. Root, cited in reference 1.

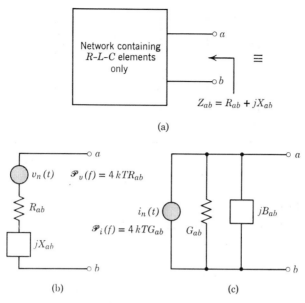

Figure 13.16

appearing across terminals ab, is given by

$$\mathscr{P}_{ab}(f) = 4kTR_{ab}(f) \tag{13.50b}$$

Hence the circuit in Fig. 13.16a can be represented by a noiseless resistor $R_{ab}(f)$ and reactance $X_{ab}(f)$ in series with an equivalent noise voltage source $v_n(t)$ whose power density spectrum is given by Eq. 13.50b. This result is the analytical statement of the Nyquist theorem. An alternative form of the Nyquist theorem can be expressed in terms of the admittance of a passive circuit in the thermal equilibrium. If $Y_{ab}(f)$, the admittance of a passive circuit across terminals ab, is given by

$$Y_{ab}(f) = G_{ab}(f) + jB_{ab}(f) \tag{13.50c}$$

then the network is equivalent to the noiseless admittance $Y_{ab}(f)$ in parallel with a noise current source $i_n(t)$ whose power density spectrum is given by

$$\mathscr{P}_{ab}(f) = 4kTG_{ab}(f) \tag{13.50d}$$

This is shown in Fig. 13.16c. By the term thermal equilibrium, we mean that all of the noise-generating elements of the circuit are at the same temperature.

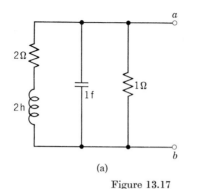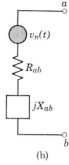

Figure 13.17

Example 13.3

Determine the power density spectrum of the noise voltage across terminals ab of the circuit shown in Fig. 13.17.

$$Y_{ab}(j\omega) = 1 + j\omega + \frac{1}{2 + 2j\omega}$$

$$= \frac{3 - 2\omega^2 + j4\omega}{2 + j2\omega}$$

$$Z_{ab}(j\omega) = \frac{2(1 + j\omega)}{3 - 2\omega^2 + j4\omega}$$

$$R_{ab}(j\omega) = \text{Re}\,[Z_{ab}(j\omega)]$$

$$= \frac{4\omega^2 + 6}{4\omega^4 + 4\omega^2 + 9}$$

$$R_{ab}(f) = \frac{16\pi^2 f^2 + 6}{64\pi^4 f^4 + 16\pi^2 f^2 + 9}$$

The power density spectrum of the equivalent noise source $v_n(t)$ in Fig. 13.17b is therefore given by

$$\mathscr{P}_v(f) = \frac{4kT(16\pi^2 f^2 + 6)}{64\pi^4 f^4 + 16\pi^2 f^2 + 9}$$

13.6 EQUIVALENT NOISE BANDWIDTH

Sometimes it is convenient to define the equivalent noise bandwidth for an electrical circuit. A system with transfer function $H(j\omega)$ and input signal power density spectrum $\mathscr{P}_i(f)$ has the mean square value of the output signal given by

$$\overline{v_0{}^2} = \int_0^\infty \mathscr{P}_i(f)\,|H(j2\pi f)|^2\,df$$

In most of the circuits the bandwidths are low enough to assume that the shot noise and thermal noise have a constant spectral density, that is, $\mathscr{P}_i(f)$ is constant, say K. Thus

$$\overline{v_0^2} = K \int_0^\infty |H(j2\pi f)|^2 \, df \tag{13.51}$$

The integral in Eq. 13.51 is constant for a given circuit. We define an equivalent noise bandwidth B with respect to some frequency f_0 as

$$B = \frac{1}{|H(j2\pi f_0)|^2} \int_0^\infty |H(j2\pi f)|^2 \, df \tag{13.52}$$

Hence

$$\overline{v_0^2} = K \, |H(j2\pi f_0)|^2 \, B \tag{13.53}$$

The significance of equivalent noise bandwidth is now evident. The rms value of a noise signal at the output of a given system is the same as that of an ideal bandpass system of gain $H(j2\pi f_0)$ and bandwidth B. It is very common to specify the equivalent noise bandwidth with respect to zero frequency, that is $f_0 = 0$. In this case,

$$B = \frac{1}{|H(0)|^2} \int_0^\infty |H(j2\pi f)|^2 \, df$$

13.7 NOISE FIGURE OF AN AMPLIFIER

From the discussion thus far it is evident that every signal is contaminated with noise. Moreover, when a signal is being processed through any system, additional noise is being added. The ratio of signal power to noise power is a good indication of the purity of a signal (or the relative level of the signal and the noise). For simplicity, we shall call this ratio the *signal-to-noise ratio*.

When a signal is amplified, additional noise generated in the amplifier is being added to the original noise in the signal. This causes deterioration in the signal-to-noise ratio of the output signal compared to that of the input signal. The ratio of signal to noise at the input to that at the output is an indication of the noisiness of the amplifier. Consider an amplifier shown in Fig. 13.18. The noise generated in the source is amplified and is

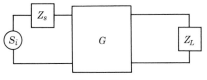

Figure 13.18

delivered to the load. In addition, some noise is generated inside the amplifier circuit and is also delivered to the load. Hence, the noise in the output is contributed by the source as well as the amplifier. We shall define the *noise figure F* of an amplifier as a ratio of the total noise power density in the load (or the output) to the noise power density delivered to the load (output) due solely to the source. If $\mathscr{P}_{nto}(f)$ and $\mathscr{P}_{nso}(f)$ represent the power density spectra of the total noise and the noise due solely to the source in the output, respectively, then by definition:

$$F = \frac{\mathscr{P}_{nto}(f)}{\mathscr{P}_{nso}(f)} \tag{13.54}$$

If $\mathscr{P}_{nao}(s)$ is the power density spectrum of the noise in the load due solely to the amplifier, then

$$\mathscr{P}_{nto}(f) = \mathscr{P}_{nso}(f) + \mathscr{P}_{nao}(f)$$

$$F = \frac{\mathscr{P}_{nso}(f) + \mathscr{P}_{nao}(f)}{\mathscr{P}_{nso}(f)}$$

$$= 1 + \frac{\mathscr{P}_{nao}(f)}{\mathscr{P}_{nso}(f)} \tag{13.55}$$

Note that the load impedance also contributes to the noise at the output. This noise contribution is included in $\mathscr{P}_{nao}$. However, this contribution is usually much smaller compared to the noise generated by the active device and the source and consequently may be ignored. It is evident that the noise figure of an amplifier is a measure of the noisiness of the amplifier relative to the noisiness of the source.

The noise figure may also be expressed in an alternative form. Let $\mathscr{P}_{si}(f)$ and $\mathscr{P}_{so}(f)$ represent the power density spectra of the desired signal at the input and the output, respectively. Then

$$\mathscr{P}_{so}(f) = \mathscr{P}_{si}(f) |H(j2\pi f)|^2 \tag{13.56}$$

If $\mathscr{P}_{nsi}(f)$ represents the power density spectrum of the noise at the source (or input), then

$$\mathscr{P}_{nso}(f) = \mathscr{P}_{nsi}(f) |H(j2\pi f)|^2$$

and, by definition (Eq. 13.54),

$$F = \frac{\mathscr{P}_{nto}(f)}{\mathscr{P}_{nsi}(f) |H(j2\pi f)|^2}$$

The substitution of Eq. 13.56 in this equation yields

$$F = \frac{\mathscr{P}_{si}(f)/\mathscr{P}_{nsi}(f)}{\mathscr{P}_{so}(f)/\mathscr{P}_{nto}(f)} \tag{13.57}$$

This is a rather significant result. The numerator of Eq. 13.57 represents the signal-to-noise power density ratio at the input terminals and the denominator represents the signal-to-noise power density ratio at the output terminals. Hence the noise figure measures the deterioration of the signal-to-noise power density ratio in the process of amplification. By the very definition it is evident that this ratio is always greater than unity and hence the signal-to-noise power density ratio always deteriorates in the process of amplification. The deterioration results, of course, from the noise contribution of the amplifier.

The noise figure F, defined in Eq. 13.54 (or Eq. 13.57), is a function of the frequency and hence is sometimes referred to as the *spectral noise figure*. In contrast, we may define an *average noise figure* $\bar{F}$ as the ratio of the total noise power at the output to the noise power contributed due solely to the source. Note that this definition is merely an extension of the definition in Eq. 13.54. In this definition we deal with the total noise power contributed over all of the frequencies. This is, therefore, an integrated or average noise figure. Thus, by definition,

$$\bar{F} = \frac{\displaystyle\int_0^\infty \mathscr{P}_{\text{nto}}(f)\,df}{\displaystyle\int_0^\infty \mathscr{P}_{\text{nso}}(f)\,df}$$

$$= 1 + \frac{\displaystyle\int_0^\infty \mathscr{P}_{\text{nao}}(f)\,df}{\displaystyle\int_0^\infty \mathscr{P}_{\text{nso}}(f)\,df} \qquad (13.58a)$$

$$= 1 + \frac{N_{\text{ao}}}{N_{\text{so}}} \qquad (13.58b)$$

where N_{ao} is the noise power at the output due solely to the amplifier and N_{so} is the noise power at the output due solely to the source noise.

From the definition it is evident that the noise figure can never be less than unity. A superior amplifier has a small noise figure. However, it should be emphasized here that the noise figure measures not the absolute but the relative quality of the amplifier. It indicates the noisiness of an amplifier relative to the noisiness of the source. It is evident from the definition that the noise figure of an amplifier can be made as close to unity as possible, merely by adding extra noise in the source. This obviously is not the proper solution for improving the performance of the amplifier, since this approach merely makes the source so noisy that the amplifier, in comparison, appears almost noise-free. The over-all signal-to-noise ratio at the output, however, deteriorates badly and consequently the output signal is much more noisy. It is therefore important not to increase the noise in the source (or to decrease signal-to-noise ratio in the input) in order to improve the noise figure. A step-up transformer in many cases solves the problem. A step-up transformer at the input increases the input noise as well as the input signal. The increased noise at the source makes the amplifier look less noisy without deteriorating the signal-to-noise ratio of the input. Hence, the noise figure is reduced, and the signal-to-noise ratio at the output terminals actually improves (see example 13.6).

Example 13.4

We shall determine the noise figure of a triode amplifier shown in Fig. 13.19. The triode will be replaced by a noiseless triode and an equivalent random noise voltage source $v_{sh}(t)$ in the grid (see Fig. 13.7). This source has a power density spectrum $4kTR_{eq}$ where $R_{eq} = 2.5/g_m$. The source resistor is replaced by a noiseless resistor of 1000 ohms in series with a random noise source $v_{ns}(t)$ of the power density spectrum $4kT \times 10^3$.

$$R_{eq} = \frac{2.5}{g_m} = \frac{2.5}{2 \times 10^{-3}} = 1250$$

and

$$\mathscr{P}_{sh}(f) = 4kT \times 1250$$

Assuming an ambient temperature of 290°K

$$\mathscr{P}_{sh}(f) = 4 \times 1.38 \times 10^{-23} \times 290 \times 1250$$
$$= 2 \times 10^{-17}$$

Similarly

$$\mathscr{P}_{nsi}(f) = 4 \times 1.38 \times 10^{-23} \times 290 \times 1000$$
$$= 1.6 \times 10^{-17}$$

Note that

$$\mathscr{P}_{nso}(f) = \mathscr{P}_{nsi}(f) |H(j2\pi f)|^2$$

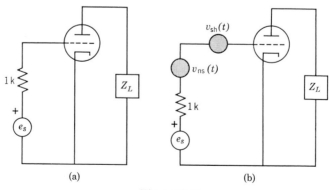

(a)   (b)

Figure 13.19

and

$$\mathscr{P}_{\mathrm{nao}}(f) = \mathscr{P}_{\mathrm{sh}}(f)\,|H(j2\pi f)|^2$$

Hence, by definition,

$$F = 1 + \frac{\mathscr{P}_{\mathrm{nao}}(f)}{\mathscr{P}_{\mathrm{nso}}(f)}$$

$$= 1 + \frac{\mathscr{P}_{\mathrm{sh}}(f)}{\mathscr{P}_{\mathrm{nsi}}(f)}$$

$$= 1 + \frac{2}{1.6}$$

$$= 2.25$$

the noise figure is commonly expressed in terms of logarithmic units as $10 \log_{10} F$ db. In this case the noise figure is

$$10 \log_{10} 2.25 = 3.5 \text{ db}$$

Note that since both $\mathscr{P}_{\mathrm{nsi}}(f)$ and $\mathscr{P}_{\mathrm{sh}}(f)$ are constant, the average noise figure is also 2.25.

Example 13.5

Determine the noise figure of a triode amplifier shown in Fig. 13.20a and calculate the rms noise voltage at the output terminals. It is given that

$$r_p = R_L = 10 \text{ k}\Omega, \quad g_m = 2.5 \times 10^{-3} \text{ mhos}, \quad R_g = 100 \text{ k}\Omega,$$

$$R_s = 1 \text{ k}\Omega \quad \text{and} \quad C = \frac{1}{\pi} \times 10^{-9} \text{ farads}.$$

The noise contribution due to the load resistance is usually negligible compared to other components and hence R_L may be assumed to be noiseless (see Problem 13 at the end of the chapter). The source resistance R_s and the grid resistance R_g will be represented by noiseless resistors in series with respective equivalent noise voltage sources, and the triode will be represented by a noiseless triode and an equivalent noise voltage source in the grid (Fig. 13.20b).

The power density spectra due to R_s, R_g, and R_{eq} are given by $4kTR_s$, $4kTR_g$, and $4kTR_{eq}$, respectively, as shown in Fig. 13.20b.

Let the transfer function relating the output voltage v_o to the grid voltage e_g be represented by $H(j2\pi f)$. It now follows that the transfer function relating the output voltage v_o to the equivalent voltage source represented by R_{eq} is $H(j2\pi f)$ and that relating v_o to the noise voltage source due to R_g is

$$\frac{R_s}{R_s + R_g}\, H(j2\pi f).$$

Similarly the transfer function relating v_o to the noise voltage source due to R_s is

$$\frac{R_g}{R_s + R_g}\, H(j2\pi f).$$

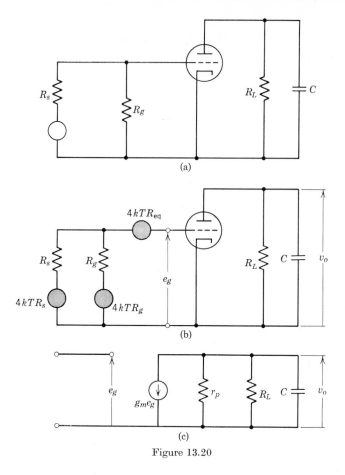

Figure 13.20

Hence, the power density spectrum of the noise voltage at the output due to R_{eq} is

$$4kTR_{eq}\,|H(j2\pi f)|^2;\qquad(13.59\text{a})$$

the power density spectrum of the noise voltage at the output due to R_g is

$$4kTR_g\left(\frac{R_s}{R_s+R_g}\right)^2|H(j2\pi f)|^2;\qquad(13.59\text{b})$$

and the power density spectrum of the noise voltage at the output due to R_s is

$$4kTR_s\left(\frac{R_g}{R_s+R_g}\right)^2|H(j2\pi f)|^2\qquad(13.59\text{c})$$

Note that the grid resistance R_g is a part of the amplifier and hence

$$\mathscr{P}_{\text{nao}}(f)=4kTR_{eq}\,|H(j2\pi f)|^2+4kTR_g\left(\frac{R_s}{R_s+R_g}\right)^2|H(j2\pi f)|^2\quad(13.60\text{a})$$

and

$$\mathscr{P}_{\mathrm{nso}}(f) = 4kTR_s\left(\frac{R_g}{R_s + R_g}\right)^2|H(j2\pi f)|^2 \tag{13.60b}$$

Therefore, the noise figure F is given by

$$F(f) = 1 + \frac{\mathscr{P}_{\mathrm{nao}}}{\mathscr{P}_{\mathrm{nso}}}$$

$$= 1 + \frac{R_{eq} + R_g\left(\dfrac{R_s}{R_s + R_g}\right)^2}{R_s\left(\dfrac{R_g}{R_s + R_g}\right)^2}$$

$$= 1 + \frac{R_{eq}(R_s + R_g)^2 + R_g R_s^2}{R_s R_g^2} \tag{13.61}$$

$$R_{eq} = 2.5/g_m = 2.5/2.5 \times 10^{-3} = 1000 \text{ ohms}$$
$$R_s = 1000 \text{ ohms} \quad \text{and} \quad R_g = 10^5 \text{ ohms}$$

Hence

$$F = 2.03$$

To obtain the rms value of the noise voltage at the output, we find the transfer function $H(j2\pi f)$. The equivalent circuit of the triode is shown in Fig. 13.20c. It is evident from this circuit that the transfer function which relates the output voltage v_o to the grid voltage e_g is given by

$$H(j2\pi f) = g_m Z$$

where

$$\frac{1}{Z} = \frac{1}{r_p} + \frac{1}{R_L} + j\omega C$$
$$= 10^{-4} + 10^{-4} + \left(\frac{1}{\pi} \times 10^{-9}\right)(j2\pi f)$$
$$= 2 \times 10^{-9}(10^5 + jf)$$

and

$$H(j2\pi f) = (2.5 \times 10^{-3})/(2 \times 10^{-9})(10^5 + jf)$$
$$= 1.25 \times 10^6/(10^5 + jf)$$

and

$$|H(j2\pi f)|^2 = 1.56 \times 10^{12}/(10^{10} + f^2) \tag{13.62}$$

The mean square of the noise voltage at the output is given by

$$\int_0^\infty \mathscr{P}_{\mathrm{nto}}(f)\, df$$

where

$$\mathscr{P}_{\mathrm{nto}}(f) = \mathscr{P}_{\mathrm{nao}}(f) + \mathscr{P}_{\mathrm{nso}}(f)$$

From Eqs. 13.60 and 13.62, we obtain

$$\mathscr{P}_{\text{nto}}(f) = 4kT \, |H(j2\pi f)|^2 \left[R_{eq} + R_g \left(\frac{R_s}{R_s + R_g} \right)^2 + R_s \left(\frac{R_g}{R_s + R_g} \right)^2 \right]$$

$$= 4 \times 1.38 \times 10^{-23} \times 290 \times \frac{1.56 \times 10^{12}}{10^{10} + f^2} \times 2010$$

$$= \frac{5 \times 10^{-5}}{10^{10} + f^2}$$

The mean square value of the output noise voltage is given by

$$\overline{v_o^2} = \int_0^\infty \frac{5 \times 10^{-5}}{10^{10} + f^2} \, df$$

$$= 5 \times 10^{-5} \times \frac{1}{10^5} \tan^{-1} \frac{f}{10^5} \Big|_0^\infty$$

$$= 2.5\pi \times 10^{-10}$$

Hence the rms value of the voltage at the output terminals is given by

$$\sqrt{\overline{v_o^2}} = 28 \; \mu\text{v}$$

Example 13.6

Find the optimum value of the source resistance R_s for the triode amplifier in Example 13.5 and calculate the corresponding noise figure.

The noise figure F is given by Eq. 13.61. Generally, $R_s \ll R_g$ and Eq. 13.61 becomes

$$F \simeq 1 + \frac{R_{eq}}{R_s} + \frac{R_s}{R_g} \qquad (13.63)$$

The optimum value of R_s can be obtained from $dF/dR_s = 0$. Thus

$$\frac{dF}{dR_s} = \frac{-R_{eq}}{R_s^2} + \frac{1}{R_g} = 0$$

or

$$(R_s)_{\text{opt}} = \sqrt{R_{eq} R_g}$$

$$= (10^3 \times 10^5)^{\frac{1}{2}}$$

$$= 10 \text{ k}\Omega$$

The noise figure for $(R_s)_{\text{opt}}$ is obtained from Eq. 13.63:

$$F = 1 + 0.1 + 0.1$$

$$= 1.2$$

If the source resistance R_s is 1000 ohms, then the optimum noise figure can be attained by using a step-up transformer of the ratio $1:\sqrt{10}$. Note that it is not desirable to obtain an optimum value of the source resistance by adding an extra 9 k in series with 1000 ohms. This will merely make the source noisy compared to the amplifier.

A Comment on Noise Figure

The noise figure is the ratio of the total noise power density spectrum of the output variable to the noise power density spectrum contributed only by the source to the output variable. A question may arise as to which output variable should be used; that is, whether we should use an output voltage or an output current. Actually the noise figure is independent of whichever we choose as the output variable. This is because the voltage and current are related by the load impedance and, since the noise figure is the ratio of the power density spectra, this factor (due to load impedance) cancels out.

Example 13.7

Determine the noise figure of a common base transistor amplifier.

In a transistor there are mainly three sources of noise: the shot noise, the partition noise, and the thermal noise. The shot noise can be accounted for by a current source $i_{sh}(t)$ across terminals ej (Fig. 13.21) and has a power density spectrum (at low frequencies):

$$\mathscr{P}_{sh}(f) = 2qI_e \tag{13.64a}$$

where I_e is the emitter current. The partition noise can be accounted for by a current source $i_p(t)$ across terminals jc and has a power density spectrum (at low frequencies):

$$\mathscr{P}_p(f) = 2q\alpha_0 I_e(1 - \alpha_0) \tag{13.64b}$$

where α_0 is the d-c current gain in a common base transistor.

The thermal noise arises due to physical resistance in the base and can be accounted for by a voltage source $v_{th}(t)$ in the base lead and has a power density spectrum:

$$\mathscr{P}_{th}(f) = 4kTr_b \tag{13.64c}$$

where r_b is the base spreading resistance. An equivalent circuit of a transistor is shown in Fig. 13.21a. In Fig. 13.21b, the equivalent circuit is shown with various noise generators, and source and load resistors. The source resistor is represented by a noiseless resistor R_s in series with a thermal noise source $v_s(t)$ which has a power density spectrum:

$$\mathscr{P}_{R_s}(f) = 4kTR_s \tag{13.64d}$$

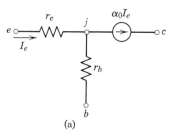

(a)

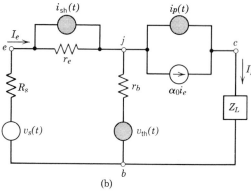

(b)

Figure 13.21

The noise generated by the transistor has three components: the components due to $i_{sh}(t)$, due to $i_p(t)$, and due to $v_{th}(t)$. It is left as an exercise for the reader to show that the transfer functions relating the load current I_L to these three sources, respectively, are:

$$H_{i_{sh}}(j2\pi f) = \frac{\alpha_0 r_e}{R_s + r_b(1 - \alpha_0) + r_e} \qquad (13.65a)$$

$$H_{i_p}(j2\pi f) = \frac{r_b + r_e + R_s}{R_s + r_b(1 - \alpha_0) + r_e} \qquad (13.65b)$$

$$H_{v_{th}}(j2\pi f) = \frac{\alpha_0}{R_s + r_b(1 - \alpha_0) + r_e} \qquad (13.65c)$$

Similarly, the transfer function relating the load current i_L to the source $v_s(t)$ is given by

$$H_{v_s}(j2\pi f) = \frac{\alpha_0}{R_s + r_b(1 - \alpha_0) + r_e} \qquad (13.65d)$$

By definition,

$$F = 1 + \frac{\mathscr{P}_{nao}(f)}{\mathscr{P}_{nso}(f)} \qquad (13.66)$$

where

$$\mathscr{P}_{nto}(f) = \mathscr{P}_{sh}(f) |H_{i_{sh}}|^2 + \mathscr{P}_p(f) |H_{i_p}|^2 + \mathscr{P}_{th}(f) |H_{v_{th}}|^2 \qquad (13.67a)$$

and

$$\mathscr{P}_{nso}(f) = \mathscr{P}_{R_s}(f) |H_{v_s}|^2 \qquad (13.67b)$$

Substituting Eqs. 13.67, 13.64 and 13.65 in Eq. 13.66, we get

$$F = 1 + \frac{r_b}{R_s} + \frac{qI_e}{2kTR_s}\left[r_e^{\,2} + \frac{1-\alpha_0}{\alpha_0}(r_b + r_e + R_s)^2\right] \qquad (13.68)$$

In a transistor the dynamic emitter resistance r_e is related to the emitter current by

$$r_e = \frac{kT}{qI_e} \qquad (13.69)$$

Substitution of Eq. 13.69 in Eq. 13.68 yields

$$F = 1 + \frac{r_b + r_e/2}{R_s} + \frac{(r_b + r_e + R_s)^2(1 - \alpha_0)}{2\alpha_0 r_e R_s} \qquad (13.70)$$

Note that there exists an optimum value of R_s for which the noise figure is minimum.

This result holds for frequencies $f < \sqrt{1 - \alpha_0}\, f_\alpha$ where f_α is the α cut-off frequency of the transistor. At lower frequencies (below 1 kc), the flicker noise becomes predominant. Hence the noise figure in Eqs. 13.68 and 13.70 is valid for intermediate frequencies. At high frequencies the partition noise increases. The general expression for the power density spectrum of the partition noise current generator is given by[11]

$$\mathscr{P}_p(f) = 2q\alpha_0 I_e(1 - \alpha_0)\frac{1 + (f/\sqrt{(1 - \alpha_0)}\,f_\alpha)^2}{1 + (f/f_\alpha)^2}$$

This reduces to Eq. 13.64b at low frequencies.

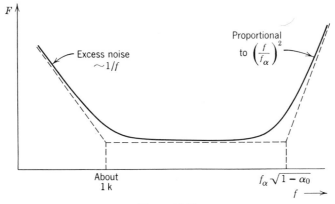

Figure 13.22

[11] For high frequency behavior, see E. G. Nielsen, "Behavior of Noise Figure in Junction Transistors," *Proc. IRE*, **45** (No. 7), 957–963 (July 1957); G. H. Hanson and A. Van der Ziel, "Shot Noise in Transistors," *Proc. IRE*, **45** (No. 11), 1538–1542 (November 1957).

The substitution of the above in Eq. 13.67 yields

$$F = 1 + \frac{r_b + r_e/2}{R_s} + \frac{(r_b + r_e + R_s)^2(1 - \alpha_0)\left[1 + \dfrac{1}{1 - \alpha_0}\left(\dfrac{f}{f_\alpha}\right)^2\right]}{2\alpha_0 r_e R_s}$$

The variation of the noise figure F with frequency is shown in Fig. 13.22.

Noise Figure in a Common Emitter Amplifier

Similar procedure may be used to calculate the common emitter amplifier noise figure. It can be shown that the noise figure of a common emitter amplifier is the same as that of a common base amplifier.[12]

13.8 POWER DENSITY AND AVAILABLE POWER DENSITY

In all of the discussion thus far the power density signifies the normalized power density, that is, the power density with respect to a 1-ohm resistor. The actual power density will depend upon the load impedance. If, for example, the current power density function in a certain impedance Z is $\mathscr{P}_i(f)$, then the actual power density (the power density being dissipated in this load) is given by $\mathscr{P}_i(f)R$ where R is the real part of the impedance Z. An energy source can yield a certain maximum power under matched conditions. The actual power density spectrum that can be extracted from a source (under the matched condition) is called the *available power density spectrum*. Consider, for example, a voltage source with a power density spectrum $\mathscr{P}(f)$ and an internal impedance $Z(j2\pi f)$ as shown in Fig. 13.23. To obtain the maximum power from such a source, the load must be

$$Z^*(j2\pi f) = R - jX$$

The actual power density delivered to the load obviously is

$$\frac{\mathscr{P}(f)}{(2R)^2}(R) = \frac{\mathscr{P}(f)}{4R} \tag{13.71a}$$

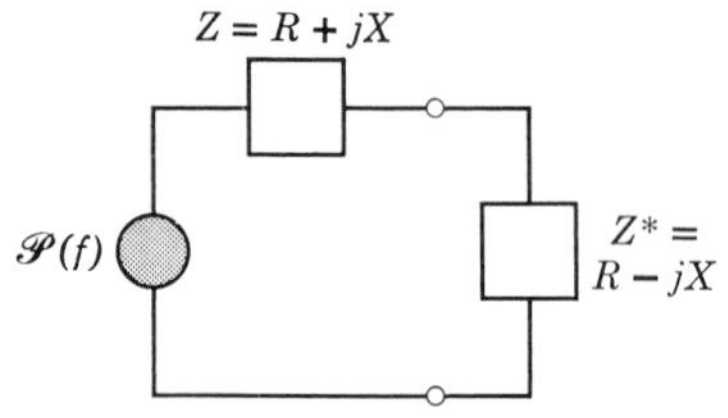

Figure 13.23

---

[12] E. G. Nielsen, cited in reference 11.

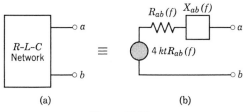

Figure 13.24

Hence the available power density spectrum is $\mathscr{P}(f)/4R$. Note that this is the actual power density dissipated in the load under matched conditions, and hence it is the maximum power density that can be extracted from the source $\mathscr{P}(f)$ with the internal impedance Z.

We shall now find the available power density spectrum due to thermal noise from a passive network containing only R-L-C elements. Such a network can be represented by an equivalent resistance $R_{ab}(f)$ in series with an equivalent reactance $X_{ab}(f)$ as shown in Fig. 13.24. The thermal noise can be represented by a voltage source of power density $4kTR_{ab}(f)$ (see Section 13.5). To extract maximum noise power from this network we must connect a load impedance $Z_{ab}{}^* = R_{ab}(f) - jX_{ab}(f)$. Under this condition the maximum thermal noise power density delivered to the load is given by

$$\frac{4kTR_{ab}}{(2R_{ab})^2}\,(R_{ab}) = kT \tag{13.72}$$

This is a rather startling result. It states that the available (thermal) noise power density from any passive R-L-C two-terminal network is a constant; given by kT. It is tacitly assumed in this discussion that all of the resistors in the network are at the same temperature T.

Note that the maximum noise power that can be extracted from any R-L-C two-terminal network in a bandwidth df is $kTdf$. Thus the available noise power from a two-terminal R-L-C network in a unit bandwidth is kT.

13.9 EFFECTIVE NOISE TEMPERATURE

We have seen in the previous section that the available power density spectrum of every R-L-C two-terminal network is kT. This result does not hold true for a two-terminal network containing sources of noise other than thermal noise (such as shot noise). Nevertheless it is possible to extend this result to all two-terminal networks by defining the effective noise temperature T_n. If the available noise power density of any two-terminal networks is $\mathscr{P}_{av}(f)$, we define T_n, the effective noise temperature of the network, as

$$\mathscr{P}_{av}(f) = kT_n \qquad (13.73)$$

or

$$T_n = \frac{\mathscr{P}_{av}(f)}{k} \qquad (13.74)$$

If $\mathscr{P}_{av}(f)$ is constant over the frequency range of interest, T_n, the effective noise temperature is also a constant given by Eq. 13.74. If, however, $\mathscr{P}_{av}(f)$ varies with frequency, T_n is a function of frequency f. The available noise power from any two-terminal network in a bandwidth df is therefore $kT_n\,df$. Note that for a network containing only R-L-C elements, the effective noise temperature T_n is equal to the ambient temperature T of the network.

13.10 NOISE FIGURE IN TERMS OF AVAILABLE GAIN

We have seen that the noise figure can be expressed as the ratio of the signal-to-noise power density spectra at the input divided by that at the output (Eq. 13.57). It is possible to express noise figure in terms of available power densities and available power gain. Consider, for example, the arrangement shown in Fig. 13.25. In this figure $\mathscr{P}_s(f)$ and $\mathscr{P}_n(f)$ represent the power density spectra of the signal and the noise voltages respectively. The thermal noise due to source impedance $Z(j\omega)$ is accounted for by $\mathscr{P}_n(f)$ and hence $Z(j\omega)$ in Fig. 13.25 is noiseless. The ratio of signal-to-noise (S/N) power density spectra at the terminals ab is given by

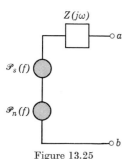

Figure 13.25

$$(S/N)_i = \frac{\mathscr{P}_s(f)}{\mathscr{P}_n(f)} \qquad (13.75)$$

Let us now find the ratio of the available signal-to-noise power density spectra. To obtain this ratio we connect the load impedance $Z^*(j\omega)$ across the terminals ab. If

$$Z(j2\pi f) = R(f) + jX(f)$$

then

$$Z^*(j2\pi f) = R(f) - jX(f)$$

and the available signal power density spectrum is given by

$$\frac{\mathscr{P}_s(f)}{[2R(f)]^2} R(f) = \frac{\mathscr{P}_s(f)}{4R(f)}$$

Similarly the available noise density spectrum is given by

$$\frac{\mathscr{P}_n(f)}{4R(f)}$$

Hence the ratio of available signal-to-noise power density spectra across terminals ab is

$$(S/N)_{av} = \frac{\mathscr{P}_s(f)}{\mathscr{P}_n(f)} = (S/N)_i \tag{13.76}$$

This is a very significant result. It states that the signal-to-noise power density ratio across any terminals is the same as the available signal-to-noise power density ratio across the same terminals. Indeed, it can be easily shown that the signal-to-noise power density spectra ratio is independent of load termination. We can take advantage of this result in finding the noise figure of an amplifier. The noise figure F of an amplifier is given by (Eq. 13.57) the ratio of signal-to-noise power density (S/N) at the input terminals divided by the same ratio at the output terminals. It is obvious from Eq. 13.76 that the noise figure F can also be expressed as the ratio of available signal-to-noise power densities at the input terminals divided by the same ratio at the output terminals. We shall designate all of the available power densities by the subscript av. Thus $(\mathscr{P}_{si})_{av}$ represents the available signal power density at the input terminals. We now have (Eq. 13.57):

$$F = \frac{(\mathscr{P}_{si})_{av}/(\mathscr{P}_{nsi})_{av}}{(\mathscr{P}_{so})_{av}/(\mathscr{P}_{nto})_{av}}$$

$$= \frac{(\mathscr{P}_{si})_{av}}{(\mathscr{P}_{so})_{av}} \frac{(\mathscr{P}_{nto})_{av}}{(\mathscr{P}_{nsi})_{av}} \tag{13.77}$$

For an amplifier we define an available power gain $\mathscr{G}$ as

$$\mathscr{G} = \frac{\text{Available signal power density at the output}}{\text{Available signal power density at the input}} \tag{13.78a}$$

It is thus apparent that

$$\frac{(\mathscr{P}_{so})_{av}}{(\mathscr{P}_{si})_{av}} = \mathscr{G} \tag{13.78b}$$

Note that the available power gain $\mathscr{G}$ is in general a function of frequency f and hence $\mathscr{G}$, the available power gain may be represented as $\mathscr{G}(f)$. Substituting Eq. 13.78 in Eq. 13.77, we get

$$F = \frac{(\mathscr{P}_{nto})_{av}}{\mathscr{G}(\mathscr{P}_{nsi})_{av}} \tag{13.79}$$

where $(\mathscr{P}_{nto})_{av}$ is the available noise power density at the output and $(\mathscr{P}_{nsi})_{av}$ is the available noise power due to source at the input terminals. If the source impedance is a passive R-L-C two-terminal network, then from Eq. 13.72 we have

$$(\mathscr{P}_{nsi})_{av} = kT \tag{13.80}$$

If the source impedance contains noise sources other than thermal noise, then

$$(\mathscr{P}_{nsi})_{av} = kT_n \tag{13.81}$$

Hereafter we shall always assume the source impedance to be a passive R-L-C network. If the source impedance is a passive R-L-C network, then Eq. 13.79 becomes

$$F = \frac{(\mathscr{P}_{nto})_{av}}{\mathscr{G}kT} \tag{13.82}$$

If the source impedance contains noise sources other than thermal, the temperature T in Eq. 13.82 should be replaced by the effective noise temperature T_n.

From Eq. 13.82, we have

$$(\mathscr{P}_{nto})_{av} = F\mathscr{G}kT \tag{13.83}$$

Thus the available noise power density at the output terminals is given by $F\mathscr{G}kT$. Note that $(\mathscr{P}_{nto})_{av}$ is composed of two components.

(1) The component $(\mathscr{P}_{nso})_{av}$ is the available noise power density at the output terminals due to noise in the source.

(2) The component $(\mathscr{P}_{nao})_{av}$ is the available noise power density at the output terminals due to noise generated in the amplifier.

Hence

$$(\mathscr{P}_{nto})_{av} = (\mathscr{P}_{nso})_{av} + (\mathscr{P}_{nao})_{av} \tag{13.84}$$

Moreover, from Eq. 13.78a,

$$(\mathscr{P}_{nso})_{av} = \mathscr{G}(\mathscr{P}_{nsi})_{av} = \mathscr{G}kT \tag{13.85}$$

Hence, from Eqs. 13.83 to 13.85, we obtain

$$(\mathscr{P}_{nao})_{av} = (F - 1)\mathscr{G}kT \qquad (13.86)$$

Thus the available noise power density at the output terminals due to amplifier noise is $(F - 1)\mathscr{G}kT$

13.11 CASCADED STAGES

When an amplifier consists of more than one stage, its noise figure can be computed in terms of the noise figures of individual stages. It is intuitively obvious that the noise generated in earlier stages is amplified by later stages, and hence the noise figure of the first stage is much more significant in determining the over-all noise figure of the amplifier. As an example, consider a two-stage amplifier as shown in Fig. 13.26. The two amplifiers have available power gains $\mathscr{G}_a$ and $\mathscr{G}_b$, respectively. The noise figure of the two amplifiers are F_a and F_b, respectively, the noise figure of amplifier b being determined under the conditions shown in Fig. 13.26b. The source impedance is equal to the output impedance of the amplifier a, and it is assumed that this impedance generates only thermal noise and has the available noise power density equal to kT.

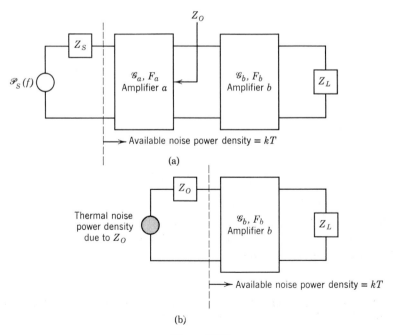

(a)

(b)

Figure 13.26

It is evident from Eq. 13.86 that the available noise power density at the output due to amplifier b alone is given by

$$(\mathscr{P}_{nao})_{av} = (F_b - 1)\mathscr{G}_b kT \tag{13.87}$$

If F_{ab} is the over-all noise figure of the amplifier, then from Eq. 13.85 it follows that the total noise power density available at the output is given by

$$(\mathscr{P}_{nto})_{av} = F_{ab}\mathscr{G}_{ab} kT \tag{13.88}$$

where $\mathscr{G}_{ab}$ is the over-all available power gain of the amplifier. It can be easily shown that

$$\mathscr{G}_{ab} = \mathscr{G}_a \mathscr{G}_b \tag{13.89}$$

Hence

$$(\mathscr{P}_{nto})_{av} = F_{ab}\mathscr{G}_a \mathscr{G}_b kT \tag{13.90}$$

As already mentioned, $(\mathscr{P}_{nto})_{av}$ consists of two components: (1) the available noise power density at the output due to amplifier b (given in Eq. 13.87), and (2) the available noise power density at the output due to the noise at the input of amplifier b. The latter component is obviously the available noise power density at the input of amplifier b multiplied by the available power gain $\mathscr{G}_b$. The available noise power density at the input of amplifier b is the available noise power density at the output of the amplifier a, and is given by (Eq. 13.83) $F_a \mathscr{G}_a kT$. Hence

$$(\mathscr{P}_{nto})_{av} = F_{ab}\mathscr{G}_a \mathscr{G}_b kT = (F_b - 1)\mathscr{G}_b kT + F_a \mathscr{G}_a \mathscr{G}_b kT$$

Hence

$$F_{ab} = F_a + \frac{F_b - 1}{\mathscr{G}_a} \tag{13.91}$$

In general, for a multistage amplifier,

$$F = F_a + \frac{F_b - 1}{\mathscr{G}_a} + \frac{F_c - 1}{\mathscr{G}_a \mathscr{G}_b} + \cdots \tag{13.92}$$

It is evident from Eq. 13.92 that the first stage is the most significant in determining the noise figure of an amplifier. Hence in low noise amplifiers the primary consideration in design of the first stage is to obtain a low noise figure even at the cost of gain.

Example 13.8

Find the noise figure of a two-stage amplifier shown in Fig. 13.27. Both tubes are identical, with parameters $g_m = 2.5 \times 10^{-3}$ mhos and $r_p = 10,000$ ohms.

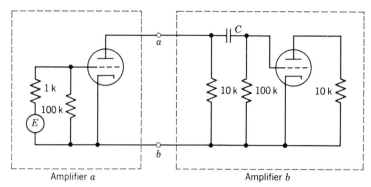

Figure 13.27

Over the frequency range of interest the coupling capacitor may be assumed to be a short circuit. For convenience we shall arbitrarily divide the amplifier into two stages as shown by the dotted blocks in Fig. 13.27. We shall first find the noise figures F_a and F_b of the two amplifiers. This can be easily obtained from Eq. 13.61. For amplifier a,

$$R_{eq} = 2.5/2.5 \times 10^{-3} = 1000$$
$$R_s = 1000 \text{ and } R_g = 100,000 \text{ ohms}$$

Substituting these values in Eq. 13.61 we get

$$F_a = 2.03$$

For amplifier b

$$R_{eq} = 2.5/2.5 \times 10^{-3} = 1000$$

R_g is the parallel combination of 10,000 ohms and 100,000 ohms. Thus $R_g \simeq$ 9100 ohms. The source impedance for amplifier b is the output impedance of amplifier a and is given by the plate resistance r_p of the first tube. Thus

$$R_s = r_p = 10,000 \text{ ohms}$$

Substituting these values in Eq. 13.61, we get

$$F_b = 2.54$$

Next we calculate the available power gains of the two amplifiers. The available gain $\mathcal{G}$ of an amplifier is given by Eq. 13.78a. Note that at any one frequency the available gain $\mathcal{G}$ can also be expressed as

$$\mathcal{G} = \frac{\text{Available signal power at the load}}{\text{Available signal power at the source}} \tag{13.93}$$

Consider amplifier a, which has a source resistance of 1000 ohms. If the signal voltage is E volts, then the available power is obtained by connecting 1000 ohms across the source terminals. The maximum power available is obviously

$$\left(\frac{E}{2000}\right)^2 1000 = \frac{E^2}{4000} \text{ watts} \tag{13.94}$$

The equivalent circuit of the output terminals of amplifier a is shown in Fig. 13.28.

The equivalent current source has a magnitude $g_m e_g$ where e_g is the voltage at the grid of first tube. From Fig. 13.27 we have

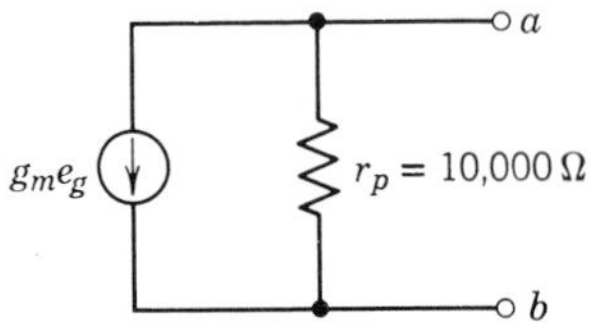

Figure 13.28

$$e_g = \frac{100}{101} E$$

and

$$g_m e_g = 2.5 \times 10^{-3} \times \frac{100}{101} E \simeq 2.5 \times 10^{-3} E$$

The maximum power available at the load terminals ab is the power delivered to the matched impedance at the load. This occurs when the load at terminals ab is 10,000 ohms and the power output under this condition is

$$\left(\frac{g_m e_g}{2}\right)^2 (10,000) = 1.56 \times 10^{-2} E^2 \tag{13.95}$$

From Eqs. 13.94 and 13.95, we obtain

$$\mathscr{G}_a = \frac{1.56 \times 10^{-2} E^2}{E^2/4000} = 62.4 \tag{13.96}$$

The over-all noise figure F_{ab} is given by

$$F_{ab} = F_a + \frac{F_b - 1}{\mathscr{G}_a}$$

$$= 2.03 + \frac{1.54}{62.4}$$

$$= 2.03 + 0.0247$$

$$= 2.0547$$

$$\simeq F_a$$

13.12 THE CASCODE AMPLIFIER

In high-frequency low-noise amplifiers, pentodes are avoided because of high noise figures (high R_{eq}). The triode amplifiers, on the other hand, tend to be unstable at high frequencies due to interelectrode capacitance which cause appreciable feedback. These difficulties are avoided by the so-called *cascode amplifier*[13] which consists of a triode grounded-cathode amplifier followed by a triode grounded-grid amplifier as shown in Fig. 13.29. The input impedance of the grounded-grid amplifier is very low and thus reduces the effect of interelectrode capacitance in the first stage. The cascode amplifier in Fig. 13.29 has approximately the same noise

[13] For an example of a cascode amplifier, see J. Pettit and M. McWhorter *Electronic Amplifier Circuits*, McGraw-Hill, New York, 1961.

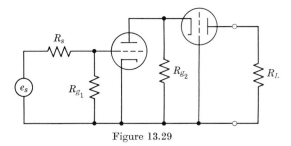

Figure 13.29

figure and gain as that of a grounded-cathode amplifier. The grounded-cathode amplifier used alone has instability problems due to feedback caused by interelectrode capacitances as mentioned above. The neutralization of interelectrode capacitances is very critical and is generally avoided.

The effectiveness of the cascode amplifier is due to the fact that the first stage has a low voltage gain (as required to minimize the effect of grid to plate capacitance to avoid instability) and a high available power gain (as required to reduce the noise figure). The available power gain of the first stage is so high that the over-all noise figure of the cascode amplifier is nearly the same as that of the first stage, that is, a grounded cathode stage.

PROBLEMS

1. Derive the rms value of the noise current in an R-L circuit.

2. Determine the power density spectrum of the noise current flowing through a series R-L-C circuit.

3. Two resistors, each of 1000 ohms, are at temperatures $300°K$ and $400°K$, respectively. Find the voltage power density spectrum at the terminals formed by the series combination of these resistors.

4. Repeat Problem 3 if the resistors are connected in parallel.

5. Determine the rms noise voltage across the output terminals of a noiseless circuit (Fig. P-13.5) when 1 k resistance is connected across the input terminals and if the voltage gain transfer function of the circuit represents the following.

(a) An ideal low-pass filter with cut-off frequency f_c.
(b) An ideal bandpass filter with a passband of f_c cycles centered around f_0.

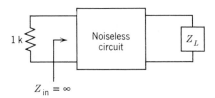

Figure P-13.5

(c) An exponential filter, $H(j\omega) = Ae^{-|\omega|/\omega_c}$.

(d) A gaussian filter, $H(j\omega) = Ae^{-\omega^2/\omega_c^2}$.

Assume the input impedance of the circuit to be infinite. Neglect the noise contribution due to the load impedance Z_L.

6. Repeat Problem 5 if now, in addition to 1000 ohms resistor a diode is connected across the input terminals as shown in Fig. P-13.6. Assume the diode to be in the

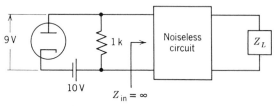

Figure P-13.6

space-charge limited region with a dynamic resistance of 6670 ohms and the cathode temperature to be 1000°K.

7. (a) Determine the power density spectrum of the noise voltage across terminals aa' of the resistive network in Fig. P-13.7 by the following two methods.

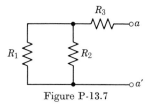

Figure P-13.7

(1) By calculating the noise power density spectrum across aa' as the sum of the noise power density spectra across aa' due to each of the three resistors.

(2) By calculating the equivalent resistance R_{eq} across aa' and finding the required power density spectrum $4kTR_{eq}$.

(b) Determine the power density spectrum of the noise voltage across terminals aa' if the resistors R_1, R_2, and R_3 are at different temperatures T_1, T_2, and T_3, respectively.

8. Determine the noise power density spectrum and the rms noise voltage across the output terminals aa' of a low-pass filter shown in Fig. P-13.8. This filter is known as the third-order Butterworth filter.

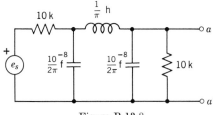

Figure P-13.8

9. Find the rms noise voltage across terminals bb' for each of the networks shown in Fig. P-13.9 by the following two methods.

(a) By calculating the power density spectrum at bb' as the sum of the power density spectra due to each individual resistor.

(b) By replacing the network to the right of terminals aa' by an equivalent impedance $Z_{aa'}$ and using Eq. 13.50.

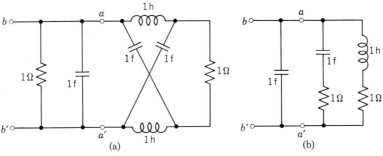

Figure P-13.9

10. Determine the power density spectrum of the noise voltage across terminals aa' of the circuits shown in Fig. P-13.10.

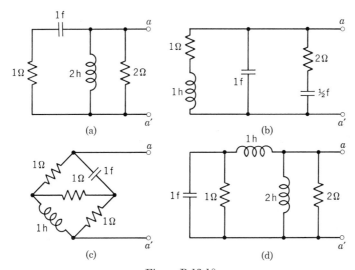

Figure P-13.10

11. Show that the equivalent noise bandwidth of the Butterworth filter in Problem 8 referred to d-c ($f_0 = 0$) is $(10^4\pi/3)$ cps.

12. (a) Calculate the equivalent noise bandwidth of the circuits referred to zero frequency if it is given that

$$H(j\omega) = (1)\ Ae^{-\alpha|\omega|}$$
$$= (2)\ Ae^{-\alpha\omega^2}$$
$$= (3)\ Sa(\omega t_0)$$
$$= (4)\ G_w(\omega)$$

(b) Calculate the equivalent noise bandwidth referred to ω_0 if

$$H(j\omega) = Sa[(\omega - \omega_0)t_0]$$

13. Solve Example 13.5 in the text without ignoring the noise contribution due to load resistance R_L.

14. A third-order Butterworth filter described in Problem 8 is connected at the output terminals of a triode amplifier (Fig. P-13.14). The source resistance is 1000 ohms. Determine the rms value of the noise voltage across the load. Evaluate the spectral and average noise figures of the amplifier. It is given that $g_m = 3000$ μmhos and $r_p = 10,000$ ohms.

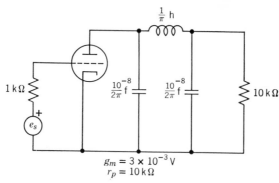

$$g_m = 3 \times 10^{-3} \text{V}$$
$$r_p = 10\,\text{k}\Omega$$

Figure P-13.14

15. Find the noise figure of the cascaded amplifier shown in Fig. 13.27 by a straightforward method using the definition of noise figure in Eq. 13.54.

16. Show that the noise figure of a grounded-cathode, grounded-grid, and grounded-plate vacuum tube amplifiers are approximately the same.

17. Show that if the effective noise temperature of the source is constant, independent of frequency, then the average noise figure $\bar{F}$ is given by

$$\bar{F} = \frac{\displaystyle\int_0^\infty F \mathscr{G}_a \, df}{\displaystyle\int_0^\infty \mathscr{G}_a \, df}$$

18. Find the noise figure of the cascode amplifier shown in Fig. 13.29.

19. Determine the noise figure of the amplifier in Example 13.5 in the text, using Eq. 13.82 or Eq. 13.86.

chapter 14

Introduction to
Information Transmission

In our discussion of communication systems in Chapter 11 the channels of transmission were assumed to be free from noise signals. Hence, the signals received were perfect replicas of the transmitted signals. In practice, however, the signals are always contaminated by unwanted signals in the process of transmission. The received signals are not perfect replicas of the transmitted signals and there is always a certain amount of uncertainty involved in the information received. This uncertainty can be reduced by increasing the signal power. The ratio of the average signal power to the noise power is an indication of the uncertainty or an error in the information received. It was indicated in Chapter 11 that the signal-to-noise ratio can also be improved by transmitting the information in a form that will occupy a larger bandwidth. An increase in bandwidth, generally, converts the signal in such a form as to make it more immune to the noise signals (for example, FM or PCM). Thus, the signal-to-noise ratio can be improved by increasing the bandwidth. In general, the uncertainty in the information received, as measured by the signal-to-noise power ratio, can be improved either by increasing the signal power or by transmitting the signal in a form which will occupy a larger bandwidth or both. In fact, we shall presently see that to maintain a given degree of uncertainty it is possible to trade the bandwidth with the signal power transmitted. To transmit a given amount of information, we can lower the signal power transmitted, provided that the bandwidth is increased accordingly. On the other hand, the information may be squeezed into a narrower bandwidth if we are willing to pay enough in signal power. The proper type of modulation can accomplish this trade between the bandwidth and the signal-to-noise ratio.

Thus far, we have been talking about information in vague terms. We shall now define the unit of information in order to base our discussion on a quantitative basis.

14.1 INFORMATION RATE: CHANNEL CAPACITY

Let us assume that we are required to transmit a response to a question which has only two possible answers: yes and no. This information can be transmitted simply by a single pulse which can assume two amplitudes: for instance, zero volts and 1 volt. We may specify that a zero-volt pulse means "no" and 1-volt pulse means "yes." Such a pulse, which can assume two states or two levels, is called a *binary pulse*. It is evident that one such pulse can transmit any of the two possible answers or two possible symbols. Hence, a single binary pulse is capable of transmitting a certain amount of information. The amount of information transmitted by a single binary pulse is defined as one unit of information and is called *bit* (short for BInary uniT). However, the definition of *bit*, as given above, is ambiguous because the amount of information carried by a pulse is not unique but depends upon the manner in which it is used. In the example given, if we want to transmit only two symbols, yes and no, we may choose to transmit the symbol yes by a group of two pulses and the symbol no by a group of three pulses. In this case, the inherent potentiality of a pulse to carry information is not completely realized and hence each pulse carries much less information than it is capable of transmitting. However, there is a maximum amount of information that can be transmitted by a single binary pulse when it is used in the most efficient manner. Again, referring back to the transmission of the two symbols, yes and no, if the two symbols are likely to occur with equal probability, then we can show that it is impossible to transmit each of the symbols by less than one binary pulse, on the average. In this case, the single pulse signifying either yes or no has been used most efficiently. The efficient use of pulses in transmitting information can be achieved by proper coding. Information theory deals with the setting up of such efficient coding systems. The efficient coding can be obtained from the knowledge of the statistical nature of the information to be transmitted. For example, in the transmission of information, certain symbols tend to occur more often than others. The symbols that occur more frequently are assigned the code of a smaller number of pulses than those that occur less frequently. In this way the given amount of information can be transmitted by a fewer number of pulses. As an example, the letters e, t, a, and o occur more frequently than letters such as x, k, q, and z in the English language. Hence, to transmit efficiently a message in English by a pulse code (like the Morse code), the code representing the letters e, t, a, and o must be shorter than the code representing the letters x, k, q, and z. It is easy to see that in order to set up a proper code a knowledge of the probability of the occurrence of each symbol is necessary. For more discussion on this subject, the reader may refer to any standard text on information theory.[1]

In light of the above discussion, we shall redefine the unit of information called *bit* as the maximum amount of information that can be transmitted by a single binary pulse.

This definition may appear, superficially, to be too restrictive as it applies only to information of a discrete nature, such as the transmission of some discrete symbols (as alphabets or numerals). However, it is a major result of information theory that any form of information to be transmitted can always be represented in binary form without a loss of generality. We have already seen in the preceding chapter that the information in a continuous bandlimited signal can be represented by a discrete number of sample values per second. It is now possible to represent these sample values by a code that uses binary pulses.

It will be shown that each communication system (or channel) is capable of transmitting a certain amount of information per second. This is called the channel capacity C. Thus, a given channel can transmit a quantity of information, at most, C bits per second. The channel capacity will be shown to be limited by the bandwidth of the system and the amount of noise power in the system.

To show this, let us assume that we are required to transmit any one of four possible symbols instead of two (like yes or no). Obviously, it is not possible to transmit this information by a single binary pulse, since it can assume only two states. But we can transmit any of the four symbols by a group of two binary pulses. Each binary pulse can assume two states, and hence a combination of two pulses will form four distinct patterns as shown in Fig. 14.1. The zero state of a pulse (absence of a pulse) is shown by a dotted line. We, therefore, need two binary pulses to transmit any

[1] See, for instance, N. Abramson, *Information Theory and Coding*, McGraw-Hill, New York, 1963; F. M. Reza, *An Introduction to Information Theory*, McGraw-Hill, New York, 1961.

Symbol	Binary digit equivalent	Binary pulse waveform	Quaternary digit equivalent	Quaternary pulse waveform
A	00		0	0 volts
B	01		1	1 volt
C	10		2	2 volts
D	11		3	3 volts

Figure 14.1

of the four possible symbols. Hence, the information transmitted per symbol is 2 bits.[2]

Alternatively, we may transmit this information by a quaternary pulse which can assume four states or four levels, for example, 0, 1, 2, and 3 volts. Each state corresponds to one of the four possible symbols. It is obvious that any one of the four possible symbols can be transmitted by a single quaternary pulse (Fig. 14.1). It follows that a single quaternary pulse can transmit the information carried by two binary pulses and hence carries 2 bits of information. In a similar way, if it is desired to transmit any one of eight possible symbols, we need a group of three binary pulses for each symbol. Since each binary pulse has two states, a combination of three pulses will yield eight distinct patterns. Each of the possible eight symbols may also be transmitted by a single octal pulse (a pulse which can

---

[2] This assumes that all the four symbols are equally likely to occur. If all of the four symbols are not equally probable, then it can be shown that by using a proper code, less than 2 bits per symbol are required, on the average. If p_i is the probability of occurrence of the ith symbol, then, on the average, a minimum of

$$\sum_{i=1}^{4} p_i \log_2 \frac{1}{p_i} \text{ bits per symbol}$$

are required. In general, if a message contains n symbols with the probability of occurrence $p_1, p_2, \ldots, p_n$, respectively, then it can be shown that, on the average, a minimum of

$$\sum_{i=1}^{n} p_i \log_2 \frac{1}{p_i}$$

bits per symbol are required to transmit such a message.

assume eight states or eight values). Hence, a single octal pulse carries 3 bits of information. It is easy to see that a pulse which can assume n distinct states or n distinct levels carries an information of $\log_2 n$ bits.

It therefore follows that the larger the number of distinct levels that a pulse can assume, the larger the information carried by each pulse. A pulse that can assume an infinite number of distinct levels carries an infinite amount of information. This means that it is possible to transmit any amount of information by a single pulse which can assume an infinite number of distinct levels. This result appears to be fantastic but it is perfectly logical and sound. If a pulse can assume an infinite number of distinct levels, then it is possible to assign one of the levels to any conceivable message or signal, no matter how large. For example, we may assign one of the infinite levels to represent the complete contents of this book. Now, if it is desired to transmit the complete contents of this book, all that is required is to transmit one pulse of the corresponding level. Since there are available an infinite number of levels, it is possible to assign one level to any conceivable message or signal of any length in this universe. Cataloging of the code in such a case may prove to be next to impossible; nevertheless, it illustrates the possibility of the transmission of an infinite amount of information by a single pulse.

At this point one may wonder why we do not use pulses that can assume an infinite number of distinct levels. There are limitations imposed upon the system by practical considerations. It should be remembered that in all of our discussion when we talk about the transmission of information by transmitting pulses we refer to the composite system that transmits the information at the transmitter and receives it at the destination. Hence, to transmit certain information, we must be able to transmit as well as receive these pulses. Moreover, we must be able to recognize the distinct levels of the pulses. Now, what can prevent us from transmitting pulses that assume an infinite number of distinct states? It is obvious that since practical considerations require that the pulses must have finite amplitudes, the infinite number of distinct states imply that each state is separated from the neighboring state by an infinitesimal amount. Since, in any practical channel, there is always a certain amount of noise signal present, it will be impossible to distinguish at the receiver, levels lying within the noise signal amplitude. Hence, the noise consideration requires that the levels must be separated at least by the noise signal amplitude.

Let us assume that S watts is the signal power transmitted, and that the signal is contaminated by the noise power of N watts in the process of transmission. The total power received is $S + N$ watts. If we assume a load of 1 ohm, then the rms value of the received signal is $\sqrt{S+N}$ volts, and the rms value of the noise voltage is $\sqrt{N}$ volts. We now want to distinguish the received signal of the amplitude $\sqrt{S+N}$ volts in the presence of the noise amplitude $\sqrt{N}$ volts. It is obvious that the input signal variation of less than $\sqrt{N}$ volts will be indistinguishable at the receiver. Hence, it follows that the number of the distinct levels that can be distinguished without error will be given by

$$M = \frac{\sqrt{S+N}}{\sqrt{N}} = \sqrt{1 + \frac{S}{N}} \qquad (14.1)$$

Hence, the maximum value of M is given by Eq. 14.1. The maximum amount of information carried by each pulse having $\sqrt{1 + S/N}$ distinct levels is given by

$$I = \log_2 \sqrt{1 + \frac{S}{N}} \qquad (14.2)$$

$$= \tfrac{1}{2} \log_2 \left(1 + \frac{S}{N}\right) \text{ bits} \qquad (14.3)$$

We are now in a position to determine the channel capacity. The channel capacity is the maximum amount of information that can be transmitted per second by a channel. If a channel can transmit a maximum of K pulses per second then, obviously, the channel capacity C is given by[3]

$$C = \frac{K}{2} \log_2 \left(1 + \frac{S}{N}\right) \text{ bits per second} \qquad (14.4)$$

In chapter 11, in connection with the bandwidth requirements of PAM signals, we showed that a system of bandwidth nf_m cps can transmit $2nf_m$ pulses per second. It was shown that under these conditions the received signal will yield the correct values of the amplitudes of the pulses but will not reproduce the details of the pulse shapes. Since we are interested only in the pulse amplitudes and not their shapes, it follows that a system with bandwidth W cps can transmit a maximum of $2W$ pulses per second. Since each pulse can carry a maximum information

---

[3] Ordinarily, in this expression S, the signal power is the maximum signal power. If, however, we consider a group of n symbols as one symbol, then S in the above expression approaches the average signal power when n is made very large. For a rigorous proof of Eqs. 14.4 and 14.5, see F. M. Reza, cited in reference 1. Also see W. W. Harman, *Principles of the Statistical Theory of Communication*, McGraw-Hill, New York, 1963; and J. C. Hancock, *An Introduction to the Principles of Communication Theory*, McGraw-Hill, New York, 1961.

of $\frac{1}{2} \log_2 (1 + S/N)$ bits, it follows that a system of bandwidth W can transmit the information at a maximum rate of

$$C = W \log_2 \left(1 + \frac{S}{N}\right) \text{ bits per second} \qquad (14.5)$$

The channel capacity C is, thus, limited by the bandwidth of the channel (or system) and the noise signal. For a noiseless channel, $N = 0$ and the channel capacity is infinite. In practice, however, N is always finite and hence the channel capacity is finite[4]

Equation 14.5 is known as the Hartley-Shannon law and is considered as the central theorem of information theory.[5]

It is evident from this theorem that the bandwidth and the signal power can be exchanged for each other. To transmit the information at a given rate, we may reduce the signal power transmitted, provided that the bandwidth is increased correspondingly. Similarly, the bandwidth may be reduced if we are willing to pay in terms of increased signal power. As stated before, the process of modulation is really a means of effecting this exchange between the bandwidth and the signal-to-noise ratio. The improvement in the signal-to-noise ratio in wideband FM and PCM can be properly understood in the light of this theorem.

It must be remembered, however, that the channel capacity represents the maximum amount of information that can be transmitted by a channel per second. To achieve this rate of transmission, the information has to be

---

[4] This is true even if the bandwidth W is infinite. The noise signal is a white noise with a uniform power density spectrum over the entire frequency range. Hence, as the bandwidth W is increased, N also increases and thus the channel capacity remains finite even if $W = \infty$. If N_0 is the noise power per cycle bandwidth, then $N = N_0 W$ and

$$C = W \log_2 \left(1 + \frac{S}{N_0 W}\right)$$

and

$$\lim_{W \to \infty} C = \frac{S}{N_0} \frac{N_0 W}{S} \log_2 \left(1 + \frac{S}{N_0 W}\right)$$

The above limit can be found by noting that

$$\lim_{x \to 0} \frac{1}{x} \log_2 (1 + x) = \log_2 e = 1.44$$

Hence

$$\lim_{W \to \infty} C = \frac{S}{N_0} \log_2 e = 1.44 \frac{S}{N_0}$$

[5] Information theory is a body of results based on a particular quantitative definition of an amount of information and is a subdivision of a broader field—the statistical theory of communication—which includes all of the probabilistic analysis of communications problems. See, for instance, P. Elias, "Information Theory" in the *Handbook of Automation, Computation and Control*, Vol. 1, Chapter 16, Wiley, New York, 1961.

processed properly or coded in the most efficient manner. The fact that such a coding is possible is one of the significant results attributed to Shannon in information theory. Actually, however, not all of the communication systems used in practice (for example AM, FM, etc.) achieve this maximum rate.

14.2 TRANSMISSION OF CONTINUOUS SIGNALS

We shall illustrate the implications of the Hartley-Shannon law regarding the exchange of bandwidth and signal-to-noise ratio by an example of a continuous signal bandlimited to f_m cps. From the sampling theorem it follows that the information of such a signal is completely specified by $2f_m$ number of samples per second. Thus, to transmit the information of such a signal, it is necessary to transmit only these discrete samples.

The next important question is: How much information does each sample contain? It depends upon how many discrete levels or values the samples may assume. Actually, these samples can assume any value, and hence to transmit such samples we need pulses capable of assuming infinite levels. Obviously the information carried by each sample is infinite bits. Hence, the information contained in a continuous bandlimited signal is infinite. In the presence of noise (finite value of N), the channel capacity is finite. It is, therefore, impossible to transmit complete information in a bandlimited signal by a physical channel in the presence of noise. In the absence of noise, $N = 0$ and the channel capacity is infinite and any desired signal can be transmitted. Obviously, it is impossible to transmit the complete information contained in a continuous signal unless the transmitted signal power is made infinite. Due to the presence of noise, there is always a certain amount of uncertainty in the received signal. The transmission of complete information in a signal would mean a zero amount of uncertainty. Actually, the amount of uncertainty can be made arbitrarily small by increasing the channel capacity (by increasing the bandwidth and/or increasing the signal power), but it can never be made zero.

It is important to realize that the uncertainty is introduced in the process of transmission. Hence, although it is possible to transmit the complete information in a continuous signal at the transmitter end, it is impossible to recover this infinite amount of information at the receiver. The amount of information that can be recovered per second at the receiver is, at most, C bits per second where C is the channel capacity. This is precisely what happens when we transmit a continuous signal by direct transmission, such as by AM and FM. In these cases, the complete information in a signal is transmitted at the transmitter. But, since a channel has a finite capacity C bps, at most, information of only C bps can be recovered at the receiver.

Alternatively, instead of transmitting all of the information at the transmitter, we may just as well approximate the signal so that its information contents are reduced to C bits per second and transmit this approximated signal which has a finite information content. It will now be possible to recover all of the information that has been transmitted. This is precisely what is done in pulse modulation. How can we approximate a signal so that the approximated signal has a finite information content per second? This can be done by a process of quantization. Consider the continuous signal bandlimited to f_m cps as shown in Fig. 14.2. To transmit the information in this signal, we need to transmit only $2f_m$ samples per second. The samples are also shown in the figure. As stated before, the samples can take any value, and to transmit them directly we need pulses which can assume an infinite number of levels. (We have seen above that although it is possible to transmit such pulses at the transmitter end, it is impossible to recover the exact heights of these pulses at the receiver due to noise.) Therefore, instead of transmitting the exact values of these pulses we round off the amplitudes to the nearest one of the finite number of permitted values. In this example, all of the pulses are approximated to the nearest tenth of a volt. It is evident from this figure that each of the pulses transmitted assumes any one of the 16 levels, and hence carries an amount of information of $\log_2 16 = 4$ bits. Since there are $2f_m$ samples per second, the total information content

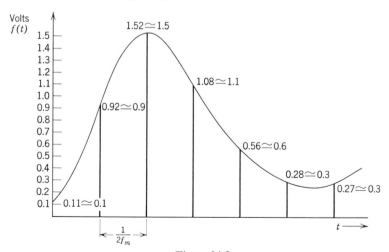

Figure 14.2

of the approximated signal is $8f_m$ bits per second. If the channel capacity is greater than or equal to $8f_m$ bits per second, then all of the information that has been transmitted will be recovered completely without any uncertainty. This means that the received signal will be an exact replica of the approximated signal that was transmitted. One may wonder whether the noise introduced in the process of transmission may not further cause an additional degree of uncertainty and thus increase the total uncertainty more than 0.1 volt in the received signal amplitude. We can easily show that, if the channel capacity is $8f_m$ bits per second, the process of transmission does not introduce an additional degree of uncertainty. Suppose we are using a channel of bandwidth f_m cps to transmit these samples, then, since the channel capacity required will be $8f_m$ bits per second, the required signal-to-noise power ratio will be given by

$$8f_m = f_m \log_2 \left(\frac{S + N}{N} \right)$$

Hence

$$\frac{S + N}{N} = 256$$

We have seen before that the number of levels that can be distinguished at the receiver is $\sqrt{(S + N)/N}$. It follows that in this case the receiver can distinguish the 16 states without error. Hence, although the process of transmission introduces some noise in the desired signal, the levels are far enough apart to be distinguishable at the receiver. This is another way of saying that a channel of the capacity of $8f_m$ bps can transmit information of $8f_m$ bps virtually without error.

14.3 EXCHANGE OF BANDWIDTH FOR SIGNAL-TO-NOISE RATIO

A given signal can be transmitted with a given amount of uncertainty by a channel of finite capacity. We have seen that a given channel capacity may be obtained by any number of combinations of bandwidth and signal power. In fact, it is possible to exchange one for the other. We shall now demonstrate how such an exchange can be effected.

Consider the transmission of signal $f(t)$ shown in Fig. 14.2. We have seen that if an uncertainty of 0.1 volt is tolerated, the information content of the signal is given by $8f_m$ bits per second. It will now be shown that this information can be transmitted by various combinations of bandwidths and signal power.

One possible way of transmission is to send $2f_m$ pulses per second (Fig. 14.2), each of which can assume any of 16 states (sixteenary pulse). In this case we must have signal-to-noise ratio so that it should be possible to distinguish 16 states. Obviously $\sqrt{S + N}/\sqrt{N} = 16$. Also in order to transmit $2f_m$ pulses per second, we need a channel of bandwidth f_m cps. Hence the required channel capacity C is given by (Eq. 14.5):

$$C = f_m \log_2 \left(\frac{S + N}{N} \right)$$
$$= f_m \log_2 (16)^2$$
$$= 8f_m \text{ bits per second}$$

Thus the channel capacity is exactly equal to the amount of information per second in the signal $f(t)$.

Alternatively we may transmit the samples in Fig. 14.2 by quaternary pulse (pulses that can assume four states). It is evident that we need a group of two quaternary pulses to transmit each sample that can assume 16 states. Now the signal-to-noise ratio required to distinguish pulses that assume four distinct states is $\sqrt{S + N}/\sqrt{N} = 4$. It is evident that in this mode of transmission the required signal power is reduced. However, we now have to transmit twice as many pulses per second, that is, $4f_m$ pulses per second. Hence the bandwidth required is $2f_m$ cps. The channel capacity C in this case is

$$C = 2f_m \log_2 \left(\frac{S + N}{N} \right)$$
$$= 2f_m \log_2 (4)^2$$
$$= 8f_m \text{ bits per second}$$

It is evident from this example that a given amount of information can be transmitted by various combinations of signal power and bandwidth and the one can be exchanged for the other. The signal $f(t)$ in the above can also be transmitted by binary pulses ($8f_m$ pulses per second) which requires $\sqrt{S + N}/\sqrt{N} = 2$ and a channel bandwidth of $4f_m$ cps. It is interesting to note that $f(t)$ may also be transmitted by a channel of bandwidth lower than f_m cps if enough signal power is transmitted (see Problem 3 at the end of the chapter).

It should be observed that the process of exchange of bandwidth and signal power is not automatic. We have to modify or transform the signal information (coding) in such a way as to occupy the desired bandwidth. In practice this is accomplished by various types of modulation. However, it should be recognized that every communication system does not achieve the full capabilities inherent in its bandwidth and the signal power used. Some modulation forms prove superior to the other forms in utilizing the channel capacity. For example, it can be shown that PCM (pulse code modulation) is more efficient than other wideband systems such as FM and PPM.

It should be noted that the amount of uncertainty in the received signal can be reduced as much as desired by making the quantized levels close enough. If, for example, it is desired to have an uncertainty in the received signal amplitude of not more than 0.05 volt, then we must approximate all of the samples to the nearest 0.05-volt level. In this case, we have a total of 32 levels for $f(t)$ shown in Fig. 14.2. The information carried by each sample pulse is now $\log_2 32 = 5$ bits, instead of 4 bits, and the information in the $2f_m$ samples is $10f_m$ bits per second. Hence, the reduction in uncertainty correspondingly increases the information to be transmitted, which necessitates a channel of a higher capacity for transmission. The channel capacity may be increased either by increasing the average signal power and/or by increasing the bandwidth. Thus, by increasing the channel capacity, it is possible to achieve an arbitrarily small amount of uncertainty. It is interesting to note that the presence of random disturbances in a channel does not, by itself, set any limit to the transmission accuracy. Instead, it sets a limit to the transmission rate for which high transmission accuracy can be achieved. This is the essence of Shannon's fundamental theorem of discrete encoding in the presence of noise. In FM systems, the channel capacity is increased by a larger bandwidth and hence the uncertainty in the received signal in FM is much smaller than in other systems which need smaller bandwidths (for example, AM). This is the reason why an FM signal has a better signal-to-noise ratio than an AM signal.

PROBLEMS

1. A voltage waveform $Sa(2000\pi t)$ is to be transmitted with an uncertainty not exceeding $\frac{1}{80}$ volt. Determine the channel capacity required (see Fig. 3.22).

2. Repeat Problem 1 for a waveform $[Sa(2000\pi t)]^2$ if the uncertainty is not to exceed $\frac{1}{64}$ volt (see Fig. 3.22).

3. Devise a scheme to transmit a continuous signal $f(t)$, shown in Fig. 14.2, with an uncertainty not exceeding 0.1 volt using a channel of bandwidth of $f_m/2$ cps. Assume that the signal $f(t)$ is bandlimited to f_m cps.

4. Repeat Problem 3 if the uncertainty is not to exceed 0.025 volt.

5. A television picture may be considered as composed of approximately 500,000 small picture elements. Each of these elements can assume 10 distinguishable brightness levels (such as black and shades of gray) for proper contrast. Determine

the amount of information in one television picture assuming that each of the 10 brightness levels are equally likely to occur. Determine the channel capacity required to transmit the television signal if 30 picture frames are transmitted per second.

6. Use the data in Problem 5 to find the minimum bandwidth required to transmit a television signal if the signal-to-noise power ratio is 1000 (30 db).

7. An announcer on a radio describes a television picture orally by 1000 words out of his vocabulary of 10,000 words. Assume that each of the 10,000 words is equally likely to occur. Determine the amount of information broadcast by the announcer in describing this picture.

8. There are 81 coins in a bag. Eighty of the coins are identical in all respects. The remaining one coin is identical to the rest, except that it is slightly heavier. What amount of information is required to locate this coin? (*Hint.* Consider the minimum number of measurements required to locate the heavier coin.)

9. If, in the above problem, it is known that one of the coins differs in weight (but is not known whether it is heavier or lighter than the others), what amount of information is required to locate this coin and find out whether it is heavier or lighter than the others?

Appendix

Laplace Transform Pairs

In the following tables it is understood that $f(t)$ is causal, that is, that the correct inverse transform of $F(s)$ is $f(t)u(t)$.

TABLE A.I

Rational Forms in s

No.	$F(s)$	$f(t)$
1.	1	$\delta(t)$
2.	$\dfrac{1}{s}$	$u(t)$
3.	$\dfrac{1}{s^n}$ $(n = 1, 2, \ldots)$	$\dfrac{t^{n-1}}{(n-1)!}$
4.	$\dfrac{1}{s+a}$	e^{-at}
5.	$\dfrac{1}{s(s+a)}$	$\dfrac{1}{a}(1 - e^{-at})$
6.	$\dfrac{1}{s^2(s+a)}$	$\dfrac{1}{a^2}(e^{-at} + at - 1)$
7.	$\dfrac{1}{(s+a)(s+b)}$	$\dfrac{1}{(b-a)}(e^{-at} - e^{-bt})$
8.	$\dfrac{1}{(s+a)(s+b)(s+c)}$	$\dfrac{e^{-at}}{(b-a)(c-a)} + \dfrac{e^{-bt}}{(a-b)(c-b)} + \dfrac{e^{-ct}}{(a-c)(b-c)}$

(continued)

TABLE A.I (cont.)

No.	$F(s)$	$f(t)$
9.	$\dfrac{s}{(s+a)(s+b)(s+c)}$	$\dfrac{-ae^{-at}}{(b-a)(c-a)} - \dfrac{be^{-bt}}{(a-b)(c-b)} - \dfrac{ce^{-ct}}{(a-c)(b-c)}$
10.	$\dfrac{1}{(s+a)^2}$	te^{-at}
11.	$\dfrac{s}{(s+a)^2}$	$(1-at)e^{-at}$
12.	$\dfrac{1}{(s+a)(s+b)^2}$	$\dfrac{1}{(a-b)^2}e^{-at} + \dfrac{(a-b)t-1}{(a-b)^2}e^{-bt}$
13.	$\dfrac{s}{(s+a)(s+b)^2}$	$\dfrac{-ae^{-at}}{(a-b)^2} - \dfrac{b(a-b)t-a}{(a-b)^2}e^{-bt}$
14.	$\dfrac{1}{(s+a)^n}\ (n=1,2,\ldots)$	$\dfrac{1}{(n-1)!}t^{n-1}e^{-at}$
15.	$\dfrac{1}{s^2+a^2}$	$\dfrac{1}{a}\sin at$
16.	$\dfrac{s}{s^2+a^2}$	$\cos at$
17.	$\dfrac{1}{s^2-a^2}$	$\dfrac{1}{a}\sinh at$
18.	$\dfrac{s}{s^2-a^2}$	$\cosh at$
19.	$\dfrac{1}{s(s^2+a^2)}$	$\dfrac{1}{a^2}(1-\cos at)$
20.	$\dfrac{1}{(s+a)(s^2+b^2)}$	$\dfrac{1}{(a^2+b^2)}\left[e^{-at} + \dfrac{1}{b}\sqrt{a^2+b^2}\sin(bt-\theta)\right]$ $\theta = \tan^{-1}\dfrac{b}{a}$
21.	$\dfrac{s}{(s+a)(s^2+b^2)}$	$\dfrac{-a}{(a^2+b^2)}\left[e^{-at} - \dfrac{1}{a}\sqrt{a^2+b^2}\sin(bt+\theta)\right]$ $\theta = \tan^{-1}\left(\dfrac{a}{b}\right)$
22.	$\dfrac{1}{(s+a)^2+b^2}$	$\dfrac{1}{b}e^{-at}\sin bt$
23.	$\dfrac{s+a}{(s+a)^2+b^2}$	$e^{-at}\cos bt$
24.	$\dfrac{s}{(s^2+a^2)(s^2+b^2)}$	$\dfrac{1}{b^2-a^2}(\cos at - \cos bt)$

(continued)

TABLE A.I (concluded)

No.	$F(s)$	$f(t)$
25.	$\dfrac{1}{(s^2 + a^2)^2}$	$\dfrac{1}{2a^3}(\sin at - at \cos at)$
26.	$\dfrac{s}{(s^2 + a^2)^2}$	$\dfrac{t}{2a}\sin at$
27.	$\dfrac{1}{s(s^2 + a^2)^2}$	$\dfrac{1}{a^4}(1 - \cos at) - \dfrac{1}{2a^3}t\sin at$
28.	$\dfrac{1}{s^4 + 4a^4}$	$\dfrac{1}{4a^3}(\sin at \cosh at - \cos at \sinh at)$
29.	$\dfrac{s}{s^4 + 4a^4}$	$\dfrac{1}{2a^2}\sin at \sinh at$
30.	$\dfrac{1}{s^4 - a^4}$	$\dfrac{1}{2a^3}(\sinh at - \sin at)$
31.	s^n	$\delta^{(n)}(t)$

TABLE A.2

Irrational and Transcendental Forms in s

No.	$F(s)$	$f(t)$
1.	$\dfrac{1}{\sqrt{s}}$	$\dfrac{1}{\sqrt{\pi t}}$
2.	$\dfrac{1}{s\sqrt{s}}$	$2\sqrt{\dfrac{t}{\pi}}$
3.	$\dfrac{1}{s^n}$ (n is not necessarily integral)	$\dfrac{t^{n-1}}{\Gamma(n)}$
4.	$\dfrac{1}{(s - a)\sqrt{s}}$	$\dfrac{1}{\sqrt{a}}e^{at}erf(\sqrt{at})$
5.	$\dfrac{2}{a}e^{-a\sqrt{s}}$ $\quad a > 0$	$\dfrac{e^{-a^2/4t}}{\sqrt{\pi t^3}}$
6.	$\dfrac{e^{-a\sqrt{s}}}{\sqrt{s}}$ $\quad a \geqslant 0$	$\dfrac{e^{-a^2/4t}}{\sqrt{\pi t}}$
7.	$\dfrac{e^{-a\sqrt{s}}}{s}$ $\quad a \geqslant 0$	$1 - erf\left(\dfrac{a}{2\sqrt{t}}\right) = erfc\left(\dfrac{a}{2\sqrt{t}}\right)$
8.	$\dfrac{\sqrt{a}}{s\sqrt{s + a}}$	$erf(\sqrt{at})$

(continued)

TABLE A.2 (concluded)

No.	$F(s)$	$f(t)$
9.	$\dfrac{1}{\sqrt{s} + \sqrt{a}}$	$\dfrac{1}{\sqrt{\pi t}} - \sqrt{a}\, e^{at} erfc(\sqrt{at})$
10.	$\dfrac{1}{\sqrt{s}(\sqrt{s} + \sqrt{a})}$	$e^{at} erfc(\sqrt{at})$
11.[a]	$\dfrac{1}{\sqrt{s^2 + a^2}}$	$J_0(at)$
12.[a]	$\dfrac{1}{\sqrt{s^2 - a^2}}$	$I_0(at)$
13.[a]	$\dfrac{1}{\sqrt{s}\sqrt{s + a}}$	$e^{-at/2} I_0\left(\dfrac{at}{2}\right)$
14.[a]	$\dfrac{1}{s + \sqrt{s^2 + a^2}}$	$\dfrac{1}{at} J_1(at)$
15.[a]	$\dfrac{1}{[s + \sqrt{s^2 + a^2}]\sqrt{s^2 + a^2}}$	$\dfrac{1}{a} J_1(at)$

[a] Functions $J_0(x)$, $I_0(x)$, $J_1(x)$, etc. are Bessel's functions and can be found in the standard tables. See, for instance E. Jahnke and F. Emde, *Table of Functions*, Dover Publications, New York, 1945.

Index